THE NORTH AMERICAN
SPECIES OF PHOLIOTA

THE NORTH AMERICAN
SPECIES OF PHOLIOTA

by Linchett
Alexander H. Smith
University of Michigan

and
L. R. Hesler
University of Tennessee

(With 115 Illustrations and 40 Drawings)

HAFNER PUBLISHING COMPANY
New York and London
1968

Printed and Published
by
Hafner Publishing Company, Inc.
31 East 10th Street
New York, N. Y. 10003

LIBRARY OF CONGRESS CATALOG CARD NUMBER: 68-55067

Printed in the United States of America.

This book was set by Topel Typographic Corporation, New York,
and printed by Noble Offset Printers, Inc., New York, N.Y. 10003.

Table of Contents

Introduction 3
  History 4
  Outline of Proposed Classification 5
  Purpose of Present Study 8
  General Description of Text Figures 9
  Acknowledgments 9
The Basidiocarp 11
  Macroscopic Characters 11
  Microscopic Characters 15
  Chemical Characters 23
The Evolutionary Tendencies Within Pholiota 24
The Intergeneric Relationships 31
Practical Importance of Pholiota 34
Taxonomic Treatment 37
  Description of Genus 37
  Key to Subgenera 38
    Subgenus Hygrotrama 38
      Section Confragosa 39
      Section Hygrotrama 44
    Subgenus Flavidula 45
      Section Flavidula 46
    Subgenus Hemipholiota 77
      Section Sordidae 78
      Section Mutabiles 91
      Section Hemipholiota 122
      Section Variabilisporae 130
    Subgenus Phaeonaematoloma 131
      Section Albivelatae 132
      Section Phaeonaematoloma 138

Subgenus Flammula 170

Subgenus Pholiota 184

   Section Pholiota 184

   Section Adiposae 192

Subgenus Flammuloides 230

   Section Flammuloides 231

   Section Carbonicola 278

   Section Spumosae 289

   Section Lubricae 325

Doubtful Species 378

Excluded Species 383

Selected Bibliography 388

List of Plates by Species 393

Index 395

Plates .. .. ,. 403

INTRODUCTION

History

Fries (1821) established Tribe xxii, *Pholiota of Agaricus,* for many of the species here placed in the genus *Pholiota.* The history of the genus may be said to start from this publication since it is the official starting date for the nomenclature of agarics. Although the Greek word *Pholiota* means scale, some glabrous species such as *Agaricus caperatus* were admitted to the group. He included sixteen species, some of which (e.g., *P. aurivella, P. adiposa, P. flammans, P. squarrosa* and *P. mutabilis*) are still included.

In the same publication Fries erected a second group, Tribe xxv, *Flammula,* with fifteen species including *Agaricus alnicola, astragalinus, spumosus, carbonarius, lubricus, lentus* and others, species which are now included under *Pholiota.* Fries made a distinction between the two tribes on the basis of the character of the veil. In *Pholiota* he stated that the veil forms an annulus, membranous or radiate-floccose, and in *Flammula* it was said to be fugacious. In 1874, however, he characterized *Pholiota* as having an annulate partial veil, but then stated that *Pholiota* passes without distinct limits into *Flammula.*

Kummer (1871) was apparently the first to assign generic rank to these two Friesian tribes. Quélet (1886) proposed the genus *Dryophila* to encompass both tribes but then divided them into subgenera *Pholiota* and *Flammula.* Since Quélet's time, authors have varied between this concept and in maintaining both tribes as genera. Earle (1909) noting that the name *Flammula* is a homonym, having been used for a genus of phanerogams previously, proposed the name *Visculus* in place of it. Earle, in the same publication, recognized the genus *Hypodendrum* Paulet (1793). It will be noted that this name is "pre Friesian." Overholts (1932) used Paulet's name since he was following the old American Code at the time, and placed in the genus species with squarrose stipes. Those with glabrous or merely fibrillose stipes were placed under *Pholiota.* He excluded species of *Flammula* from his treatise.

In more recent times it has been observed that some of the species of the *Pholiota-Flammula* group exhibit a germ pore broad enough to cause the spore apex to appear more or less truncate. Based chiefly on

3

this character, Singer and Smith (1946b) proposed the genus *Kuehnero-myces* for certain species in which the character was readily observable under ordinary magnifications with a compound microscope. More recently Singer (1957) proposed *Pachylepyrium* for certain species in which the spores are exceptionally heavily pigmented, smooth, and relatively thick-walled. Pleurocystidia were said to be lacking.

Despite the comment by Fries, upon which Quélet apparently acted, students of agarics since 1874 for the most part maintained *Pholiota* and *Flammula* as separate genera. Among these were some of the leading agaricologists of Europe: Ricken (1915), Rea (1922) and Lange (1935-40). In North America Peck (1897) (1908), Atkinson (1900), Murrill (who used Karsten's name *Gymnopilus* in place of *Flammula*), Kauffman (1918, 1926), and Overholts (1927) accepted the same generic concepts. In 1953 Kühner and Romagnesi followed Quélet (1886) in using the name *Dryophila* in that author's original concept.

Singer and Smith (1946, p. 264) expressed the opinion that the generic differences between *Pholiota* and *Flammula* in the sense of modern authors were too slight to justify maintaining both. In this respect they reiterated Quélet's (1886) opinion, but Singer (1951) sought to divide the group along lines other than originally indicated by Fries. This was a constructive move and has been followed by such recent authors as Moser (1955). Singer (1963) has given us the most detailed analysis of the whole group to date and it is the one which we have used as a point of departure for our study. Singer's work is of such importance that we include here the outline of his classification:

Pholiota

Subgenus *Hemipholiota,* type *P. destruens.*
    Sect. 1. *Hemipholiota*
          2. *Sordidae,* type *Dryophila sordida*
          3. *Albocrenulatae,* type *P. albocrenulata*
          4. *Myxannulatae,* type *P. nameko*

Subgenus *Pholiota,* type *P. squarrosa*
          5. *Pholiota*
          6. *Adiposae,* type *P. adiposa*
          7. *Subflammantes,* type *P. subflammans*

Subgenus *Flammula,* type *Flammula flavida*
          8. *Flammula*
          9. *Lubricae,* type *P. lubrica*
             subsect. *Polychrominae,* type *P. polychroa*
                        Spumosinae, type *P. spumosa*
       10. *Sericellae,* type *Agaricus scambus*
       11. *Privignae,* type *P. privigna*
       12. *Glutinigerae,* type *P. glutinigera*

Our proposed classification follows by way of comparison:

Outline of Proposed Classification of Pholiota

I. Subgenus *Flavidula*

Section *Flavidula*
  Stirps *Curvipes*: *P. curvipes, P. multifolia, P. subsulphurea,*
    P. squamulosa
  Stirps *Aurea*: *P. aurea, P. fulvella, P. granulosa, P. erinaceella,*
    P. pseudosiparia
  Stirps *Cinchonensis*: *P. cinchonensis*
  Stirps *Curcuma*: *P. curcuma, P. murrillii, P. minutula, P. lactea,*
    P. proximans, P. fagicola, P. subechinata
  Stirps *Corticola*: *P. corticola, P. cyathicola, P. pseudolimulata*
  Stirps *Erinacea*: *P. erinacea*

II. Subgenus *Hygrotrama*

Section *Confragosae*: *P. anomala, P. punicea, P. canescens, P. confragosa*
Section *Hygrotrama*: *P. subangularis*

III. Subgenus *Hemipholiota*

Section *Sordidae*
  Stirps *Discolor*: *P. striatula, P. mutans, P. discolor, P. brunnea,*
    P. davidsonii, P. aurantioflava, P. gummosa
  Stirps *Serotina*: *P. serotina, P. kalmicola*
Section *Mutabiles*
  Stirps *Mutabilis*: *P. mutabilis, P. caespitosa, P. tennessensis, P. veris*
  Stirps *Marginella*: *P. marginella, P. albovirescens, P. deceptiva,*
    P. umbilicata, P. albo-olivascens, P. bridgii
  Stirps *Obscura*: *P. obscura, P. nigripes, P. galerinoides,*
    P. tahquamenonensis
  Stirps *Vernalis*: *P. pallida, P. subpapillata, P. conica, P. atripes,*
    P. populicola, P. vernalis
  Stirps *Depauperata*: *P. depauperata*
Section *Hemipholiota*
  Stirps *Destruens*: *P. destruens* (and if distinct *P. heteroclita*
    and *P. comosa*)
  Stirps *Albocrenulata*: *P. albocrenulata*
  Stirps *Olivaceodisca*: *P. olivaceodisca*
Section *Variabilisporae*: *P. variabilispora*

IV. Subgenus *Phaeonaematoloma*

Section *Albivelatae*
Stirps *Albivelata*: P. *albivelata*, P. *sipei*
Stirps *Cubensis*: P. *cubensis*, P. *duroides*, P. *johnsoniana*
Section *Phaeonaematoloma*
Stirps *Silvatica*: P. *silvatica*, P. *aberrans*
Stirps *Myosotis*; P. *myosotis*, P. *humidicola*
Strips *Elongata*: P. *elongata*, P. *olympiana*
Stirps *Subochracea*: P. *subochracea*, P. *subcaerulea*, P. *burkei*,
    P. *subgelatinosa*, P. *parvula*, P. *pusilla*, P. *ornatula*,
    P. *melliodora*, P. *flavescens*, P. *lutescens*, P. *prolixa*,
    P. *californica*, P. *contorta*

V. Subgenus *Flammula*

Section *Flammula*: P. *alnicola*, P. *abieticola*, P. *subvelutina*,
    P. *flavida*, P. *oregonensis*, P. *malicola*

VI. Subgenus *Pholiota*

Section *Pholiota*
Stirps *Fulvosquamosa*: P. *fulvosquamosa*
Stirps *Schraderi*: P. *schraderi*, P. *sola*, P. *scabella*
Stirps *Squarrosa*: P. *squarrosa*, P. *kodiakensis*
Section *Adiposae*
Stirps *Squarrosoides*: P. *rigidipes*, P. *penningtoniana*, P. *terrestris*,
    P. *subcastanea*, P. *barrowsii*, P. *squarrosoides*, P. *romagnesiana*,
    P. *angustifolia*
Stirps *Adiposa*: P. *adiposa*, P. *flammans*, P. *aurivelloides*,
    P. *aurivella*, P. *lucifera*, P. *connata*, P. *hiemalis*, P. *subvelutipes*,
    P. *filamentosa*, P. *squarroso-adiposa*, P. *abietis*, P. *simulans*,
    P. *limonella*, P. *angustipes*

VII. Subgenus *Flammuloides*

Section *Flammuloides*:
Stirps *Virgata*: P. *virgata*, P. *pseudograveolens*
Stirps *Olivaceophylla*: P. *olivaceophylla*, P. *castanea*
Stirps *Adirondackensis*: P. *adirondackensis*, P. *flavopallida*,
    P. *agglutinata*
Stirps *Condensa*: P. *condensa*, P. *subminor*, P. *bakerensis*, P. *iterata*,

P. *sequoiae*, P. *alabamensis*.
Stirps *Decorata*: P. *decorata*, P. *humii*, P. *vinaceo-brunnea*,
P. *velaglutinosa*, P. *rubronigra*
Stirps *Ferruginea*: P. *ferruginea*, P. *sienna*, P. *ferrugineo-lutescens*,
P. *hypholomoides*, P. *rufodisca*
Stirps *Occidentalis*: P. *abruptibulba*, P. *verna*, P. *rivulosa*,
P. *occidentalis*, P. *fulvodisca*, P. *subfulva*
Section *Carbonicola*
Stirps P. *carbonaria*, P. *fulvozonata*, P. *subsaponacea*, P. *luteobadia*,
P. *highlandensis*, P. *molesta*, P. *brunnescens*
Section *Spumosae*
Stirps *Sphagnicola*: P. *sphagnicola*, P. *paludosella*, P. *sphagnophila*,
P. *chromocystis*
Stirps *Graveolens*: P. *graveolens*
Stirps *Scamba*: P. *scamba*, P. *pulchella*, P. *calvini*, P. *tetonensis*,
P. *pseudopulchella*, P. *totteni*, P. *gregariformis*, P. *scamboides*,
P. *subdefossa*
Stirps *Subamara*: P. *subamara*
Stirps *Stratosa*: P. *stratosa*
Stirps *Spumosa*: P. *baptistii*, P. *spumosa*, P. *velata*, P. *vialis*,
P. *piceina*
Section *Lubricae*
Stirps *Astragalina*: P. *astragalina*
Stirps *Fibrillosipes*: P. *coloradensis*, P. *sublubrica*, P. *armeniaca*,
P. *subcarbonaria*, P. *fibrillosipes*, P. *luteola*, P. *spinulifera*
Stirps *Lubrica*: P. *lubrica*, P. *subtestacea*, P. *harenosa*, P. *gruberi*,
Stirps *Polychroa*: P. *polychroa*, P. *avellaneifolia*, P. *trullisata*,
P. *foedata*, P. *milleri*, *groenlandica*
Stirps *Crassipedes*: P. *biglowii*, P. *macrocystis*, P. *subflavida*,
P. *crassipedes*
Stirps *Innocua*: P. *virescentifolia*, P. *brunneidisca*, P. *jalopensis*,
P. *innocua*, P. *lurida*
Stirps *Lenta*: P. *fulviconica*, P. *acutoconica*, P. *squalida*, P. *lenta*

Summarizing our concept, we place in *Pholiota* all species with smooth spores (with one possible exception, P. *aurea*), the spore deposit rusty-brown to yellow-brown, typically with at least a minute germ pore at the spore apex and at least an inner veil typically present as shown by fibrils on the stipe (see p. 14). In accordance with our detailed characterization of *Pholiota* we transfer to it all species of *Gymnopilus-Flammula* complex with smooth spores. *Agrocybe* and *Conocybe* featured by a cellular pileus cuticle and truncate spores are recognized by both Singer and ourselves as the core of the Bolbitiaceae. Many of these in which an annulus is present were at one time or another placed in *Pholiota*.

Purpose of the Present Study

Since previous taxonomic accounts of *Pholiota* and *Flammula* concerned with the North American species have not been based on a modern approach to a study of the basidiocarp, it was important to re-evaluate species concepts for even the so-called common species. Singer's treatment was a cross-sectional study of the genera and families of the Agaricales and did not purport to be even reasonably complete for this group in any region. Also, it was not concerned primarily with comparative studies of species in the larger groups.

In addition, while a cross-sectional study such as Singer's was of great value in aiding mycologists to gain perspective in relation to the genera of the agaricales, its very scope prevented it from dealing with the larger genera in detail. Before generic concepts can be established on anything like a stable foundation, the monographs must follow in the wake of Singer's cross sectional study. The present contribution should be regarded as a step in this direction..

It soon became evident in our study that the pholiotoid agarics of North America were far more numerous than we had expected. In fact it was only upon the completion of this work that we finally realized how much basic exploration remained to be done. Our description of over 75 previously undescribed species is evidence of the diversity of the flora, and we do not claim to have found all that occur here—that would be presumptuous indeed. It should be realized, but is not, apparently, in some quarters, that there is no region on the face of the earth that has been explored completely for any group of fungi. Fungi, unfortunately or fortunately, depending on your point of view, move around, so that one must always take the migration factor into account. Also, in spite of the collecting that has been done even in the restricted areas such as the British Isles where collecting has been done for years, there is no good representation of the British agaric flora in their herbaria—this now is being remedied by such workers as Dennis, Reid, Watling and others— but the situation reflects the changing thinking on the study of agarics over the last fifty years. If such a situation prevails in the British Isles, what about the United States? Here we have had to deal with a much larger more complicated flora with fewer people studying it. To the extent that these factors have operated in our country, we are just that much farther behind such areas as the British Isles and Scandinavia in the problem of a basic inventory of our species and in learning their relationships. In view of this the number of "new" species in this work needs no apology. If one is due it is for not having more than one lifetime in which to complete the work.

Our collecting procedures have been organized around a sampling process of working in the various forest associations of North America in the various climatic regions. We know from intensive collecting in selected areas such as the Great Smoky Mountains National Park, and the devastation left in the wake of logging operations in the Upper Peninsula of Michigan, that the only approach to a reasonably complete knowledge of our flora, especially as it pertains to wood-decay fungi in general, is to follow the fruiting of fungi in such areas from spring through fall regularly from the time the slash first starts to "produce" until it is reduced to humus. This involves working during unfavorable as well as during favorable seasons. Smith has made an attempt to do this, to the extent that time and facilities permitted, in the hardwood slashings near Emerson, Michigan in Chippewa County. It is only after attempting such a program that one can realize fully the futility of going into an area for a single season, and then thinking that the agaric flora has been "collected." Even after a good season, one obtains only a partial picture. One season, of course, is always better than none.

Our purpose here, we wish it clearly understood, is not to present the complete picture of *Pholiota* in North America, but to present a modern treatment of sufficiently broad scope to allow one interested to ascertain the identity of most of the collections he makes, and to help him recognize and understand the lines along which species are evolving, and where worthwhile opportunities for critical studies in culture can be made for further elucidation of complex species groups.

General Description of Text Figures

The drawings of the spores as reproduced are at an approximate magnification 1900 times. The details are shown somewhat schematically as it was difficult to work with a camera-lucida on details less than 0.3 μ in diameter. The drawings of cystidia are approximately × 1000 but for *Pholiota macrocystis* the magnification is approximately 600. In the cystidia it was not always possible to see the clamp at the crosswall because in the course of crushing the amount to bring the entire cell into full view it often broke at the cross wall. Sometimes the oblique septum of the clamp shows but more often than not it did not show simply because it was impossible to orient the cystidium to get a perfect medial optical section in the right plane to show it.

Acknowledgments

The aid rendered in this study by institutions and individuals has been indispensable.

Each of us has had valuable support of the National Science Foundation through a series of grants of funds.

Type specimens and other collections have been made available to us on loan. For these loans, we extend our grateful acknowledgment to the following persons and institutions:

Dr. Sten Ahlner, Curator, the Rijksmuseum, Stockholm; Mr. C. Bas,

Curator, The Rijksherbarium, Leiden; Dr. Meinhard Moser, Boden-biologisches Institut, Imst, Austria; Dr. G. Taylor, Director, Royal Botanic Gardens, Kew; Dr. R. Watling, Royal Botanic Garden, Edinburgh; Dr. H. E. Bigelow, University of Massachusetts, Amherst; Dr. Kenton L. Chambers, Oregon State University, Corvallis; Dr. James Kimbrough, Curator, The University of Florida; Dr. Patricio Ponce de León, Curator, The Chicago Natural History Museum, Chicago; Dr. Richard Korf, Curator, Cornell University, Department of Plant Pathology Herbarium; Dr. I. MacKenzie Lamb, The Farlow Herbarium, Harvard University; Dr. Clark T. Rogerson, Herbarium, The New York Botanical Garden, New York City; and Mr. Stanley Jay Smith, The Herbarium, New York State Museum, Albany. We also acknowledge the generosity of Dr. H. E. Bigelow, who made his photographs of *Pholiota* species available to us; and finally, our thanks to more than a score of devoted and zealous amateur mushroom hunters for the many interesting and new species they have communicated to us for study.

Four courtesies extended in aid of field work we wish to acknowledge the wholehearted cooperation of the National Park service for the opportunity to collect in the Great Smoky Mts. National Park, Mt. Rainier National Park, the Olympic National Park and in the Rocky Mountains National Park. These areas play a most important role in preserving large tracts of our native forests for posterity and of course this means the preservation of all the elements of the forest biota. We wish also to acknowledge similar courtesies extended by the staff of the United States Forest Service, United States Department of Agriculture, from the forest superintendants as well as the rangers and other field personnel. Their help has been of inestimable value in locating quickly the type of site desired for a particular problem. Their patience with the working as well as recreating public is a model for all to follow. Beyond this, however, we wish to particularly acknowledge the facilities placed at the disposal of Smith and his party at the Priest River Experimental Forest, a unit of the Intermountain Forest and Range Experiment Station, Mr. Joseph Pechanec, Director. The location is ideal for the study of *Pholiota,* being as it is in the center of the Idaho white pine belt.

The University of Michigan Biological Station, Dr. A. H. Stockard, Director, was our most important central Great Lakes base of operations, but we also wish to acknowledge the opportunity granted Smith by the Huron Mountains Club and its Wildlife Foundation for the privilege of collecting in the virgin forests now dedicated by the Club as a natural area.

THE BASIDIOCARP

Macroscopic Characters

In *Pholiota,* the gross features of the basidiocarp—the pileus, flesh (context), lamellae, and stipe—are now as important in taxonomy as they were in the Friesian era. An analysis of the details relative to each structure gives some indication of their use in taxonomy.

Pileus. In our experience, the colors and surface characters of the pileus are highly important in the identification of species. On the other hand, the size, shape, habit of growth, and habitat are of lesser value, and are merely supplemental to those of color and surface features.

In general, the predominant colors of the pileus are in the yellow and brown series. In a relatively few species, there are red tints which modify the browns and yellows. Grays and general lack of pigmentation are present in some, but species with permanent pure white pilei have not been encountered. The pileus is whitish in *P. destruens,* but it develops colors toward maturity, and in *P. lutescens* the pileus is at first white but gradually becomes lemon-yellow. A common color pattern is that the central portion of the pileus is darker than that of the marginal area; the disc may be brownish, and the marginal area buff to yellowish. Often the colors are of darker tints in the "button" stage than at maturity. A rare color-display is found in *P. polychroa;* the surface of the pileus is of many colors—purplish when young, then changing to buff or yellowish, or often to olive to greenish on the marginal area, the disc remaining more or less purplish or becoming yellow to orange. Colors and color-patterns are valuable in distinguishing species.

Surface modifications are, in many species, noteworthy, and their character should be determined. The pileus surface may be glabrous; or, in other species, it may be fibrillose, and the fibrils may be aggregated into scales. Pronounced development of scales is striking in the subgenus *Pholiota;* see *P. squarrosa, P. squarrosoides, P. terrestris,* and others.

It is important to determine whether the fresh pileus is dry or viscid. When truly viscid, the surface will display a zone of gelatinized hyphae when sections of the pileus are mounted in KOH. In doubtful cases final decision as to whether a pileus is viscid must rest on such a microscopic

11

examination (see also pages 21-22) . In a high degree of gelatinization, the pileus surface is glutinous or slimy when wet.

The diameter of the pileus may vary, with the species, from 10 mm or less to 10-20 cm. In a large number of species the pileus is 2-5 cm broad. Pileus shape tends to be convex then becoming more or less expanded. In some species it is umbonate, and in a few the disc may be depressed. Size and shape, however, are usually of relatively minor value in taxonomy. The basidiocarps, in some species, are caespitose; in other species they may be scattered or solitary on the substratum. Their habit of growth varies with the species, but these characters are likewise of somewhat limited taxonomic value since field observations indicate that here the supply of available food is an important factor.

Species of *Pholiota* are found growing on soil, wood, or humus. Some seem restricted in their habitat; for example, a few species, such as *P. highlandensis* and *P. carbonaria,* grow on burned areas around charcoal. In *P. sphagnicola,* the basidiocarps grow among sphagnum—a rather specialized habitat. A few wood-inhabiting species seem to be confined to either hardwood or coniferous wood; but others are found on both. Habitat in itself is usually of secondary importance in critical identification.

In this study we have made no use of the hygrophanous or non-hygrophanous character of the flesh. We have not seen every species in the fresh state, and for many species records of this character are not available. For those studied too often the caps are "subhygrophanous" indicating at best a state not too valuable as a taxonomic character. However, there are exceptions.

Context. The color, odor, and taste of the pileus context (flesh) should be noted in fresh material.

Color is constant enough to be of value at the species level. The flesh may be yellowish, more rarely brownish, or often white or pallid. In *P. avellaneifolia* the flesh of the pileus is white, but when cut it slowly becomes pinkish buff. Other color changes taking place on injury to the context will be found in the text. In many species the color may be white to pallid at first but in old specimens becomes distinctly yellow. This makes it difficult to use the color of the context as a taxonomic character because weather conditions as well as age seem to influence this change. Also, in sterile or semisterile basidiocarps, there is often a decided development of yellowish pigment—to the confusion of the taxonomist.

Odor is, in many species, not distinctive. However, in a few it is both noticeable and distinctive, and should be recorded. Odors described for the various species are fragrant (in *P. humii, rubronigra, stratosa, subvelutina, scamba*) ; or in *P. melliodora,* of honey; in a very few species the odor is of coal-tar (*P. graveolens*) ; rarely is it raphanoid (in *P. vernalis*) ; and in *P. squarrosa* some collections have an odor of garlic. The odor of freshly unhusked green corn is noticed in some collections of subgenus

Flammuloides. In view of the present emphasis on "chemical characters" in the fungi it must be kept in mind that both taste and odor are based on particular chemicals and hence may be as important as, for instance the color change with iron salts.

Taste, like odor, is not distinctive in great numbers of species. It is bitter in *P. astragalina, gregariiformis, alnicola, multifolia,* and in *P. scabella* it is described as bitter-acrid. Taste is mawkish (a term used by Murrill) in *P. hypholomoides,* of radish in *P. schraderi,* subalkaline in *P. flavida,* and nutty in *P. angustifolia, johnsoniana,* and *oregonensis.* A characteristic odor and taste are rarely similar to each other, but both are farinaceous in *P. harenosa,* and raphanoid in *P. fulvosquamosa.*

In summary, color of the context is an important macroscopic character but one subject to certain confusing variations. Odor and taste may be only of confirming or supplemental value, but deserve more study.

Lamellae. A significant character of the gills is their color in the young stage. At maturity, the color is in the yellow-brown to rusty series and is then of little or no value in distinguishing species. The gills may be pallid when very young but soon become some shade of yellow or in some species avellaneous. Occasionally, one encounters a species in which the gills become stained when bruised or in age (*P. aurantiobrunnea, multifolia*). Gill width and spacing may be of some importance when in extremes (distant or crowded, very broad or very narrow). In *P. multifolia,* for example, they are noticeably crowded and narrow—characters which aid in field identification of this species. Gill attachment offers little assistance in an effort to separate species of *Pholiota.* The typical condition when young is adnate and in age adnexed or somewhat decurrent.

Stipe. We have customarily recorded the stipe dimensions in our descriptions, but, only in rare and extreme instances is stipe-length of value. In *P. malicola* var. *macropoda,* the stipe measures 10-18 cm long and 10-25 mm thick—whence the varietal name. However, in addition to this obvious character, there are other distinctive features. Stipe width is a much better index for species recognition, but a great majority have stipes 5-15 mm diam. However, a few species exhibit very slender, short, delicate stipes.

Surface characteristics of the stipe are important and are to be noted. In one species, the stipe may be glabrous, in another fibrillose or scaly. Usually the veil remnants and cuticular hyphae are dry, but in *P. adiposa* the scales are notably gelatinous. Stipe color should be observed; in many species the stipe is more or less concolorous with the pileus. In others, the apical and basal portions may differ markedly from each other since the base of the stipe often darkens. It should be determined whether the stipe darkens, with maturation, from the base up, or is rusty brown from the very beginning.

Inner Veil. As the basidiocarp reaches maturity, there are present, in most species, remnants of an inner veil, or cortina, as a ring on the upper portion of the stipe. This ring of fibrils is commonly brownish from spores which have lodged on them. The ring or zone of veil-remnants is usually inconspicuous and often evanescent. Its color (often either white or yellow) in the early stages of the basidiocarp should be noted. When strongly developed, the veil may be membranous and persistent, as in *P. albivelata.* In one species, *P. velaglutinosa,* the elements are gelatinous, and the veil is described as glutinous. In other species, the veil breaks so that remnants cling to the margin of the pileus, a condition described as appendiculate. Finally it appears that in some species the inner veil is absent. In *P. nigripes* for example, no trace of such a veil was found, even in young basidiocarps. With the exeception of the glutinous veil, and the veil which forms a membranous persistent annulus, the color of the inner veil is its most valuable feature for taxonomic emphasis.

Outer veil. The development of the veils was studied by Sawyer (1917) for *P. adiposa* and *P. flammans.* It is now apparent that the species he studied were *P. squarroso-adiposa* and *P. flammans.* The outer veil, or blematogen as he used the term, may be regarded as part of the ground tissue within which the active differentiation of the basidiocarp occurs, and the amount to which this layer develops varies with the species. In such species as *P. squarrosa* this layer continues to grow along with the differentiating basidiocarp to the point that at maturity conspicuous aggregations of its hyphae persist as scales. As Sawyer pointed out the hyphal arrangement in the blematogen tissue is at first perpendicular to the developing cap surface. Hence as these hyphae elongate they become decumbent and by the expansion of the cap become aggregated into separate fascicles oriented toward the cap margin away from the disc, but often standing straight up (squarrose) on the disc. These scales are innate (firmly attached to the pileus). At maturity they appear to be a direct outgrowth from the pileus. When the gelatinous layer forms underneath them however, there is no solid connection to the cap and they can be easily washed away by rains. It is difficult in *Pholiota* to distinguish at all times between a partial and an outer veil as in most cases over the stipe the two tissues appear grown together and the fibrils assigned to each are better identified by their position on the stipe. As already pointed out those of the inner veil leave the zone nearest the apex of the stipe. Veil material left on the stipe below this is likely to be mostly outer veil material. For the species without well developed scales on the pileus it must be recognized that the development of the outer veil is reduced. In the subgenus *Pholiota,* in keeping with the derivation of the name, the central feature is the presence of numerous scales on the pileus and these scales are to be interpreted as remains of the blematogen. However, the structure of the scales themselves is important taxonomically. In some the end-cells of the hyphae may be somewhat cystidioid, in some the hyphal walls may be slightly thickened, colored or encrusted, etc.

In summary, the more important taxonomic macroscopic characters in *Pholiota* are color and surface features of the pileus, color of pileus context, color of the gills and the surface characters of the stipe. The texture of the inner veil becomes a valuable character when it forms a persistent, membranous annulus, or leaves copious remnants. Finally, the color of the inner veil when young is regarded here as of some value in distinguishing species.

Microscopic Characters

In the present study and in line with the hyphal approach to the study of the basidiocarp, we have placed emphasis on hyphal end-cells, whether occurring as pileo- caulo- pleuro- or cheilo- cystidia, the types of hyphae making up the various tissues, and hyphal detail in the veil in so far as the available material allowed this. The spores, of course, were studied on a modern basis with due emphasis on wall features as well as size and shape. The features offering the most value for taxonomy appear to us to be spore size, spore shape, presence or absence of pleuro-cystidia and if present their type, the structure of the pileus cuticle, the presence or absence of caulocystidia and whether the hyphae of the subhymenium gelatinize or not.

Spores. We have examined spores mounted in 2% KOH and in Melzer's reagent when studying dried material. Water and 2% KOH are now both regularly used on fresh material. The spores under a good oil immersion lens when viewed individually free from the tissues of the basidiocarp appear ochraceous to ochraceous tawny, tawny or some shape of pale to dark cinnamon. Whenever possible spores from deposits were examined; however for most collections including many of the types, deposits of spores were not available. Under these circumstances we checked the spores found on the apex of the stipe while in the process of looking for caulocystidia. We did not find enough caulohymenium in the species studied to create a situation similar to that found by bolete investigators in *Leccinum* where there is a fairly extensive caulohymenium at times and the spores produced on its basidia are very different in size and shape from those on the basidia of the hymenophore.

Spore deposits should be taken on white paper and air-dried or dried over silica gel before the color is recorded. There is a characteristic range in color, or color spectrum, for the genus. In this respect *Pholiota* is like other large genera such as *Psathyrella, Coprinus, Russula,* etc. The central color is a dull rusty brown to cinnamon brown and there are variations to reddish, earth brown or paler to ochraceous or clay-color to olive-yellow (in *P. olivaceodisca*). We believe that by using standardized spore prints by the drying methods suggested here, more can be done with the color of the spore deposit as a taxonomic character at the infrageneric level than we have done. We simply do not have the necessary data at this time. We do know, for instance, that in some species such as *P. polychroa* the spores are quite dark when moist, but we do not have properly dried spores for comparisons. One of the major problems still to be resolved in relation to *Pholiota* and the *Geophila* group of genera (*Psilocybe, Naematoloma* and *Stropharia*) demands critical observations on the color of the spore deposits, since this is at present the only major distinction between the two groups.

The spore wall for the genus is smooth by definition, but two species are admitted in which one can find irregularities on the surface of some of the spores (e.g. *P. aurea*). In thickness the wall ranges from less than 0.25 μ to 0.5 μ for the majority of the species, but in a number it is from 0.5–1.5 μ thick. The apical end is typically furnished with a germ pore, but in most species it is not broad enough to affect the outline of the spore apex as seen in optical section. In a relatively small number of species the spore apex appears somewhat truncate to distinctly truncate because of the width of the pore. It is the small-spored species of this group that Singer and Smith at one time segregated as the genus *Kuehneromyces*. However, we have found all degrees of the development of the germ pore from a broad one causing the apex of the spore to appear truncate to one so small it could hardly be discerned with a 1.4 NA oil immersion lens. On the basis of the material we have examined the truncate spore apex does not correlate well enough with other features of the basidiocarp to justify a group at the rank of genus or subgenus. This was a surprize to us, as it may be to others. We have found on some specimens that the pore, on spores from four-spored basidia is small and does not change the configuration of the spore apex, but on larger spores from 2-spored basidia the pore was larger and in some the apex could be termed truncate. As we see it, the important feature is the presence of the pore, not its width. Singer's (1963, p. 549) statement ". . . always with a broad truncate germ pore" simply does not hold up if you look at the spores. We might add that it is the spore which is truncate at the apex, not the germ pore. Singer's statement should be read this way.

When viewed from the front (face view), spores in *Pholiota* are usually elliptic. In the same mount, however, a species may exhibit a range in form from elliptic to ovate or subovate with one or the other usually dominating. In a large number of species the shape in face view is rather monotonously elliptic, with a smaller percentage in a field being subovate. In such instances little use can be made of spore-shape in the taxonomy of the genus. On the other hand, a few notable exceptions occur as in *P. pulchella,* in which the spores in optical section in face view are distinctly ovate to broadly subfusoid. They are also rather thick walled. In side-view (profile), it is common, in large numbers of species, to find that the spores are inequilateral to some degree, or vary in a different pattern to phaseoliform (bean-shaped). In our descriptions we have tried to indicate the degree to which the spore is inequilateral by the use of three terms: *obscurely, somewhat* and simply *inequilateral.* In an obscurely inequilateral spore in profile the ventral line in optical section is humped slightly on the side toward the apex—if one were to make a medial transverse section of the spore. The dorsal line, however, is "humped" slightly back of this medial section or about at the medial position, but in a transverse line across the spore the two humps do not coincide at their peaks. The degree to which the suprahilar plage is depressed will then be the factor most important in determining the category: if slightly depressed the spore is said to be *somewhat inequilateral.* If not or scarcely at all depressed the term *obscurely inequilateral* is used. If the suprahilar depression is distinct and the spore is drawn out to a more or less narrowed apex the unqualified term *inequilateral* applies. The term bean-shaped or phaseoliform means exactly what it says: the profile of a navy bean.

Spores in *Pholiota* vary with the species from small (3.5–5 × 2.5–3 μ) in *P. flammans,* to relatively large in *P. albocrenulata* (10–14–18 × 5.5–7–8 μ). In the bulk of the species, however, the spores fall in a range in length of 6–9 μ. In subgenus *Flammuloides* this is particularly true; there is one group of about fifty species in which they measure 5–7.5 × 3.5–4.5 μ.

Although reactions of the spore wall with iodine (Melzer's solution) have not been emphasized greatly in the study of brown spored agarics, we have found a group of species (subgenus *Flammula*) in which the spores are a darker reddish brown in it than when revived in KOH—in other words they are somewhat dextrinoid. This feature correlates so well with absence of pleurocystidia and bright yellow pilei that it is used as a major feature in redefining the subgenus. In *P. brunneidisca* a few spores show a violet-brown coagulated content in Melzer's reagent.

Basidia. These structures are normally clavate and 4-spored, and are of such uniformity in *Pholiota* that their importance in taxonomy as morphological structures showing differences is minor indeed. It is true that in some species they are relatively large, up to 40 × 10 μ, but most often they are 22–28 × 5–6 μ or smaller. In some species both 2- and 4-spored basidia were found, but none were consistently 2-spored only. At times the content of the cell may be brown in KOH, but this is not a constant feature of the type that can be used in species recognition. However, it is of theoretical interest in that in this genus some hyphae and their end-cells can serve as a container for certain compounds and still perform such basic functions as producing spores. More will be said of this feature under the heading of gloeocystidia.

Pleurocystidia. Sterile end-cells interspersed among the basidia in the hymenium are common and often conspicuous. In form, one encounters two general types: 1) those which project conspicuously beyond the hymenium, and 2) those which are more or less buried in it and project only slightly or not at all.

1. The projecting type. The term *Flammula*-type is no longer appro-

priate for this type as a name since the type species of *Flammula* does not have pleurocystidia. In shape this type is basically fusoid-ventricose. There is a long narrow pedicel, a broad submedial enlargement and a long often tapered neck ending in an obtuse to subacute apex. In many species the wall is uniformly rather thin, but in some the wall is obviously thickened at least over the ventricose region. In the following account the dividing line between "thick" and "thin" is at 0.5 μ. In some species less than half the cystidia will show a thickened wall. In others nearly all the cystidia will have walls 1.5–3 μ thick. There is an interesting problem here in the nature of the cell wall which needs critical study. We have used this wall feature as a sectional character in *Flammuloides* in order to focus attention upon it.

In some species the neck is more or less of equal diameter but in others it tapers gradually outward to the apex. In *P. macrocystis* the neck is rather uniformly constricted at its base. The apex, in a few species, may be encrusted and varies from acute to obtuse or broadly rounded. The content of these cystidia is of some interest. As revived in KOH many are found to have a homogeneous plug of yellow material which more or less fills the neck and may fill or nearly fill the ventricose portion also. Since chrysocystidia are described by some authors as having a yellow content in ammonia, or becoming differently colored with other dyes, the question as to whether these large cystidia are leptocystidia (which are said to lack distinctive content), or gloeocystidia of the type called chrysocystidia, is worth some thought. A discussion of this point is included under chrysocystidia. We have used the presence of these large pleurocystidia as the major feature of subgenus *Flammuloides*.

2. Chrysocystidia. In subgenus *Hemipholiota* as well as in section *Pholiota*, pleurocystidia of a kind different from the *Flammuloides* type are encountered. In general, these are non-projecting, clavate, often with an apical short protuberance, and often with an amorphous yellowish content in the enlarged portion as revived in weak bases such as KOH. Not infrequently the amorphous content is present only in some of the cystidia as seen in a given gill section, the others having a hyaline homogeneous content. This type of pleurocystidium (with the amorphous content) is termed a chrysocystidium if it has the refractive content or inclusion as revived in KOH. Their presence is used here as one of the features for distinguishing subgenus *Pholiota*. Accompanying these, one also often encounters pleurocystidia which are more or less clavate and at the same level as the basidia in the hymenium, but in contrast to the true chrysocystidia, their contents are partially or wholly brown. Since all these types of buried to very slightly projecting pleurocystidia are of about the same type and size, they have here been used to group together the species showing them. It should be understood that we recognize this collection of sterile end-cells as colored basidioles, true chrysocystidia and small leptocystidia, but in this group they intergrade to a remarkable extent. The point in our plan, which has some significance, is that it is

in this group that it appears that we are dealing with a group in which chrysocystidia are originating, and that various stages of development will be encountered, depending on which chemicals or stains one uses to differentiate the physical properties of the cell content.

We have also found that while the morphological types already outlined are in the main distinct, there are many species in which intergradation between types occur. In *P. simulans,* for instance, the pleurocystidia (as chrysocystidia) measure up to 58 μ long—as long as for many of the *Flammuloides*-type and are fusoid-pointed. To this one can add other information such as that in a number of the characteristically chrysocystidiate species such as *P. prolixa,* the amorphous-refractive inclusion becomes red in Melzer's reagent, indicating a chemical difference in the material involved when compared with species in which the chrysocystidial inclusion is merely dingy yellowish to scarcely colored in Melzer's. In *P. aurea* some of the basidioles, as revived in KOH, have an amorphous content resembling that of true chrysocystidia.

In our estimation one of the most interesting features discovered in the course of the present study is that cystidial shape and content are not necessarily correlated, and that the characterization of "chrysocystidia present" is hopelessly inadequate by itself in describing the cystidia of a *Pholiota*. A major feature of *Pholiota* is the diversity in cystidial content —as indicated in our descriptions. It deserves a special study by microchemical tests. It is hopeless to try and limit the term chrysocystidia in this genus to the end-cells of the hyphae of the laticiferous system as these occur in the hymenium. In *P. sola* we have observed hyphae with the content of oleiferous hyphae which ended in basidia with spores attached and with the basidia having the same distinctive content as the hyphae from which they originated. In short, *Pholiota* is a most interesting genus from the standpoint of the content of the hyphal cells.

The absence of pleurocystidia is the most difficult feature to use, since one must first search for imbedded cystidia, but there appears to be a group of species in which hymenial cystidia are truly absent. For this group it is actually best to check dried material because it is rather easy to spot the refractive inclusion in the hymenium of a chrysocystidium before one makes out the outline of the cell around it.

Cheilocystidia. By definition these are the hyphal end-cells on the gill edge which do not produce basidiospores. They may be in the form of basidioles, resemble the pleurocystidia in shape, or have their own distinctive morphological characters. They may also have distinctive content in the form of amorphous refractive material or a dull brown homogeneous content. In the subgenus *Pholiota* in some species the chrysocystidia found as pleurocystidia can also be found in the hymenium covering the gill edge. This is by no means unexpected. The same can be said for the types of pleurocystidia which approach in some measure true chrysocystidia. If fertile basidia occur on the gill edge these types are also to be expected there. In subgenus *Flammuloides* the cheilocystidia are often smaller than the pleurocystidia but basically the same type.

In general cheilocystidia tend to vary in morphology more than pleurocystidia, but they are typically reasonably constant for a species and in many instances do furnish valuable taxonomic characters. In fact the situation is roughly parallel to that found in *Galerina* (Smith and Singer 1964). In certain species the cheilocystidia are nine-pin-shaped, in others they are cylindric to filamentous or elongate-clavate, in others they are long- or short-fusoid to fusoid-ventricose, aciculate, vesiculose, spathulate, etc. The length of the neck varies with the species from short and thick to long and narrow and, of course, this is reflected in whether the apex is broadly rounded, obtuse or subacute. In some the neck is not uniform in diameter or evenly tapered but instead is somewhat moniliform, constricted to knobby or more rarely, branched. Encrusted or thick-walled cheilocystidia are rare.

The size varies with the species being small in some (14–20 μ long) and up to 75 μ long in others. The range in width for the genus is about like that for *Mycena, Galerina* and *Psathyrella,* rarely do they measure over 20 μ wide in the broadest part. Rarely are the cheilocystidia longer than the pleurocystidia. In *P. innocua* and in *P. simulans* the wall may be thickened noticeably over the ventricose portion or the apex. In *P. sola* they are often septate. In a collection from Alaska they are evidently somewhat gelatinous since in revived sections they usually appear agglutinated to each other. In no instance did we find the dark brown pigment present in a sufficient number of cells to impart color to the gill edge (but see *P. fagicola* and *P. hiemalis* with yellow gill edges). However, in species which show darkening of the gill edges from bruising, one can often find numerous colored cells in the damaged zone. This is a feature common throughout the Agaricales including the boletes.

Gill trama. The typical pattern for the genus consists of a central strand of subparallel to slightly interwoven non-gelatinous hyphae with cells varying from 3–6 μ wide, in some species, and to 12–20 μ in others and with some degree of inflation present at maturity. The walls are typically smooth and hyaline to slightly colored but in *P. bridgii* they are distinctly thickened and dark colored. Since a good share of our studies are from dried material not examined by either of us in the fresh state, we have tried to be conservative in using the degree of cell inflation and width of cell before inflation as taxonomic characters of significance, but it is probable that more detailed studies will reveal more differences on the order of those we have observed: hyphae 3–6 μ diam. as compared to 12–20 μ, and smooth vs. encrusted walls.

Perhaps the most outstanding single feature of the gill trama in *Pholiota* is the manner in which the hyphae of the subhymenium gelatinize to produce a distinct translucent zone (in KOH or H_2O mounts). We tried to correlate this feature with the presence of a gelatinous pileus epicutis and found the following: 1) Species in which both the cuticle of the pileus and the subhymenium are gelatinous. This may be said to be typical for the genus. 2) Those with a dry pileus and dry floccose subhymenium. This is the second largest group. 3) Those in which the cuticle is gelatinous but the subhymenium is not, as in *P. atripes, P. brunnea, P. innocua, P. pallida* and a few others. 4) Those with a non-gelatinous pileus epicutis but with a gelatinous subhymenium as in *P. squarrosa,* the type of the genus.

Pileus trama. The hyphae composing the trama (context) of the pileus commonly are disposed either radially or interwoven. In the radial type, tangential sections reveal the transverse ends of the hyphae suggesting a psueudoparenchyma. A radial section, however, will reveal the true arrangement and type of element. In the interwoven type, tangential sections merely show the hyphae interlaced. An intermediate type, radial-interwoven, is not infrequent, and is distinguished by radially-disposed hyphae, but these hyphae, instead of being parallel, are interwoven. In some instances, we have described the pileus trama as vesiculose; but whether this condition results from poorly dried material, or represents the true structure is not clear. We have not encountered truly amyloid hyphae in either the pileus cutis or context. However, one reaction we have observed with Melzer's reagent may have some significance. In a number of species, when the pileus context was revived in KOH, the hyphae revived exceptionally well and were seen to have a colloidal-appearing content (granular but homogeneous). Sections mounted in Melzer's show these same hyphae to have a cinnabar red to orange yellow content. This is a very striking reaction but one for which as yet the significance is not clear. It is the main difference between *Pholiota limonella* Peck and *P. squarroso-adiposa* Lange. However, it is a wide-spread reaction among the fungi. Smith has observed it in *Macowanites* (in the astrogastraceous fungi), in *Leccinum,* in the Boletaceae, and here in *Pholiota* to name the larger groups. In nearly all of these the very well revived hyphae in KOH with their colloidal-appearing content enabled the Melzer's reaction to be accurately predicted.

In most species examined, the pileus trama is homogeneous and is uniform throughout in structure. In *P. stratosa,* however, it is duplex; the outer (upper) half being loosely radial-interwoven; the inner (lower) half compactly radial. In *P. macrocystis,* the outer portion is of large vesiculose elements, and the inner of narrower elements.

Pileus Cuticle. The covering of the pileus in its simplest form is a more or less undifferentiated surface area—not greatly distinct in structure from that of the context. Examples of species in which the cuticle is not sharply differentiated include *P. angustifolia, anomala, duroides* and *scabella.* In a slightly more modified dermal layer, surface hyphae are darker and often with thicker walls than those of the tramal area. In some species the surface hyphae are repent, and with a few or no erect to semi-erect hyphae; in such a condition, the pileus is glabrous. In several species, however, hyphae, often darker brown and in clusters, occur in a more or less erect or even reclining position, and are seen on the pileus as scales. In more rare instances, erect specialized cells, clavate or cylindric, are present as pileocystidia. When the hyphae bearing these elements are erect and numerous they form what is known as a trichodermium. This latter type occurs mostly in subgenus *Flavidula* in varying degrees.

In viscid and glutinous species, a zone of the surface hyphae, when wet, becomes gelatinized. Thus, the cuticle is gelatinous, and in sections in KOH it is translucent, or glassy. The zone may be narrow or broad (50–400 μ), and very distinct under the microscope even under low magnification. In this gelatinous zone, hyphae or hyphal remnants persist for a long time even in mature pilei. Shaffer (1966) has recently discussed the modifications which hyphal walls undergo to produce a viscid or slimy layer (pellicle) and has pointed out how it is possible to have hyphae imbedded in slime (secreted by the cell) without the cell wall becoming involved through disintegration. In *Pholiota* both types undoubtedly occur but in our studies we were unable to distinguish clearly any cuticle of the pellicle type in which none of the gelatinization came from hyphal walls. In *Pholiota* the common occurrence is for the cuticle hyphae to have hyphal walls that gelatinize to some degree.

Usually, the gelatinous cutis rests on another zone, usually of brownish hyphae—the hypodermium. The hyphal components of it are often periclinal in arrangement, but in some species are more or less radial, and not infrequently their walls are encrusted. In some species a hypodermium is not differentiated. We regard the hypodermium in *Pholiota* as the upper zone of the pileus context, not part of the cuticle. This is because of the poorly defined nature of the zone, and too often the only differentiation is the presence of a small amount of pigmentation.

The general type of pileus cutis—whether of repent, dry hyphae, or of gelatinous hyphae—is highly important taxonomically at the subgenus, and species levels, and has been used to a great extent in this study.

Pileocystidia. In a comparatively few species, single-celled elements stand more or less erect on the pileus surface. These terminal cells, called pileocystidia, are differentiated, and they may be distinguished morphologically from a mere hyphal tip. We found pileocystidia in tufts in *P. canescens* and in *P. minor.* In the latter, they are similar to the cheilocystidia (subfusoid). Likewise, pileocystidia were found rarely in a few other species, but here they were scattered rather than in tufts. We have assigned to pileocystidia only minor taxonomic value since they are not a feature of very many species and those having them are not obviously closely related among themselves. In subgenus *Flavidula* they form the terminal cell of the trichodermial hypha and are treated as part of the trichodermium.

The stipe cutis, with few exceptions, is dry; in *P. adiposa,* however, the hyphae of the scales on the stipe are gelatinous. This is a diagnostic character for *P. adiposa* and a few other species. In a large number of species in subg. *Flammuloides* the hyphae at the stipe apex darken strongly in KOH. This is a feature of some significance, especially in the study of dried specimens.

Caulocystidia. In all *Pholiota* material examined in this work, longitudinal sections of the stipe apex (between the pileus and the annular zone) have been prepared and have been examined for caulocystidia. In many species caulocystidia were absent; in many others they were present and readily found. In instances where present, their morphology, is one of two types: 1) those which were similar to the cheilocystidia (or even the pleurocystidia, if present) ; and 2) those which differed in shape from the lamellar cystidia. In general, they may be scattered along the surface, or, in some species, may occur in distinct clusters or rosettes.

The taxonomic value of caulocystidia is, in our view, somewhat uncertain. In some collections of a species, they were found; in other collections of the same species they appeared to be absent. This situation was encountered sufficiently in these studies to cause avoidance of any considerable use of these structures in the separation of species or larger entities. Further study of their occurrence is necessary to a clear understanding of their significance in *Pholiota* systematics, but studies should be based on fresh material. Large thin-walled vesiculose cells in particular are often difficult to revive.

Clamp connections. For practical purposes, clamp connections were found in all species of *Pholiota* studied (except for *P. fulvosquamosa* and *P. cinchonensis*) . In rare instances, we assume that they escaped detection, either because they were very small and inconspicuous, or they were indeed very rare in their occurrence. We are not yet ready to assume that when not found in the course of ordinary examination they are not present to some extent somewhere in the basidiocarp. Because of their (almost?) universal presence in *Pholiota,* they offer no help in the separation of taxa, a situation in contrast to that in the genus *Crepidotus.*

Chemical Characters

KOH was used as a standard mounting medium and the usual darkening of hyphal walls from ochraceous to rusty brown was noted as occurring but has not been given particular emphasis in infrageneric classification simply because it did not seem practical. No red or green reactions as one frequently finds in other genera—*Panus, Cortinarius,* etc. were noted. KOH on the fresh basidiocarp usually gave some degree of browning reaction, but more studies are needed here as our data are necessarily incomplete, though the KOH reactions are apt to be at least somewhat similar on both fresh and dried material. KOH often dissolves the yellow to brown pigment to some extent. This is readily observed in the mounting medium.

$FeSO_4$ has been tested to some extent, mostly in recent years, and the typical reaction is olive to bright green. From preliminary studies we suspect most species of reacting, but the time required for the color change may vary considerably. Hence some reports of negative reactions may be unreliable. The situation will probably turn out about like it has for *Inocybe* (Stuntz per. com.) and our observations verify his, namely that here also almost all species react, but some more slowly than others. We have obtained green reactions with *P. macrocystis* and *P. flavopallida,* malachite green in *P. agglutinata,* instantly olive in *P. lurida, P. milleri* and *P. stratosa* and in *P. molesta* no change at all.

The reactions with Melzer's reagent are interesting and of considerable help taxonomically in some areas. Subgenus *Flammula,* as indicated elsewhere, is defined on the combination of dextrinoid spores and lack of pleurocystidia. We regard it as unusual that the spores of so many species of *Pholiota* are paler in Melzer's reagent than in KOH. In one species, *P. brunneidisca,* a few of the spores showed a dark purple-brown content— a feature unique in the family Strophariaceae as far as we are aware, and for which we have no explanation. The pileus context gives a bright orange-red reaction in Melzer's reagent as noted for *P. limonella.* This character is found in *Macowanites, Pholiota* and *Leccinum*—to name some obviously unrelated groups. It can usually be predicted by the colloidal appearance of the cell content in KOH as previously pointed out. As yet we need data on fresh material of these fungi to ascertain the difference in the reaction between fresh and revived hyphae. Our studies on this feature are from dried material revived directly in Melzer's reagent.

A critical study of the cystidial content of all *Pholiota* species is now in order to explore the value of the content as a taxonomic character, and to evaluate the category of chrysocystidia in relation to differences in chemical content of these organs. (See discussion of chrysocystidia p. 00)

EVOLUTIONARY TENDENCIES WITHIN PHOLIOTA

In as much as the concept of *Pholiota* proposed here is much broader than that of Singer (1963) some comment on it and the category of subgenus are particularly appropriate. By way of background it might be mentioned that when we began our study we had no intention of merging either *Kuehneromyces* or any part of *Phaeomarasmius* with *Pholiota.* Several factors, as will appear in the following discussion, caused us to change our view point. With the aid of a 1.4 N. A. Leitz apoch. objective we found that the spore of many species of *Phaeomarasmius* had a distinct though minute germ pore, and that the spore generally, as concerns shape and wall thickness was so similar, in many of the species Singer placed in *Phaeomarasmius,* to the typical *Pholiota* spore that no real basis could be found for distinguishing two genera on spore features.

Singer (1963, p. 593, line 14 from bottom) writes as follows concerning the problem of distinguishing *Pholiota* from *Phaeomarasmius*: "The genus *Phaeomarasmius* differs from *Pholiota* in size and habit, in spores with callus or with continuous spore wall rather than with germ pore, in the constant absence of cystidia or—if the sections of *Pholiota* without chrysocystidia are considered—in a different structure of the epicutis (the scales either made up of appressed fibrils, or else epicuticular hyphae gelatinized in the Pholiotas). Undoubtedly, the group *Pholiota tuberculosa, P. curvipes* and *P. lucifer* ss. Kühner & Romagnesi comes, among all Pholiotas, closest to *Phaeomarasmius*. They have an epicutis which is of cutis-structure with many hyphal fascicles ascending just as in other Pholiotas and not forming a trichodermium, . . . its hyphae being not so broad as in *Phaeomarasmius* and never so short, with a slight incrustation from the brown pigment but not conspicuously so, and never thick walled. The spores are here small, so that a confusion with the original group of *Phaeomarasmius* is out of the question, while the smaller-spored species with often thinner-walled epicuticular elements never have the bright colored veil characteristics for the three *Pholiota* species just mentioned."

In view of Singer's comments let us consider here in detail how we have found the various features involved to be distributed in North American population of concern to us. Of the species placed in *Phaeomarasmius* by Singer and included here we have:

1. *P. erinaceella*—no germ pore.
2. *P. curcuma*—with a minute pore.
3. *P. erinacea*—no apical pore.
4. *P. confragosa*—no germ pore.

Additional species which would be placed in *Phaeomarasmius* by the features of the pileus cuticle (but not included by Singer) are:

1. *P. pseudosiparia*—minute pore present. Pileus cutis of globose encrusted cells.
2. *P. granulosa* with a minute pore; pileus cutis a "collapsed" trichodermium, hyphal walls rusty-cinnamon, and slightly roughened.
3. *P. proximans*—minute pore present; pileus cutis normal for *Phaeomarasmius*.
4. *P. prominans* var. *subauripes*—minute pore present; pileus cutis a trichodermum (collapsing).
5. *P. cinchonensis*—no germ pore, no clamps; pileus cutis with suberect rusty brown hyphae.
6. *P. lactea*—distinct germ pore; pileus cutis with encrusted sphaerocysts.
7. *P. subechinata*—germ pore minute; pileus cuticle a trichodermium, hyphae encrusted.
8. *P. fagicola*—no germ pore. Pileus cuticle a collapsed trichodermium.

9. *P. squamulosa*—lacking a pore. Pileus cutis not *Phaeomarasmius*-like.
10. *P. curcuma var. lanatipes*—pore present; cuticle like that of *Phaeomarasmius*.
11. *P. minutula*—apex of spore truncate from pore; pileus cuticle of encrusted appressed tubular hyphae.
12. *P. murrillii*—pore minute. Pileus cuticle a trichodermium but hyphae not strongly encrusted or dark brown in KOH.
13. *P. pseudolimulata*—apical pore present; pileus cuticle a trichodermium with smooth to encrusted hyphal walls.
14. *P. corticola*—spore with a "callus." Pileus cuticle a tangled turf of brown encrusted hyphae.
15. *P. cyathicola*—no germ pore; cutis not like *Phaeomarasmius*.
16. *P. punicea*—no pore. Cuticle ± as in *P. confragosa*.
17. *P. canescens*—pore minute; pileus cuticle somewhat Phaeomarasmioid.

Of the second group eleven have spores with germ pore, and in one it is broad enough to cause the spore apex to be somewhat truncate. Counting all the species with a pore and a cuticle of the type Singer admits as characteristic of *Phaeomarasmius,* we have ten species. For the known North American species with central stipes, then, it is clear that the *Phaeomarasmius* type of pileus cuticle is more frequently correlated with a germ pore at the spore apex than not—by a score of two to one. On this basis the correlation of lack of a germ pore with the presence of a Phaeomarasmioid pileus cuticle as a feature distinguishing *Phaeomarasmius* as a genus is best abandoned.

The nature of the epicutis of the pileus is such that its features do not lend themselves as well to tabular presentation as does the presence or absence of a germ pore at the apex of the spore. Singer has raised the point of the meaning of a typical trichodermium as against appressed hyphae in fascicles with the ends ascending. The problem of using the presence of a trichodermium as a generic character in this instance cannot be considered independently from the problem of the origin of such an epicutis.

If a parallel situation may be regarded as of some value in indicating the direction of evolution we may review the situation in *Pluteus* where the *P. cervinus* complex (Section *Pluteus*) contains species with a cutis of tubular hyphae (including the end-cell). In other words this cutis, as regards hyphal differentiation, must be regarded as primitive, for the primitive hypha generally in Basidiomycetes is of this type. Smith (unpublished data) has been able to observe all degrees of hyphal differentiation starting with the enlargement of the hyphal end-cells to a somewhat cystidioid condition, and a general shortening of the cells in the cuticular hyphae. These cystidioid end-cells have a tendency to be somewhat ascending either singly or in fascicles, and as this development progresses a condition is approached which is used to recognize section

Hispidoderma—a tangled mass of hyphal end-cells cystidioid in shape. As the shortening process continues the cystidia become shorter and more compactly arranged until a hymenium-like layer results. In *Pluteus* it is certainly evident that the hymeniform type of cuticle could have originated in this manner with fewer changes in the genome of the group than by any other means.

The same explanation of this formation of the trichodermium of *Phaeomarasmius* is equally as plausible. The name *Pholiota* means scale and this is the keynote to a good share of the genus. Here we find what we have termed the "collapsed" trichodermium meaning that the layer is sparse enough when the pileus is mature so that the hyphal elements do become more or less decumbent as the pileus expands. Since we have filamentous, intermediate (collapsed trichodermium) and trichodermial types as well as the granulose type in *Pholiota,* it appears more logical to us to assume that the more complex type evolved from the undifferentiated type.

On this basis we do not admit that the cuticle types as used by Singer have any value in delimiting genera in the present case. The color of the veil in *P. proximans* is much like that of *P. curvipes,* so we also exclude veil color as having any generic significance. In fact, it seems clear to us that the major aspects of evolution in *Pholiota* have been concerned with cuticle types.

In view of the strong likelihood that the trichodermial type of cuticle originated in the manner just discussed, we consider *Phaeomarasmius* as a genus to be distinguished by its more or less eccentric stipe in addition to the cuticle type (trichodermium), and large spores as proposed by Singer. In this way, the genus is found to occupy an end position in the *Flavidula* branch of *Pholiota.* That so many intermediate species are still in our flora, can hardly indicate that more genera should be recognized. We regard the *Flavidula* line to have bifurcated with species having a *Cystoderma*-type cuticle as one branch, and those leading to the *P. erinacea* type forming the other.

Thus *Pholiota aurea* appears to us to be more in the "orbit" of *Pholiota* than in *Cystoderma.* Because of its size it is very distinct from the other species, but the same size range (or nearly so) is found in *Cystoderma.* The thin-walled at times slightly ornamented spores are the best reason for excluding *P. aurea* from *Pholiota.* This point should be studied by EM photographs.

One uniting feature of the whole group (*Flavidula*) as we have outlined it is that the hyphal walls become a darker brown or change to brown upon the application of KOH.

We do not put any generic emphasis on the presence or absence of cheilocystidia as we feel that this is a more minor character best used at the species or section level.

A second feature which rather well unifies this whole subgenus is the general tendency to produce a rather persistent yellow pigment with the result that color throughout the subgenus falls rather strikingly into a spectrum from pale yellow to rich reddish brown. Since this is also a feature of the subgenus *Flammuloides* and subg. *Pholiota,* (the bulk of the genus), we believe the pigmentation pattern supports our conclusions in regard to the probable path of evolution as based on the structure of the pileus cuticle. Hence we have used Romagnesi's admirably descriptive name, *Flavidula,* for this group.

To us it is also an indication of a connection to *Pholiota* that *P. corticola* and *P. cyathicola* have a gelantinous subhymenium—a very prominent feature in subgenera *Flammuloides* and *Pholiota.*

We have found pleurocystidia present as pseudocystidia on *P. murrillii,* leptocystidia in *P. erinacea, P. pseudolimulata, P. corticola P. cyathicola, P. anomala,* and *P. canescens*—the latter two not typical of the central group in *Phaeomarasmius.* To us, however, this means that in this group as in most groups of Agaricales, some species do develop cystidia and that as a character it does not correlate with the other features of *Phaeomarasmius.*

Because the problem of *Phaeomarasmius* (type species), *Tubaria* and certain other brown-spored agarics with small basidiocarps needs to be made the object of a special study involving E.M. photographs of spores, our purpose here is to merely group in *Pholiota* the species we suspect belong there in a natural classification and obviously do not claim to have investigated all ramifications of the problem of the borderline taxa. *Phaeomarasmius* is thus maintained at least temporarily for the species with eccentric stipes or lateral attachment of the pileus to the substratum.

Kuehneromyces. This genus was proposed by Singer and Smith (1946) for *Pholiota* species with truncate spores. In the course of the present study this feature came under critical scrutiny with some interesting results. In *P. minutula* of subg. *Flavidula* we found that with a 1.4 N.A. oil immer. lens the larger spores appeared truncate. In a number of specimens of *Pholiota aurivelloides* the spores, or at least many of them, appeared truncate. It will be noted in the descriptions that for many species the germ pore is large enough to affect to some degree the configuration of the spore apex. To this one might add that by far the majority of species included in our concept of *Pholiota* have spores with an apical pore. The unavoidable question, then, is not one of the presence or absence of a pore, but rather how large it is—and it is here that the main character for *Kuehneromyces* as a genus breaks down. For the spore in most of the species included by Singer (1963) is not "always with a broad truncate germ pore" (l.c., p. 549). We even noted one instance of a basidiocarp with two and four-spored basidia where the large spores were truncate but those on four-spored basidia were not. Singer attempted to correlate the truncate spore with other features such as lack of dermato-cystidia but again this does not hold because so many of the species have caulocystidia. In short the evidence, as presented in the following descriptions, convinced us that *Kuehneromyces* was untenable as a genus.

For the most part its species have their relationships with others in subgenus *Hemipholiota,* with the result that the truncate spore as a character is used to define a section with several stirpes which show intergradation with *Naematoloma, Stropharia* or *Psilocybe.*

In our estimation the North American species Singer placed in *Pachylepyrium* finds a logical place along with section *Confragosae* as a subgenus (*Hygrotrama*) in *Pholiota.* The thick walled spore (wall 0.5-1.8 μ thick) as well as the intense pigmentation are found in other species not closely related but obviously in *Pholiota, P. pulchella* for instance, with the spore wall about 0.5 μ thick. Both features are merely a matter of degree of development. The color spectrum of the spore deposit for *Pholiota* is from ferruginous to earth-brown, to yellow-brown ("bister" etc.) to cinnamon-brown to clay-color or more ochraceous, and within this range, in our estimation, it is forcing the issue to make generic groupings with one of these shades as a major character.

The subgenus *Pholiota* with *P. squarrosa* as type pin-points the name as associated with scaly species lacking any gelatinization in the pileus cuticle. Here, however, the subhymenium is usually gelatinous whereas in subg. *Flavidula* it is rarely gelatinous. Hence, in many respects the type of the genus is close to subg. *Flavidula* as far as anatomical features are concerned. However, the most widely known (and as it turns out the most frequently misidentified species) are in section *Adiposae,* where, through the development of gelatinous layers in the cuticle, we see the beginnings of a connection to subg. *Flammuloides.*

Flammuloides as a subgenus contains the largest number of species of any of the subgenera and the species may be said to have evolved in an almost routine manner, since the characters are largely different patterns of pigmentation, slight but constant differences in spore size, features of pleuro-, cheilo-, and caulocystidia, favored substrata, and the usual odd characters of one type or another which crop out in most of the larger groups of Agarics in general—in fact speciation in subgenus *Flammuloides* may be characterized as monotonous.

Subg. *Flammula* as typified by *F. flavida* necessitated a shift in the use of the name from cystidiate species with non-dextrinoid spores to acystidiate species with at least weakly but distinctly dextrinoid spores. This is one of those unfortunate changes in the meaning of a name which cannot be helped. It is brought about by the type-system in nomenclature.

From the standpoint of evolution subg. *Hemipholiota* is most interesting since it is in this group that we have placed the "primitive" species of *Pholiota* such as *P. discolor, P. mutans* and *P. striatula.* These connect to *Galerina* mostly and indicate to us the probable area of origin of the genus. More important, however, is the frequent appearance of chryso-cystidia and types approaching chrysocystidia. When Smith (1951) mono-graphed *Naematoloma* he was not aware that there are more species of rusty-brown spored agarics with chrysocystidia than there are species of *Naematoloma* with purple-brown spores, and hence included some brown-spored fungi in *Naematolma*. These are transferred to subg. *Phaeanaema-taloma*. Some have a truncate spore and some do not. Because of the number of variations of the chrysocystidial type found in this subgenus, we believe that this type of cystidium had an independent origin in this group and that certain aspects concerning cystidial content have been maintained through the rest of the genus regardless of the morphology of the cystidium. The development of the apical germ pore of the spore has occurred in all subgenera, but in *Hemipholiota* it appears to have become linked in some measure with the absence of pleurocystidia. Thus real intergradation with *Psilocybe* results, since the spore deposit in the latter genus is vinaceous-brown in some species not too dissimilar from those of stirps *Vernalis*.

But *Hemipholiota* contains a number of evolutionary segments. The type, *P. destruens* stands out in the group as an odd-sized species much as *P. aurea* stands out in subg. *Flavidula*. The *P. albivelata* group con-nects obviously to ́*Stropharia* not only by the well developed annulus but by the presence of chrysocystidia. The spores are not "broadly truncate" it is true, but neither are they in *Stropharia squamosa*. In short, from subg. *Hemipholiota* as treated here we have the basic group from which the other subgenera including *Phaeonaematoloma* most likely evolved.

The major lines of evolution in the genus as we see them, may be summarized as follows:

1) The development of gelatinous layers—in pileus cuticle and sub-hymenium—subg. *Flammuloides*.

2) The development of the outer veil to form dry scales as it breaks on both pileus and stipe—subg. *Pholiota* (type species) .

3) The development of "dry" species either with a granulose outer covering (veil) or trichodermium as a pileus cuticle in the extreme forms—subg. *Flavidula*.

4) A development leading toward *Stropharia, Naematoloma* and *Psilo-cybe* (the "*Geophilia*" group) . This we distinguish as a separate taxon because the features of a truncate spore and presence of chrysocystidia become linked in *Pholiota* to make a unified group distinct from *Hemipholiota*. The interesting feature here is that in reality these two features are not any more closely linked in the "*Geophila*" group than in *Pholiota*. In *Geophila* we have purple brown-spored fungi most of which have more or less truncate spores, and *many* of which have chrysocystidia. In fact, with the present study as a background, it is now clear to us that if *Pholiota* is to be maintained as distinct from "*Geophila*" the color of the spore deposit makes a better distinction

than the presence of chrysocystidia combined with a glabrous or nearly glabrous pileus.

It is interesting to note in this arrangement that the most clearly defined subgenera, *Flavidula* and *Flammuloides,* are the terminal or near terminal groups. That *Hemipholiota* represents the basic gene pool from which evolutionary lines diverged, and that subg. and sect. *Pholiota* by accident of typification represents a small group not too far removed from *Flavidula.* Finally, the overall trend of evolution, particularly in *Hemipholiota,* shows a progression toward "*Geophila.*" Thus as we have outlined the genus here we have used the category of subgenus to indicate the major gene-pools within the group and the major trends from them, with, we admit, the type subgenus and section actually left at a level that would ordinarily be regarded as a stirps, though, it must be admitted, a central one as far as the genus as a whole is concerned.

The relationships outlined here are merely a confirmation of the original ideas of L. Quélet (1886) . It is most unfortunate that the generic names *Dryophila* and *Geophila* are not tenable under the rules.

The problem of the relationships of smaller groups to each other is difficult in this genus, in particular since the only evidence that can be brought to bear on them at present is somewhat subjective as far as macroscopic features are concerned.

The division of *Flavidula* into two major lines is somewhat subjective in that it is only in the extremes that the *Cystoderma*-type of pileus cutis is truly distinct from the trichodermial type. A gene change to cause the cells to be short and wide rather than long and narrow admittedly would not need to be very great. Hence one cannot say that *P. granulosa,* for instance, originated from other species with a more or less granulose cuticle—it might as well have arisen from a species with trichodermial hyphae having relatively long narrow cells.

INTERGENERIC RELATIONSHIPS

In our opinion the genus *Pholiota* originated from *Galerina* or *Galerina*-like species. We find in *Galerina* the development of an apical pore in the basidiospores, and all degrees of development from a thin spot termed a callus to a pore which in a few species is broad enough to cause the apex to be obscurely truncate—in other words a pore about the size found in most species of *Pholiota*. In *Galerina* we also find the subhymenium gelatinizing in a few smooth spored species. The same may be said for gelatinous layers in the pileus cuticle but we do not consider this as important in intergeneric relationships as the others because most genera of Agarics show some degree of cuticle gelantinization. To us the important feature between the two genera is the shift in emphasis of the important characters.

GALERINA	PHOLIOTA
1) Spore apex, a fair number with pore more or less distinct.	1) Pore characteristic of most species.
2) Subhymenium. Gelatinous in a few species.	2) Gelatinous in most species.
	3) Over 75% of the species.
3) Pileus cuticle gelatinous in some part, less than 25% of species.	4) Dark brown to cinnamon brown in great majority, yellow to tawny in a few.
4) Spore color yellow to fulvous in great majority.	

In other words, the features which appear in *Galerina* have become combined to be characteristic of the genus in *Pholiota*. This spells out a probable direction of evolution that is difficult to deny and does not bring into the discussion any gastromycetous ancestors. Just as *Pholiota* has evolved in several directions so has *Galerina* and it is in one of these lines that we find the trend toward *Pholiota*. *Pholiota mutans*, *P. discolor* and *P. striatula* approach *Galerina* so closely that when monographing the latter genus the question arose as where to place them. A second major trend in *Galerina* is toward or into *Cortinarius*. *G. odorata* and *G. cortinarioides* are readily mistaken for small *Cortinarii*. If this connection is accepted, it is of course logical to place *Pholiota* beside *Galerina* in the *Cortinariaceae*.

If we now consider the species placed in *Hemipholiota* and *Phaeonaematoloma* we can find direct trends toward the Strophariaceae; since the yellow pigmentation, the apical germ-pore of the spore and particularly cystidial types are all found in the Strophariaceae in about the same pattern. If one disregards the color of the spore deposit, he has no features left by which *Pholiota* can be distinguished from the Strophariaceae. We are concerned here with many species so it cannot be claimed that there are only a few intermediates. As features relating *Pholiota* to "*Geophila*" we find that most of the rusty brown spored specied with a truncate spore-apex have small spores which exhibit a slight tendency to become compressed (*P. vernalis*). In *Psilocybe*, to which this stirps connects many more species have compressed spores so here again we have a situation in which certain characters prominent in one genus are found in a less developed state in a related, presumably more primitive, genus.

As to chrysocystidia, we find them in many more different states of development from species to species in *Pholiota* than in "*Geophila*" where they are more uniform as to the nature of the inclusion. Here however the claim cannot be made that this cystidial type is more "primitive" in *Pholiota* and more advanced in "*Geophila*" because in the number of species involved and in the diversity of this type of cystidium both are large groups and show about the same gamut of changes. In other words in a comparison of subg. *Phaeonaematoloma* and "*Geophila*" as to chrysocystidia and related types, the two groups merge rather evenly. This might be used as an argument for dividing *Pholiota* and placing those species with chrysocystidia and related types in *"Geophila,"* but it must be remembered that the type of *Pholiota* has these cystidia as well as lacking gelatinous layers in the pileus cuticle. Consequently we have adhered to the classical distinction between the two—the color of the spore deposit—as being the most useful feature and the one leaving us with the fewest intermediate species.

Pachylepyrium Singer (1957) is to our minds a superfluous genus. It ,is admitted that when Singer erected it it seemed quite distinct but in view of the present study, like *Kuehneromyces*, it falls by the wayside. There are a number of species in *Pholiota* with thick walled (0.5 μ ±) spores dark in color—*P. pulchella* as already mentioned, so this feature appears in viscid as well as dry species. In fact it is found occasionally throughout the genus. The character follows about the same pattern of appearance as thickened cystidial walls, only species with the latter are concentrated in one section by definition.

The subject of relationships should not be dropped, however, without a few comments concerning *Inocybe*. Like certain other genera, this one is an anomaly in that it is readily recognized at sight by the *"Inocybe* aspect"* and yet when its important macroscopic and microscopic features are put down on paper the recognition of the genus from the description is most difficult. If we eliminate the species with angular to nodulose spores as not presenting a problem, we find the basic features of the smooth spored species to read very much like those of *Pholiota* in a number of respects. The color of the spore deposit is not too different (clay-color to yellow-brown or earth-brown) ; cheilocystidia are practically universally present, pleurocystidia are frequently present, and veil development is copious in a number of species.

The points of difference are that to our knowledge gelatinizing hyphae in the subhymenium are not found in *Inocybe* and few if any species have a viscid pileus caused by the hyphal walls of the epicuticular hyphae gelatinizing. Actually, *Inocybe* is conspicuous among the large brown-spored genera because of the lack or almost complete lack of the last mentioned feature. Also, the over-all picture from an ecological standpoint is different. *Inocybe* like *Cortinarius* is a conspicuously terrestrial genus. *Pholiota* is a conspicuously lignicolous one—so much so that one retains reservations in his own mind even in regard to species which are described as terrestrial. The pileus surface is also quite different—in most *Inocybe* species it is of dry matted radial fibrils quite different from the non-viscid *Pholiota* species. In *Inocybe* lamprocystidia are common, in *Pholiota* they are limited to a single section and may be regarded as not so clearly differentiated. We do not know of any *Inocybe* species with true chrysocystidia. Our over-all impression of the two genera, then, is that any similarities between them are more likely explained as parallelisms than as indicating close relationship. This conclusion is in line with that of previous authors and has not been supplanted by the additions to *Pholiota* included in the present treatise.

Lastly, a few comments on the gastroid genus *Nivatogastrium* are in order. When Singer and Smith (1959) described this genus they related it to *Pholiota* and nothing we have discovered since has indicated a different alignment. The gelatinous layer in the glebal trama was described as hymenopodium, whereas the subhymenium was described as cellular and non-gelatinous. The homologies as we see them now are that the gelatinous layer we have termed subhymenium corresponds to the hymenopodium in *Nivatogastrium*. This is not a contradiction, in fact it is very likely a situation brought about by the gastroid condition. It is common in the *Hymenogastraceae* for the one to three cells below a basidium to inflate greatly thus producing a layer, whereas in *Pholiota* cells in a similar position do not enlarge to form a layer and in fact are continuous with the gelatinous layer. By definition the subhymenium is the layer giving rise to the hymenium.

The real problem, however, is: How does *Nivatogastrium* fit into the the picture of evolution to or from *Pholiota*? We believe the genus is a gastroid extension of *Flammuloides*. It is difficult to visualize a lignicolous fungus fruiting under the cold conditions of the snow-line in the mountains having its direct ancestors hypogeous in the soil. More important, however, is the fact all major anatomical characters connect to *Flammuloides* and we know of no hypogeous species with such a combination of features. Hence we regard the genus as a reduced agaric.

PRACTICAL IMPORTANCE OF PHOLIOTA

Edibility. From the standpoint of edibility we would list *P. squarrosoides* and *P. barrowsii* as the best in the genus and among the good edible species on this continent. We cannot recommend *P. squarrosa* as highly because it tends to develop a disagreeable flavor, and there are certain strains of it which do not cook up well-flavored even if young specimens are used. Also Shaffer (1965) has reported a "mild" case of poisoning by it. The *Pholiota aurivella* group has long been used for the table without much regard for species identity as it turns out. We recommend them as average, but the slime should be wiped from the pileus before using them and this also removes the scales. Kühner and Romagnesi (1953 p. 328) give *P. adiposa* one star—which is about where we would rate the American variants. However, they list *P. mutabilis* with 3 stars meaning excellent, and Dr. Bille-Hansen of Copenhagen informs us that in Denmark it is rated high because of its excellent flavor. It has not been used much in this country as far as we are aware, but in the Pacific Northwest it is abundant and could well be on the choice list. It is also easy to recognize in the stages most desirable for eating by the numerous recurved scales on the stipe.

However, *Pholiota* as a genus in the enlarged modern concept may contain some species at least mildly poisonous. Also, since in their general aspect some species resemble the *Galerina* species of the *Autumnalis* complex, and since this group contains some very poisonous ones, no one should eat a *Pholiota* without being sure it is identified accurately and that the species is known to be edible. None of the species recommended above resemble possible poisonous species closely except *P. mutabilis* which in stature somewhat resembles the *G. autumnalis* group.

Kühner and Romagnesi list *P. lubrica, P. spumosa,* and *P. carbonaria* (*Flammula carbonaria* Fries sensu authors), under *Dryophila* as edible with one star—meaning average. We have all of these in North America, but in view of the many closely related species described as new and for which we have no information on edibility we cannot recommend them. We cannot help but call to mind the case of *Togaria aurea* (Fr.) W. G. Smith (*Pholiota aurea* of the present work) which is recommended as choice in Europe (3 stars in Kühner and Romagnesi), but in Alaska Wells and Kempton (1965) have found that a number of people are consistently poisoned by it. This pattern as regards edibility is a real threat in the group, and promiscuous testing of species whose edibility is not known is definitely discouraged.

PHOLIOTA SPECIES AS THE CAUSE OF WOOD-DECAY. From our point of view based on field observations it is obvious that this genus plays a major role in slash disposal in both deciduous and conifer forests. As evidence of this we need only to cite the occurrence of *Pholiota polychroa* on oak slash 3-5 years old as observed by Smith near Ann Arbor, and the frequency with which *Pholiota decorata* and *Pholiota spumosa* occur on conifer slash in the Rocky Mountains and Pacific Northwest. In addition to these activities certain species obviously play an important role as root-rot fungi, namely *Pholiota terrestris* and *Pholiota squarrosa*. In the Trout Lake area of the San Juan Mountains of southwestern Colorado it was a common sight to see large clusters of this species at and near the bases of both aspens and conifers—it is often impossible to be sure of which conifer species, but Engleman Spruce is certainly involved. In view of this feature of *Pholiota squarrosa* locally in this one area, and the presence of variants in the species based on such features as color of the basidiocarps in one and an odor of garlic in another it is clear that the species is variable. From field observations, however, we suspect that perhaps one of the most active root-rotting fungi in the genus at least in the Pacific Northwest is *Pholiota terrestris* which fruits from buried wood and dead roots. The clusters nearly always appear terrestrial, which is why the species epithet was applied.

Another complex, very common in the conifer forests of the Rocky Mountains, is that here designated as subgenus *Flammula*. These fungi are often common during wet summers in the Salmon River country of Idaho. In the Sawtooth Wilderness Area giant clusters are often encountered under such conditions. Here again we have a number of morphological variants that need to be carefully compared, in culture, as to nutritional requirements and other cultural characters.

In the Lake States *Pholiota squarrosoides* is one of the major causes of decay in logs of *Acer saccharum* and *Tilia glabra*. In fact the decaying trunks of the latter are reduced in very short time. Smith followed the course of decay in one tree near Ann Arbor. The log was relatively sound when discovered with a few basidiocarps of *P. squarrosides* on it. Four years later there was almost nothing left of it. In the interval, during two seasons, large masses of basidiocarps were observed. *P. albocrenulata* causes a heart rot of maple trees, at least the basidiocarps occur in a pattern indicating this, but we have no data of our own to indicate the extent of damage produced or the rate of decay. The fungus can attack trees down to 6″ DBH. In fact, *P. albocrenulata* is to be regarded as one of the characteristic species of the beech-maple association, but was found on ponderosa pine in New Mexico by Barrows and Isaacs.

Cottonwood and Lombardy poplar are commonly attacked by *Pholiota destruens*. This fungus appears to form a primary decay as fruiting bodies often occur on the cut surface of the stump or log-ends. This species has been studied in some detail in culture.

Anyone collecting in irrigated country where Lombardy poplars were planted along the ditches many years ago has probably seen this species. These trees are now being cut down because of die-back and over-maturity. One will find this species in quantity on the stumps or logs during cool wet weather in November. On one trip through the John Day country of Oregon during November, we observed basidiocarps of this species on almost every log or stump of cottonwood or Lombardy poplar in a fifty mile stretch.

In summary, we can say from our own observations that *Pholiota* is a genus in which physiological specialization has progressed along the lines of using various components of wood for its nutriment, and no mycorrhizal forms clearly belonging here are known. The opposite is true for *Hebeloma* in which it is very likely true that all or nearly all the species are mycorrhiza formers. As we have treated *Pholiota* here we regard it as the major genus of wood-rotting agarics having colored spores.

TAXONOMIC TREATMENT

TAXONOMIC TREATMENT

PHOLIOTA (Fr.) Kummer

Der Führer in die Pilzkunde, p. 22. 1871

Agaricus trib. Pholiota Fries, Syst. Mycol. 1: 240. 1821.
Agaricus trib. Flammula Fries, Syst. Mycol. 1: 250. 1821.
Hypodendrum Paulet, Traité Champ., pl. 137. 1825.
Flammula (Fr.) Kummer, Der Führer in die Pilzkunde, p. 22. 1871.
Pholiota (Fr.) Quélet, Champ. Jura et Vosges, p. 124. 1872-73.
Flammopsis Fayod, Ann. Sc. Nat. Bot. VII, 9: 356. 1889.
Dryophila Quélet, Enchir. Fung. p. 66. 1886.
Visculus Earle, Bull. N. Y. Bot. Gard. 5: 437. 1909.
Kuehneromyces Singer & Smith, Mycologia 38: 504. 1946.
Pachylepyrium Singer, Sydowia 11: 321. 1957.

Description of Genus

Pileus diameter variable from species to species (1-20 cm), pileus convex to conic, more rarely hemispheric, then plane, at times umbonate, more rarely depressed; dry, moist, viscid or slimy; of various colors; scaly, fibrillose, or glabrous; context thick or thin, often more or less concolorous with the surface; odor and taste mild or not distinctive, or more rarely distinctive; lamellae variously attached but rarely decurrent, brownish at maturity, paler at first and then white, pallid, yellowish, or brownish; narrow to broad; close to distant; stipe often darker colored at the base, scaly, fibrillose, or nearly glabrous, dry or (very rarely) viscid, solid or hollow, central; inner veil arachnoid and fugacious, more rarely membranous and forming a persistent, superior to median annulus, sometimes appendiculate; outer veil virtually undeveloped, or in many species leaving remnants as fibrils or conspicuous scales, rarely the scales viscid; spores ellipsoid to ovoid or subovoid in face view, often inequilateral to phaseoliform in profile, wall medium thin to moderately thick and double, smooth, germ-pore present, in some species obscure or not discernible, sometimes broad and the spore-end truncate; basidia clavate, 2- 4-spored; pleurocystidia present in many species, sometimes as chrysocystidia, absent in others; cheilocystidia almost always present and either similar to the pleurocystidia (if present) or different, more rarely as chrysocystidia; gill

37

trama usually subparallel, sometimes more or less interwoven, at times forming a mediostrate and then the subhymenium gelatinous; pileus trama more or less homogeneous, its hyphae disposed radially to interwoven; cuticle filamentous, often of repent hyphae and dry, or again the surface hyphae gelatinizing and forming a gelatinous zone which usually rests on a distinct zone of brownish hyphae—a hypodermium, or hypodermium not differentiated; pileocystidia rare; clamp connections present, and found in nearly all species (rarely not found) ; caulocystidia at the apex absent, or present and then scattered or in tufts, at times similar to the lamellar cystidia; growing on wood, sawdust, débris, humus, soil, or more rarely in sphagnum beds or on charcoal.

TYPE SPECIES: *Pholiota squarrosa.*

Key to Subgenera of Pholiota

1. Pileus cuticle lacking any gelatinous layers (surface granulose to fibrillose or scaly, or rarely canescent, glabrous and hygrophanous 2
1. Pileus cuticle with a layer of gelatinized hyphae in some part (surface may be glabrous to scaly) 4
   2. Pileus glabrous and hygrophanous or merely silky to canescent over the surface (see Subg. Hemipholiota) .... Subg. *Hygrotrama*
   2. Pileus dry, scaly to granulose or coarsely fibrillose 3
3. Pileus and stipe scaly to coarsely fibrillose (but not granulose) and chrysocystidia (or similar cells) present in hymenium. ....
.... Subg. *Pholiota*
3. Pileus fibrillose, scaly or granulose, lacking chrysocystidia in hymenium
.... Subg. *Flavidula*
   4. Pleurocystidia absent; spores at least weakly dextrinoid ....
.... Subg. *Flammula*
   4. Not as above 5
5. Pileus and stipe typically distinctly scaly at the time the veil breaks; chrysocystidia or somewhat similar structures present in hymenium
.... Subg. *Pholiota* Sect. *Adiposae*
5. Not as above 6
   6. Pleurocystidia present and promiently projecting ....
.... Subg. *Flammuloides*
   6. Pleurocystidia not as above 7
7. Pleurocystidia absent or if present as leptocystidia then not projecting appreciably .... Subg. *Hemipholiota*
7. Pleurocystidia present as chrysocystidia .... Subg. *Phaeonaematoloma*

Subgenus **Hygrotrama** subg. nov.

Pileus glaber vel subfibrillosus, udus, hygrophanus vel subhygrophanus, non-viscidus.

TYPUS: *Pholiota subangularis.*

Key to Sections

1. Spores with wall less than 0.5 μ thick (usually less than 0.25 μ thick)
.... Section *Confragosae*
1. Spores with wall 0.5 μ thick or more .... Section *Hygrotrama*

Section **Confragosae** (Singer) comb. nov.

Phaeomarasmius section *Confragosi* Singer, Sydowia 15: 75. 1962.

In this group are placed species with a non-viscid moist and more or less hygrophanous pileus which is glabrous except possibly for some superficial veil remnants or is canescent at first. Pleurocystidia are absent or inconspicuous, if present they are not the type known as chrysocystidia.

If the pileus is viscid or has gelatinized subcutis and pleurocystidia are absent to inconspicuous see subgenus *Hemipholiota*.

Key to Species

1. Clavate-rostrate pleurocystidia scattered in the hymenium ....
.... *P. anomala*
1. Pleurocystidia present as pseudocystidia or subcapitate or absent 2
  2. Growing on charred wood; pileus dark red .... *P. punicea*
  2. Not as above 3
3. Pleurocystidia present and mostly capitate .... *P. canescens*
3. Pleurocystidia absent .... *P. confragosa*

    1. Pholiota anomala Peck, Bull. Torrey Club 22: 202. 1895.
Illustrations: Text figs. 483, 486.

Pileus 1.5–2.5 cm broad, at first hemispheric or subconic, then convex, hygrophanous, broccoli-brown when moist, pale yellow or cream colored when dry, warm buff in dried plants, glabrous.

Lamellae adnate or decurrent, pale, becoming brownish ferruginous, in dried plants ochraceous-orange to cinnamon, medium close or slightly distant, rather narrow (3–4 mm).

Stipe 3–6 cm long, 2–6 mm thick, whitish or brownish, fibrillose or glabrous, hollow with irregular transverse partitions, or filled with a cottony tomentum, equal. Veil forming a slight, finally evanescent annulus.

Spores 7–10 × 4–5.5 μ, smooth, apical pore small but distinct; shape in face view elliptic to somewhat oval, in profile mostly somewhat inequilateral varying to bean-shaped; color in KOH distinctly yellow singly (individual spores), with a tawny tinge as seen in groups; in Melzer's reagent merely yellowish; wall about 0.25 μ thick, spores not readily collapsing.

Basidia 26–30 × 5–7 μ, 2-, and 4-spored, clavate, hyaline in KOH, yellowish in Melzer's reagent; sterigmata seen up to 15 μ long with typical basidiospores attached, these sterigmata filamentous and 1.5–2 μ diam. Pleurocystidia 27–35 × 4–8 μ, clavate-rostrate to fusoid, at the same level in the hymenium as the basidia (many of them could have been 1-spored basidia), hyaline, smooth, thin-walled. Cheilocystidia 33–52 × 4–8 μ, narrowly clavate with flexuous pedicels, the apex in some subcapitate, in others spathulate (as if starting to branch), some with a lateral bulge, some ventricose at base; hyaline, smooth, thin-walled, content homogeneous. Caulocystidia 30–70 × 5–9 μ, more or less resembling the cheilocystidia but more variable in shape.

Gill trama of parallel non-gelatinous hyphae 5–10 μ broad, walls thin and smooth; subhymenium of the same type of hyphae but narrower. Pileus cuticle of more or less appressed narrow (2–4 μ) hyaline non-gelatinous hyphae; hypodermial region lacking special differentiation. Context hyphae interwoven, cells inflated to 15 μ, walls thin, smooth and yellowish. All hyphae inamyloid. Clamp connections present.

HABIT, HABITAT, AND DISTRIBUTION: On sticks and leaves, California, January. Type studied.

OBSERVATIONS: Apparently it is known only from the type collection. There is a collection by William Herbst, from Pennsylvania, labelled *Pholiota anomala,* but it is not a *Pholiota.* Its spores are globose and slightly roughened and 4–5 μ diam. Our description is based entirely on the type. *P. anomala* can be recognized by the inconspicuous rostrate pleurocystidia, the evanescent annulus, and a peculiar cavernous internal structure of the stipe. It is not to be confused with *Flammula anomala* Peck (Bull. Torrey Bot. Club 22: 202. 1895) which has globose echinulate spores and which Kauffman (1926) transferred to *Paxillus.* Murrill (1917) placed it under *Gymnopilus.*

2. Pholiota punicea sp. nov.
Illustrations: Text fig. 37.

Pileus 1–1.5 cm latus, convexus, glaber, obscure sangineus. Lamellae adnatae confertae latae, obscure sanguineae. Stipes 1.5–2 cm longus, 2–3 mm crassus, sursum albozonatus. Sporae 7.5 × 4.5–5 μ (9–10 × 5–6 μ). Pleurocystidia desunt. Cheilocystidia 32–50 × 4–16 μ, breve clavata vel ovata. Specimen typicum in Herb. Univ. Mich. conservatum est; legit prope Takilma, Ore. 6 Nov. 1937, Smith 8507.

Pileus 1–1.5 cm broad, hemispheric-convex, glabrous, more or less expanding, blood red, margin subplicate. Context reddish brown.

Lamellae adnate or adnexed, moderately close, broad, red.

Stipe 1.5–2 cm long, 2–3 mm thick, 5 mm when compressed, minutely fibrillose, with a white fibrillose zone, striated longitudinally, some slightly enlarged below.

Spores 7.5–8.5 × 4.5–5 μ (9–10 × 5–6 μ), wall thin but double, no apical pore visible, elliptic to ovate in face view, in profile somewhat bean-shaped to elliptic, rusty cinnamon in KOH, dingy ochraceous in Melzer's reagent (paler), in optical section a small apiculus showing.

Basidia 26–30 × 5–9 μ, (2-) and 4-spored, narrowly clavate to sub-cylindric, the hymenium pale dull cinnamon as revived in KOH, many basidia with hyaline refractive content of amorphous material variously disposed, in Melzer's reagent yellowish. Pleurocystidia present only as scattered pseudocystidia in the hymenium, 20–33 × 3–5 μ, crooked, content dark cinnamon in KOH. Cheilocystidia 32–50 × 4–16 μ, versiform, short-clavate to ovate, 15–30 × 7–10 μ, with the wall very slightly thickened and pale cinnamon in KOH, ventricose at base (6–8 μ) with a long narrow flexuous neck and subacute apex, hyaline and thin-walled, utriform to dumb-bell-shaped with the enlarged apex as broad as the ventricose portion and rarely with a secondary septum in the constriction, hyaline in KOH and collapsing readily. Caulocystidia clavate to irregularly ventricose, 40–80 × 5–11 μ, walls thickened (at times irregularly) and hyaline to yellowish in KOH. Gill trama of parallel to somewhat interwoven, non-gelatinous hyphae with dull cinnamon to ochraceous often asperulate walls (as revived in KOH), cells inflating to 12–15 μ in the central portion and rather short; subhymenium of small somewhat thick-walled cells rusty brown in KOH, not gelatinous. Pileus cutis of appressed non-gelatinous hyphae 4–10 μ diam. the walls dull rusty cinnamon in KOH and often roughened with incrusting material. Context hyphae very pale cinnamon in KOH, walls slightly incrusted to smooth, cells inflated to 15 μ more or less, interwoven, Clamp connections present, all hyphae inamyloid to weakly dextrinoid.

HABIT, HABITAT AND DISTRIBUTION: On a burned stump, at the California-Oregon state line, Nov. 6, 1937, Smith 8507, type.

OBSERVATIONS: This is a third species in the stirps *Confragosa* if the section were to be divided into stirpes. The blood red glabrous pileus distinguishes it at once from *P. canescens* in the field if one compares basidiocarps which have lost the annulus or annular zone. It differs from *P. confragosa* in redder colors, growing on charred wood, in the caulocystidia tending to have thick walls, and in lacking a membranous veil.

3. Pholiota canescens sp. nov.

Pileus 8–22 mm latus, late convexus, albocanescens, subhygrophanus. Lamellae late adnatae, ferrugineae, latae, confertae. Stipes 2–3.5 cm longus, 1.5–2.5 mm crassus, ferrugineus, albofibrillosus; annulatus. Annulus albus. Sporae 5–7.5 × 3.8–5 μ. Pleurocystidia 30–40 × 7–9 μ, subcapitata. Cheilocystidia 34–76 × 4–6 μ, filamentosa vel subcapitata.

Specimen typicum in Herb. Univ. Mich. conservatum est; legit prope Mt. Hood, Ore. 28 Sept. 1922, C. H. Kauffman.

Pileus 8–22 mm broad, broadly convex, obtuse, covered with small whitish appressed silky canescence composed of elements of the sparse trichodermium, at length these grouped into small fascicles or squamules, color ferruginous ("Kaiser brown") beneath this coating when moist, somewhat hygrophanous and paler when dried (as in *P. confragosa*). Context concolorous 1–1.5 mm thick, odor and taste not distinctive.

Lamellae broadly adnate, ferruginous ("Kaiser brown") at maturity, rather broad (4–5 mm), narrowed to cap margin, close to crowded, thin, edges entire.

Stipe 2–3.5 cm long, 1.5–2.5 mm thick, equal, "cinnamon rufous," clothed by silky fibrils or appressed whitish scales up to the delicate membranous fragile spreading annulus, above ring even, pruinose, concolorous within except for the narrow whitish stuffed axis.

Spores 5–7.5 × 3.8–5 μ, elliptic to ovate in face view, slightly inequilateral in profile, smooth, pale cinnamon in KOH slightly paler in Melzer's reagent, germ pore minute.

Basidia 17–24 × 3.5–5 μ, clavate, 4-spored. Pleurocystidia 30–40 × 7–9 μ, slightly ventricose, apex capitate or subacute, not projecting greatly beyond the basidia. Cheilocystidia 34–76 × 4–6 μ, filamentous or apex enlarged and subcapitate, very numerous and conspicuous.

Gill trama subparallel, hyphae 5–9 μ broad, walls rusty cinnamon in KOH; subhymenium not distinctive. Pileus cutis of appressed brown hyphae bearing a sparse trichodermium of hyaline to pale brownish hyphae 5–15 μ diam., the terminal cell of a filament cystidioid. All hyphae inamyloid. Clamp connections present.

HABIT, HABITAT AND DISTRIBUTION. On decayed wood, among mosses, Oregon, September, (type, Kauffman, 9–28–22).

OBSERVATIONS: This species is clearly closely related to *P. confragosa* but differs in the spores having a minute germ pore, the presence of pleurocystidia, redder colors and the pileus is less hygrophanous.

4. **Pholiota confragosa** (Fr.) Karsten, Hattsvampar (Bidr. Finlands Natur och Folk, p. 304. 1879.

Agaricus confragosus Fries, Epicr. Syst. Myc. p. 169. 1838.
Phaeomarasmius confragosus (Fr.) Singer, Lilloa 22: 577. 1951.
Illustrations: Text figs. 35-36; pl. 9a.

Pileus 1–4 (5) cm broad, obtuse to convex expanding to broadly convex or nearly plane, surface moist and hygrophanous beneath a whitish covering of fibrils which become aggregated into minute squamules or remain appressed causing surface to appear canescent, when fresh dark reddish cinnamon to deep vinaceous-cinnamon, fading to pale cinnamon buff or retaining a reddish tone. Context thin, fragile, concolorous with surface, odor and taste not distinctive.

Lamellae bluntly adnate to slightly decurrent, close, moderately broad (about 3 mm), pale rufous to cinnamon becoming dark reddish cinnamon in age, edges pallid and minutely fimbriate.

Stipe 2–6 (8) cm long, 1.5–5 mm thick, equal or enlarged downward, soon becoming hollow, with a superior flaring membranous to submembranous annulus, pallid above annulus and silky to pruinose, in age pinkish tan; below the annulus more or less concolorous with pileus or paler and typically paler than pileus in herbarium specimens, with veil remnants variously distributed, base usually with white matted mycelium.

Spores 6.5–9 × 4–5 (6) μ, smooth, dull cinnamon in KOH when mature, dark reddish cinnamon in deposit, broadly obscurely bean-shaped in profile, in face view broadly elliptic to ovate, no apical pore present, in Melzer's reagent paler colored than in KOH.

Basidia 4-spored, 20–26 × 5–8 μ, narrowly clavate, hyaline (to dingy cinnamon at base) in KOH. Pleurocystidia none. Cheilocystidia abundant, 36–60 × 4–8 μ, hyaline in KOH, near base slightly ventricose and some narrowed to a slight pedicel, forward of the ventricose part flexuous-cylindric and 4–6 μ thick, the wall here thin to slightly thickened (see old specimens), apex obtuse to subacute. Caulocystidia scattered, similar to cheilocystidia, 40–70 × 4–8 μ, hyaline in KOH, smooth, thin-walled for the most part, often lacking a basal enlargement.

Gill trama of parallel non-gelatinous hyphae with cells 5–10 μ wide and in age considerably more inflated, walls slightly thickened and hyaline or pale cinnamon, toward the narrow cellular subhymenium the hyphae with darker cinnamon walls. Pileus cutis with a sparse trichodermium of hyphae with walls thickened up to 1 μ, asperulate and hyaline or nearly so in KOH, in age or on standing in KOH very pale tan, the cells 8–25 μ diam., and mostly elongate but not rarely subglobose, terminal cells clavate to broadly fusoid; hypodermium not distinct in young pilei but in old ones a layer of hyphae with cinnamon colored walls showing, these smooth to asperulate. Context hyphae thin-walled, interwoven, cells 8–20 μ diam., hyaline to pale cinnamon in KOH. Clamp connections present. All hyphae inamyloid.

HABIT, HABITAT AND DISTRIBUTION: On rotting logs of hardwoods and conifers, not rare during late summer and fall in the Great Lakes area of North America southward as well as eastward, and on the Pacific Coast.

OBSERVATIONS: This is a most interesting species in view of the failure of the trichodermial elements to become dark cinnamon in KOH.

MATERIAL EXAMINED: MAINE: Bigelow 2970, 3859, 3055, 3082, 3241. MICHIGAN: Harding 205. Shaffer 3712, 5416. Smith 9-22-29, 41715, 57619. NORTH CAROLINA: Meyer 14245. NEW YORK: Kauffman 8-23-24, 8-26-14; Smith 690, 875. OHIO: Walters 5-26-46. OREGON: Smith 19768. WASHINGTON: Smith 16700. CANADA—NOVA SCOTIA:

Smith 799. ONTARIO: Kelly 994; Smith 4432, 4375. QUEBEC: Smith 61702.

Section **Hygrotrama**

The species placed here shows thicker spore walls than occur in other stirps when spores of the same size are compared. The apical pore is obscure in some spores. This is the genus *Pachylepyrium* of Singer, who states (1963, p. 559) that the genus differs from *Kuehneromyces* in the color of the spores and the character of the surface of the pileus and in habitat. We do not agree that the degree of thickening in the spore wall is of any generic significance here since throughout the genus the spore wall is not what one would term thin in the sense that the term applies to the Tricholomataceae. To us the situation is more like that found by Smith (Smith & Zeller, 1966) in *Rhizopogon*. In this genus the spore wall varies from thin up to 0.5 μ thick (which is scarcely to be regarded as thin), but Morten Lange found one species with spore walls up to or over 1.5 μ thick. As to spore color, it is within the range of that of subg. *Pholiota*. Hence there is no use trying to use either of these characters to establish a genus in this complex. In the absence of E M photographs of the spores of *Pholiota* in general it is premature to use the number of layers in the wall as a generic character here. In all of the stirpes so far discussed for this subgenus the spores approach those of *P. subangularis* in wall thickness.

We have one species known to date in North America: *P. subangularis*.

5. **Pholiota subangularis** nom. nov.

Kuehneromyces carbonicola Smith, Sydowia Suppl. 1: 53. 1957. (non *Pholiota carbonicola* Singer, 1963)
Illustrations: Text figs. 175-176; pl. 1.

Pileus 1-3 (4) cm broad, broadly convex with an incurved margin, expanding to plane or nearly so, "natal-brown" at first but gradually becoming paler (to "warm-sepia"), hygrophanous, fading to a bright or a dingy tawny, lubricous, glabrous or with a faint marginal zone of pallid fibrils from the thin veil. Context fragile, watery brown fading to buff; odor and taste none.

Lamellae adnate, seceding at times, more or less ochraceous tawny (paler when young, darker in age), broad, edges somewhat fimbriate.

Stipe 3-5 cm long, 2.5-3.5 mm thick, lower three-fourths silky from the remnants of a thin veil and at first with a superior fibrillose zone where the veil breaks, apex naked and shining, watery brown above, darker brown below and becoming bister from the base upward in age.

Spores 8–11.5 × 6–6.5 × 7–9 μ, elliptic in profile view, angular-ovate in face view varying to ovate or to kite-shaped, smooth in KOH, with a thick wall for the genus (0.5–1.8 μ), rich reddish cinnamon in KOH and in Melzer's, apical pore present and apex more or less truncate, pore 1–1.5 μ wide.

Basidia 23–26 × 8–10 (11) μ, clavate, hyaline in KOH. Pleurocystidia none. Cheilocystidia 20–26 × 8–13 μ, abundant but readily collapsing and not easily demonstrated on old gills, fusoid-ventricose with short necks and obtuse to subacute apex, hyaline, smooth, thin-walled.

Gill trama parallel, pale cinnamon in KOH, hyaline in H₂O when fresh but with hyaline incrusting particles along the walls. Subhymenium not gelatinous. Pileus trama floccose-interwoven. Cuticle of compactly appressed enlarged hyphal cells with ochraceous walls in H₂O when fresh, and dark rusty brown revived in KOH, the cells more or less ellipsoid (10–18 μ in diameter) and hyphae radial, pigment mostly in the wall, incrustations not conspicuous. Clamp connections present.

HABIT, HABITAT AND DISTRIBUTION. Densely gregarious on burned soil, Idaho and Wyoming, June and July.

OBSERVATIONS: The lubricous pileus, dull reddish brown color, and mild taste distinguish it. In KOH the color of the spores would seem to suggest a relationship with *Conocybe* but the other characters do not bear this out.

MATERIAL EXAMINED: IDAHO: Smith 44640 (type), 44809, 65015, 65056, 71453. WYOMING: Solheim 3957; Smith 34354, 34646, 34862.

Subgenus **Flavidula** subg. nov.

Pileus siccus, fibrillosus vel squamulosus, luteus, luteofulvus, fulvus vel badius. Stipes glaber, fibrillosus, granulosus vel non squarroso-squamulosus.

TYPUS: *Pholiota curvipes.*

Species with a pileus trichodermium of non-gelatinous hyphae and typically having the cells more or less inflated or often sphaerocyst-like are placed here if in addition the spores are tawny to cinnamon-brown or dark yellow-brown in KOH and have smooth walls. In some species the epicutis of the pileus consists of innate appressed non-gelatinous hyphae. A germ pore may or may not be present at the spore apex, and if present it is usually so small that a 1.4 N.A. oil immersion lens is often needed to see it clearly. The cells of the hyphae forming the trichodermium in section *Flavidula* may be thin or thick-walled, and smooth or incrusted, but become a dark rusty brown color in KOH. This latter reaction we consider an important feature of the subgenus. An annulus may or may not be present. The pileus generally appears dry and appressed fibrillose to echinate-squamulose. Species with an hygrophanous pileus are not admitted to section *Flavidula*. Species having pale colored spores (yellowish to nearly hyaline) and with the wall thin are retained in *Tubaria*. Clamp connections are present in all but *P. cinchonensis*. No species with a gelatinous layer in the pileus cuticle is admitted.

As here defined, many of the species included by Singer (1956) in *Phaeomarasmius* are excluded because of the combination of pale colored spores and hygrophanous pilei. We are here restricting *Phaeomarasmius* to the small species with eccentric stipes in addition to the characters emphasized by Singer. This interpretation is consistent with the features of the type species. However a detailed critical study of *Tubaria* and *Phaeomarasmius* must now be made to more clearly delimit them from *Pholiota*. For one thing, E M photographs of the spore-wall are badly needed since the layering in the wall is important in determining generic limits. In the present work we have tried to bring together those taxa which we believe connect so well to *Pholiota* that there is no valid reason for excluding them. Actually many of them were described in *Pholiota* and *Flammula* originally. Species with chrysocystidia are arbitrarily excluded from this subgenus. They are found in *Phaeonaematoloma* and *Pholiota*. However, brown cells (basidioles and/or basidia) are often encountered in species of *Flavidula*. Not infrequently these can be observed bearing spores, and so unquestionably are true basidia.

To us it is obvious that subg. *Flavidula* connects to *Tubaria* to the extent that it will take a very careful study to properly dispose of all the questionable species. The subgenus is also very closely related to *Galerina* sect. *Inoderma*. The only way to accurately distinguish between them is to place generic emphasis on the line delimiting the plage of the spore in the *Galerinae,* but at the same time one must point out that many species of *Galerina* in other sections have truly smooth spores and that a number of these show *Pholiota* characters, such as the gelatinous subhymenium (in the *G. sideroides* group) .

Section **Flavidula**

Characters as given in the description of the subgenus.

Key to Stirpes

1. Pileus appressed fibrillose when young, not hygrophanous, becoming appressed squamulose to diffracted scaly in age; epicuticular hyphae not greatly inflated .... Stirps *Curvipes*
1. Not as above 2
   2. Pileus cuticle granulose-tomentose (of chains of inflated cells, these often disarticulating to produce the granulose texture) or the spores large (9–12 × 5.5–7 μ, or both .... Stirps *Aurea*
   2. Not as above 3

3. Clamp connections absent; known from Jamaica ....
.... Stirps *Cinchonensis*
3. Not as above—clamps readily demonstrated 4
4. Pleurocystidia present .... Stirps *Corticola*
4. Pleurocystidia absent 5
5. Hyphae of pileus epicutis mostly thick-walled .... Stirps *Erinacea*
5. Hyphae of pileus epicutis not as above .... Stirps *Curcuma*

Stirps Curvipes

The epicutis of the pileus consists of hyphae becoming cinnamon in KOH, but the cells are less inflated than those in the other stirpes and the walls are not as coarsely or extensively incrusted or ornamented. The gradations between species in this stirps are such that one might regard it as a single variable taxon. A critical study of the behavior in culture of these variants is badly needed because the apparent introgression is of a pattern common to the fleshy fungi generally often in groups not readily culturable. Lacking this approach, we present here the taxa as we can recognize them in nature. The color of the veil, Singer to the contrary notwithstanding, does not distinguish this stirps from the others (except for stirps *Cinchonensis*).

Key

1. Stipe about 2 mm diam; pileus ferruginous and finely squamulose
.... *P. squamulosa*
1. Not as above 2
2. Taste mild; lamellae broad and at maturity subdistant ....
.... *P. curvipes*
2. Taste of raw context distinctly bitter 3
3. Stipe (3) 4–10 (12) mm. thick; lamellae narrow and crowded ....
.... *P. multifolia*
3. Stipe 2.5–3 mm. thick; cespitose; lamellae broad and subdistant ....
.... *P. subsulphurea*

6. Pholiota multifolia (Pk.) comb. nov.
Flammula multifolia Peck, Bull. Torrey Club 32: 79. 1905.
Gymnopilus multifolius (Pk.) Murrill, North Amer. Fl. 10: 204. 1917.
Illustrations: Text figs. 1-2; pls. 2-3.

Pileus 5–8 cm broad, convex, subumbonate, dry, "cadmium yellow" (brilliant yellow) when young, then more tawny or "Xanthine orange" when mature, sometimes paler on the margin and darker at the center, glabrous or obscurely fibrillose from veil patches, margin incurved. Context fairly thick in large specimens, pale yellow to bright yellow, soon sordid rusty brown where injured, odor slight, taste bitter.

Lamellae adnexed, rounded behind, concolorous or "pinard yellow" (paler yellow than pileus), narrow, crowded, soon spotted or stained rusty brown to orange-brown from injury, edges crenulate, often with yellow or reddish-yellow glandular drops.

Stipe (2) 3–7 (10) cm. long, (2) 4–10 mm thick, yellow, floccose, fibrillose to the apical zone or nearly glabrous finally, equal or slightly thickened at the base, solid, tough. Veil yellowish, fibrillose, evanescent.

Spores 6.5–9 × 4.5–5 (5.5) μ, ovate to elliptic in face view, somewhat inequilateral to obscurely bean-shaped in profile, smooth, rich tawny in KOH, germ pore obscure and very minute.

Basidia 25–30 × 5–7 μ, narrowly clavate, yellow revived in KOH, 4-spored or occasionally apparently two-spored. Pleurocystidia present as brown basidioles 24–42 × 4–7 μ. Cheilocystidia (20) 30–50 (75) × (4) 5–9 μ, filamentose-capitate, hyaline to yellow in KOH or some rusty brown, in clusters, thin-walled, smooth, rarely with a secondary septum below the head (shaped much as in those of *P. curvipes*). Caulocystidia none found.

Gill trama interwoven to subparallel, hyphae 3–12 μ in diam. in broadest part, walls thin and yellowish in KOH, hyphal cells inflated only in age; subhymenium of narrow non-gelatinous hyphae. Pileus cuticle of non-gelatinous radially arranged hyphae with thin smooth walls 4–12 μ diam. and the terminal cells merely tapered to the apex. Hyphae of context interwoven, cells thin-walled, yellow in KOH and in Melzer's reagent many small needle-like crystals often grouped into burr-like masses in the mounts, walls all inamyloid. Clamp connections present.

HABIT, HABITAT AND DISTRIBUTION: On logs, sawdust and decaying wood of deciduous trees of ash, aspen, maple etc. New York, North Carolina, Missouri, Michigan and Canada, June to October.

OBSERVATIONS: The narrow, crowded, spotted and stained lamellae together with the yellow to tawny hues of the pileus, and the bitter taste are a good set of field characters. It is close to *P. curvipes* but the latter has broader more distant gills and a mild taste. We do not emphasize the lack of caulocystidia as observed so far as an important feature since in Smith 67009 with pilei up to 7 cm wide they were present as clusters of clavate thin-walled cells. The taste of this collection was not recorded.

A yellow pigment dissolves into the KOH mounting medium and in Melzer's the presence of pale dextrinoid burr-like to star-like aggregations of needle-like crystals is unique in our experience. This species is the most "Gymnopilus-like" of the section as far as pigmentation is concerned, and is likely to be confused with that genus until the spores are examined.

Flammula expansa was considered identical with this species by

Text Fig. 1.

FIGS. 1 & 2, cheilocystidia and spores of *P. multifolia;* 3 & 4, cheilocystidia and spores of *P. curvipes;* 5 & 6, spores and cheilocystidia of *P. subsulphurea* (type) ; 7 & 8, spores and cheilocystidia of *P. squamulosa;* 9 & 10, cells from the pileus cutis of *P. aurea,* and spores; 11 & 12, cheilocystidia and spores of *P. erinaceella;* 13 & 14 & 15, caulocystidia, spores and cheilocystidia of *P. pseudosiparia.*

Kauffman but Peck described it as having white flesh and a mild taste. *Pholiota tuberculosa* (Fr.) Kummer is apparently very close to *P. multifolia,* but on the data available we do not regard them as synonyms.

MATERIAL EXAMINED: MICHIGAN: Harding 77, 84, 117, 161, 186, 232, 346, 393. Pennington 9-13-07. Potter 2801, 14219. Smith 22131, 32059, 32035, 33866, 33894, 35877, 42034, 42370, 50064, 51023, 57078, 57865, 61426, 67009. Thiers 688. MISSOURI: Peck (type of *Flammula multifolia*). NEW MEXICO: Barrows 3085. NORTH CAROLINA: Hesler 24842. TENNESSEE: Smith 10894. WASHINGTON: Flett (Mich). CANADA—ONTARIO: Smith 4718.

7. Pholiota curvipes (Fr.) Quél., Champ Jura et Vosges p. 230. 1872.

Agaricus curvipes Fries, Epicr. Syst. Myc. p. 168. 1838.
Dryophila curvipes (Fr.) Quélet, Enchir. Fung. p. 69. 1886.
Illustrations: Text figs. 3-4; pl. 4a.

Pileus (1) 2–5 (6) cm. broad, obtuse to convex, the margin incurved, becoming broadly convex or nearly plane, at times with a low obtuse umbo; surface dry, opaque, fibrillose, the epicutis becoming broken up into small appressed to slightly recurved squamules, squamules around the disc often small and inconspicuous, at times the extreme margin lacerate-fibrillose or appendiculate from the remains of the thin veil; color brilliant yellow to ferruginous yellow or finally ferruginous ("Mars yellow" to "Cadmium-yellow" or "ochraceous-orange"). Context thin, pliant, yellow. Odor and taste mild.

Lamellae moderately close to subdistant, broad, adnate, whitish in small buttons but soon yellow and finally more or less cinnamon from the spores, edges even but in age crenulate.

Stipe 2–5 (9) cm long, 2–5 (7) mm thick, curved or ascending, more or less concolorous with the pileus, equal, tubular, apex clear yellow, floccose fibrillose, becoming more or less rusty brown from handling. Veil pale yellow, fibrillose, forming an evanescent fibrillose zone where it breaks.

Spores 6–8.5 (9) × 3.5–4.5 (5) μ, rusty brown in KOH, smooth, in face view elliptic to ovate, in profile somewhat bean-shaped, wall scarcely thickened, no germ pore visible.

Basidia 20–26 × 4.5–6 μ, 4-spored, yellow in KOH or some with rusty brown content, yellow pigment diffusing in the mount from the hymenium. Pleurocystidia none. Cheilocystidia 24–42 (60) × 3–9 μ, cylindric to narrowly clavate to more or less capitate and flexuous down to the base, often in tufts, yellowish hyaline or with ochraceous to pale tawny content, thin-walled, smooth. Caulocystidia 28–60 × 4–9 μ, similar in shape to cheilocystidia but often more highly colored.

Gill trama parallel to somewhat interwoven, hyphal cells enlarged in age, walls thin and yellowish in KOH, hyphae narrower near subhymenium; subhymenium not distinctive. Pileus cuticle of fascicles of appressed hyphae with cinnamon to reddish cinnamon walls smooth to slightly incrusted as revived in KOH, cells inflated to 20 μ at times, end-cells usually merely narrowed to an obtuse to subacute apex. Clamp connections present. All tissues inamyloid.

HABIT, HABITAT, AND DISTRIBUTION: On logs, stumps and sawdust of hardwoods, especially aspen, rarely on conifer logs such as *Larix*: Maine, New York, Michigan and Missouri, in the United States, and Ontario in Canada.

OBSERVATIONS: This species, *P. multifolia* and *P. subsulphurea* inter-grade. However, the characters given in the key will serve to distinguish most collections. Although the hyphae of the pileus cuticle are mostly of uninflated cells, some inflated cells do occur and this is evidence, in our estimation, of the evolutionary tendency toward the *P. erinaceella* type. Singer believed that the similarities between these fungi constituted a parallelism and were not an indication of true relationship. We hold the opposite view. We have followed Singer in recognizing both *P. tuber-culosa* and *P. curvipes*. Some authors regard them as synonyms.

MATERIAL EXAMINED: MAINE: Bigelow (Tenn. 23833). MICH-IGAN: Harding 131, 139, 151, 161, 162, 186, 187, 232, 386, 393, 422; Langdon 11-8-93; Kauffman 6-6-10; Shaffer 612, 1753, 2167, (MICH); Smith 33-967, 33-1104, 9547, 9558, 15060, 18855, 21468, 21559, 25606, 25712, 25753, 25837, 33822, 33894, 36310, 36350, 36692, 37587, 38399, 38849, 39687, 66971, 68792; Thiers 688, 2665, 2729, 2746, 3059 (MICH): TENNESSEE Hesler 14195 (TENN): CANADA (ONTARIO): Beards-lee 9-3-21.

8. Pholiota subsulphurea sp. nov.
Illustrations: Text figs. 5-6.

Pileus 10–15 mm latus, convexus, siccus, demum subsquamulosus flavus. Contextus luteus, amarus. Lamellae subdistantes, latae, adnatae, subsulphureae. Stipes 2.5–3 cm longus, 2.5–3 mm crassus subsulphureus, deorsum fulvus, vellum luteum. Sporae 6.5–7.5 × 4–4.5 μ, leves. Pleuro-cystidia desunt. Cheilocystidia 28–64 × 6–10 μ; filamentoso-capitata. Specimen typicum in Herb. Univ. Mich. conservatum est; legit prope Tahquamenon Falls, Mich. 29 June 1953 Smith 41356.

Pileus 10–15 mm broad, convex with an incurved margin, becoming plane or nearly so, surface dry and matted-fibrillose, becoming somewhat areolate to diffracted squamulose; color bright yellow (rich sulphur-yellow), in age near orange-yellow; margin at first appendiculate from veil remnants. Context yellow but readily staining rusty, cutis quickly rusty brown in KOH (NH₄OH reaction weaker), odor none, taste very bitter.

Lamellae close becoming subdistant, horizontal, adnate, moderately broad, sulphur-yellow young, near tawny mature, edges flocculose.

Stipe 2.5–3 cm long, 2.5–3 mm thick, equal, bright yellow, floccose-squamulose to the annular zone, pruinose above, staining rusty brown from base up or where handled or where in contact with bases such as KOH. Veil fibrillose, yellow.

Spores 6.5–7.5 × 4–4.5 (9 × 3.5) μ smooth, lacking an apical pore, tawny in KOH, in Melzer's reagent merely yellowish; shape in face view elliptic to oblong, in profile slightly bean-shaped.

Basidia 4-spored, 18–23 × 4.5–6 μ, narrowly clavate, yellow to clay-color in KOH (many sporulating basidia with dark rusty brown content seen). Pleurocystidia none. Cheilocystidia abundant, flexuous-capitate as in *P. erinceella*, 28–46 × 6–10 μ, bright yellow in KOH, thin-walled, smooth, wall hyaline. Caulocystidia 30–60 × 8–14 μ, in shape similar to cheilocystidia but head broader and often flattened, yellow to orange in KOH.

Gill trama of subparallel to interwoven thin-walled hyphae bright yellow in KOH, oleiferous hyphae orange-yellow; subhymenium not distinctive (very narrow and not gelatinous). Pileus cuticle a tangle of hyphae 5-14 μ diam., the cells tubular to somewhat inflated but typically more than 4 times longer than broad, pale tawny to pale cinnamon in KOH, thin-walled, walls smooth to minutely roughened; terminal cells somewhat cystidioid. Clamp connections present. All tissues inamyloid.

HABIT, HABITAT, AND DISTRIBUTION: Clustered on a log of *Fagus,* Tahquamenon Falls State Park, Mich. June 29, 1953, Smith 41356 (type), and from Oakland County, Smith 73247, 73269.

OBSERVATIONS: This species is close to *P. curvipes* but it at once distinguished in the field by the very bitter taste. From *P. multifolia* which has a bitter taste, it differs in broad subdistant gills at maturity and by having numerous caulocystidia over the upper half of the stipe. We seldom find *P. curvipes* cespitose. We assume that *P. fagicola* is not bitter. It is described as having distant arcuate gills.

9. Pholiota squamulosa (Murr.) Kauffman, Amer. Journ. Bot. 13: 29. 1926.

Gymnopilus squamulosus Murrill, North Amer. Fl. 10: 201. 1917
Illustrations: Text figs. 7-8.

Pileus 2 cm broad, convex, not fully expanding, uniformly ferruginous, gibbous, surface dry, finely squamulose, margin entire, concolorous.

Lamellae adnate, ferruginous to fulvous at maturity, crowded, broad, plane, edges yellowish and somewhat crenulate.

Stipe 2 cm long, 2 mm thick, tapering downward, short, subconcolorous, fibrillose, rather tough.

Spores 8–9.5 × 4–5 μ, smooth, lacking an apical pore; in face view ovate to elliptic, in profile slightly bean-shaped to obscurely inequilateral, in KOH tawny to pale tawny, in Melzer's reagent nearly hyaline, walls about 0.3 μ thick.

Basidia 20–25 × 6–7 μ, 4-spored, yellow in KOH, nearly hyaline in Melzer's reagent. Pleurocystidia none. Cheilocystidia 36–52 × 7–11 μ, narrowly clavate to filamentous with a capitate apex, content clear yellow in KOH, wall thin, smooth and hyaline. Caulocystidia not studied (material insufficient).

Gill trama of subparallel hyphae with cells becoming inflated to 12 μ or more in places, walls ferruginous-brown in KOH, smooth to asperulate, subhymenium of narrower hyphae than the central area but otherwise the same. Hyphae of context with yellow walls in KOH and nearly hyaline in Melzer's reagent, cells 6–14 μ diam. or more inflated, walls thin and smooth to (rarely) minutely asperulate. Cuticle not reviving well but no pigment-encrusted hyphae found, dark red-brown in KOH (the typical color change for the group, only very accentuated). Clamp connections present. All hyphae inamyloid.

HABIT, HABITAT, AND DISTINCTION: On dead wood near the New York Botanical Gardens, Sept. 13, 1910. Known only from the type locality.

OBSERVATIONS: The type material was so scanty that no sections were attempted to determine if caulocystidia were present. We recognize this species provisionally since the possibility of its being *P. muricata* is not excluded. The data that are obtainable from the type are admittedly inadequate. However, it is significant that no sphaerocysts were seen in the sections made of the pileus cuticle, and no heavy pigment incrustations were observed on the cuticular hyphae.

Stirps Aurea

In this stirps, with the exception of *P. fulvella,* it is known that the epicutis of the pileus contains many cells more or less isodiametric to keg-shaped. In this respect and in the KOH reactions there is a strong parallel to *Cystoderma* of the Tricholomataceae. *P. fulvella* is placed here because of the large spores and lack of cheilocystidia.

Key

1. Spores 9–13 (14) μ long 2
1. Spores shorter 3
    2. Stipe 3–4 mm. thick .... *P. fulvella*
    2. Stipe 3–5 cm thick .... *P. aurea*
3. Cheilocystidia clavate to subglobose, 20–30 × 9–18 μ ...... *P. granulosa*
3. Cheilocystidia (at least many of them) with a flexuous pedicel and clavate at the tip, or fusoid-ventricose 4
    4. Cheilocystidia (40) 50–115 × 3.5–6 × 9–16 μ .... *P. erinaceella*
    4. Cheilocystidia 28–40 × 7–11 μ .... *P. pseudosiparia*
    4. Cheilocystidia 26–40 × 8–16 μ; Caulocystidia often boomerang-shaped (see no. 12., *P. subechinata*)

10. **Pholiota fulvella** (Pk.) comb. nov.

Flammula fulvella Peck, J. M. Macoun, in D. S. Jordan, Fur Seals of the North Pacific 3: 584. 1899.
Gymnopilus fulvellus (Pk.) Murrill, Mycologia 4: 253. 1912.

Pileus 1.2–2.4 cm broad, convex or nearly plane, subtawny, glabrous, dry, the margin deflexed or incurved. Context whitish.

Lamellae adnate or slightly decurrent, somewhat tawny, inclining toward ochraceous-tawny, thin, subdistant.

Stipe 2.5 cm long, 3–4 mm thick, concolorous, fibrillose or fibrillose-squamulose, equal, solid.

Spores 9–12 × 5.5–7 μ, elliptic to irregularly ovate in face view, inequilateral in profile, smooth, germ pore not distinct.

Basidia 30–43 × 7–10 μ, 4-spored. Pleurocystidia and cheilocystidia none. Caulocystidia none.

Gill trama of hyphae 4–7 μ broad in subparallel arrangement, yellowish brown in KOH. Pileus cutis of appressed hyphae but some more or less erect, brown, and incrusted. Pileus trama of interwoven hyphae yellowish brown in KOH, dark brown in Melzer's reagent. Clamp connections present.

HABIT, HABITAT, AND DISTRIBUTION: On low ground, St. Paul Island, Bering Sea. Known only from the type.

In our study of the type we were unable to find either pleurocystidia or cheilocystidia. We place the species here with some reservations. For instance, we doubt if the pileus was actually glabrous. On the assumption that it was not, we have placed the species here. The evidence for this is that incrusted brown epicuticular hyphae were demonstrated which must have formed squamules at first. The large spores and lack of cheilocystidia would seem to place the species near *P. aurea*—if one disregards size of the basidiocarp.

11. **Pholiota aurea** (Fr.) Kummer, Der Führer in die Pilzkunde p. 85. 1871.

Agaricus aureus Fries, Syst. Myc. 1: 241. 1821.
Togaria aurea (Fr.) W. G. Smith, Syn. British Basid. p. 122. 1908.
Phaeolepiota aurea (Fr.) Konrad & Maublanc, Icon. Select. Fung. 6: 11. 1924-1928.
Agaricus vahlei Fries, Syst. Myc. 1: 240. 1821.
Lepiota pryrenacea Quélet, Champ. Jura & Vosges supp. 16, p. 1 (reprint). 1887.
Illustrations: Text figs. 9-10; pls. 5-6.

Pileus 7–20 (30) cm diam., convex to obtusely campanulate young, expanding to obtusely umbonate or nearly plane finally; colors orange-buff to orange-ochraceous in buttons, usually becoming paler in age, rarely merely ochraceous; surface dry, granulose to unpolished (in age when most of the veil particles have weathered away) ; margin often appendiculate with veil remnants. Context pallid and unchanging when cut or bruised, firm, moderately thick in the disc; odor mild to slightly pungent, taste mild to slightly astringent.

Lamellae pallid in buttons, becoming more or less concolorous with or darker than pileus at maturity, adnate or at times with a short decurrent tooth, moderately broad, close, edges entire and concolorous.

Stipe 10–15 (25) cm long, (1.5) 3–5 (6) cm in diam. at apex, enlarging downward to subclavate; more or less concolorous with the pileus though sometimes darker at the apex; surface dry and unpolished; smooth and glabrous above the annulus, below the latter peronate with a covering similar to that of the pileus; annulus flaring, membranous, persistent to mid-maturity, finally becoming pendulous and disappearing in extreme age; the peronate sheath separable to the base of the stipe. Context whitish or somewhat streaked with orange down the center and the cortex longitudinally fibrous, stuffed becoming hollowed; base of stipe white mycelioid and with a few short white poorly developed rhizomorphs.

Spore deposit light yellow-brown to orange-buff. Spores 10.7–13 (14) × 5–6 μ, yellowish to clay-color in KOH and with one large central oil drop, somewhat elliptic in face view, in profile somewhat inequilateral, inamyloid, smooth or some with minute markings, wall thin and many spores collapsing, no germ pore evident under oil immersion.

Basidia hyaline to pale brownish in KOH, usually 4-spored, clavate, thin-walled, occasionally with a highly refractive body as revived in KOH. Pleurocystidia absent or rarely clavate-mucronate and brownish in KOH, measuring 26–30 × 7.5–8.5 μ. Cheilocystidia none (edge entirely fertile) .

Gill trama of subparallel to parallel hyphae with yellowish to brownish thin to slightly thickened walls as revived in KOH; subhymenium of narrow (2–3 μ) non-gelatinous hyaline hyphae. Epicutis of pileus of inflated often isodiametric cells 12–25 μ diam., smooth or with one to several short finger-like or knob-like projections over the apex of the terminal cells of the chain, the walls thin to slightly thickened, pale yellowish in Melzer's reagent but orange-cinnamon in KOH. Clamp connections present.

HABIT, HABITAT, AND DISTRIBUTION: Caespitose-gregarious often near the edges of roads under *Alnus,* September to October, Pacific Northwest to Alaska, rare, but when it fruits it is found in quantity.

OBSERVATIONS: As is indicated in the synonymy, this species has been placed in a number of genera. We did not suspect what we now regard as its true relationships until after completing our study of this subgenus. Both *P. erinaceella* and *P. granulosa* in particular have basically the same type of pileus epicutis with the cells having the same type of KOH reaction. It can be characterized as the *Cystoderma*-type, which implies that not all the cuticular cells are sphaerocysts. In *Flavidula* there are two major lines of development. The first leads to the type of cutis found in *P. erinacea* where there is no disarticulation of the cutis cells and there is a tendency for the hyphae to develop thick colored walls. The second line is to the *Cystoderma*-type. Singer (1963) placed *Togaria* with *aurea* as the only species near *Lepiota*. We believe the resemblance to be superficial. The spores in KOH are pale tawny and thin-walled more like a *Tubaria* spore than any other type. But *Tubaria* also demonstrates the development of the *Cystoderma*-type pileus cutis. The large size of the basidiocarps should not influence any one to use this feature to establish relationships here. It has been amply shown throughout this paper that size is of no value in delimiting infrageneric or generic groups among pholiotoid fungi. In *P. aurea* the ornamentation of the spores is very minute, and in a way contradicts our definition of "spores smooth" for the genus. But here one has a choice of which spores he wishes to emphasize, the smooth ones or those with ornamentation, and this of course tends to vitiate the character as one of importance as far as relationships are concerned. The situation here is more like that in *Rhizopogon,* another genus of smooth-spored fungi, where, if one wishes, it can be claimed that some of the species have slightly ornamented spores. It should also be kept in mind that as far as *P. aurea* is concerned, *Tubaria,* to which it might be truly related, is a genus containing species with both smooth and ornamented spores. Thus in our opinion, a monotypic genus here serves no useful purpose either from a practical or theoretical consideration, and we have placed the species in line with previous tradition.

In Europe *P. aurea* is considered a good edible species but in Alaska Wells and Kempton (1965) have reported cases of "mild" poisoning from it. Bach (1956) made an excellent study of the physiology and ecology of this species. From Bach's study it is apparent that the fungus is not restricted to a single forest tree, and we would judge that its occurrence under alder in the Pacific Northwest is indicative of a habitat filled with nutrients rather than one indicating a symbiotic relationship with the alder.

MATERIAL EXAMINED: WASHINGTON: Imshaug 1801; Smith 3050, 3117, 3355 30448, 30859, 31491, 39843. CANADA (BRITISH COLUMBIA) Odell 1922. Reported from Alaska by Wells and Kempton (1965) and their specimens examined.

12. **Pholiota erinaceella** (Pk.) Peck, N.Y. State Mus. Bull. 122: 152. 1908.
Agaricus detersibilis Peck, N. Y. State Mus. Ann. Rept. 28:49. 1876.
Agaricus erinaceellus Peck, N. Y. State Mus. Ann. Rept. 30: 70. 1878.
Phaeomarasmius erinaceellus (Peck) Singer, Lilloa 22: 577. 1951.
Illustrations: Text figs. 11-12; pl. 4a, 7b.

Pileus 1–3 (4) cm broad, obtusely conic to convex expanding to broadly convex or nearly plane, rarely with a slight obtuse umbo; surface dry and granular-squamulose with tufted squamules soon breaking into a powder, margin for a short time appendiculate with veil fragments; color evenly dark rusty brown ("auburn") or "Brussel's brown" or "Mars brown"), in age the ochraceous ground color showing to give a paler yellow-brown effect. Context olive-yellowish fading to dingy buff; thin midway to margin; with $FeSO_4$ olive, with KOH, dark red-brown; odor slight; taste metallic to bitterish.

Lamellae pallid to pale cinnamon-buff, becoming pale ochraceous tawny or finally dull tawny, broad, adnexed at maturity crowded, edges crenulate.

Stipe 3–4 (6) cm long, 2.5–4 mm thick, equal, stuffed becoming hollow, coated with granules and squamules like those on pileus, apical region above veil line pallid and pruinose, downward slowly glabrescent as veil remnants disappear; annulus merely a zone of fibrils to rarely submembranous.

Spore deposit pale dingy cinnamon; spores 6–8 (9) × 4–4.5 μ, smooth, wall slightly thickened (about 0.25 μ), dingy cinnamon as revived in KOH, in Melzer's reagent more ochraceous, suboblong to elliptic in face view, slightly bean-shaped in profile, no apical pore present as seen under an ordinary oil immersion lens.

Basidia 4-spored, 18–23 × 5–6 μ, narrowly clavate, yellow in KOH and also in Melzer's reagent. Pleurocystidia none. Cheilocystidia abundant (40) 50–115 × 3.5–6 × 9–16 μ, cylindric to flexuous with an apical capitellum, thin-walled, smooth, content hyaline or ochraceous, rarely narrowly clavate. Caulocystidia present over apical region of stipe and shaped like the cheilocystidia or more of them narrowly clavate, measuring up to 120 μ long and many with slightly thickened ochraceous-tawny walls in the lower half as revived in KOH, smooth or with some debris adhering.

Pileus cutis of chains of inflated to subglobose cells 18–36 × 12–20 μ and readily disarticulating, with rusty cinnamon walls in KOH and rather heavy patches of rusty cinnamon incrustation, in Melzer's the walls pale colored and the incrusting material inconspicuous. Hyphae of content floccose and interwoven, yellowish to hyaline in Melzer's or KOH. Clamp connections present. All hyphae inamyloid.

HABIT, HABITAT, AND DISTRIBUTION: Solitary to gregarious on rotting hardwood logs, northern United States and Canada, particularly abundant in old hardwood slashings late in the summer or early fall; Overholts reported it from Missouri.

OBSERVATIONS: The large capitate to subcapitate cheilocystidia, the more or less isodiametric cells of the pileus epicutis which soon disarticulate, and the even colors all make this one of our most distinctive species. *Pholiota muricata* is said to differ in having distinctly yellow gills when young. This is not the color in the material we have seen of Peck's species. In veil characters and cheilocystidia, however, the two should appear very similar. It is possible that *P. muricata* and *P. erinaceella* have been confused in the Michigan flora as Singer (1955) describes *P. erinaceella* as having yellowish gills. Smith confirmed this identification. At that time a species more like *P. granulosa* was passing under the name *P. muricata* in the United States.

MATERIAL EXAMINED: MICHIGAN: Harding 109; Shaffer 2208; Smith 33-788, 21770, 25869, 33222, 33229, 37177, 39112, 39458, 41667, 41760, 41769, 41809, 41998, 49691, 49928, 50474, 57637, 57985, 61340, 66989, 67154, 67028, 73029; Thiers 704. MARYLAND: Smith 73064. NEW YORK: Kauffman 9-2-21; Peck, Lake Pleasant (type); Smith 228.

13. Pholiota pseudosiparia sp. nov.
Illustrations. Text figs. 13-15.

Pileus 5–8 mm latus, late convexus, siccus, granulosus, sordide fulvus. Lamellae latae, confertae, adnatae, pallide luteae. Stipes 1–2 cm longus, 0.5 mm crassus, sursum pallide ochraceus, deorsum subfulvus. Sporae 7–7.5 μ longae, 4–4.5 μ crassae. Pleurocystidia desunt. Cheilocystidia 28– 40 × 7–11 μ, filamentoso-capitata. Specimen typicum in Herb. Univ. of Mich. conservatum est; legit prope Pellston, Mich., 6 Juli, 1953 Smith 41513.

Pileus 5–8 mm broad, convex to broadly convex, the margin straight, surface dry and granular from cells of the epithelium, many of these becoming free in the mounts; colors dingy ochraceous to dull tawny and fading to pale yellow or cinnamon buff. Context yellowish, thin, soft, odor and taste none.

Lamellae close broad, adnate, yellowish young, then ochraceous tawny, edges minutely crenulate.

Stipe 1–2 cm long, 0.5 mm thick, equal, pallid ochraceous and pruinose above, dingy tan and pubescent below, the hairs delicate.

Spores 7–7.5 × 4–4.5 μ, oblong to subovate in face view, in profile somewhat bean-shaped, smooth, tawny in KOH and wall slightly thickened (spore not collapsing readily), apex with a minute hyaline spot as a rudimentary pore.

Basidia 4-spored, hyaline to yellowish in KOH, clavate, 26–30 × 5–7 μ. Pleurocystidia none. Cheilocystidia 28–40 × 7–11 μ, flexuous-capitate to narrowly clavate and some fusoid-ventricose, hyaline in KOH, smooth, thin-walled. Caulocystidia abundant, often a terminal cell in a series of 2–3 cells, 26–40 × 7–11 (16) μ, somewhat cystidioid (narrowed to an obtuse apex), walls thin and ochraceous, smooth to minutely asperulate.

Gill trama of inflated hyaline cells with thin smooth walls, hyphae more or less subparallel; subhymenium a narrow indistinct zone. Pileus cutis an epithelium of globose to ovate cells with incrusted pigment, walls yellow in KOH, thin. Clamp connections present. All hyphae inamyloid.

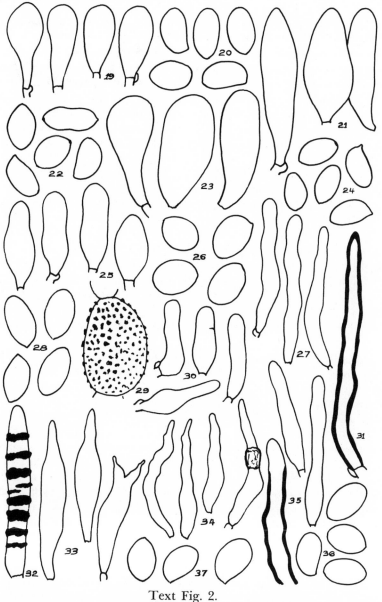

Text Fig. 2.

Figs. 19, 20 & 21, cheilocystidia, spores and caulocystidia of *P. granu-losa;* 22 & 23, spores and cheilocystidia of *P. curcuma* var. *curcuma;* 24 & 25, spores and cheilocystidia of *P. curcuma* var. *lanatipes;* 26 & 27, spores and cheilocystidia of *P. minutula;* 28, 29 & 30, spores, cell from pileus hypodermium, and cheilocystidia of *P. lactea;* 31, 32, 33 & 34, thick walled setiform cell from pileus cuticle, encrusted cell from pileus cutis, pleurocystidia, and cheilocystidia of *P. erinacea;* 35 & 36, cheilocystidia and spores of *P. confragosa;* 37, spores of *P. punicea.*

HABIT, HABITAT, AND DISTRIBUTION: Scattered on hardwood logs, Maple River, Emmet County, Michigan, July 6, 1953, Smith 41513 (type), also 41667 and 73301.

OBSERVATIONS: The distinguishing features are the pileus epithelium of globose disarticulating cells with distinct incrustations of pigment, the large caulocystidia, spores of the *P. granulosa* type, and cheilocystidia of much the same type as found in *P. squamulosa*. As dried the color of the basidiocarp is very pale. This species would be best placed in the *Flocculina* group were it not for the well pigmented spores with the very minute pore.

Naucoria mexicana is described as having pallid distant gills in contrast to *P. pseudosiparia* which has close yellowish gills. The spores of *N. mexicana* were pale ochraceous tawny under the microscope and no pore was noted under high dry magnifications. A few pleurocystidia similar to the subfilamentose cheilocystidia were seen. Also, Murrill described the stipe as tough and fulvous. We believe that the two species are distinct on the differences indicated and do not accept Singer's statement that *N. mexicana* is a synonym of *Pholiota muricata* (Singer, 1963, p. 597). The globose cells of the pileus cutis indicate that both are closely related, but before transfering *N. mexicana* to *Pholiota* we would prefer to make a critical study of the *Phaeomarasmius-Tubaria* problem.

14. Pholiota granulosa (Pk.) comb. nov.

Flammula granulosa Peck, in V. White, Bull. Torrey Bot. Club 29: 561. 1902.
Illustrations: Text figs. 19-21; pl. 29b.

Pileus 1–3.5 cm broad, convex and remaining broadly convex, margin long remaining incurved, surface dry and covered by a dense coating of minute erect fibrillose squamules over disc, but those toward margin more or less granular and more appressed, margin at first hung with the delicate remnants of the yellow ("antimony yellow") veil; color of epicutis bright rich yellow-brown ("amber brown" to "Sudan brown"), the yellowish ground color showing between the squamules. Context thin, watery-ochaceous, unchanging when cut, odor and taste mild; in KOH instantly dark brown, in FeSO$_4$ soon olive-black.

Lamellae rather narrow (3–4 mm broad in large fruiting bodies), broadest near stipe and tapered toward pileus margin, bluntly adnate, close to crowded, pale yellow young ("chamois" to "antimony-yellow"), spores not obscuring the yellow ground color, not becoming spotted, edges even.

Stipe 3–5 cm long, 2–3.5 mm thick, soon tubular to hollow, equal, with a pallid pad of mycelium at base, upper part pale yellow like the gills, below the veil-line thinly scurfy-fibrillose from veil remnants that are yellow to concolorous with the squamules of the pileus, in age becoming dark rusty brown from the base upward.

Spores 7.5–9 × 4–4.5 × 4.5–6 *μ*, smooth, elliptic to somewhat ovate in face view, slightly bean-shaped in profile or with the ventral line merely straighter than the dorsal line, slightly compressed (at least some of the spores), color in KOH rather bright yellow-brown, paler in Melzer's, apex with a very minute pore.

Basidia 4-spored, 20–25 × 7–9 *μ*, yellowish as revived in KOH. Pleurocystidia none. Cheilocystidia narrowly clavate to subglobose, 20–30 × 9–15 *μ*, walls hyaline to golden ochraceous revived in KOH but when fresh pale cinnamon, showing some tendency for the wall to thicken, very few of them fusoid-ventricose to utriform. Caulocystidia 26–40 × 9–18 *μ*, clavate, subelliptic or broadly fusoid-ventricose, walls thin but rusty cinnamon in KOH.

Gill trama of subparallel hyphae with yellowish walls in KOH, smooth and thin as revived in KOH, the cells 8–15 *μ* diam., (inflated in age), narrower toward the poorly formed indistinct subhymenium. Pileus cutis of filaments aggregated into fascicles and with the cell walls thin, rusty cinnamon in KOH and nearly smooth to asperulate or finely roughened, terminal cells somewhat cystidioid to merely elliptic; subcutis of appressed rusty-cinnamon hyphae smooth to incrusted and narrower than those in the fascicles (in the latter 8–15 *μ* diam.) Context of hyphae paler than those of subcutis (in KOH) to merely yellowish, interwoven. Clamp connections present. All tissues inamyloid (color not much different from that seen in KOH mounts.)

HABIT, HABITAT, AND DISTRIBUTION: Solitary to widely gregarious on debris and wood of conifers and harwoods, June to September; Maine to Michigan. The description is from Smith 9546, from near Pontiac, Mich.

OBSERVATIONS: The distribution of this species in North America remains to be ascertained, since there is such a strong possibility of confusion between *P. muricata, P. erinaceella, P. limulata* and *P. granulosa.* According to the Friesian descriptions *Agaricus muricatus* has broad adnexed-seceding gills and a rather strongly squamulose stipe below the veil-line. The description of *Naucoria muricata* in Kühner & Romagnesi reads more like that of *P. erinaceella,* especially in regard to the cheilocystidia. Certainly the account by Pearson (1949) under *Naucoria muricata* describes a species different from *P. granulosa* on the basis of cheilocystidia alone. It seems that the best characterization of *Pholiota muricata* that can be made at present is that it is a yellow-gilled *P. erinaceella.*

Flammula limulata is close to *P. granulosa.* To try and resolve this problem specimens collected and identified by Lars Romell were borrowed from the Riksmuseet at Stockholm. The following is a detailed description of the microscopic features of this material:

Spores 7–9 × 4–5 *μ*, smooth, apical pore very minute; shape in face view elliptic to subovate, in profile obscurely bean-shaped to obscurely inequilateral; color in KOH pale cinnamon, in Melzer's reagent about the same; wall about 0.25 *μ*.

Basidia 18–21 × 5–6 μ, 4-spored, nearly hyaline in KOH, narrowly clavate to subcylindric. Pleurocystidia none. Cheilocystidia 23–30 × 9–14 μ, clavate to nearly utriform; walls thin, smooth, yellow to hyaline; content homogeneous. Caulocystidia rare, merely as decumbent clavate to subfusoid hyphal tips with slightly thickened (about 0.5 μ) walls dark chestnut in KOH.

Gill trama of subparallel hyphae with tan to rusty red walls in KOH, smooth, cells 3–6 (10) μ, wide; subhymenium cellular, non-gelatinous, hyphal walls merely yellowish in KOH. Pileus cuticle a "collapsed" trichodermium of heavily incrusted hyphae dark rusty brown to chestnut; the cells 8–18 μ broad and mostly rather short, some as sphaerocysts but these not disarticulating. Context hyphae yellowish in KOH, cells smooth and inflated. All hyphae inamyloid. Clamp connections present (text figs. 480-482).

As can be readily ascertained, the spores are about the same but *F. limulata* has much heavier ornamentation on the trichodermial hyphae. The gill trama is much more highly colored also. Both characteristically occur on conifer wood. We do not regard these two as synonyms. Although *P. granulosa* was described from conifer wood, the Michigan collections were all on wood of hardwoods. A portion of White's type was examined. In it most of the cheilocystidia were hyaline, but the basidiocarp was obviously young. It seems quite likely that Josserand's (1965) excellent account of *"Naucoria (Floccularia) limulata"* actually applies to *P. granulosa.* Because of the discrepancies between the features of the Romell specimen cited above and Josserand's description we are using the name which is based on North American collections.

MATERIAL EXAMINED: MAINE: White (the type). MICHIGAN: Mazzer 4035; Smith 7-19-29, 9546 (typical), 25912, 32393, 49933, 57367, 61408, 61435, 73083, 73133.

Stirps Cinchonensis

Stipe with a white annulus; clamp connections apparently absent.

15. Pholiota cinchonensis Murrill, Mycologia 5: 33. 1913.

Pileus 1.5 cm broad, becoming plane, ochroleucous to ochraceous, dry, granular-tomentose, striate, margin straight.

Lamellae adnate, with a decurrent tooth, isabelline, narrow (1–2 mm broad).

Stipe 1.5 cm long, 1 mm thick, paler than the pileus, glabrous or nearly so, sometimes with fibrils on the lower part, base attached to a white mat of mycelium, equal. Veil forming a white, nearly central, sometimes ample annulus.

Spores 6–8 × 4.5–5.5 μ, in face view elliptic, in profile slightly inequilateral, smooth, no germ pore visible.

Basidia 20–28 × 5–6 μ, 1-, 2- and 4-spored, sterigmata stout. Pleurocystidia none. Cheilocystidia 38–54 × 2–6 μ, cylindric to slightly clavate, in dried material mostly shrivelled and not reviving. Caulocystidia (material sparse so no sections were made.

Gill trama interwoven, yellowish in KOH, reddish brown in Melzer's reagent. Pileus cutis of appressed hyphae bearing scattered to numerous more or less erect rusty brown hyphae as revived in KOH and reddish brown in Melzer's. Clamp connections none.

HABIT, HABITAT, AND DISTRIBUTION: On wood, Jamaica, December–January. Type studied.

OBSERVATIONS: This species is rather anomalous because of the white annulus and lack of clamp connections on the hyphae of the basidiocarp. We regard our characterization of it as tentative. With more specimens available for study for instance it may be found that some clamps are present.

Stirps Curcuma

The pileus cuticle is more of a trichodermium in this stirps than in the others, including the feature that the cells do not disarticulate.

Key

1. Growing on hemlock; odor when fresh aromatic; taste resembling that of birch twigs .... *P. murrillii*
1. Not as above 2
    2. Pileus 2–6 mm broad; spore wall up to about 0.5 μ thick .... *P. minutula*
    2. Pileus 1–3 cm broad; spore wall closer to 0.25 μ thick 3
3. Pileus pale yellow to pale tan when fresh; spores with a distinct pore .... *P. lactea*
3. Not as above 4
    4. Cheilocystidia clavate to vesiculose, walls typically yellow in KOH .... (see *P. granulosa* also) .... *P. proximans* and variants
    4. Cheilocystidia utriform, fusoid-ventricose, subcylindric, etc. but not as above 5
5. Lamellae distant and arcuate .... *P. fagicola*
5. Lamellae close 6
    6. On conifer wood; lamellae subdistant; cheilocystidia elongate-pedicellate with enlarged apex .... *P. subechinata*
    6. On hardwood; lamellae close; cheilocystidia clavate, utriform to fusoid-ventricose .... *P. curcuma* and variants

16. Pholiota curcuma (Berk. & Curt) comb. nov.
Agaricus curcuma Berkeley & Curtis, Ann. & Mag. Nat. Hist. II; 12: 421. 1853.

Phaeomarasmius curcuma (Berk. & Curt.) Singer, Schw. Zeitschr. Pilzk. 34: 60. 1956.
Illustrations: Text figs. 22-23.

var *curcuma*

Pileus 10–20 (35) mm broad, obtusely conic when young, expanding to broadly campanulate to convex or finally nearly plane, surface dry and appearing echinate (with minute erect squamules), toward margin appearing granular and squamules poorly formed, color bay to rusty-fulvous ("bay" becoming "amber-brown") finally ochraceous tawny, evenly colored. Context thin, lax, pale dingy ochraceous when mature, odor and taste none; olive with FeSO$_4$.

Lamellae close, moderately broad, bluntly adnate, dingy ochre-yellow scarcely changing, edges concolorous with faces.

Stipe 1.5–3 cm long, about 1.5 mm thick at the slightly enlarged apex, dingy brownish and in age becoming darker rusty brown from the base upward, thinly covered by appressed buff-colored fibrils from a very thin veil.

Spores 7–9 × 3.5–4.5 (5) μ, smooth, with a minute apical pore, in profile slightly bean-shaped to obscurely inequilateral, in face view elliptic to ovate, tawny in KOH and paler and dingier in Melzer's sol.

Basidia 4-spored, 18–23 × 5–7 μ, narrowly clavate to subcylindric when sporulating, yellowish hyaline in KOH. Pleurocystidia none. Cheilocystidia 26–40 (50) × 8–15 μ, utriform, broadly fusoid-ventricose, subclavate, thin-walled hyaline to yellow from pigment in the walls, smooth.

Gill trama of gigantic hyphal cells with thin non-gelatinous smooth walls yellow in KOH, the cells 10–25 μ wide and greatly elongated; subhymenium indistinct. Pileus cutis a trichodermium of hyphae with inflated cells up to 20 μ or more in diam., the walls of the cells thin but yellow in KOH and with coarse patches of rusty cinnamon pigment incrusting them; hyphae of subcutis narrower and some tubular but with the walls mostly heavily incrusted also. Context hyphae thin-walled, smooth, ochraceous in KOH. All hyphae inamyloid. Clamp connections present.

HABIT, HABITAT, AND DISTRIBUTION: Solitary to scattered on aspen logs during the summer and fall, South Carolina, Michigan, and Wyoming.

OBSERVATIONS: The features which at once distinguish this species from *P. granulosa* are the mostly hyaline utriform to broadly ventricose cheilocystidia and the very coarse pigment incrustations on the cells of the pileus trichodermium. The germ pore is minute but readily visible especially on the larger spores. The cells of the trichodermial hyphae vary from narrowly ventricose to subglobose, and the terminal cell is often elliptic to clavate—not fusoid-ventricose. *Phaeomarasmius suberinaceellus* Singer is indicated as having clavate cheilocystidia and the

North American material he cites more than likely belongs in *P. granulosa* as this is the common species around Douglas Lake, Mich. *P. curcuma* is distinct because of the very heavy dark colored pigment incrustations of the trichodermial hyphae.

MATERIAL EXAMINED: IDAHO: Smith 54130, 65985, 73450, 73451, 73452. MICHIGAN: Smith 33-971, 31. WYOMING: Smith 34429.

16a. Pholiota curcuma var. **lanatipes** var. nov.
Illustrations: Text figs. 24-25.

Pileus 7–20 mm latus, late convexus, siccus, squamulosus, subcastaneus. Lamellae confertae, latae, adnatae, pallide ochraceae demum fulvae. Stipes 1.5–3 cm longus, 1–1.5 crassus, subannulatus, deorsum fulvus. Sporae 7–8 × 3.5–4 μ. Pleurocystidia desunt. Cheilocystidia 20–32 × 7–12 μ, clavata vel fusoide ventricosa. Specimen typicum in Herb. Univ. Mich. conservatum est; legit prope Lewiston, Mich. 3 Juli 1963, Smith 66988.

Pileus 7–20 mm broad, broadly convex with an incurved margin, expanding to plane or nearly so, surface dry and densely and minutely tufted-squamulose, dark rusty reddish brown overall, slowly becoming slightly paler. Context thin, yellowish, taste mild, with $FeSO_4$ olive; with KOH dark russet.

Lamellae close, broad, adnate, pale dingy ochraceous, when mature dull rusty brown; edges crenulate.

Stipe 1.5–3 cm long, 1–1.5 mm thick, equal, thinly fibrillose below and at first with a delicate submembranous annulus, at times veil remnants hanging on pileus margin, becoming rusty brown below, near apex about cinnamon buff, apex silky pruinose. Veil ochraceous, submembranous to fibrillose.

Spores 7–8 × 3.5–4 μ, smooth, dull tawny to darker rusty brown in KOH, oblong to subelliptic in profile with the ventral line (in optical section) almost straight, in face view elliptic to ovate and some obscurely angular, apical pore present as a minute apical discontinuity, wall estimated at 0.25 μ thick.

Basidia 4-spored, 20–25 × 5–6 μ, hymenium yellow in KOH. Pleurocystidia 20–32 × 7–12 μ, clavate, utriform or broadly fusoid-ventricose with rounded apex, smooth, thin-walled, hyaline in KOH.

Gill trama of more or less parallel hyphae with cells in central area 8–15 μ broad, and with ochraceous smooth walls in KOH but toward subhymenium 3–6 μ wide and walls paler; subhymenium not truly differentiated as a layer. Pileus epicutis a shortened trichodermium of inflated hyphal cells 10–25 μ wide with conspicuous plates or patches of rusty cinnamon deposits (as seen both in KOH and in Melzer's reagent), the end-cell often smaller than the penultimate cells and ovate to elliptic in optical section, cell walls thin and ochraceous. Clamp connections present. All tissues inamyloid.

HABIT, HABITAT, AND DISTRIBUTION: Scattered on hardwood logs, Lewiston, Michigan, July 31, 1963, Smith 66988 (type), 66992.

OBSERVATIONS: This variety is distinguished primarily by the heavy veil for the size of the basidiocarps.

17. Pholiota subechinata sp. nov.

Pileus 10–25 mm latus, late convexus, siccus, fibrilloso-squamulosus, fulvus. Lamellae latae, subdistantes, adnatae, luteae demum fulvae. Stipes 2.5–3.5 cm longus, 1.5 mm crassus, flexilis, subluteus, deorsum fulvus. Sporae 7–9 × 4–4.5 μ. Pleurocystidia desunt. Cheilocystidia 26–40(50) × 8–16 μ, subclavata. Specimen typicum in Herb. Univ. Mich. conservatum est; legit prope Mt. Adams, Wash. 19 Oct. 1954, Smith 49291.

Pileus 10–25 mm broad, convex to convex-depressed, surface dry and minutely fibrillose-squamulose, squamules erect over disc and more appressed near the margin, tawny to darker rusty brown. Context yellowish, thin, fairly lax, odor none, taste not recorded.

Lamellae broad, subdistant, adnate, seceding, dull yellow young, darker fulvous than pileus when mature, edges flocculose.

Stipe 2.5–3.5 cm long, 1.5 mm thick, equal, fairly pliant, dull yellowish above, soon dark fulvous from the base up (over all as dried), thinly coated to the evanescent veil-line from the remnants of the veil, with a pad of yellowish mycelium at base.

Spores 7–9 × 4–4.5 μ, smooth, germ pore very minute, dingy ochraceous in Melzer's reagent, in KOH cinnamon, oblong to elliptic in face view and some obscurely angular, somewhat to distinctly bean-shaped in profile.

Basidia 4-spored, 22–30 × 5–7 μ, yellowish hyaline in KOH, narrowly clavate. Pleurocystidia none. Cheilocystidia 26–40 (50) × 8–16 μ, mostly somewhat enlarged at apex (the widest part) but apex varying from rounded to truncate or subacute, rarely bifurcate, walls thin, smooth and hyaline in KOH (reminding one of those of *P. erinaceella* but not as capitate). Caulocystidia with rusty cinnamon thin walls usually smooth, 35–60 × 8–12 μ, fusoid to boomerang-shaped, terminal or arising laterally from hyphae of stipe cortex.

Gill trama regular, of yellowish to brownish hyphae with smooth scarcely thickened walls; subhymenium not distinctive. Pileus cutis a trichodermium of hyphae mostly with short broad cells (1-2 times as long as broad), the walls slightly thickened or thin and many with coarse plates of incrusting material, in KOH dark red (near "Bay"), end-cells subglobose to elliptic or ovate. Clamp connections present. All tissues inamyloid.

HABIT, HABITAT, AND DISTRIBUTION: On a conifer log, on the upper Cispus River, Washington, near Mt. Adams, Oct. 19, 1954, Smith 49291 (type).

OBSERVATIONS: The sphaerocyst-like cells in the trichodermial hyphae of the pileus would seem to indicate stirps *Aurea*. However, no disarticulation of the cells was noted. The caulocystidia are unique as known to date in this subgenus, but need further study in relation to veil elements.

The diagnostic features of this species are the habitat on conifer logs, the coarse pigment deposits on at least a fair number of the trichodermial hyphae and the large number of subglobose cells in many of the hyphae, the cheilocystidia of the *P. erinaceella* type, and the broad subdistant gills. The conifer-inhabiting members of this section in North America are rare and occur solitary. There are more than those described here, but our data on them are very incomplete.

Some might be inclined to regard *P. subechinata* as a synonym of *P. muricata* but the latter is said to occur on beech, have a densely fibrillose stipe below the veil-line, and nothing is said of the gills spotting rusty as in *Gymnopilus* species. *P. subechinata* has a thin fibrillose veil leaving only inconspicuous scattered patches on the stipe, the gills become rusty spotted, and the ornamentation of the pileus is not granulose. Because of these possible differences we believe it wiser to consider the conifer inhabiting fungus as a different species. It is readily distinguished from *P. granulosa* by its cheilocystidia. In the latter they are mostly short-clavate to ovate.

18. **Pholiota murrillii** nom. nov.

Gymnopilus aromaticus Murrill, North Amer. Fl. 10: 203. 1917. (not
 Pholiota aromatica Orton, 1960)
Illustrations: Text figs. 477-479.

Pileus about 3 cm broad, convex to expanded, surface conspicuously floccose, areolate with age, yellowish-ferruginous margin lacking striae. Context whitish, aromatic; taste like that of birch twigs.

Lamellae adnexed, crowded, rather narrow, yellow to bright ferruginous.

Stipe 2–3 cm long, 4 mm thick, cylindric, densely yellow-fibrillose, chrome yellow, solid, hard, whitish within.

Spores 7.5–9.5 × 4–5 μ, smooth, apical pore minute and not visible on all spores, shape in face view ovate to elliptic, in profile mostly more or less bean-shaped; color in KOH more or less ochraceous tawny, not appreciably different in Melzer's reagent; wall about 0.3 μ thick.

Basidia 24–30 × 4.5–7.5 μ, 4-spored, narrowly clavate, in KOH lemon-yellow, duller in Melzer's reagent (yellow pigment diffusing copiously in mounts in KOH). Pleurocystidia 26–35 × 3–7 μ, present as pseudocystidia, with dingy yellowish granular content (in Melzer's mounts) and much granular to minutely granular material pervading the mount and the content disappearing from the "pseudocystidia," in KOH the content homogeneous. Cheilocystidia 28–42 × 4–9 μ, versiform: filamentous-subcapitate with a flexuous pedicel, slightly ventricose below and equally broad at apex, subtibiiform as in some species of *Galerina,* etc., their content yellow to orange-brown in KOH. Caulocystidia 36–48 × 5–8 μ, cylindric-capitate to fusoid-ventricose.

Gill trama subparallel to interwoven, cells 5–12 (finally) with thin smooth walls, the layer bright yellow in KOH; subhymenium of narrow compactly arranged non-gelatinous hyphae also yellow in KOH. Pileus cutis a collapsed trichodermium of non-gelatinous thin-walled smooth hyphae, 6–15 μ diam., with walls ochraceous in KOH (on isolated cells, or in masses of cells fulvous), cells mostly elongated and end-cells clavate to cystidioid; hypodermial hyphae arranged compactly in a layer about the color of the context. Context with an orange-fulvous layer toward the hymenophore of ochraceous somewhat refractive but not gelatinous hyphae above. Clamp connections present. All hyphae inamyloid.

HABIT, HABITAT, AND DISTRIBUTION: On dead hemlock, New York, August. Type studied.

OBSERVATIONS: This species is distinguished from *P. curvipes* by its odor and taste, and more subtibiiform cells as caulocystidia. The figures are from the type.

19. Pholiota minutula sp. nov.
Illustrations: Text figs. 26-27.

Pileus 2–6 mm latus, convexus, siccus, fibrillosus, sordide ochraceo-brunneus. Lamellae latae, confertae, vel subdistantes, argillaceae demum fulvae. Stipes 2–3.5(4) mm longus, –1 mm latus, fibrillosus. Vellum luteo-brunneum. Sporae 7–9 × 5–6 μ, subtruncatae. Pleurocystidia desunt. Cheilocystidia 26–40 × 4–7 μ, anguste clavata vel subfilamentosa. Specimen typicum in Herb. Univ. Mich. conservatum est; legit prope Dexter, Mich. 5 Oct. 1944, Smith n. 34229.

Pileus 2–6 cm broad, convex becoming broadly convex, surface dry and densely fibrillose, the fibrils fringing the margin for a time after the veil breaks, dingy yellow-brown fresh, drying dingy clay-color.

Lamellae broad, close to subdistant, adnate or with a decurrent tooth, dingy tan becoming dull rusty brown, edges slightly crenulate.

Stipe 2–3.5 (4) mm long, less than 1 mm thick, shaggy-fibrillose from veil fibrils and colored about like the pileus, apex pruinose.

Spores rusty cinnamon in KOH under the microscope, 7–9 × 5–6 μ, wall up to 0.5 μ thick, smooth, elliptic to ovate in face view, elliptic to obscurely inequilateral in profile, with a distinct apical pore causing apex to appear slightly truncate in large spores.

Basidia 24–30 × 6–7.5 μ, 4-spored, hyaline in KOH, clamped at base. Pleurocystidia none. Cheilocystidia 26–40 × 4–7 μ, flexuous-filamentous to narrowly clavate or near base slightly ventricose, thin-walled, smooth, hyaline or ochraceous in KOH. Pileus cutis of appressed non-gelatinous tubular hyphae 2–5 μ diam., ochraceous in KOH and with tawny incrustations arranged in a variable pattern. Context hyphae mostly hyaline to yellow in KOH and thin-walled. Clamp connections present. All hyphae inamyloid.

HABIT, HABITAT, AND DISTRIBUTION: Scattered on bark of living cotton-wood tree, Dexter, Mich., Oct. 5, 1949, Smith 34229, type.

OBSERVATIONS: This is a shaggy little species about the size of *Mycena corticola* but with different spores. It differs from *Naucoria horizontalis* in smaller spores (14–18 × 6–7 μ for the latter). It differs from *P. corticola* in lacking pleurocystidia and in having the well developed germ pore at the spore apex. The color of the spores is about that of *P. aberrans* but the wall is not quite as thick. This species is one of the reasons for not recognizing the genus *Pachylepyrium*. It has the spore features of that genus but, as *Pholiota* species have evolved, it is in a different line.

20. Pholiota lactea sp. nov.
Illustrations: Text figs. 28-30.

Pileus 1–2 cm latus, convexus, fibrillosus, siccus, pallide luteus. Lamellae latae, late adnatae, confertae, albidae demum pallide brunneae. Stipes 2–4 cm longus, 1–2.5 mm crassus, sursum pallidus, deorsum subbadius. Sporae 8–10 × 4.5–5 μ. Pleurocystidia desunt. Cheilocystidia 28–36 × 8–12 μ, clavata vel fusoide ventricosa. Specimen typicum in Herb. Univ. Mich. conservatum est; legit prope Lower Tahoma Creek, Mt. Rainier Nat'l. Park, Wash. 4 Oct. 1952, Smith 40539.

Pileus 1–2 cm broad, convex, expanding to broadly convex, surface dry and fibrillose, somewhat areolate in age, pale yellow to pallid (near "warm buff") over all or with the disc darker (pale clay-color), margin finally whitish and long remaining appendiculate from veil remnants. Context firm, colored like the surface, odor and taste not distinctive.

Lamellae broad, broadly adnate, close, whitish when young, becoming pale dull brown.

Stipe 2–4 cm long, 1–2.5 mm thick at apex, equal to a small basal bulb, pallid above, dingy red-brown below, at first decorated with veil remnants which terminate in an evanescent annular zone.

Spores 8–10 × 4.5–5 μ, somewhat inequilateral in profile, in face view narrowly ovate to elliptic, smooth with a distinct apical pore; rusty cinnamon in KOH, wall thickened, plage area not differentiated.

Basidia 20–23 × 7–8 μ, 4-spored, hyaline in KOH. Pleurocystidia none. Cheilocystidia abundant (edge heteromorphic), 28–36 × 8–12 μ, clavate to fusoid-ventricose with only slightly narrowed neck and rounded apex, smooth, thin-walled, hyaline in KOH. Caulocystidia abundant near apex of stipe, 28–45 × 6–11 μ, subcylindric to ventricose at base and neck elongated to an obtuse apex; walls flexuous and thin to slightly thickened.

Gill trama subparallel, of inflated thin-walled hyphae, hyaline in KOH; subhymenium not distinctive. Pileus trama floccose-interwoven, the hyphal walls smooth and yellowish in KOH. Pileus cuticle a layer of fulvous (in KOH) walled hyphae with incrusting pigment, with cells considerably enlarged (15–50 μ in diam.) and often elliptic to subglobose. Terminal cells often clavate, yellow-fulvous in KOH. Clamp connections present. All hyphae inamyloid.

HABIT, HABITAT, AND DISTRIBUTION: Gregarious on soil, lower Tahoma Creek, Mt. Rainier Nat'l. Park, Washington, Oct. 4, 1952, Smith 40539, Type.

OBSERVATIONS: This species connects to section *Inoderma* of *Galerina,* but there is no demarcation of the plage area of the spores as in those species. If *P. lactea* were to be placed in *Galerina* it would more properly belong in section *Porospora.* However, in its spore characters and the characters of the pileus cutis it falls naturally in this section of *Pholiota.* The discovery of such species as this in our estimation clearly connects *Pholiota* to the *Galerina-Tubaria* complex. The basidiocarps of *P. lactea* are a pale buff as dried, but show the typical darkening reaction of the stipe and pileus cutis when revived in KOH.

21. Pholiota proximans sp. nov. var. proximans.
Illustrations: Pl. 8a.

Pileus 1–3 cm latus, convexus, squamulosus, luteofulvus. Lamellae confertae, adnatae, luteae. Stipes 2–3 cm longus, 1.5–2.5 cm crassus, ochraceo-brunneus, tenuiter fibrillosus. Sporae 7–9 × 4–5 μ, leves. Pleurocystidia desunt. Cheilocystidia 26–35 × (9)10–22 μ, clavata vel subvisiculosa. Specimen typicum in Herb. Univ. Mich. conservandum est; legit prope Tahquamenon Falls State Park, Michigan, 22 June 1955, Smith 49607.

Pileus 1–3 cm broad, convex with an incurved margin, expanding to broadly convex or nearly plane, surface dry and covered by minute erect cones of fibrils over the disc, toward margin the squamules recurved to appressed; color bright yellow brown ("auburn" to "Sudan brown") and not changing much in age. Context thin, yellow, slowly yellowish brown by maturity, odor none, taste mild.

Lamellae broad, close, depressed-adnate and readily seceding, dingy ochraceous young, concolorous with pileus when mature, edges even but minutely flocculose.

Stipe 2–3 cm long, 1.5–2.5 mm thick, becoming tubular, attached by a pad of mycelium, surface slightly fibrillose scurfy from a rudimentary veil, ochraceous over all when fresh and near "buckthorn brown" (dark clay color) in age, but not darkening from the base up on aging, with KOH soon dark rusty brown.

Spores in deposit "russet" to "tawny"; in H_2O mounts golden tawny, dull cinamon revived in KOH, in Melzer's reagent bright ochraceous tawny; 7–9 × 4–5 μ, elliptic to oblong in face view but not infrequently obscurely angular, in profile obscurely inequilateral to bean-shaped, wall slightly thickened, apical pore present but minute.

Basidia 18–22 × 5–6 μ, 4-spored, hymenium yellow in H_2O fresh and as revived in KOH. Pleurocystidia none. Cheilocystidia 26–35 × 9–22 μ, with yellow walls in H_2O fresh and as revived in KOH, narrowly clavate to nearly vesiculose, wall slightly thickened irregularly (appearing as if somewhat ornamented).

Gill trama hyaline or yellowish in H_2O fresh, hyphae yellow in KOH on sections but hyaline as seen individually, walls thin and smooth to minutely asperulate, cells greatly elongated and 6–15 μ wide. Pileus cutis a trichodermium the hyphae separating into fascicles to form squamules, cells more or less inflated (15–20 μ wide), walls thin to somewhat thickened, rich reddish cinnamon in KOH, ornamentation fine but readily visible (not in the form of coarse plates and patches), terminal cells often cystidioid. Clamp connections present. All hyphae inamyloid.

HABIT, HABITAT, AND DISTRIBUTION: Gregarious on hardwood logs, Tahquamenon Falls State Park, Mich. June 22, 1955. H. E. Bigelow (Smith 49607, type).

OBSERVATIONS: This species differs from *P. granulosa* in that the stipe did not darken to a deep rusty brown from the base upward—and old basidiocarps were present in the collection—the gills are broad and become ventricose, and the terminal cells of the trichodermial hyphae show a tendency toward having thick walls in some hyphae of a squamule. The veil is rudimentary. Smith 66977 gave an olive black reaction with $FeSO_4$. Apparently this is typical of the species, but the type was not tested when fresh.

MATERIAL EXAMINED: IDAHO: Smith 53801. MICHIGAN: Smith 36658, 36693, 36871, 37049, 49607, 49645, 61068, 63514, 63516, 66969, 66977, 67011. NEW MEXICO: Isaacs 2687.

21a. Pholiota proximans var. subauripes var. nov.

Pileus 1–3 cm latus, fibrillose squamulosus, fulvo-ochraceus. Lamellae ochraceae, confertae, sublatae. Stipes fulvo-ochraceus. Specimen typicum in Herb. Univ. of Mich. conservatum est; legit prope Telluride, Colo., Smith 52459.

Pileus 1–3 cm broad, convex with an incurved margin expanding to broadly convex or nearly plane, surface dry and minutely fibrillose-squamulose over disc and appressed-squamulose near margin, color golden fulvous fresh, dull ochraceous dried. Context thin, yellow, odor and taste not distinctive.

Lamellae ochraceous when young, becoming dull fulvous, dull yellow-brown as dried and darker than dried pileus, moderately close, broad, adnate-seceding, edges even.

Stipe 2–4 cm long, 1–2.5 mm thick, equal, becoming tubular, concolor with pileus and the same when well dried, (not darkening from base upward), but in age dingy yellow-brown over all, veil rudimentary.

Spores 7–9 (10) × 4–5 μ, smooth, rusty brown in KOH, paler in Melzer's reagent, in face view oblong to subovate, occasionally somewhat angular, in profile somewhat bean-shaped to obscurely inequilateral, with a very minute but distinct apical pore.

Basidia 4-spored, narrowly clavate, 20–24 × 6–8 μ, yellow in KOH. Pleurocystidia none. Cheilocystidia clavate 18–30 × 9–15 μ, walls smooth and bright yellow in KOH. Caulocystidia scattered, clavate, 26–40 × 9–15 μ, thin-walled, walls yellow in KOH, smooth.

Gill trama of inflated subparallel hyphae with thin yellow walls (in KOH), narrower near the indistinct subhymenium. Pileus trama of hyaline to yellow-walled smooth inflated hyphal cells. Pileus cuticle a trichodermium, the elements of inflated smooth (rarely asperulate) yellow to tawny cells with thin-walls. Clamp connections present. All tissues inamyloid.

HABIT, HABITAT, AND DISTRIBUTION: Solitary to gregarious on aspen, Colorado, Smith 52459 (type), 50051, 51539, 52459, 52668.

OBSERVATIONS: This variety may be confused with *P. curvipes* in the field because of its bright yellow color but the cheilocystidia are different.

    22. Pholiota fagicola (Murr.) Kauffman, Amer. Journ. Bot. 13: 28. 1926.

Gymnopilus fagicola Murrill, North Amer. Fl. 10: 201. 1917.

Pileus 2 cm broad, hemispheric, not fully expanding, slightly umbonate, uniformly fulvous, cespitose, surface dry, densely imbricate-squamulose.

Lamellae adnate, melleous to ferruginous, distant, arcuate, broad, edges beautifully crenulate and yellow.

Stipe 3 cm long, 2 mm thick, ochraceous, becoming darker at the base, rough with rather coarse fibrils, equal, slender, rather tough, solid, dry.

Spores (5.5) 6–8.5 (9) × (3.5) 4–5 μ, elliptic in face view inequilateral to bean-shaped in profile, smooth, no germ pore visible. Basidia 24–28 × 5–6 μ, 4-spored. Pleurocystidia present as brown basidioles 24–30 × 4–6 μ, Cheilocystidia 25–66 × 5–9 μ, in tufts, cylindric-capitate, colorless or brown. Caulocystidia scattered, few, cylindric-capitate, similar to the cheilocystidia.

Gill trama subparallel, hyphae 6–9 μ wide, yellow to brownish in KOH, subhymenium not gelatinous. Pileus trama radially interwoven. Pileus cutis a well-defined zone of yellowish brown hyphae to dark rusty brown, bearing mounds of more or less erect columns of hyphae and some clavate pileocystidia 34–52 × 6–10 μ. Clamp connections present.

HABIT, HABITAT, AND DISTRIBUTION: On a beech log, July, New York. Type studied.

OBSERVATIONS: The arcuate distant yellow-margined gills appear to distinguish this species from *P. curvipes* but the relationship is close. *P. curvipes* as a rule is not densely imbricate-squamulose on the pileus. See *P. tuberculosa sensu* Orton (1960) also.

Stirps Corticola

This group is featured by species having pleurocystidia. *P. erinacea* of the next stirps shows these in some collections but not in others.

Key

1. Spores 6–7 × 3.5–4 μ .... *P. cyathicola*
1. Spores larger 2
   2. Pleurocystidia 26–30 × 5–8 μ, clavate-rostrate ....
   .... *P. pseudolimulata*
   2. Pleurocystidia 40–60 × 10–16 μ .... *P. corticola*

23. Pholiota pseudolimulata sp. nov.

Pileus 10–20 mm latus, subumbilicatus, siccus, squamulosus, fulvous. Lamellae latae, distantes, adnatae. Stipes 1–2 cm longus, 1–1.5 mm crassus, sursum luteus, deorsum fibrillosus. Sporae 7–9 × 4–5 μ. Pleurocystidia 26–30 × 5–8 μ, clavatorostrata. Cheilocystidia 26–35 × 9–18 μ, clavata. Specimen typicum in Herb. Univ. Mich. conservatum est; legit prope Emerson, Mich., 9 Aug. 1963, Smith 67107.

Pileus 10–20 mm broad, convex-depressed, the margin long remaining incurved, surface dry, covered over all except marginal area by very fine erect dull tawny brown fibrillose squamules, fibrils toward margin more appressed and not as well organized into squamules, ground color pale dingy ochraceous. Context thin, but not fragile, yellowish.

Lamellae broad, distant to subdistant, yellowish, when dried more rusty brown than pileus, adnexed, edges minutely floccose.

Stipe 1–2 cm long, 1–1.5 mm thick, equal fistulose, concolor with pileus below veil-line from fibrils and patches similar to scales on pileus, yellowish and faintly pruinose above, with a mycelial pad at base.

Spores 7–9 × 4–5 μ, elliptic in face view, slightly bean-shaped in profile, smooth, tawny in KOH and Melzer's reagent, with a minute apical pore.

Basidia 4-spored, 18–23 × 4–6 μ, narrowly clavate, hymenium yellow in KOH. Pleurocystidia clavate-rostrate, 26–30 × 5–8 μ, neck narrowed to a needle-like apex, content homogeneous. Cheilocystidia clavate, 26–35 × 9–18 μ, wall thickened slightly and surface mottled from slight unevenness (or irregular wall thickenings?), walls bright ochraceous in KOH.

Gill trama parallel, hyphae with yellow walls that are non-gelatinous; subhymenium indistinct. Pileus cutis a trichodermium the elements of which become aggregated to form scales on the pileus, the cells of the hyphae inflated (up to 25 μ) and ovate to clavate; walls smooth to slightly incrusted, reddish cinnamon in KOH and thin. Clamp connections regularly present.

HABIT, HABITAT, AND DISTRIBUTION: Scattered on hardwood logs, Emerson, Mich. Aug. 9, 1963 (Smith 67107, type).

OBSERVATIONS: It is very doubtful if the pleurocystidia are one-spored basidia. No sign of a spore attached was ever seen and the material was in excellent condition. The clavate cheilocystidia immediately place this species near *Naucoria limulata,* see Josserand (1965). The distinctive features of *P. pseudolimulata* are the heavily incrusted hyphae, the pleurocystidia, and the habitat on hardwoods. At the present time we are not prepared to state that *"Flammula limulata"* occurs in North America.

24. **Pholiota corticola** (Murrill) comb. nov.
Naucoria corticola Murrill, Mycologia 4: 77. 1912.

Pileus 1–1.5 cm broad, convex to subexpanded, surface avellaneous, isabelline, innate-fibrillose with slight tufts (resembling *Panus stipticus*), dry, margin undulate, incurved when young. Context thin.

Lamellae adnate, dull whitish to bay-fulvous, broad, heterophyllus, rather distant.

Stipe 1 cm long, more or less 1 mm thick, yellow, cylindric equal, glabrous at apex, whitish pubescent below.

Spores 7–9.5 × 4.5–5 μ, elliptic to ovate in face view, slightly inequilateral in profile, smooth, with a small apical callus, dark reddish tawny under the microscope.

Basidia 18–23 × 5–7 μ, 2- and 4-spored. Pleurocystidia 40–60 × 10–16 μ, irregularly clavate, subcylindric, or narrowly fusoid-ventricose, often with a secondary septum in the upper portion, at times with a brown pigment, walls thin and smooth. Cheilocystidia 37–44 × 5–8 μ, more or less resembling the pleurocystidia, occasionally secondarily septate.

Gill trama subparallel to slightly interwoven, the hyphae 3–7 μ broad and non-gelatinous; subhymenium distinctly gelatinous as revived in KOH. Pileus cuticle a tangled turf of rather long brownish incrusted hyphae. Clamp connections present.

HABIT, HABITAT, AND DISTRIBUTION: On bark of a stump, Jamaica, December-January. Type studied.

OBSERVATIONS: No caulocystidia were found but so little material was available for examination that we do not regard our observation as final. The structure of the subhymenium is that of a *Pholiota* rather than a *Galerina,* especially since the species is not related to those few *Galerina* species showing a tendency to have a gelatinous subhymenium. This feature is also against placing it in *Phaeomarasmius* even though the pileus is a trichodermium. The question of the presence of a veil also needs further study from fresh material as the original description does not actually rule out the possibility of a rudimentary veil being present.

25. Pholiota cyathicola (Murrill) comb. nov.
Naucoria cyathicola Murrill, Mycologia 4: 77. 1912.

Pileus 7–12 mm broad, hemispheric-umbonate to convex, isabelline, umbo pale-fulvous, dry, innately fibrillose, margin even.

Lamellae squarely adnate, whitish to pale ochraceous, distant.

Stipe 2 cm long, 1.5 mm thick, cylindric, isabelline, fibrillose, cartilaginous. Veil not evident except as fibrils on stipe and pileus.

Spores 6–7 × 3.5–4 μ, elliptic in face view, ends often subacute, in profile slightly inequilateral, smooth, dark tawny in KOH, no germ pore evident.

Basidia 16–20 × 4–5.5 μ, 4-spored. Pleurocystidia 44–69 × 9–12 μ and fusoid-ventricose, or saccate-pedicellate, imbedded and 30–45 × 10–18 μ, thin-walled, smooth, hyaline or nearly so in KOH. Cheilocystidia 28–37 × 8–12 μ, fusoid-ventricose with obtuse apex, smooth, thin-walled.

Gill trama with a central non-gelatinous stratum of subparallel hyphae 2–4 μ broad; subhymenium gelatinous. Pileus cutis of non-gelatinous brown obscurely incrusted hyphae more or less appressed to surface, beneath this a layer of appressed non-gelatinous hyphae. Clamp connections present.

HABIT, HABITAT, AND DISTRIBUTION: On dead trunks of tree ferns, Jamaica. Type studied.

OBSERVATIONS: This species, obviously related to *P. corticola* in the structure of the gill trama, presence of pleurocystidia and spore features, is, because of the gelatinous subhymenium somewhat peripheral in subg. *Flavidula*.

Stirps Erinacea

This stirps features characteristically thick-walled elements in the trichodermium of the pileus and is peripheral in the genus.

26. Pholiota erinacea (Fr.) Rea, Brit. Basid. P. 121. 1922.

Agaricus erinaceus Fries, El. Fung. p. 33. 1828.
Naucoria erinaceus (Fr.) Gillet, Champ de Fr. p. 543. 1874.
Dryophila erinacea (Fr.) Quélet Enchir. Fung. p. 69. 1886.
Agaricus aridus Persoon, Myc. Eur. 3: 193. 1828.
Phaeomarasmius aridus (Pers.) Singer, Lilloa 22: 577. 1951.

Phaeomarasmius erinaceus (Fr.) Kühner, Encyc. Myc. 7:33. 1935.
Illustrations: Text figs. 31-34; pl. 8b.

Pileus 5–15 mm broad, usually convex, sometimes slightly depressed on the disc or disc slightly umbonate, surface dry and densely covered by fibrillose scales, the squamules erect and nearly spine-like over the disc, toward the margin somewhat appressed, the edge usually fimbriate with over-hanging fibrils; color medium to dark rusty brown ("auburn" "russet" or paler and "ochraceous-tawny"), paler and more ochraceous near the edge. Context thin and fairly tenacious, pallid brownish, becoming pallid, odor not distinctive, taste not recorded.

Lamellae close to subdistant, broad, bluntly adnate, whitish becoming pinkish-cinnamon or darker.

Stipe 8–15 mm long, 1–2 (2.5) mm thick, equal or base somewhat enlarged, stuffed by a narrow pith, pliant and tough, lower portion densely squarrose-scaly with fine fibrillose squamules, somewhat silky above the fringe left by the broken veil, pallid brownish above, dark rusty-red below.

Spores 7–10 × 4–5.5 (9–11 × 6–8) μ, smooth, relatively thin-walled (many seen collapsed in mounts in Melzer's reagent) pale dingy ochraceous in KOH, yellowish to pale tawny in Melzer's reagent, broadly ovate to subrhomboid in face view varying to elliptic, in profile elliptic to broadly elliptic, some slightly compressed dorsiventrally, apiculus distinct, no apical pore present.

Basidia 1-, 2-, and 4-spored, 18–22 × 7–9 μ, hyaline to pale ochraceous in KOH and Melzer's reagent, narrowly clavate. Pleurocystidia scattered, 30–42 × 7–10 μ, fusoid-ventricose with subacute apex, hyaline, thin-walled, smooth, in some pilei apparently absent. Cheilocystidia 20–35 × 4–9 μ, ventricose at base and with an elongated often crooked and branched neck ending in a subacute to acute apex, neck portion with thin hyaline walls but in basal part the walls often yellowish as revived in KOH. Caulocystidia present as the cystidial to cylindric end-cells of thick-walled encrusted hyphae, the cells 35–80 × 5–10 μ diam., also seta-like cells present 50–100 × 7–9 μ with an elongated flexuous hyaline distal half ending in the subacute apex.

Gill trama of subparallel interwoven hyphae with yellow to tawny walls in KOH but the walls at most only slightly thickened; subhymenium scarcely differentiated, not gelatinous. Pileus cuticle of fascicles of thick-walled hyphae the cells tubular to inflated and with walls heavily incrusted, hyphae with end-cells tubular to cystidioid, cells 6–9 μ diam. when tubular and up to 15 μ when inflated, the subcutis a thin layer of non-gelatinous brown-walled hyphae appressed-interwoven and with thinner walls than in hyphae of epicutis. Clamps regularly present. All tissues inamyloid to weakly dextrinoid.

HABIT, HABITAT, AND DISTRIBUTION: Scattered on twigs of *Corylus* and *Betula,* Northern United States and Canada, not common.

OBSERVATIONS: The spore size is variable in this species as is also the number of sterigmata borne on a basidium. Hence we have not attempted to recognize variants based on this feature. The spores described here for Harding 261 are very similar to those described by Kühner & Romagnesi (1953). Josserand and Smith (1941) made a critical comparison of European and North American material.

It should also be pointed out here that the spores are intermediate between the *Pholiota* and *Tubaria* types. Since the species has been placed previously in *Pholiota* we include it here for practical reasons pending a critical restudy of *Phaeomarasmius, Tubaria* and *Flocculina*. Such a study should include EM photographs of the spores. Singer (1963, p. 595) states: "After having worked with *Phaeomarasmius* intensively in several continents, I have come to the conclusion that the arrangement first proposed by me in 1947 and maintained here is correct." On the basis of our study as of the present, and as indicated earlier, we would limit *Phaeomarasmius* to his subgenus and section under that name. His subgenus *Carpophilus* in our estimation does not give sufficient emphasis to the typical *Pholiota*-type of spore as found in many of its species.

Subgenus **Hemipholiota** Singer, Emended
Sydowia 15: 70. 1961.

In this group are included the remaining species with: 1) characteristically truncate spores, or 2) leptocystidia present or absent but if present scarcely projecting beyond the basidia. The subhymenium may or may not be gelatinous, and the pileus may be moist, dry or with a gelatinized subcutis or epicutis. If chrysocystidia are present and the stipe and pileus are distinctly scaly see the subgenus *Pholiota*. If the pileus is moist and hygrophanous but lacks gelatinous layers in the cutis, and chrysocystidia are present, the species belongs in *Hemipholiota*. *Pholiota discolor* was originally described as viscid so we have placed it here. If chrysocystidia are present and the stipe is not scaly see sect. *Phaeonaematoloma,* and *P. caespitosa* and *P. tennesseensis* in Section *Mutabiles.*

Key to Sections

1. Pleurocystidia lacking; pileus viscid and context thin; spores not truncate (but see *P. davidsonii*) ; stipe mostly under 5 mm thick ....
.... Section *Sordidae*
1. Not as above 2
   2. Spores truncate and chrysocystidia typically absent; spores seldom
     up to 10 μ long .... Section *Mutabiles*
   2. Not as above 3
3. Pleurocystidia absent; stipe (5) 8–15 (50) mm thick; spores not trun-

cate .... Section *Hemipholiota*
3. Not as above. Spores often with more than one germ pore near apex
.... Section *Variabilisporae*

Section **Sordidae** Singer, Emended
Sydowia 15: 70. 1961.

This section is retained for species with a viscid pileus, relatively thin somewhat hygrophanous context, non-truncate spores (but see *P. davidsonii*) and lacking pleurocystidia. The subhymenium may be gelatinous or not.

Type species *P. oedipus* (Cooke) Orton

Key to Stirpes

1. Spore apex with a slight wall thickening around the apical pore ....
.... Stirps *Serotina*
1. Spore apex lacking any differentiation around the apical pore ....
.... Stirps *Discolor*

Stirps Discolor
Key

1. Spores from 4-spored basidia 8–10 × 4–5.5 (6) μ 4
1. Spores from 4-spored basidia 5–8 × 3–5 μ 2
   2. Pileus pale yellow; spores 4–5 μ wide .... *P. contorta*
   2. Not as above 3
3. Pileus with strong olive tones .... *P. gummosa*
3. Pileus orange to tawny; lamellae spotted brownish .... *P. aurantioflava*
   4. Pileus context very soft and watery; stipe 1.5–3 mm thick 5
   4. Pileus context fairly pliant; stipe 3–6 mm thick 7
5. Cheilocystidia 6–15 μ wide .... *P. striatula*
5. Cheilocystidia 5–9 μ wide 6
   6. Gills broad and subdistant (see *P. subdefossa*) .... *P. mutans*
   6. Gills narrow and close .... *P. discolor*
7. Pileus dull reddish brown when young and fresh; stipe becoming rusty brown below .... *P. brunnea*
7. Pileus yellowish to tawny (on disc); stipe pallid below ....
.... *P. davidsonii*

27. **Pholiota striatula** sp. nov.
Illustrations: Text figs. 38-39; pl. 9b.

Pileus 1–3.5 cm latus, convexus, viscidus, hygrophanus, melleobrun-

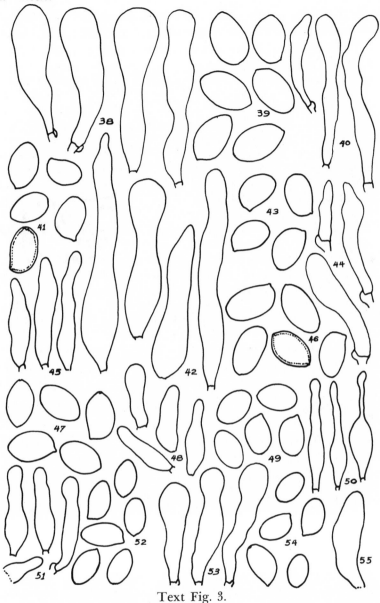

Text Fig. 3.

Figs. 38 & 39, cheilocystidia and spores of *P. striatula;* 40 & 41, cheilocystidia and spores of *P. mutans;* 42 & 43, cheilocystidia and spores of *P. discolor;* 44, 45 & 46, caulocystidia, cheilocystidia and spores of *P. brunnea;* 47 & 48, spores and cheilocystidia of *P. davidsonii;* 49 & 50, spores and cheilocystidia of *P. aurantioflava;* 51 & 52 cheilocystidia and spores of *P. olivaceodisca;* 53-55, cheilocystidia, spores and caulocystidia of *P. contorta.*

neus, glaber, striatulatus. Lamellae adnatae, breve decurrentes, latae, sub-distantes, brunneolae. Stipes 3–5 cm longus, 1.5–3 mm crassus, pallidus, submelleus, deorsum floccosus. Annulus evanescens. Sporae 8–10 × 4.5–5.5 μ. Pleurocystidia nulla. Cheilocystidia 35–61 × 6–15 μ, subcapitata-filamentosa. Caulocystidia 20–65 × 6–16 μ. Specimen typicum in Herb. Univ. of Mich. conservatum est, legit prope Ophir, Colo. 17 Aug. 1956. Smith 52341.

Pileus 1–3.5 cm broad, convex, becoming expanded plane or margin slightly arched, viscid and hygrophanous, pale butterscotch color when young, darker butterscotch in age before fading to near pale pinkish buff, glabrous except for veil fragments over marginal area when young, striatulate when moist. Context moderately thick, but very soft and watery; odor none, taste mild.

Lamellae broadly adnate to short-decurrent, moderately broad to broad, subdistant, pallid-brownish becoming clay-color, edges minutely white-crenulate.

Stipe 3–5 cm long, 1.5–3 mm thick, pallid, tinged dilute honey color over all, with soft fibrillose patches up to the broken, evanescent annulus, base spongy but not darkening, equal or base slightly enlarged.

Spores 8–10 × 4.5–5.5 μ, smooth, apical pore extremely minute (under 1.4 N.A. lens); shape in face view broadly elliptic to subovate, in profile obscurely inequilateral to slightly bean-shaped; in KOH pale ochraceous tawny, in Melzer's reagent nearly the same color; wall about 0.3 μ (or slightly more) thick.

Basidia 24–28 × 5–6 μ, 2- and 4-spored, clavate, hyaline in Melzer's reagent. Pleurocystidia none. Cheilocystidia 35–61 × 6–15 μ filamentose-capitate to clavate or many with one or more enlargements beneath the apical enlargement, some spathulate at apex, walls thin smooth and hyaline, content homogeneous, but with small (1–3 μ diam.) thickenings of refractive material adhering to interior walls variously in some of the cells. Caulocystidia 20–65 × 6–15 μ versiform, (similar to cheilocystidia).

Gill trama of subparallel hyphae 6–17 μ broad, walls of cells thin hyaline and smooth; subhymenium indistinct, (cut ends of narrow hyaline non-gelatinous hyphae). Pileus cutis a thin gelatinous pellicle of narrow (3 μ ±) hyphae with smooth thin walls, loosely interwoven, hyaline in KOH; hypodermial region not differentiated. Context hyphae inter-woven, hyaline, walls thin and smooth. Clamp connections present. All hyphae inamyloid.

HABIT, HABITAT, AND DISTRIBUTION: On soil and debris, under aspen, Colorado, August.

OBSERVATIONS: This agaric is distinguished by its colors, rather broad, subdistant, and white-crenulate lamellae. The cheilocystidia are large and conspicuous. The caulocystidia are in tufts and resemble the cheilo-cystidia. It might suggest *P. pusilla,* which has narrow gills which are at first white and has a white stipe with a ferruginous base, as well as smaller spores and cheilocystidia. It is closest to *P. mutans* from which the more poorly formed annulus, wider cheilocystidia and differently colored pileus distinguish it.

MATERIAL EXAMINED: Colorado: Smith 52341 (type from Ophir).

28. Pholiota mutans sp. nov.
Illustrations: Text figs. 40-41; pl. 7d, 8c.

Pileus 1–3 cm latus, late convexus, olivaceo-brunneus demum olivaceo griseus vel sordide luteo-olivaceus, viscidus, glaber. Lamellae adnato-decurrentes, convertae demum subdistantes, latae, pallidae, demum sub-fulvae. Stipes 2.5–4 cm longus, 2–3.5 mm crassus, cavus, deorsum incrasa-tus sursum albus, sericeus; annulus albus, submembranaceus. Sporae 7–9 × 4–5 μ. Pleurocystidia desunt. Cheilocystidia 30–62 × 5–7 μ, elongato-clavata, subfilamentosa vel subcapitata. Specimen typicum in Herb. Univ. Mich. conservatum est; legit prope Sharon Hollow, Mich. 27 May 1937. Smith 6225.

Pileus 1–3 cm broad, convex, becoming plane or in age with a slightly turned-up margin, "clove-brown" to "olive-brown" at first (olive-brown) becoming "pale olive-buff" on margin, subhygrophanous, fading to "clay-color" or "Saccardo's umber" (dark ochraceous-brown), disc often "Isabella color" for a time, opaque at first, viscid, glabrous except for a slight fibrillose marginal zone, edge often with floccose flecks of veil tissue, becoming striate before fading. Context watery, soft, pale brownish umber, becoming ochraceous; odor earthy, taste mild.

Lamellae broadly adnate-decurrent, close or nearly subdistant, (25–30 reach stipe), 3 tiers of lamellulae, moderately broad, (broadest at base), a few forked next to stipe, pallid to whitish at first, crenulate.

Stipe 2.5–4 cm long, 2–3.5 mm thick fleshy-watery, hollow, equal or slightly enlarged below, white mycelioid at base, sparsely fibrillose up to the well-formed submembranous, whitish annulus, white and silky pruinose above and below annulus.

Spores 7–9 × 4.5–5.5 μ, smooth, apical pore scarcely visible under 1.4–N.A. obj., wall less than 0.2 μ thick but visible as a double line; in face view elliptic, rarely subovate, in profile slightly bean-shaped; in KOH pale ochraceous tawny, in Melzer's reagent pale ochraceous.

Basidia 4-spored, 23–30 (37) × 6–7.5 μ, clavate, hyaline in KOH, faintly yellow in Melzer's reagent. Pleurocystidia none. Cheilocystidia 30–62 × 5–7 μ, narrowly clavate, cylindric, or slightly ventricose near the base, sometimes subcapitate, often flexuous or constricted, smooth, content homogeneous (in KOH). Caulocystidia 40–110 × 4–6 (12) μ, similar to pleurocystidia, clavate, subcapitate, to fusoid-ventricose, thin-walled, smooth, content homogenous.

Gill trama of parallel hyphae 5–10 μ broad, floccose, cells short and inflated (finally), walls thin, hyaline and smooth, subhymenium cellular and cells indistinctly outlined in KOH but not truly gelatinous. Pileus cutis a thin gelatinous layer of narrow (2–3 μ) hyaline interwoven hyphae with thin smooth walls; hypodermial region not distinct from the context. Context of closely interwoven thin-walled hyaline to yellowish hyphae with inflated cells. Clamp connections present. All hyphae inamyloid.

HABIT, HABITAT, AND DISTRIBUTION: On debris of elm, basswood, and aspen, Michigan and Colorado, May, June and October.

OBSERVATIONS: This is a rather anomalous agaric, but is better placed in *Pholiota* than *Tubaria*. In aspect it is more like *Agrocybe* than any other genus, but it lacks the diagnostic characters of that genus. It is readily destroyed by insects, as is *P. veris,* but the spores are not truncate. It is very close to *P. striatula* but that species differs in wider cheilo- and caulocystidia and in the spores lacking a germ pore. Also, the annulus in *P. mutans* is typically well-formed.

We were at first inclined to place this species in *Pholiota oedipus* (Cke) P. D. Orton but finally decided against it. There is no doubt that if one maintains a "broad" species concept, one could treat *P. oedipus* *P. striatula* and *P. mutans* as variants of a single species. However, in the past much confusion has been caused by lumping North American species with European ones before a truly critical comparison has been made of both. It is difficult for us to visualize how anyone would have ever referred our fungus to *Hypholoma.*

MATERIAL EXAMINED: Colorado: Smith 52225; MICHIGAN: Smith 6205, 6225 (type), 6277, 36319, 71531. Washington: Smith 13134, 14134.

29. Pholiota gummosa (Lasch) Singer, Lilloa 22: 517. 1951.

Agaricus gummosus Lasch, Linnaea 3: 406. 1828.
Flammula gummosa (Lasch) Kummer, Der Führer in die Pilzkunde, p. 82, 1871.
Dryophila gummosa (Lasch) Quélet, Enchir. Fung. p. 70. 1886.
Illustrations: Text figs. 62-64.

Pileus 2–5 cm broad, at first hemispheric, then convex, mamillate at first but generally obtuse or even slightly depressed in age, with the margin inrolled and regular but often becoming straight or irregularly undulating, when young slightly greenish, then clear pale citrine, showing often reddish to brownish red on disc, at times uniformly of these colors in age, viscid at first, then dry, decorated with brownish squamules very appressed and often not apparent at maturity. Context fairly thin, clear yellow, odor of herbs, taste mild or slightly raphanoid.

Lamellae merely close, unequal, adnate to appearing slightly decurrent, fairly narrow (3–7 mm), pale yellow finally yellowish brown with paler edges.

Stipe 3.5–8 cm long, 3–8 mm thick, pliant, cylindric to crooked or twisted, in some attenuated downward, stuffed, at first yellowish pallid to clear citrine, becoming rusty (tawny) below, with traces of reddish mycelium, decorated with zones and patches of veil remnants. Cortina yellowish pallid, remains disappearing almost entirely.

Spores 5.5–7 × 3.5–4 μ, smooth, apical pore distinct but apex not truncate; shape in face view ellipsoid, in profile oblong to ellipsoid; color in KOH dark yellow brown, in Melzer's paler; wall 0.25 μ thick.

Basidia 4-spored, 18–20 × 6–7 μ, clavate, hyaline in KOH, yellowish in Melzer's reagent. Pleurocystidia none, except for clavate bodies with ochraceous content in KOH. Cheilocystidia filamentous 24–36 × 5–8 μ, broadest at capitate apex, hyaline, smooth, thin-walled, content homogeneous. Caulocystidia 28–42 × 7–12 μ clavate, subutriform or more rarely fusoid ventricose, smooth, thin-walled, hyaline, arising from a gelatinous subhymenium over apex of stipe, content hyaline but coagulated and wrinkled in some cells.

Gill trama with a central area of hyaline subparallel floccose hyphae 4–12 μ diam. walls thin, smooth, hyaline; subhymenium a distinct gelatinous interwoven layer of narrow hyaline hyphae. Pileus cutis a well developed layer of narrow gelatinous hyphae 3–5 μ diam. smooth, hyaline in KOH; hypodermial zone not distinct. Context hyphae interwoven, hyphae with inflated cells, walls thin, smooth, hyaline in KOH. Clamp connections present. All hyphae inamyloid.

HABIT, HABITAT, AND DISTRIBUTION: Romagnesi reports it as fairly common in the spring or fall on wood or soil.

OBSERVATIONS: Kühner & Romagnesi (1953) and Romagnesi (1956 pl. 58 lower figs.) describe a species which they consider to have chrysocystidia. In our mounts we did not find any with the hyaline refractive inclusion as revived in KOH, but some clavate cells with yellow content were observed. In either case, depending on ones definition of chrysocystidia, the species would not fall in section *Lubrica* of Singer or in our subgenus *Flammuloides*. Our description is translated and condensed from that of Romagnesi (1956) and our microscopic data are from excellent specimens by Josserand. We do not recognize the species, in this concept, from North America, but include the description for comparative purposes. The name has appeared in the American literature, mostly for a cystidiate species with yellowish gills but otherwise very close to *P. lenta*. From Romagnesi's painting it appears that *P. gummosa* (as *Dryophila*) resembles clusters of *Naematoloma fasiculare* on the one hand (except for the viscid pileus and lack of green gills) or greenish clusters of *P. polychroa*. Pilat (1959) illustrates elongate cystidia of the *P. lenta* type (pl. 130, as *Flammula gummosa*). We have used here the most clearly established concept of the species we could find by European authors. We do not insist it *is* the concept of Fries since none of the illustrations—Pilat's or Romagnesi's closely resemble the Friesian paintings. Kühner (1946) has studied the species in culture. He describes allocystidia in his cultures of both diploid and haploid mycelium. They remind one of the cheilocystidia of some of the species we have included in the present work.

30. Pholiota discolor (Pk.) Saccardo, Syll. Fung. 5: 744. 1887.
Agaricus discolor Peck, Buffalo Soc. Nat. Sci. Bull. 1: 50. 1873.
Illustrations: Text figs. 42-43.

Pileus subcaespitose, 1–3 cm broad, convex, becoming plane or slightly depressed, hygrophanous, cinnamon-rufous and striatulate on the margin when moist, bright ochraceous yellow when dry, glabrous, thin.

Lamellae adnate or with a decurrent tooth, pallid then pale ferruginous, finally brown, narrow, close.

Stipe 2.5–7 cm long, 1.5–3 mm thick, whitish or pallid, fibrillose-striate, equal, hollow. Veil forming a distinct, persistent annulus.

Spores 7–9 × 4–5.5 μ, elliptic to broadly so in face view, slightly inequilateral in profile; smooth; germ pore not evident; very pale yellowish in KOH under microscope.

Basidia 22–26 × 6–7 μ, (2-, 4-spored. Pleurocystidia none; cheilocystidia 45–68 × 5–9 μ, usually long-cylindric, often obscurely to slightly ventricose, more rarely capitate.

Gill trama slightly interwoven, hyphae 4–7 μ broad. Subhymenium not distinctive. Pileus trama interwoven. Cuticle of repent hyphae, bearing erect, scattered or clustered colorless hyphae, the terminal elements as ventricose or subclavate pileocystidia, 25–95 × 10–13 μ. Caulocystidia absent, but at times the terminal cells of the more or less colorless hyphae are cystidioid and project outward. Clamp connections present.

Habit, habitat, and distribution: On wood, New York, September. Type studied.

Observations: In his original description, Peck described the pileus as viscid. We found the type devoid of any gelatinous hyphae on the pileus and therefore regard the species as not viscid. But this conclusion needs to be reaffirmed from an examination of fresh material, as Peck was usually right on such matters. However, Peck himself confused this species with *Galerina autumnalis,* a species with distinctly ornamented spores, and this concept (of a species with rough spores) was continued for many years in the North American literature.

Dennis (1953) reported on this species, but he described it as having spores with an apical germpore and cheilocystidia 20–30 × 7 μ. These features do not check with our study of the type.

31. Pholiota brunnea sp. nov.
Illustrations: Text figs. 44-46; pl. 10.

Pileus 1–2.5(3) cm latus, late convexus, glaber sed ad marginem fibrillosus, viscidus, sordide vinaceo-brunneus. Lamellae adnatae, brunneolae demum fulvo-cinnamomeae, confertae, latae. Stipes 2–5 cm longus, 3–6 mm crassus, aequalis, deorsum fulvus, fibrillosus; sursum pallide argillaceus, sericeus. Sporae 8–10 × 4–5 μ, ellipsoideae. Pleurocystidia desunt. Cheilocystidia 24–40 × 5–8 μ, clavata vel subfusoideo-ventricosa, tenuitunicata. Caulocystidia 25–40(60) × 5–8 μ, clavata, obclavato-mucronata vel cylindrica. Specimen typicum in Herb. Univ. Mich. conservatum est; legit prope Upper Payette Lake, Idaho, 30 Aug. 1962. Smith 66294.

Pileus 1–2.5 (3) cm broad, caespitose, convex becoming broadly convex, margin incurved at first and decorated with a fringe of fibrils, viscid, moist, hygrophanous, "verona brown" (dark dull cinnamon) to "warm sepia," becoming near "buckthorn brown," fading to dingy ochraceous, margin often splitting in age. Context pinkish buff, fading to watery brown; odor and taste not distinctive.

Lamellae adnate, becoming adnexed, when young watery brown, then dull rusty cinnamon (like *Galerina autumnalis*), close, broad, edges even, pallid.

Stipe 2–5 cm long, 3–6 mm thick, equal, rusty-fulvous below, with the buff remains of the veil variously distributed over main portion, apex pale pinkish buff and fibrillose silky, dingy honey-brown beneath the fibrils.

Spores 8–10 × 4–5 μ, smooth, in face view elliptic to ovate, in profile elliptic to obscurely inequilateral, apical pore minute, wall about 0.3 μ thick, in KOH dark cinnamon, in Melzer's reagent a paler cinnamon.

Basidia 27–30 × 6–9 μ, 4-spored, clavate, yellowish in KOH to hyaline, yellowish in Melzer's reagent. Pleurocystidia none. Cheilocystidia abundant, 24–40 × 5–8 μ, clavate to subfusoid-flexuous or fusoid-ventricose, thin-walled, smooth, hyaline to yellowish in KOH, content homogeneous. Caulocystidia 25–40 (60 × 5–8 μ, clavate cylindric to cylindric-flexuous, or obclavate-mucronate, smooth, thin-walled, walls yellowish in KOH, content homogeneous.

Gill trama of parallel to interwoven hyphae with short to long cells with thin hyaline to yellowish smooth walls and homogeneous to colloidal content (in fine globules); merging gradually into the cellular nongelatinous subhymenium. Pileus cutis of appressed hyphae 2–5 μ wide, in a subgelatinous layer grading imperceptibly to the context (no hypodermium differentiated structurally), the hyphae at the base of the cutis darker in color (in KOH) than remainder, the hyphae smooth to asperulate. Context hyphae 8–15 μ diam. cells inflated, walls thin smooth and yellowish in KOH, content "colloidal." All hyphae inamyloid.

HABIT, HABITAT, AND DISTRIBUTION: Cespitose on conifer wood, Squaw Meadows, Valley County, Idaho. Aug. 30, 1962. Smith 66294, type.

OBSERVATIONS: This species appears at first to belong in the *P. malicola* group but differs in the brown rather than yellow pileus and non-dextrinoid spores. The basidiocarps show a strong superficial resemblance to those of *Galerina autumnalis* but spores and cystidial features separate them sharply. It is not related closely to *P. mutans* though one might get this impression from comparing descriptions. The caulocystidia vary from simple projecting hyphal tips to cells resembling the cheilocystidia.

32. Pholiota davidsonii sp. nov.
Illustrations: Text figs. 47-48.

Pileus 2–3 cm latus, late convexus, luteofulvus, glaber viscidus. Caro luteola. Lamellae subdecurrentes, brunneae confertae, latae. Stipes 2–3 cm longus, 3–5 mm crassus, obscure pallidus, sursum pruinosus, deorsum fibrillosus. Sporae 8–10(12) × 4–5(6–6.5) μ. Pleurocystidia desunt. Cheilocystidia 20–32 × 5–7 μ, subcylindrica vel subventricosa, tenuitunicata. Caulocystidia clavata, 8–15 μ diam. Specimen typicum in Herb. Univ. Mich. conservatum est; legit. prope Estes Park, Colorado, (Rocky Mts. Nat'l. Park), Ross Davidson 112.

Pileus 2–3 cm broad, convex, slightly hemispheric, yellowish tawny, glabrous, slightly viscid when wet. Context thick on disc, thin on margin, tinged yellowish.

Lamellae adnate-subdecurrent, brown (color when young not recorded), close, broad, edges whitish and minutely fimbriate.

Stipe 2–3 cm long, 3–5 mm thick, dingy-pallid, apex pruinose, elsewhere sparsely fibrillose, equal. Veil white, rather heavy-arachnoid but not membranous, appendiculate, fugaceous.

Spores 8–10 (12) × 4–5 (6–6.5) μ, smooth, dark rusty brown in KOH, a paler tawny-cinnamon in Melzer's sol., smooth, with a distinct apical germ pore which in the giant spores causes the apex to appear truncate; elliptic to ovate in face view, somewhat inequilateral in profile; wall 0.3–0.5 μ thick (estimated).

Basidia 25–32 × 6–8 μ, 4-spored or rarely 2-spored (large spores seen in diads.), hyaline in KOH and yellowish in Melzer's reagent. Pleurocystidia none. Cheilocystidia very inconspicuous, 20–32 × 5–7 μ, buried in the hymenium of the gill-edge, subcylindric to ventricose or a few fusoid-ventricose, thin-walled, hyaline in KOH, content homogeneous. Caulocystidia present as clavate end-cells of stipe hyphae, 8–15 μ diam. and variable in length, hyaline, walls thin and smooth, content homogeneous.

Gill trama of floccose hyphae 5–10 μ diam. (gills all young) somewhat interwoven to parallel; walls thin, smooth and hyaline to yellowish revived in KOH; subhymenium of cellular construction and not gelatinous, the cells 4–8 μ diam. Pileus cutis a layer of hyphae 3–6 μ diam. with incrusted walls, the zone refractive in KOH indicating presence of slime but individual hyphae clearly delimited; hypodermial zone of more deeply colored incrusted hyphae. Context hyphae hyaline to yellowish in KOH, 6–15 μ diam; smooth, thin-walled. All hyphae inamyloid. Clamp connections present.

HABIT, HABITAT, AND DISTRIBUTION: On soil under spruce. Aug. 28, 1959, Rocky Mts. National Park, Colo., Ross Davidson 112, type.

OBSERVATIONS: This species although described from rather young specimens is worth placing on record as it shows that two-spored basidia very likely produce the large spores which are truncate at the apex, whereas the 4-spored basidia produce spores with the apical pore distinct but the spore apex is not truncate. It is because of such species as this that we have abandoned *Kuehneromyces* as a genus.

In our description the measurements of the basidiocarp are from dried immature specimens, but the spores have been studied both from a deposit and from the gills of the oldest basidiocarp. This species is to be regarded as having about the stature and proportions of *Pholiota spumosa*. Since cystidial features are more reliable at the time sporulation begins, we believe that the absence of pleurocystidia and the very inconspicuous cheilocystidia can be trusted to be reliable species characters here.

The dried basidiocarps remind one of *Naematoloma capnoides* to a great extent, but spore features and the absence of chrysocystidia rule this out. It is named in honor of the collector, Dr. Ross Davidson who has worked so much on the forest fungi of the Rocky Mountains.

33. Pholiota aurantioflava sp. nov.
Illustrations: Text figs. 49-50; pl. 11a.

Pileus 2–4 cm latus, obtusus demum plano-umbonatus, viscidus, aurantiacus vel aurantiofulvus, squamulosus, glabrescens. Lamellae adnatae, confertae, latae, luteolae, tactu brunneo-maculatae. Stipes 3–5 cm longus, 2–4 mm crassus, deorsum aurantio-brunneus, sursum luteus, fibrillosus. Sporae 6–7.5 × 4–5 μ. Pleurocystidia desunt. Cheilocystidia 26–44 × 3.5–7 μ, ventricoso-rostrata et subcapitata. Specimen typicum in Herb. Univ. Mich. conservatum est; legit prope Nordman, Idaho, 8 Oct. 1956. Smith 54274.

Pileus 2–4 cm broad, obtuse with a curved-in margin, expanding to plano-umbonate or at times margin arched, color between zinc orange and tawny with margin paler and yellowish, viscid, at first spotted with minute squamules above marginal area or over all, glabrescent, slightly striate in age. Context concolorous, pliant; odor and taste not distinctive.

Lamellae adnate, depressed-adnate in age, close, broad, pale yellowish, finally brownish from spores, edges soon serrulate and staining dingy where bruised.

Stipe 3–5 cm long, 2–4 mm thick, equal or nearly so, base soon dingy orange-brown, apex yellowish. Veil pallid and fibrillose, not leaving a distinct zone.

Spores 6–8 × 4–5 μ, smooth, wall slightly thickened, apical pore very minute; in face view elliptic (usually fairly broadly elliptic), in profile elliptic to subelliptic; in KOH dingy ochraceous and with a central refractive globule, wall thin but with a mucilaginous ochraceous thickening against it as revived in KOH, in Melzner's reagent dull tawny (and the mucilaginous material not evident).

Basidia 26–30 × 6–8 μ, 2- and 4-spored, hyaline in KOH, yellowish in Melzer's sol. Pleurocystidia none. Cheilocystidia 26–44 × 3.5–7 μ, ventricose-rostrate, the neck flexuous and 2–3 μ thick, apex subacute to subcapitate, (shape much as in the *Galerina sideroides* group—almost tibiiform), walls thin smooth and hyaline, content homogeneous. Caulocystidia abundant, versiform: 15–20 × 8–10 μ and clavate, tibiiform and 36–50 × 4–6 × 2–3 × 3.5 μ, and 35–50 × 3–5 μ and nearly setiform, all hyaline in KOH, smooth and with thin-walls.

Gill trama of floccose parallel to subparallel hyphae 4–10 μ broad and cells inflating even more in age, dull rusty ochraceous in KOH to merely dingy ochraceous, walls smooth and thin; subhymenium gelatinous, of narrow interwoven hyphae. Pileus cutis a very thick gelatinous pellicle of widely separated interwoven hyphae with gelatinous walls, hyphae 2–3 μ diam. and yellowish to hyaline, smooth; hypodermial region of more highly colored (ochraceous) smooth floccose hyphae 4–10 μ diam., and thin-walled. Context hyphae ochraceous in KOH, thin-walled, smooth and cells often much inflated. All hyphae inamyloid. Clamp connections present.

HABIT, HABITAT, AND DISTRIBUTION: On debris of conifers, Nordman, Idaho, Oct. 8, 1956. Smith 54274, type.

OBSERVATIONS: In the dried condition the pilei are evenly a rather distinct yellow, the disc and margin being the same color. The stipes are browner but have not darkened distinctly in drying as occurs for so many *Pholiota* species. The stipe tissue in KOH does not darken distinctively. *P. aurantioflava* is a most unusual species in that the basiodicarps when fresh resemble those of subgenus *Flammula* in both appearance in the field and in the combination of moderately dextrinoid spores and lack of pleurocystidia. The gelatinous subhymenium and cheilocystidia connect to stirps *Sideroides* of *Galerina*. It appears that the more *Galerina* and *Pholiota* are studied the more intermediates we find. This situation is of importance in evaluating the families of rusty brown and purple-brown spored agarics. Because of such intermediate species as this the connection from *Galerina* to *Pholiota* subg. *Flammula* is solidly established, for here the aspect of the basidiocarp is clearly with a group of *Pholiotae* lacking pleurocystidia, but the microscopic features of subhymenium still indicate the stirps *Sideroides* of *Galerina*.

Stirps Serotina

The peculiar "doughnut-like" thickening around the apical pore is the feature emphasized here. It is not conspicuous but it could be the forerunner of a spore apex resembling that of *Boletus truncatus*. No relationship, of course, is implied between the two just mentioned. The pleurocystidia are very inconspicuous.

The same spore feature is found in *P. paludosella*, but there it is not so distinct or present on as many spores.

Key

1. Gills very wide; gelatinous subhymenium very well developed; pileus yellowish white .... *P. kalmicola*
1. Gills only moderately broad; subhymenium a poorly defined layer; pileus pale alutaceous on disc, margin olivaceous .... *P. serotina*

34. Pholiota serotina sp. nov.
Illustrations: Text figs. 70-71.

Pileus 2–4 cm latus, hemisphericus vel late convexus, viscidus, sub-squamulosus, pallide alutaceus. Lamellae adnatae, demum sinuatae, confertae, latae, albidae demum ligno-brunneae. Stipes 4–5 cm longus, gracilis, fibrillosus, deorsum brunnescens, sursum pallidus. Vellum fibrillosum. Sporae 7.5–9(11.5) × 4–5 (5.5) μ. Pleurocystidia inconspicua, fusoide ventricosa, 18–24 × 6–9 μ. Specimen typicum in Herb. Univ. of Mich. conservatum est; legit prope Ann Arbor, 12 Nov. 1911, C. H. Kauffman.

Pileus 2–4 cm broad, at first subhemispheric, then broadly convex, margin decurved, pinkish buff, the center minutely dotted by innate scales, later taking on pale olive color towards margin, slightly incarnate tinted on the disc from the dotlike scales, with a distinct viscid pellicle, even on margin. Context concolor, thin.

Lamellae adnate, then sinuate-uncinate, or with faint decurrent lines, medium broad (4–5 mm), close, of equal width, white at first, covered when young by a cortinate veil, at length gray-brown ("wood brown") and dusted by ferruginous spores, edges entire.

Stipe 4–5 cm long, 2–4 mm thick, slender, subequal and tapered slightly downward, at first covered with fibrillose subsilky covering, brunnescent, tubular and white within, becoming brown later. Veil cortinate, evanescent.

Spores 7.5–9 (11.5) × 4–5 (5.5) μ, smooth, apical pore distinct and in most spores surrounded by a wall thickening evident in an optical-section view of the spore; shape elliptic to oblong in face view or varying to slightly irregular in outline, in profile view obscurely inequilateral to subelliptic, wall up to about 0.5 μ thick in KOH mounts, tawny in KOH and not much change in Melzer's reagent.

Basidia 18–24 × 6–8.5 μ, 2-spored and 4-spored, obese, yellowish in KOH, orange-yellowish in Melzer's reagent. Pleurocystidia 18–24 × 6–9 μ, resembling basidioles or rarely with a neck 4–5 μ diam., very inconspicuous, content as revived in KOH homogeneous, hyaline. Cheilocystidia 22–35 × 7–12 μ, fusoid-ventricose to ventricose- capitate, usually more ochraceous than the pleurocystidia, smooth, thin-walled. Caulocystidia none.

Gill trama of subparallel floccose hyphae ochraceous in KOH, with thin smooth walls, cells 3–10 μ diam., subhymenium of narrow subgelatinous hyphae in a poorly defined layer. Pileus with a tangled layer of encrusted hyphae 4–9 μ diam., those at surface collapsing as if gelatinized (hence surface may be viscid) ; hypodermial region more compact and highly colored. Context hyphae poorly revived but interwoven and cells inflated. Clamp connections present. All hyphae inamyloid (merely ochraceous in Melzer's reagent).

Habit, habitat, and distribution: On soil, Michigan and Pennsylvania, September-November. Rare.

Observations: The distinctive feature of this species is the differentiation at the spore apex (fig. 71). It is not conspicuous, but we believe significant taxonomically. In view of the description of the pileus as viscid (by Kauffman) we are inclined to interpret the collapsing surface hyphae as producing this effect, but the anatomical basis for the viscid character is to be regarded as questionable here. The pleurocystidia are so widely scattered and inconspicuous that their presence is of little help to the taxonomist. It is a peculiar fungus which should be critically restudied from fresh material.

Material examined: MICHIGAN: Type, Kauffman, Ann Arbor, Nov. 12, 1911; PENNSYLVANIA: collected by Kauffman.

35. Pholiota kalmicola (Murr.) comb. nov.
Hebeloma kalmicola Murrill, North Amer. Fl. 10: 218. 1917.
Illustrations: Text figs. 72-74.

Pileus 2.5–3.5 cm broad, convex expanding to convex-depressed, not umbonate, uniformly yellowish white to cream colored, surface moist, slightly viscid, subglabrous, margin entire and concolorous, not striate. Context thin; odor none, taste slightly unpleasant.

Lamellae adnexed or sinuate, yellowish white to dirty white, very broad, moderately close, thin, entire and concolorous on the edges.

Stipe 5 cm long, 3 mm thick, slender, cylindric, equal, fibrillose, slightly darker than the pileus, hollow.

Spores 7–9 × 4–5 μ (9–12 × 5–6 μ), smooth, apex differentiated much as in *P. serotina*, shape in face view oblong to elliptic for 4-spored basidia, suboblong and obscurely angular for those from 2-spored basidia, in profile oblong to subelliptic; tawny or paler in KOH and about the same color in Melzer's reagent; walls 0.3–0.4 μ thick.

Basidia 17–21 × 6–8 μ, 4-spored and 2-spored, utriform, hyaline to yellow in KOH and in Melzer's reagent. Pleurocystidia scattered, 18–26

× 8–14 μ, clavate, clavate-mucronate or broadly fusoid-ventricose, wall smooth, thin, hyaline, content hyaline to yellow in KOH and homogeneous (with aspect of chrysocystidia but lacking the inclusion as revived in KOH). Cheilocystidia similar to pleurocystidia or varying to vesiculose-pedicellate. Caulocystidia not studied.

Gill trama a central hyaline strand of floccose hyphae with cells smooth, thin-walled, inflated, and hyaline in KOH; subhymenium a broad gelatinous band of narrow (2 μ) hyaline branched hyphae. Pileus trama of hyaline floccose interwoven hyphae with inflated thin-walled smooth cells; above it a hypodermial region of bright rusty brown (in KOH) incrusted inflated cells and above this a gelatinous pellicle of yellow, narrower (4–7 μ) nearly smooth tangled hyphae. Clamp connections present. All hyphae inamyloid.

HABIT, HABITAT, AND DISTRIBUTION: Gregarious on a much-decayed mossy stump of *Kalmia latifolia,* Virginia, October. Type studied.

OBSERVATIONS: The spore size as given in Murrill's original description is slightly erroneous. The spores, gill trama, pileus trama and habitat on wood make this a typical *"Flammula"* of the Friesian classification. The portion of the type examined was in part sterile, which accounts for the pale gills. The stature is much like that of *Pholiota myosotis,* but no chrysocystidia were found. The cystidia which are present are more properly classed as leptocystidia. The species is most closely related to *P. serotina* by its peculiar spore feature but has much wider gills. Both show the same pattern of variation in spore size and shape. In *P. serotina,* however, the subhymenium is poorly defined whereas in *P. kalmicola* it is more highly developed than in any other *Pholiota* known to us.

Section **Mutabiles Konrad & Maublanc,** Encyc.
Myc. 15: 158. 1948

Kuehneromyces Singer & Smith, Mycologia 38: 504. 1946.

As limited here the section includes only those species with truncate spores measuring consistently less than 9 μ long.

Type species: *Pholiota mutabilis.*

Key to Stirpes

1. Stipe scaly below annulus or stipe 4–12 mm thick. ...... Stirps *Mutabilis*
1. Not as above 2
   2. Pileus lacking a gelatinized pellicle .... Stirps *Marginella*
   2. Pileus with pellicle gelatinized 3
3. Gills more or less olive-fuscous mature .... Stirps *Depauperata*
3. Gills some shade of rusty brown when mature 4

4. Gills broad at maturity .... Stirps *Obscura*
4. Gills narrow .... Stirps *Vernalis*

Stirps Mutabilis

In this group are placed first of all species with a distinctly scaly stipe and glabrous pileus as well as two additional species with stipes 4–12 mm thick in which the pileus is viscid or at least has a thin gelatinous pellicle but in which the veil is not developed enough to produce scales on the stipe. *P. veris* is often riddled by insect larvae by the time the spores are formed.

Key

1. Pileus dull cinnamon fading to yellowish; stipe distinctly scaly below
   annulus at time veil breaks .... *P. mutabilis*
1. Not with above combination of features 2
   2. Chrysocystidia present in hymenium 3
   2. Chrysocystidia absent 4
3. Veil yellow; yellow pseudocystidia present in the hymenium ....
   .... *P. caespitosa*
3. Veil remnants on stipe yellow-brown; pseudocystidia absent ....
   .... *P. tennessensis*
   4. Hypodermial zone of pileus with cell walls hyaline in KOH and
      about 1 μ or slightly more thick .... *P. albo-olivascens*
   4. Hypodermial zone of brown hyphae with thin walls as seen in
      KOH .... *P. veris*

36. Pholiota mutabilis (Fr.) Kummer, Der Führer in die Pilzkunde p. 83. 1871.

Agaricus mutabilis Schaeff. ex Fries, Syst. Myc. 1: 245. 1821.
Pholiota mutabilis Quélet, Champ. Jura et Vosges, p. 94. 1872.
Dryophila mutabilis Quélet, Enchir. Fung. p. 69. 1886.
Kuehneromyces mutabilis (Fr.) Singer & Smith, Mycologia 38: 505. 1938.
Illustrations: Text figs. 123-124; pls. 12-14.

Pileus 1.5–6 cm broad, obtuse when young (rarely papillate), becoming campanulate or broadly conic while the margin is still strongly incurved, expanding to convex or plane or retaining a low broad abrupt umbo, the margin often remaining decurved, hygrophanous, reddish cinnamon to dull cinnamon or clay-color ("Verona brown" to "clay-color" to "ochraceous-tawny" or "sayal-brown" at maturity), fading to pale alutaceous (near "pinkish-buff" or yellower and near "ochraceous-buff" on disc), fading on the disc first or in a zone between disc and margin, surface glabrous or with inconspicuous white fibrils from the veil when very young, smooth, lubricous to viscid from a more or less separable pellicle (merely moist after heavy rains have washed off the pellicle), margin closely translucent striate when moist, opaque when faded. Context thin except in the disc, moderately soft, watery to moist and pallid; odor weak, agreeably spicy (neither raphanoid nor farinaceous), taste mild or slightly unpleasant but not bitter.

Lamellae broadly adnate to subdecurrent when young, later usually distinctly decurrent (more so than in other species), close to crowded, broad in the inner third (± 5 mm in a medium-sized mature cap), pallid when young, developing a dull buff tinge and eventually becoming almost "sayal-brown" (dull cinnamon).

Stipe 4–10 cm long, 2–12 mm thick, pallid at first over all except basal portion, soon becoming brownish and finally blackish brown from base upward, equal or nearly so, tapered toward the base at times, stuffed becoming hollow, below the annulus covered almost to base with distinct pallid to brownish recurved scales (scales sometimes indistinct in dried material), base of stipe either naked or covered by a white velutinous mycelial tomentum, somewhat silky-striate above annulus. Veil forming an apical or subapical membranous annulus; annulus sometimes scaly on the lower side, or at times ring merely a zone of fibrils.

Spore deposit cinnamon ("Verona-brown" to "cinnamon"); spores 5.5–7.5 × 3.7–4.5 (6) μ, smooth, ovate in face view or subelliptic in profile, obscurely inequilateral to subelliptic; apex truncate from a well-developed pore; smooth, wall fairly thin, in cross section terete to slightly compressed; pale tan in KOH, in Melzer's pale tawny to tawny.

Basidia 20–23 × 4–5 μ, 4-spored. Pleurocystidia none. Cheilocystidia 17–29 × 3.3–7 μ, abundant, thin-walled, hyaline in KOH, subcylindric to fusoid-ventricose, some with a slight capitellum at apex or more or less capitate from a mucilaginous secretion. Caulocystidia scattered to fasciculate, sometimes apparently absent (always check young material), more or less like cheilocystidia in size and shape.

Gill trama somewhat interwoven, hyphae 3–5 (12) μ broad, hyaline and smooth in KOH or with brownish incrusting pigment on the walls (more pronounced in age), walls slightly thickened as revived in KOH. Pileus trama of interwoven, irregular, hyaline hyphae with inflated cells and smooth walls at first, but in old basidiocarps with somewhat thickened walls. Pileus epicutis a gelatinous pellicle; hypodermium a region of hyaline hyphae 2–3 μ diam. of brownish hyphae not structurally different from context. Clamp connections present.

HABIT, HABITAT, AND DISTRIBUTION: Caespitose to gregarious on hardwood logs, stumps or more rarely on buried wood, also abundant on conifer wood in the Pacific Northwest; widely distributed in North America.

OBSERVATIONS: One naturally expects that a species with such a scaly stipe would at first have veil remnants on the pileus, but we have never found it this way. It is one of the most prolific species we have, as shown in the photograph (pl. 22). It is not uncommon to find the base of a dead tree literally covered by it.

The basidiocarps are fairly persistent with the result that clusters are sometimes found which have washed out to various degrees of yellow and the slime in the epicutis is largely removed leaving the layer with a loosely interwoven appearance and with the hyphal walls rather clearly outlined. In fact we were at first inclined to recognize a species on this feature but gave it up for lack of any substantial correlated difference. The reason, apparently, for the longevity of the basidiocarps is the manner in which the hyphae slowly develop walls up to 1.5 μ thick and which separate from the middle lamella, as can be seen in frayed or broken walls. The hyphae of the gill trama and adjacent pileus trama in particular show this feature. In such weathered specimens the veil material may be weathered away to the degree that causes confusion in recognizing the species. Such specimens may still be readily recognized, however, by the very small ventricose-rostrate cheilocystidia, rather thick-walled spores for their size, lack of pleurocystidia, and scattered small caulocystidia, though the latter feature is somewhat unreliable as the cells are often difficult to locate on revived tissue. Caulocystidia were found on a specimen from Sweden determined as this species by Romell and given to Kauffman. We have found them rare to absent on most American collections in restudying dried material. Further observations on this feature based on fresh material are desirable.

This species was found to cause a rot of ground wood pulp by Robak (1933). In culture the fungus grew about 5 mm per day and produced a strong red-brown color in the medium. It did not seem to be very destructive but apparently was common. The fungus was fruited in culture. The wood used was ground spruce from Norway.

MATERIAL EXAMINED: ALASKA: Wells 1959 #2, 6-29-64 #7S. COLORADO: Barrows 1356 (Mich); Smith 51470, 51761, 51829, 52271. IDAHO: Smith 54156, 59156. MAINE: Bigelow 3047, 3728, 3839 (all Mich.). MICHIGAN: Harding 150. NEW YORK: Kauffman 9-16-22. NORTH CAROLINA: Hesler 11467, 12701. OREGON: Cooke 25-le (Mich.); Smith 19540, 19548, 23820. TENNESSEE: Hesler 9107, 9332, 2536, 12701, 13967; Sharp 107 (FH). Smith 10478, 10566. WASHINGTON: Kauffman 10-14-25; Imshaug 1020; 1219, 1765, 226; Smith 13261, 13426, 13620, 13709, 13741, 13918, 14265, 14524; 14821, 16163, 16252, 30212, 39856, 39904, 47549, 49022, 49158. WYOMING: Solheim 3776. CANADA—BRITISH COLUMBIA: Waugh 27533, Bowman 34567 (DAOM). NOVA SCOTIA: Wehemeyer 783. ONTARIO: Kelly 1187 (Mich).

37. Pholiota tennesseensis sp. nov.
Illustrations: Tex figs. 125-127; pl. 15.

Pileus caespitosus, 1.5–3.5(7) cm latus, eburneo-albus demum ebur-

neo-flavus vel "light-buff" tinctus colore obscuro-olivaceo, disco "chamois" demum "warm-buff," denique obscure flavo-albus, fibrillosus, squamuosus vetus. Caro alba; odore et gustu mitis. Lamellae adnatae vel adnato- decurrentes, albae deinde flavidae, denique "honey-yellow" demum "clay- color," confertae, medio-latae. Stipes 2–3.5(6) cm longus, 5–8(10) mm crassus, albidus vel tinctus colore flavido, obscure flavido-brunneus, fibrillosus. Velum album, arachnoideum, fugax. Sporae (4.5)5–7(7.5) μ, ellipsoideae vel subovoideae, leves, truncatae. Pleurocystidia desunt; cheilocystidia 22–48 × 4–9 μ, ventricosa demum cylindrica. Cuticula gelatinosa. Caulocystidia versiformia. Specimen typicum in Herb. Univ. Tenn.; legit in Knoxville, Tennessee, November 18, 1945, Hesler 18848.

Pileus caespitose, 1.5–3.5 (7) cm broad, viscid, ivory white to "ivory- yellow," or "light-buff" with an obscure olive tint, disc "chamois" to "warm-buff," finally dingy yellowish-white over all, with scattered brown- ish fibrils, usually becoming scaly in age, margin even, at first appendicu- late. Context white, at maturity yellowish under the cuticle; odor and taste not distinctive.

Lamellae adnate, or adnate-decurrent, at times more or less adnexed, at first white or pallid, soon yellowish, finally dull yellow to yellow-brown ("honey-yellow" to "buckthorn-brown" or "clay-color), close, moderately broad, edges even or nearly so.

Stipe 2–3.5 (6) cm long, 5–8 (10) mm thick, whitish with a yellowish tint, apex white-silky, elsewhere with dingy yellowish brown fibrils or scales, equal or tapering downward, stuffed then hollow. Veil white, arachnoid, leaving a superior annular fibrillose zone, fugaceous.

Spore deposit dark yellow-brown ("Prout's brown" to "snuff- brown") ; spores (4.5) 5–7 (7.5) × 3.3–4 μ, elliptic to ovate in face view, obscurely inequilateral in profile, wall only slightly thickened (not enough to estimate thickness), tawny to near amber brown in KOH, merely pale reddish tawny in Melzer's reagent, smoch, apex obscurely truncate.

Basidia 24–30 × 5–7.5 μ, 4-spored, clavate, hyaline in KOH, yellow- ish in Melzer's sol. Pleurocystidia scattered as chrysocystidia, 31–46 × 8–12 μ, clavate-mucronate to obclavate to more or less fusoid-ventricose, as revived in KOH with the typical hyaline amorphous mass of material in the enlarged part or in the broad pedicel, thin-walled, smooth, yellow- ish in Melzer's. Pseudocystidia filamentous to clavate 25–34 × 5–10 μ, bright yellow in KOH, scattered in hymenium. Cheilocystidia 18–26 (48) × 4–9 μ, fusoid-ventricose to utriform, apex obtuse to rounded, often with yellowish content in KOH but content homogeneous. Caulocystidia mostly clavate as projecting terminal cells of hyphae, 33–60 × 5–8 μ, thin-walled, hyaline to yellowish in KOH and Melzer's sol.

Gill trama of subparallel hyphae with cells elongate, tubular or nearly so (until old age), non-gelatinous, (3) 4–8 (12) μ wide, thin-walled, hyaline to yellow in KOH and Melzer's reagent; golden yellow oleiferous hyphae numerous (as revived in KOH) ; subhymenium of interwoven filamentous hyphae 2–3.5 μ diam., hyaline and subgelatinous as revived in KOH. Pileus cutis a gelatinous pellicle of interwoven hyphae hyaline to bright ochraceous in KOH, tubular, 3–5 μ diam.; golden lactiferous (or oleiferous?) hyphae also in the layer; hypodermial zone not structurally distinct from context (possibly containing more oleiferous hyphae). Context hyphae (3) 6–12 (22) μ wide, cells becoming greatly inflated, golden oleiferous hyphae also present. Clamp connections present. All hyphae inamyloid but occasional small masses of amyloid debris noted.

HABIT, HABITAT, AND DISTRIBUTION: Clustered to gregarious on soil in lawns, Tennessee, November-December, Hesler 18848 type, and 17246, 18848, 18871, and 25006.

OBSERVATIONS: This is a most interesting species from the standpoint of the yellow-brown spore deposit, tendency for the subhymenium to gelatinize, the obscurely truncate spores and presence of chrysocystidia. It is excluded from *Naematoloma* by the color of the spore deposit. The bright yellow pseudocystidia in the hymenium are fairly rare in the material examined to date but we feel they are significant as a species character. We would not emphasize the amyloid debris at this time as a taxonomic character, though it must be admitted that this sort of material is very rare in the genus as we have studied it to date. In the herbarium the bright yellow pseudocystidia distinguish this species from *P. caespitosa*. In the field *P. caespitosa* is basically whitish and has a yellow veil. *P. tennesseensis* has yellowish brown scales on the stipe, and the pileus when young is pale yellow or tinged with olive.

38. Pholiota caespitosa sp. nov.
Illustrations: Text figs. 128-130.

Pileus 3–5 cm latus, convexus demum late convexus, viscidus, fibrillo-so-squamulosus, subalbidus demum pallide luteus, ad margineum appendiculatus. Contextus albus. Lamellae adnato-decurrentes, subdistantes, latae, luteae. Stipes caespitosus, 4–5 cm longus, 6–10 mm crassus, albidus demum luteus, deorsum fibrilloso-squamulosus. Velum copiosum. Sporae 5.5–7.5 × 3.5–4(4.5) μ. Pleurocystidia ut chrysocystidia, 23–42 × 6–9 μ, clavato-mucronata vel fusoide ventrisosa, Specimen typicum in Herb. Univ. Tenn. conservatum est; legit Anderson County, Tennessee. 31 Oct. 1943, Hesler No. 15908.

Pileus densely caespitose (30–50 in each clump), 3–5 cm broad, convex, viscid, densely fibrillose when young, becoming fibrillose scaly, scales more conspicuous on disc, basic color whitish, scales becoming (at maturity) "chamois," margin incurved and more or less appendiculate. Context firm, moderately thick, white; odor and taste mild (or slightly like Irish potato).

Lamellae adnate-decurrent, finally sinuate, near "honey yellow" to "buckthorn brown," nearly subdistant, medium broad, edges rough (serrulate), many lamellulae present.

Stipe 4–5 cm long, 6–10 mm thick, somewhat flattened from pressure of crowding, whitish, fibrillose-scaly up to ring, naked above, scales "chamois," surface dry, interior hollow. Veil fibrillose, copious, yellow, leaving an evanescent, fibrillose flaring ring.

Spores 5.5–7.5 × 3.5–4 (4.5) μ, dull tawny in KOH, paler and more ochraceous in Melzer's reagent, apex in many spores somewhat truncate from a distinct apical pore, in face view oblong to elliptic or some ovate, in profile slightly bean-shaped to oblong or obscurely inequilateral, wall relatively thin (0.25 μ ±).

Basidia 18–23 (24–35) × 5–7 μ, variable in length, 4-spored, clavate hyaline in KOH, yellowish in Melzer's reagent. Pleurocystidia 23–42 × 6–9 μ, clavate-mucronate to fusoid-ventricose, rarely merely clavate, apex subacute to obtuse, wall smooth thin and hyaline, content as revived in KOH with the typical hyaline refractive inclusion of chrysocystidia, refractive body merely yellowish in Melzer's reagent. Cheilocystidia 20–32 × 5–9 μ, utriform, fusoid-ventricose to subfusoid, hyaline to yellowish in KOH, walls smooth, thin, hyaline, content homogeneous. Caulocystidia 23–35 × 5–9 μ, clavate to narrowly subfusoid, usually remaining agglutinated to stipe tissue in KOH mounts, thin-walled, hyaline to yellowish and content homogeneous.

Gill trama of a floccose central strand of parallel hyphae 5–15 μ diam.; walls thin, smooth, hyaline to yellowish, somewhat refractive; subhymenium of narrow gelatinous to subgelatinous hyphae hyaline in KOH. Pileus cutis a gelatinous pellicle of mostly non-gelatinous hyphae 3–6 μ diam. with very pale ochraceous smooth walls; hypodermium of floccose hyphae with smooth to asperulate darker ochraceous-brown walls, hyphae 4–10 μ diam. Context hyphae hyaline to ochraceous, smooth, the hyphal cells inflated greatly in age. Stipe hyphae perfectly hyaline in KOH except for the agglutinated caulocystidia and the narrow cells which bear them, both ochraceous in KOH. All hyphae inamyloid. Clamp connections present.

HABIT, HABITAT, AND DISTRIBUTION: Densely caespitose on sawdust. Anderson County, Tenn. Oct. 31, 1943. Hesler 15908 type.

OBSERVATIONS: This is a most interesting species in a number of ways, particularly in that it is intermediate between sect. *Pholiota* and Sect. *Kuehneromyces* since the spores, at least many of them are sufficiently truncate to place the species in the latter group, and the species is clearly related to *P. veris*. The distinctive field features include the densely cespitose habit, its whitish fibrillose scaly pileus, the yellowish scales, yellow gills and white stipe which does not darken in KOH in the apical area.

39. **Pholiota veris** nom. nov.

Kuehneromyces rostratus Singer & Smith, Mycologia 38: 510. 1946.
(non *Pholiota rostrata* Vel. 1921).
Illustrations: Text figs. 131-132; pls. 16-17.

Pileus 2–6 cm broad, obtuse when young, soon convex to campanulate-convex, finally plane or depressed and sometimes the center perforated, rarely slightly umbonate, margin incurved at first, surface moist and hygrophanous, when young "clay-color" to "sayal-brown" (tan to dull cinnamon) slowly becoming paler and the margin often avellaneous when water-soaked, fading finally to warm-buff (yellow) to whitish, with a thin viscid to subviscid pellicle, glabrous at maturity, at first with fibrils along the margin, margin even at first, becoming translucent striatulate. Context concolorous with surface and more or less hygrophanous, gradually tapering outward, very fragile; taste mild, odor not distinctive.

Lamellae adnexed-sinuate to adnate and rounded, often with a decurrent tooth, pallid to pallid tan ("pinkish buff") when young, near clay-color to cinnamon when mature, moderately broad, (usually about 5 mm broad near stipe), close to crowded, thin, edges even.

Stipe 4–9 cm long, 4–12 mm thick, watery-pallid or subconcolorous, but paler than pileus, subequal or tapering upward from a ventricose midportion, characteristically long, fleshy, interior stuffed but soon hollow, somewhat squarrulose-squamulose on lower surface of annulus and for a short distance downward, usually glabrescent in age, silky to furfuraceous and whitish above the annulus, at the base appressed white fibrillose.

Spore deposit about "snuff-brown"; spores 5.5–7.5 × 3.7–4.8 μ, at maturity elliptic to ovate or indistinctly lentiform in face view, about the same in profile or more narrowly elliptic, wall double (?), apex truncate to obscurely truncate, wall smooth, not thick enough to measure, pale tan revived in Melzer's sol.

Basidia 20–24 × 5–6 (7) μ, 4-spored. Pleurocystidia 36–66 × 3–6 μ, erratic in occurrence, absent in many sections, narrowly fusoid-ventricose with a long slender neck and acute to subacute apex, thin-walled and smooth. Cheilocystidia 38–62 × 4–9 μ, ventricose-rostrate, neck 2–3.5 μ thick, apex acute to subacute, content homogeneous, thin-walled, smooth, hyaline in KOH. Caulocystidia 30–80 × 5–8 μ, in dense clusters, cylindric-clavate, sometimes a few similar to cheilocystidia. Pileus cutis a thin gelatinous pellicle of appressed hyphae; hypodermium a dingy brown zone scarcely differentiated structurally.

HABIT, HABITAT, AND DISTRIBUTION: On logs and debris, and especially sawdust of hardwoods such as oak and beech logs, (Smith 36675 on dung), Maryland, Ohio, Michigan, North Carolina and Tennessee, April-July.

OBSERVATIONS: The pleurocystidia are usually present in damaged areas, a situation not infrequently encountered in *Psilocybe*. This is one of the most distinctive species of the subgenus by virtue of its pale color faded, extreme fragility dried, and rather wide delicate stipe. Some of the spores in mounts of the type appear slightly compressed.

MATERIAL EXAMINED: MARYLAND: Kauffman, 5-20-19, as *"Pholiota* sp."* (MICH). MICHIGAN: Bartelli 2209, 2219; Harding 79; Smith 9510, 15002 (type), 15021, 21467, 25535, 28740, 321148, 32149, 36301, 36321, 36369, 36416, 36620, 36675, 38980, 41293, 51346, 66253, 66355, 66509, 66640, 71505, 71515, 71519, NORTH CAROLINA: Hesler 20411. OHIO: Walters 5-21-42, 5-20-46. TENNESSEE: Hesler 20411, 21314, 21322, 21346. WISCONSIN: Shaffer 740.

Stirps Marginella

This group contains species lacking a gelatinous pellicle on the pileus. The final test for viscidity here is to section freshly matured pilei to demonstrate that no gelatinous layer is present. In the remaining stirpes old basidiocarps of any of the species may have the pellicle obliterated by erosion, so young specimens, if available, should be sectioned. In *P. albo-virescens* we find a very close parallel to *Naematoloma fasciculare* but with a yellow-brown spore deposit.

Key

1. Basidiocarps with a distinct pseudorhiza; taste bitter ....
.... see *P. olympiana*
1. Not as above 2
    2. Stipe distinctly yellow at first; gills at first pallid becoming greenish .... *P. albo-virescens*
    2. Stipe not colored as above 3
3. Cheilocystidia 30–50 × 7–12 μ, basal portion often ochraceous in KOH, arising from a cellular region with cells having ochraceous walls in KOH .... *P. deceptiva*
3. Not as above 4
    4. Pileus soon umbilicate; on debris of *Thuja*; stipe bister ....
.... *P. umbilicata*
    4. Not as above 5
5. Pileus olive-yellow fading to whitish; pleurocystidia 25–46 × 6–9 μ, abundant .... *P. albo-olivascens*
5. Pileus red to red-brown or dark cinnamon, not whitish when faded
.... 6
    6. Pileus subferruginous; gill trama of hyphae more or less thin-walled and nearly hyaline in KOH .... *P. marginella*
    6. Pileus dark dull cinnamon; gill trama at maturity cellular from hyphal cells inflated 10–25 μ, and with walls 0.5–1.5 μ thick as well as rusty brown in KOH .... *P. bridgii*

40. Pholiota albovirescens sp. nov.

Pileus 0.8–3 cm latus, convexus, non viscidus, sericus, in medio "Naples yellow," tinctus viridi colore, marginibus "sea-foam green," cum maculis ferruginosis, margine planus. Caro albida demum flavida; odore mitis, gustu amarus. Lamellae adnatae cum dente decurrentes, albidae deinde "citron-green" demum "olive-green," brunnaceae, angustae, perconfertae. Stipes 3–5 cm longus, 2–5 mm crassus, concoloratus vel pallidior, base aeruginosus, flexuosus, sericus. Velum album, arachnoideum. Sporae 5.5–7.5 × 3.5–4(4.5) µ, ellipsoideae demum subovoideae in fronte, parvum inaequilaterales in imagine obliqua, leves, truncatae. Pleurocystidia (16)25–32 × 6–11 µ, clavata, mucronata; cheilocystidia 18–25 × 3–7 µ, clavata vel subventricosa demum ampullacea. Cuticula ex hyphis repentibus composita. Fibulae adsunt. Specimen typicum in Herb. Univ. Tenn.; legit prope Gatlinburg, Tennessee, 12, August 1965, Hesler 28185.

Pileus caespitose, 0.8–3 cm broad, convex, becoming more or less expanded, often obtusely umbonate, not viscid, subhygrophanous, silky, center "Naples yellow," tinged greenish, marginal half "seafoam green," with ferruginous stains, margin even, at times appendiculate. Context whitish or more or less concolorous; odor mild, taste bitter.

Lamellae adnate, with a decurrent tooth, at first whitish, becoming "citron-green" to "olive-green," brownish where bruised, finally brown from the spores, very crowded and narrow.

Stipe (1) 3–5 cm long, 2–5 mm thick, more or less concolorous with the pileus varying to straw colored, base becoming rusty brown, often compressed, flexuous, equal or attenuated upwards, silky, dry, hollow. Veil white, arachnoid, often leaving a faint ring, also remnants adhering for a time to pileus margin.

Spores 5.5–7.5 × 3.5–(4.5) µ, ellipsoid to subovoid in face view, slightly inequilateral in profile, smooth, truncate.

Basidia 16–20 × 5–6 µ, 2- or 4-spored. Pleurocystidia (16) 25–32 × 6–11 µ, clavate-mucronate, rarely merely clavate, sometimes brownish, buried. Cheilocystidia 18–25 × 3–7 µ, clavate to subventricose, varying to fusoid-ventricose.

Gill trama subparallel, hyphae 3–6 µ broad; subhymenium not distinctive. Pileus trama of hyphae radially arranged to somewhat interwoven. Cuticle of pileus of radially arranged repent hyphae. Clamp connections present. All tissues inamyloid.

HABIT, HABITAT, AND DISTRIBUTION: On logs and buried wood of hardwoods, Tennessee, June-August.

OBSERVATIONS: The color-pattern suggested *P. ochrochlora* (Fr.) Orton, but this latter species has scales on the pileus disc and on the stipe, the gills are at first straw-yellow, the taste mild, pleurocystidia absent, and finally Orton in his description (1960) stated nothing about the spores being truncate. The species most similar to *P. albovirescens* is

Naematoloma fasciculare but the color of the spore deposit and the inconspicuous pleurocystidia lacking a refractive content prevent assignment there.

MATERIAL EXAMINED: TENNESSEE: Hesler 10399, 28185 (type).

41. Pholiota deceptiva sp. nov.

Illustrations:

Pileus circa 10 mm latus conico-campanulatus demum plano-umbonatus, lubricus, sordide melleus, demum pallide ochraceus; lamellae argillaceae, angustae demum latae, confertae, adnatae; stipes 1–2 cm longus, 1 mm crassus, aequalis, sursum pallide luteus, deorsum demum subfulvus; annulus fibrillosus; sporae 7–9.5 × 4–4.5 μ, leves, subtruncatae; pleurocystidia desunt; cheilocystidia 30–50 × 7–12 μ. Typus: Smith 63819 (MICH); legit prope Tahquamenon Falls, Michigan. 2 Aug., 1961.

Pileus about 10 mm broad, campanulate with a conic umbo, expanding to plano-umbonate much as in *Galerina triscopa,* surface subviscid to lubricous but soon dull, dingy honey-yellow and drying pale ochraceous.

Lamellae clay color mature, narrow to moderately broad, close, adnate, edges pallid-fimbriate.

Stipe 1–2 cm long, 1 mm thick, very slender, equal, yellowish above, very soon dark yellow-brown below, as dried evenly tawny overall (darker than pileus), with an apical fibrillose annulus and a few fibrils or fascicles of veil fibrils adhering below, apex pruinose.

Spores 7–9.5 × 4–4.5 μ, smooth, in face view ovate to elliptic, in profile mostly obscurely inequilateral, wall not more than 0.25 μ thick, apex slightly truncate from a distinct apical pore, bright cinnamon to ochraceous cinnamon in KOH, about the same color in Melzer's reagent.

Basidia 4-spored, 18–23 × 7–9 μ, subcylindric to clavate, hyaline in KOH, yellowish in Melzer's sol. Pleurocystidia none seen. Cheilocystidia abundant 30–50 × 7–12 μ, fusoid-ventricose, thin-walled and hyaline or near base the wall thickened slightly and ochraceous, fusoid-ventricose and tapered to an obtuse to subcapitate apex or with one or more absorted knobs near apex. Caulocystidia more or less similar to pleurocystidia. Gill trama of parallel bright ochraceous-rusty-walled hyphae 3–9 μ in diam., walls scarcely thickened; subhymenium becoming cellular and at gill edge conspicuously so with the cells bright rusty ochraceous-walled in KOH and walls slightly thickened. Pileus cutis of appressed nongelatinous hyphae 3–6 μ diam.; The hypodermial region, which has cells enlarged to about 15 μ in the wider ones, the walls bright rusty ochraceous. Clamp connections present, all hyphae non-amyloid.

HABIT, HABITAT, AND DISTRIBUTION: On a hardwood log, Tahquamenon Falls State Park, Mich. Aug. 2, 1961. Smith 63819, type.

OBSERVATIONS: This species is peculiar because of the large cheilocystidia with the bright ochraceous slightly thick-walled cells at the base, and the *Galerina triscopa* aspect, but with spores having a truncate apex. In the dried material the gills appear moderately broad though on fresh material they were noted as narrow. *P. tahquamenonsis* has narrow cheilocystidia not bright ochraceous at base, and the basidiocarp hyphae generally are much less ochraceous when revived.

42. Pholiota umbilicata sp. nov.
Illustrations: Text figs. 133-134.

Pileus 2–3 cm latus, campanulato-convexus, umbilicatus, non viscidus, "Sayal brown" deinde "pinkish buff," glaber. Caro concolor; odore et gustu mitis. Lamellae adnatae, "Sayal brown" vel "snuff brown," confertae, marginibus albo-fimbriatae. Stipes 3 cm longus, 2–3 mm crassus, "bistre," flexuosus. Velum faciens fugacem annulum. Soorae 6–8 × 3.5– 4.5 μ, ellipsoideae demum subovoideae, leves, truncatae. Pleurocystidia 16–18 × 4–5 μ, clavata demum ampullacea, pauca. Cheilocystidia 25–35 × 3–5 μ, filamentosa, gracilo-clavata vel ventricosa. Cuticula ex hyphis repentibus composita. Specimen typicum in Herb. Univ. Mich. conservatum est; legit in Pend d'Oreille National Forest, Copeland, Idaho, legit L. E. Wehmeyer, 11 Sept. 1922.

Pileus 2–3 cm broad, campanulate-convex, becoming umbilicate, hygrophanous, not viscid, dull cinnamon ("Sayal brown") moist, fading to pale tan ("pinkish buff") hence hygrophanous, at first margin faintly translucent-striate, glabrous margin tending to remain decurved. Context thin, pliant, concolorous with surface, 2 mm thicker near disc, thinner at margin; odor and taste mild.

Gills broadly adnate, dull cinnamon ("Sayal brown" to "snuff-brown"), narrow, acuminate toward pileus margin, seceding, crowded, edges white fimbriate.

Stipe 3 cm long, 2–3 mm thick, equal, dark yellow-brown ("bister"), darker within, narrowly stuffed, flexuous, slightly tapering, tough to subcartilaginous, pruinose above the apical indistinct evanescent annulus, below the veil-line variegated with white silky fibrils.

Spores 6–7.5 (9) × 4–5 (6.5) μ, ovate to broadly elliptic in face view, obscurely inequilateral in profile, smooth, apex rather broadly truncate from a prominent apical pore, in cross section terete to slightly compressed, pale cinnamon in KOH and ochraceous in Melzer's reagent (paler), wall about 0.3 μ thick.

Basidia 15–20 × 6–7 μ, clavate, 4-spored, hyaline in KOH and Melzer's reagent. Pleurocystidia rare, absent on some sections, 22–26 × 4–8 μ, clavate-rostrate (like 1-spored basidia) to fusoid-ventricose or nearly filamentous, hyaline, thin-walled. Cheilocystidia 25–36 × 4–8 μ, narrowly clavate to fusoid-ventricose or some nearly cylindric, very delicate and difficult to revive. Caulocystidia present above veil-line, similar to the cheilocystidia (subcylindric to clavate or somewhat fusoid-ventricose), thin-walled, delicate and reviving poorly.

Gill trama of subparallel to interwoven non-gelatinous hyphae with thin smooth to slightly roughened walls, the cells 3–8 μ diam., and tubular to somewhat inflated; subhymenium an indistinct narrow non-gelatinous zone. Pileus cutis of non-gelatinous hyaline hyphae 3–6 μ diam. and tubular, thin-walled, the layer hyaline-yellowish in KOH; hyphae beneath wider (6–12 μ) and with brownish walls in KOH but no true hypodermium present, the hyphal walls smooth to somewhat incrusted. Context hyphae inflated to 15 μ, thin-walled, hyphae interwoven, yellowish in KOH to hyaline and about the same color in Melzer's reagent. Clamp connections present.

HABIT, HABITAT, AND DISTRIBUTION: On debris of *Thuja plicata,* Idaho, September. Type collected at Copeland, Sept. 11, 1922 by C. H. Kauffman and L. E. Wehmeyer.

OBSERVATIONS: This species is known only from the type, and a large part of the material was used up in checking the microscopic characters. It is distinguished by its umbilicate hygrophanous non-viscid pileus, small pleurocystidia, and the delicate cheilocystidia which revive very poorly. It belongs in the *P. marginella* group since the pileus cutis is not gelatinous, the gills however are narrow as in *P. vernalis.* Under an oil immersion lens the spores are more obviously truncate than in typical *P. vernalis* and we suspect that in a spore deposit they will be found to have a redder tone. We feel that this taxon is worth placing on record because its features approach closely certain species of *Psilocybe* from the Pacific Northwest.

43. Pholiota albo-olivascens sp. nov.
Illustrations: Text figs. 135-138.

Pileus (1)2–3(5) cm latus, convexus, se extendens, viscidus, hygrophanus, albus siccatus, "Isabella-color" humidus, appressus sericus et similis pelli villosae, margine striatus maddidus. Caro tenuis, demum alba, odore et gustu mitis. Lamellae adnatae deinde adnatae-decurrentes, albae deinde "Dresden brown" demum "snuff-brown," medio-latae, confertae; marginibus albo-denticulatae. Stipes 3–5 cm longus, 2–4 mm crassus, albidae deinde furvae, sericae, aequales. Velum arachnoideum, album, permanentem demum fugacem annulum ostendens. Sporae 6–9 × 3.8–4.5 μ, ellipsoideae demum ovoideae in fronte, parvum inaequilaterales in imagine oblique, leves, truncatae. Pleurocystidia 24–46 × 6–8 μ, clavata demum ventricosa, appendiculata; cheilocystidia 30–37 × 4–6 μ, obclavata, fusoidea. Cuticula gelatinosa. Fibulae non inventae. Specimen typicum in Herb. Univ. Tenn. conservatum est; legit in Cades Cove, Blount County, Tennessee, 16 May 1953, Hesler 20814.

Pileus (1) 2–3 (5) cm broad, convex, expanding, at times wavy, viscid, hygrophanous, white when dry, olive-yellow moist ("Isabella-color"), fading from disc outward, surface appearing glabrous but actually appressed-silky and plush like under a lens, margin even when dry, striate when wet. Context rather fragile, thin, white, darker when wet; odor and taste mild.

Lamellae adnate to adnate-decurrent, at first white then dark yellow-brown ("Dresden brown" to "snuff-brown"), medium broad, close, reaching margin of pileus, edges white-denticulate.

Stipe 3–5 cm long, 2–4 mm thick, whitish, dingy in age, dry, silky, striate, equal, usually curved, spongy then hollow. Veil delicate, webby, white, forming an apical, persistent to subfugaceous annulus, often brownish from spores.

Spores 6–7.5 × 4–4.5 μ (6–9 × 3.8–4.5 μ in some caps), smooth; wall 0.4 μ thick ($\pm$), apex obscurely truncate from a small apical pore; in face view ovate to elliptic, in profile obscurely inequilateral, occasionally a spore seen with a lateral bump; tawny in KOH, slightly more cinnamon in Melzer's.

Basidia 4-spored, 18–23 (26) × 5–7 μ, hyaline in KOH and pale yellow in Melzer's reagent. Pleurocystidia abundant 25–46 × 6–9 μ, clavate-rostrate to mucronate, the neck often as long or longer than the enlarged portion in old specimens, walls thin, hyaline, smooth, content homogeneous, cystidium yellowish and with homogeneous content in Melzer's reagent. Cheilocystidia 28–44 × 4–9 μ, ventricose near base and with a long neck 3–4 μ wide in some, and ending in a subacute apex, wall in neck usually flexuous, thin, hyaline in KOH or Melzer's. Caulocystidia 33–58 × 6–11 μ, clavate to obscurely fusoid-ventricose because of the irregular wavy walls and variously spaced protrusions, some with an acute apex and the neck back of it about 2 μ diam., walls thin and hyaline and smooth.

Gill trama of hyphae subparallel interwoven, cells often short and up to 16 μ diam., walls thin and hyaline in KOH to slightly brownish-ochraceous, yellowish in Melzer's reagent; subhymenium indistinct at first, finally cellular in age, not gelatinous. Pileus trama with a thin cutis of somewhat gelatinous hyphae tubular and 2.5–4 μ diam., hyaline and appressed; hypodermium of greatly inflated hyphae (cells 10–20 μ) hyaline in KOH and walls about 1 μ thick with the middle lamella evident in mounts revived in KOH. Context hyphae floccose-interwoven, hyaline in KOH and pale yellow in Melzer's, 8–15 μ diam. Hyphae of stipe apex hyaline in KOH, walls smooth. Clamp connections present.

HABIT, HABITAT, AND DISTRIBUTION: On hardwood logs and chips, Tennessee, May, Hesler 20814, type; Cades Cove, Great Smoky Mts. Nat'l. Park, May 16, 1953.

OBSERVATIONS: This is a most distinctive species by reason of the broad close gills, abundant pleurocystidia, pale colors, and lack of a positive KOH reaction in the hyphae of the upper part of the stipe. In this genus this feature is almost always correlated with the absence of darkening in the stipe as the latter ages. P. albo-olivascens appears to be most closely related to P. veris.

One of the interesting features of our study of this species is that very rarely one can find a "pleurocystidium" on the apex of which is a single spore and the upper part of the sterigmata for a distance of 10–15 μ back from the spore is seen to have a colored wall thickened and resembling the spore wall and is continuous with the latter. We cannot see how a spore attached in this manner could ever be discharged in the manner of the spores borne in the normal way on 4-spored basidia with very fine hyaline sterigmata. To us it indicates that the change from active spore discharge to a state of no spore discharge by the basidium can occur in a single basidiocarp. This may have some interest to those studying the relationships of *Pholiota* to gastromycetous fungi. Several points need to be clarified in regard to this feature as follows: The cells producing the spores appear to be cystidia, not basidia, as far as their shape is concerned. What is their nuclear history? Thousands of cystidia without spores are found to one with a spore, so it is not proper to classify all the pleurocystidia as one-spored basidia. The homology, however, seems obvious. It is interesting to note that this same sort of modification of the sterigmata—becoming thick-walled and continuous with the spore wall, has been noted for other rusty-brown spored agarics by Heim and others, and is not infrequent in the form-order "Agarico-gastrales."

44. **Pholiota marginella** Peck, Rep. N.Y. State Mus. 51: 289. 1898. Illustrations: Text figs. 139-140.

"Pileus fleshy, convex becoming nearly plane, glabrous, hygrophanous, yellowish red or subferruginous when young or moist, then commonly striatulate on margin, yellowish buff or whitish when dry, the young margin slightly silky with the whitish fibrils of the veil; lamellae close, thin, adnexed, minutely eroded on the edge, whitish becoming dark ferruginous; stem flexuous, subequal fibrillose, pruinose or mealy above the slight evanescent annulus, stffed or hollow, pallid or whitish, sometimes with a white mycelial tomentum at the base; spores elliptic, .00024 to .0003 in. long, .00016 to .0002 broad."

"Pileus 1–2 in. broad; stem 2 to 4 in. long, 2 to 4 lines thick."

"Single or caespitose on decaying wood. North Elba, June."

"The species is related to *P. marginata,* from which it differs in its paler color, even or merely striatulate margin, adnexed lamellae and uniformly colored stem."

The above is quoted from the original description. Smith's notes on the type follow: Pileus epicutis of interwoven appressed hyaline nongelatinous hyphae 3–5 μ diam. with clamps at the septa (mounted in KOH), beneath this an area of more compactly interwoven hyphae yellowish in KOH but not forming a distinct hypodermium. Context hyphae (5) 10–20 μ diam., yellowish in KOH or nearly hyaline, the cells more or less inflated. Gill trama of interwoven short broad hyphal cells 6–15 μ diam., nearly hyaline in KOH except toward subhymenium where they are pale tawny. Pleurocystidia none found. Cheilocystidia abundant, 32–44 × 6–9 μ, fusoid-ventricose with short to long necks and subacute apex, if elongated the neck often flexuous to moniliform (with irregular swellings and constrictions) .

Basidia 14–17 × 6–7 μ, 4-spored, hyaline in KOH. Spores 7–8.4 × 4.4–5 μ, smooth, apical pore distinct and apex somewhat truncate, ovoid to ellipsoid, pale tawny is KOH.

Smith noted that the gills were neither as close nor as narrow as in *P. vernalis*. The diagnostic features of the species are the subferruginous young pileus, broad close gills (as contrasted to narrow crowded gills in *P. vernalis*) , whitish gills when young and the whitish stipe. Singer and Smith (1946) confused this species with *P. vernalis* and published a very cumbersome description under the latter name which encompassed a number of taxa. At present, we suspect with Overholts (1927) that *P. marginella* is rather common on conifer wood and debris in the mountains both in eastern and western United States but our data on individual collections are not complete enough for critical comparisons. For further comment see *P. vernalis*.

45. Pholiota bridgii sp. nov.
Illustrations: Text figs. 141-143.

Pileus 1–4 cm latus, convexus vel planus, glaber, udus, sordide cinnamomeus deinde argillaceus. Lamellae confertae, adnatae, secedentes, angustae vel medio-latae, sordide cinnamoneae. Stipes 2–6 cm longus, 1.5–3.5 mm crassus, caespitosus, sursum atro-brunnescens. Velum fibrillosum. Sporae 6–7.5(8) × 3.8–4.2(4.5) μ, leves truncatae. Cheilocystidia 28–42 × 7–11 μ, versiformia. Specimen typicum in Herb. Univ. of Mich. conservatum est; legit prope Mt. Shasta, Calif., 11 July 1963, Wm. Bridge Cooke 34315.

Pileus 1–4 cm broad, broadly convex, expanding to nearly plane, surface glabrous, hygrophanous, brown when moist, fading to pale dingy clay-color, not viscid.

Lamellae close, adnate-seceding, narrow to moderately broad, dull cinnamon when mature.

Stipe 2–6 cm long, 1.5–3.5 mm thick, cespitose, base coated with appressed whitish mycelium, becoming very dark brown from base up to apex; cortina scanty, apex pruinose.

Spore deposit near clay color. Spores 6–7.5 (8) × 3.8–4.2 (4.5) μ, smooth, apex somewhat truncate from the apical pore; shape in face view narrowly ovate to suboblong, in profile slightly inequilateral, wall about 0.25 μ thick; in KOH the walls dull cinnamon, in Melzer's reagent about the same color as in KOH or paler.

Basidia 18–23 × 5–7 μ, 4-spored, hyaline in KOH, narrowly clavate. Pleurocystidia none. Cheilocystidia abundant, 28–42 × 7–11 μ subcylindric to subfusoid or somewhat fusoid-ventricose, apex subacute to obtuse, wall smooth, thin, hyaline or near base slightly cinnamon. Caulo-cystidia versiform, 30–56 × (7) 9–16 μ, subcylindric with various con-strictions, fusoid-ventricose with narrow neck and acute apex or sub-clavate, wall often thickened to 0.5–1.2, and often colored in pedicel.

Gill trama as revived in KOH cellular with cells 10–25 μ diam. having rusty brown walls thickened to 0.5–1.5 μ and "double" in optical section, subhymenium also of dark cinnamon cells but narrow and wall often finely encrusted. Pileus cuticle with an epicutis of hyphae 2–5 μ diam., with minutely asperulate walls and not gelatinous. Hypodermial zone of greatly inflated hyphal cells (to 20 μ) with rusty brown thick-ened walls. Context of greatly inflated hyphal cells also thick-walled (0.5–1.5 μ). Clamp connections present. All hyphae inamyloid.

Caespitose on a rotten *Abies concolor* log, Wagon Camp, Mt. Shasta, California, July 11, 1963. William Bridge Cooke 34315, type; elevation 5700 ft.

OBSERVATIONS: This species differs from *P. obscura* in smaller spores, large thick-walled cells comprising the gill trama, close narrow gills at first, and lack of a gelatinous pellicle on the pileus. It is closest to *P. marginella* in most features but differs in the much more greatly inflated cells of the gill trama and the darker color of the stipe when fresh. Also, in *P. bridgii* there is a distinct colored hypodermial region of hyphal cells with slightly thickened walls.

Stirps Obscura

In this group are placed the viscid small spored species with narrow stipes and broad gills in which the stipe below the annulus is not con-spicuously scaly. The gills are yellow-brown at maturity or cinnamon. This group continues into the next to form a single complex.

Key to Species

1. Spores 2.5–3 μ broad .... see *P. subochracea*
1. Spores 2.5–5 μ wide 2
  2. Veil absent; stipe blackish below .... *P. nigripes*
  2. Veil evident on young basidiocarps 3
3. Stipe whitish; pileus olive-yellow, moist .... see *P. albo-olivascens*
3. Stipe soon darker colored 4
  4. Large clavate pleurocystidia present .... *P. galerinoides*
  4. Not as above 5
5. Veil rudimentary, all traces soon gone (see *P. atripes* also) .... *P. obscura*
5. Stipe, when veil breaks, with a thin membranous annulus .... *P. tahquamenonensis*

46. Pholiota obscura sp. nov.

Pileus 1–2.2 cm latus, obtuse conicus, demum planus, lubricus demum viscidus, obscure "ochraceous tawny" demum "cinnamon buff." Caro concolor; odore et gustu mitis. Lamellae adnatae, latae, subdistantes, "ochraceous tawny," leviter se obscurantes naturae. Stipes 2–3 cm longus, 2–3 mm crassus, infra obscure brunneus, supra furvus. Velum fugax, cineraceo-coriaceum. Sporae 7–9(10) × 3.8–4.5(5) μ, ellipsoideae vel ovoideae, leves, truncatae. Pleurocystidia desunt. Cheilocystidia 25–44 × 5–8 μ, subfusoidea vel ampullacea, cervice leviter vel constricta. Cuticula cingulum angustum gelatinosum. Caulocystidia 25–37 × 5–7 μ, cheilocystidiorum similia. Specimen typicum in Herb. Univ. Mich. conservatum est; legit prope McCall, Idaho, June 23, 1962, Smith 65011.

Pileus cespitose, 1–2.2 cm broad, obtusely conic with a straight margin, expanding to plane or the margin slightly uplifted and wavy, surface lubricous to viscid and shining, translucent striate to disc when moist and then dull ochraceous tawny, fading to cinnamon buff. Context thin, fragile, watery, concolorous with surface, odor and taste none, $FeSO_4$ and KOH both no reaction.

Lamellae broad, adnate, subdistant, ochraceous tawny and not changing color much on maturing, edges fimbriate.

Stipe 2–3 cm long, 2–3 mm thick, equal, watery, fragile, dark reddish brown below, tawny above, at first faintly fibrillose from grayish buff veil fibrils, veil very thin and soon evanescent, apex faintly pruinose and at first striate.

Spores 7–10 × 3.5–4.5 μ, smooth, wall very slightly thickened (about 0.25 μ), apex truncate from an apical pore, in face view distinctly ovate varying to elliptic, in profile somewhat inequilateral, a small number slightly compressed and rarely one slightly angular; in KOH cinnamon to tawny, in Melzer's reagent slightly paler.

Basidia 4-spored, 20–24 × 6–8 μ, hyaline to yellowish in KOH and Melzer's reagent, clavate. Pleurocystidia present in the hymenium between the gills (rarely on gill surface), 20–28 × 7–12 μ, broadly fusoid-ventricose to subclavate or elliptic, thin-walled, hyaline in KOH, content homogeneous. Cheilocystidia (20) 26–45 × 5–10 μ, utriform, fusoid-ventricose or ventricose-rostrate, wall in neck flexuous, hyaline in KOH, wall very slightly thickened to thin, smooth, cell content homogeneous as revived in KOH.

Gill trama of narrow (3–8 μ) parallel to interwoven hyphae, walls thin, pale cinnamon to nearly hyaline in KOH, yellowish in Melzer's reagent; subhymenium non-gelatinous, in age cellular from inflation of cells. Pileus cutis a thin gelatinous layer in which are imbedded hyaline tubular hyphae 2–6 μ diam. (in age the layer often obliterated); hypodermial zone of inflated (8–15 μ ±) hyphal cells with ochraceous to rusty brown walls as revived in KOH, the walls thin and color fading as the mount stands. Clamp connections present. Some amyloid debris present in places in a mount but all hyphae inamyloid.

HABIT, HABITAT, AND DISTRIBUTION: Caespitose on rotton wood, Idaho, June, Smith 65001 type, 58682, 65043, 65131, 65154, all from near McCall, Idaho.

OBSERVATIONS: In Smith 65131 the hymenophoral trama when fresh became pale rusty brown to dark ochraceous in KOH. The type, however, was not tested when fresh. Also, the gills appeared close when fresh but as dried there is no appreciable difference in gill spacing between it and other collections. We hesitate to emphasize the presence of pleurocystidia between the gills as an important taxonomic character. *P. obscura* is distinct from *P. vernalis* by its broad gills which are typically subdistant, *P. galerinoides* has abundant pleurocystidia, incrusted hyphae in the pileus (hypodermial zone) and small cheilocystidia.

47. Pholiota tahquamenonensis sp. nov.
Illustrations: Text figs. 144-145.

Pileus 2.0–2.5 cm latus, planus, margine laceratus, "buckthorn brown," deinde "pale pinkish buff," disco "warm buff," glabrosus, viscidus. Caro fragilis; odore et gustu mitis. Lamellae adnatae, paene "buckthorn brown," latae, confertae demum subdistantes, demum ventricosae. Stipes 2 cm longus, 3 mm crassus, supra pallidus, infra obscure flavido-brunneus, ad imum albae rhizomorphae. Velum fasciens tenuem, medianum ,membraneaceum annulum. Sporae 6–8 × 3.8–4.5(5) μ, ellipsoideae demum subovoides, leves, truncatae. Pleurocystidia 36–47 × 2–3 × 3–4 μ, ampullacea, cervice longa, apicibus acuta vel subcapitata; cheilocystidia similia. Cuticula gelatinosa. Specimen typicum in Herb. Univ. Mich. conservatum est; lectum in Tahquamenon Falls State Park, Michigan, 6 July, 1959, Smith 60944.

Pileus 2–2.5 cm broad, plane with a lacerate margin in age, glabrous, moist, viscid when young, "buckthorn brown" (yellow-brown) fading to pale pinkish buff, rather strongly hygrophanous, disc finally pale yellow ("warm buff"). Context fragile, odor and taste mild.

Lamellae adnate, seceding, broad, close to subdistant, dull yellow-brown (near "buckthorn-brown"), ventricose in age, edges slightly fimbriate.

Stipe 2 cm long, about 3 mm thick, equal, pallid above, dull yellow-brown below, with white rhizomorphs at the base, with a thin median membranous annulus.

Spores 6–8 × 4–5 μ, smooth, in face view mostly ovate but varying to elliptic, in profile obscurely inequilateral to ovate, wall thickened to about 0.25 μ, apex obscurely to distinctly truncate from an apical pore, apiculus minute but present as seen in a profile optical-section; tawny to pale tawny in KOH individually, paler in Melzer's reagent individually but in groups slightly dextrinoid.

Basidia 20–24 × 5–7 μ, clavate, 4-spored, hyaline in KOH, yellowish in Melzer's reagent. Pleurocystidia rare to scattered, most abundant in hymenial area between the gills, 35–50 × 2–3 × 3–4 μ, very narrowly ventricose at base and tapered to an acute to subcapitate apex, the neck flexuous, rarely the apical region moniliform to variously contorted, hyaline, thin-walled, smooth. Cheilocystidia 30–50 × 4–7 × 3–4 μ, hyaline, thin-walled, smooth, more or less ventricose at base, neck narrow and flexuous, often somewhat moniliform in apical third. Caulocystidia none located.

Gill trama of subparallel non-gelatinous hyphae with inflated cells, the cells shorter near the pileus trama and more elongate toward the gill edge, 4–14 μ or more wide, walls smooth, thin, hyaline to yellowish in KOH, and only slightly more yellowish in Melzer's reagent. Pileus cutis a thin layer of appressed gelatinous narrow (2–3.5 μ) tubular thin-walled hyphae. Context hyphae 4–12 μ diam., walls brownish to hyaline in KOH, hypodermial area not structurally differentiated. Clamp connections present. All hyphae inamyloid.

HABIT, HABITAT, AND DISTRIBUTION: On rotten wood, Tahquamenon Falls State Park, Michigan, Luce County, July 6, 1959. Smith 60944, type.

OBSERVATIONS: This species is smaller than *P. veris* and many of the cheilocystidia are almost tibiiform as in stirps *Sideroides* of *Galerina*. This feature at once distinguishes it from *P. veris* microscopically, if one has depauperate specimens of the latter at hand. Here again the species is not known from more than the type locality and type collection, but we felt it worthwhile to place it on record because of the cheilocystidia and the general stature of the *Galerina sideroides* group—at least in the larger basidiocarps.

48. Pholiota nigripes sp. nov.
Illustrations: Text figs. 146-148.

Pileus 0.8–3.5 cm latus, late convexus, glabrosus, lubricus, obscure "buckthorn brown" recens, deinde opacus demum cinnamomo-brunneus deinde "ochraceous tawny" vel "pinkish buff," margine leviter striatus. Caro tennuis, aquosa, concolor; odore et gustu mitis. Lamellae depresso-adnatae, secedens, furvo-coriaceae recentes, confertae, latae. Stipes 3–6 cm longus, 1.5–2.5 mm crassus, infra brunneus vel niger, sursum pallide "buckthorn brown," glaber. Velum deest. Sporae 7–9.5 × 3.8–4.5(5.3) μ, ellipsoideae demum oblongae, leves, truncatae. Pleurocystidia desunt; cheilocystidia 27–50 × 4–10 μ, fusoidea demum ventricosa, cervix longa, gracilis, sursum decrescens, apicibus acuta. Cuticula repens. Caulocystidia 27–54 × 4–10 μ, cheilocystidiorum similia. Specimen typicum in Herb. Univ. Mich.; lectum in Idaho County, Idaho, 27 June, 1962. Smith 65040.

Pileus 0.8–3.5 cm broad, margin incurved at first, pileus becoming broadly convex or remaining obtusely umbonate, surface glabrous, lubricous when fresh and moist, hygrophanous, pale "Buckthorn brown" (dark clay color) to cinnamon brown and fading to ochraceous tawny or finally pinkish buff, margin faintly striate before fading. Context thin, watery, concolorous with surface; odor and taste mild; no reaction with $FeSO_4$.

Lamellae depressed-adnate and seceding, dingy butterscotch-color young, dull rusty brown in age, close, broad, edges minutely eroded.

Stipe 3–6 cm long, 1.5–2.5 mm at apex, equal or nearly so, dark rusty brown to blackish below, pale watery buckthorn-brown at apex, glabrous and naked or apex faintly pruinose, with a few faint fibrillose streaks below. Veil absent on all specimens observed.

Spores 7–9.5 × 4–5 (5.3) μ, ovate to elliptic or some nearly oblong in face view, in profile view ovate to obscurely inequilateral; smooth, relatively thick-walled (up to 0.5 μ); apical pore distinct but apex mostly slightly truncate; pale dull cinnamon to tawny in KOH, not changing color appreciably in Melzer's reagent.

Basidia 18–22 × 7.5–9 μ, 4-spored, clavate, hyaline in KOH, yellowish in Melzer's reagent. Pleurocystidia none. Cheilocystidia abundant, 27–50 × 4–10 μ, narrowly fusoid to fusoid-ventricose, tapered from a basal inflated area 5–10 μ diam. to a neck 4–6 μ diam. midway to apex and apex acute to subacute, thin-walled, smooth, hyaline in KOH. Caulocystidia thin-walled, scattered or in groups, 36–50 × 9–15 μ and clavate or ventricose (6–12 μ) at base and tapered to an acute to subacute apex, neck often flexuous, portion below ventricose part often with ochraceous walls in KOH, otherwise walls hyaline.

Gill trama parallel to subparallel, the hyphal cells short and 5–10 μ wide, walls thin to slightly thickened but middle lamella not clearly evident, not gelatinous; subhymenium indistinct, not gelatinous; walls of hyphae nearly hyaline to dingy ochraceous in KOH and slightly more ochraceous brown in Melzer's reagent. Pileus cutis a thin layer of tubular hyaline subgelatinous hyphae 2.5–4 μ diam., walls smooth; hypodermial region of non-gelatinous thin-walled hyphae with pale dingy ochraceous walls in KOH, the cells inflated to 22 μ more or less, toward the gill trama the hyphae with slightly thicker walls but middle lamella not showing distinctly; all hyphae inamyloid (ochraceous orange to paler in Melzer's reagent). Clamp connections present.

HABIT, HABITAT, AND DISTRIBUTION: Caespitose on conifer logs, Idaho, June and July; Trueblood 18 (MICH); Smith 65040 type, 65059, 65225, 65323.

OBSERVATIONS: The absence of a veil is a distinctive feature, but buttons should be checked. The thin gelatinous pellicle may become obliterated in age and this may cause some trouble in placing some collections. The spores are distinctly larger than in *P. atripes,* the latter has a distinct veil, and its pilei are paler and yellower as dried.

49. **Pholiota galerinoides** sp. nov.

Pileus 10–15 mm latus, glabrosus, "russet" demum cinnamomeo-brunneus deinde pallide fulvus. Odore et gustu non proprius. Lamellae late adnatae, latae, confertae vel subdistantes, paene "russet" demum brunneae recentes, concolores maturae, marginibus crenulatae. Stipes 1–2 cm longus, paene 1.5 mm crassus, pallido-brunneus deinde obscurior, infra veli reliqua. Sporae 7–9.5(10.5) × (3.5)4–5 μ, ellipsoideae vel oblongae, planae, truncatae, crassitunicatae. Pleurocystidia 28–42 × 9–14 μ, clavata; cheilocystidia 20–38 × 4–7 μ, ampullacea. Cuticula non accurate distincta. Caulocystidia acervatim, pleurocystidis et cheilocystidiis similia. Specimen typicum in Herb. Univ. Mich.; lectum in Mt. Rainier National Park, 6 Oct. 1952, Smith 40612.

Pileus 10–15 mm broad, convex with a straight margin, expanding to broadly convex to nearly plane, surface viscid, glabrous, "russet" to "cinnamon brown," fading to dark rusty brown, hygrophanous, translucent-striate on margin before fading, when faded a dingy ochraceous tan. Context thin, very fragile, odor and taste not distinctive.

Lamellae broad, close to subdistant, broadly adnate, russet to cocoa-color when young, concolorous with moist pileus when mature, edges minutely crenulate.

Stipe 1–2 cm long, about 1.5 mm thick, equal, fragile, tubular, paler than the gills near apex, soon very dark russet brown over basal area, lower portion dotted with flecks of veil tissue, apex pruinose, in age nearly glabrous.

Spores 7–9 (10.5) × (3.5) 4–4.5 μ, smooth, wall slightly thickened, apex truncate from a small apical pore; in face view narrowly elliptic to oblong, in profile nearly oblong to obscurely inequilateral, pale ochraceous in H_2O when fresh, pale cinnamon as revived in KOH; apiculus small but readily apparent; in Melzer's reagent pale cinnamon.

Basidia 4-spored, 18–22 × 5–6 μ, hyaline in KOH and Melzer's reagent, clavate. Pleurocystidia 28–42 × 9–14 μ, clavate to utriform, hyaline in KOH, content homogeneous, thin-walled, smooth. Cheilocystidia 20–35 × 4–7 μ, lanceolate to ventricose-rostrate, the neck often only 2 μ thick, apex acute to subcapitate, hyaline, thin-walled, content homogeneous. Caulocystidia scattered, clavate, mostly thin-walled but wall colored in KOH and in some slightly incrusted. Hyphae of the stipe cortex bright cinnamon in KOH and smooth, cells 8–18 μ wide.

Gill trama of parallel non-gelatinous hyphae with incrusted cinnamon-colored walls (especially near the thin nongelatinous subhymenial area). Pileus trama of interwoven cinnamon colored pigment incrusted hyphae and revived in KOH. Pileus cutis a well developed pellicle of gelatinous hyphae 3–5 μ diam., hyaline in KOH and with incrustations only on the hyphae nearest the context. Clamp connections present. All hyphae non-amyloid.

HABIT, HABITAT, AND DISTRIBUTION: On a wet seepage swampy area on very decayed conifer wood, Carbon River, Mt. Rainier National Park, Wash., Oct. 6, 1952. Smith 40612, type.

OBSERVATIONS: This is a *Psilocybe*-like species in pigmentation save that the spores are pale ochraceous in water mounts of fresh material. Deposited spores on the stipe were near cinnamon brown but this should be checked from a deposit on white paper. The clavate to utriform pleurocystidia and very small ventricose-rostrate cheilocystidia make a peculiar combination of cystidial features. It is a curious feature that the hyphae of the stipe cortex should be smooth when those of the gill and pileus trama show incrustations.

Stirps Vernalis

Lubricous to viscid species with small spores and narrow gills key out here if the stipe is not conspicuously squamulose below the veil-line. This stirps approaches *Psilocybe* very closely even in the color of the spore deposit, in fact a problem exists here as to just how certain species should be placed generically.

Key

1. Stipe not discoloring from base up and its hyphae not becoming rusty brown in KOH .... *P. pallida*
1. Not as above 2
    2. Pleurocystidia present .... *P. subpapillata*
    2. Not as above 3
3. Pileus sharply conic; veil rudimentary .... *P. conica*
3. Pileus convex or with an obtuse umbo 4
    4. Hyphal walls in gill trama and adjacent pileus trama thickening to 1–1.2 μ .... *P. atripes*
    4. Hyphal walls of gill trama not becoming appreciably thickened 5
5. Caulocystidia none; annulus thick, superior, striate above ....
.... *P. populicola*
5. Caulocystidia present; annulus soon evanescent .... *P. vernalis*

    50. **Pholiota pallida** sp. nov.
Illustrations: Text figs. 149-150; pl. 18a.

Pileus 10–15 mm latus, plano-convexus, deinde depressus, glabrosus, viscidus, pallido-coriaceus; odore et gustu mitis. Lamellae adnexae, concolores, confertae, angustae, marginibus planae. Stipes 3–4 cm longus, 2–3 mm crassus, concolor, basis distorta. Velum tenue. Sporae 6–7.5 × 3.5–4.5 μ, ellipsoideae vel ovoideae, truncatae, leves. Pleurocystidia desunt; cheilocystidia 33–46 × 5–10 μ, clavato-capitata, obclavata, ampulla-

cea, apicibus nonnumquam furcata vel ramosa. Cuticula gelatinosa. Caulocystidia 27–54 × 6–13 μ, clavata, fusoidea, ventricosa. Specimen typicum in Herb. Univ. Mich.; lectum prope Payette Lakes, Idaho, 3 Aug., 1964. Smith 68837.

Pileus 10–15 mm broad, plano-convex with the margin incurved, expanding to shallowly depressed and with an arched margin, surface glabrous, thinly viscid, color watery cream color (about like pale butter scotch), evenly colored, when dried pale yellow to whitish. Context thin, pallid, odor and taste not distinctive, KOH and $FeSO_4$ both negative.

Lamellae close, narrow to moderately broad, adnexed, pale cream color becoming rusty brown as spores mature, edges even, concolorous with faces in young stages.

Stipe 3–4 cm long, 1.5–3 mm at apex, 3–6 mm at base, concolorous with young pileus throughout, not discoloring in age or on drying, with an inconspicuous fibrillose zone left where veil breaks, nearly naked downward to the white tomentose base, variously crooked and twisted downward, apex fibrillose-punctate.

Spores 6–7.5 × 3.5–4.5 μ, elliptic to ovate in face view, subelliptic to obscurely inequilateral in profile, smooth, tawny in KOH, and slightly darker in Melzer's reagent; wall thickened to about 0.25 μ (estimated) thick, apex obscurely to distinctly truncate from an apical pore.

Basidia 4-spored 16–21 × 5–6 μ, narrowly clavate, hyaline in KOH, yellowish in Melzer's reagent. Pleurocystidia none. Cheilocystidia scattered, 33–46 × 6–10 μ, subcylindric to obscurely fusoid-ventricose (tapered to an obtuse or rounded apex from a slightly ventricose base), hyaline, thin-walled, rarely with 1–2 protuberances around apex. Caulocystidia 4–7 μ diam., length variable (20–50 μ long), filamentous to narrowly clavate; stipe tissue not darkening in KOH. Gill trama of hyphae parallel to subparallel the cells becoming inflated to 12 μ or more in age and relatively short; subhymenium indistinct, hyphal walls thin, hyaline to pale yellowish in KOH and not much change in Melzer's reagent (in-amyloid). Pileus cutis a moderately thick layer (3–8 hyphae) of hyaline subgelatinous tubular thin-walled hyphae with smooth walls; hypodermial region of wider hyphae the walls thin and yellowish to hyaline in KOH and orange ochraceous in Melzer's reagent. Context hyphae about like hypodermial hyphae. Clamp connections present.

HABIT, HABITAT, AND DISTRIBUTION: On a conifer log, cespitose; Lake Fork Creek, Payette Lakes, Idaho, Aug. 3, 1964. Smith 68837, type.

OBSERVATIONS: This species is unusual in that the hyphae of the stipe do not become dark in KOH. The over-all pale color is also distinctive in relation to the others of the stirps *Vernalis*. It is somewhat intermediate between stirps *Vernalis* and stirps *Marginella* in the features of the gills and pileus cutis.

51. Pholiota atripes sp. nov.
Illustrations: Text figs. 151-152.

Pileus 1–3 cm latus, planus, lucide flavo-brunneus, nitidus, glaber. Lamellae adnatae, flavo-albae deinde flavo-brunneae, confertae vel stipatae, marginibus palido-serrulatae. Stipes 3–5 cm longus, 2–4 mm crassus, apice flavo-brunneus, albi obscuro-brunneus. Sporae 5–7.5 × 3.5–4 μ, ellipsoideae vel subovoideae, truncatae, pariete crassae, leves. Pleurocystidia desunt; cheilocystidia 30–50 × 7–10 μ, clavata vel subfusoidea. Cuticula gelatinosa. Caulocystidia desunt. Specimen typicum in Herb. Univ. Mich.; lectum prope Ledgewood, Wyoming, 28 Juni, 1959, L. E. Wehmeyer.

Pileus 1–3 cm broad, broadly convex with a decurved margin expanding to plane or with the disc slightly depressed, surface glabrous, viscid, light yellow-brown (collected in faded condition). Context thin, pliant, odor and taste not recorded.

Lamellae adnate, yellowish white, becoming pale to dark clay color when mature, crowded, narrow, bluntly adnate to slightly adnexed, edges serrulate and whitish.

Stipe 3–5 cm long, 2–4 mm thick, fibrous, apex light yellow-brown, the remainder dark brown to blackish brown, very dark in KOH, base white-mycelioid. Veil thin, fibrillose, leaving an apical evanescent fibrillose zone, with scattered fibrils lower down on the stipe.

Spores 5–7 (7.5) × 3.5–4 μ, smooth, in face view elliptic to ovate, in profile obscurely inequilateral, terete, wall thickened to about 0.3 μ, apical pore distinct and apex slightly truncate, in KOH pale tawny, slightly darker tawny in Melzer's reagent.

Basidia 18–22 × 5–6.5 μ, 4-spored, clavate, hyaline in KOH, yellowish in Melzer's reagent. Pleurocystidia none. Cheilocystidia 30–50 × 7–10 μ, clavate to obtusely fusoid-ventricose, thin-walled, smooth, or with 1–2 apical projections in some. Caulocystidia scattered, clavate, similar to cheilocystidia in size or longer, pedicels in some yellowish in KOH.

Gill trama regular, hyphae somewhat interwoven; the subhymenium thin and not distinctive, hyphae of central area with cells 4–12 (15) μ wide, the walls as revived in KOH and Melzer's reagent thickened to 1–1.2 μ and with the middle lamella readily visible (1.3 N.A. objective), walls smooth and ochraceous to brownish in KOH, orange-ochraceous in Melzer's reagent. Pileus cutis a thin layer of gelatinous hyphae 2–4 μ diam., tubular, hyaline in KOH, walls finally asperulate; hypodermial region of interwoven thin-walled hyphae cells 6–15 μ diam. and dingy ochraceous in KOH, this layer occupying about half the pileus trama, the other half of hyphae with thickened walls like those of the gill trama and colored ochraceous to brownish in KOH, more orange-brownish in Melzer's reagent. Clamp connections present.

HABIT, HABITAT, AND DISTRIBUTION: On decayed conifer wood, Wyoming (type) and Idaho, Smith 68312, 68507.

OBSERVATIONS: The pilei are pale yellow as dried, a strong contrast to the dark stipes. The species is most closely related to *P. vernalis* but the thickened hyphal walls of the gill trama and adjacent pileus trama are unusual in the genus. It is close to *P. bridgii* but has a gelatinous pileus cutis and smaller cells in the trama of the hymenophore.

52. Pholiota conica sp. nov.
Illustrations: Pl. 18b.

Pileus 1–2.5(3) cm latus, acute conicus deinde conico-campanulatus, margin fibrillosus, siccus, "ochraceous-tawny" demum "buckthorn-brown," denique "warm-buff." Caro coriacea deinde pallida; odore et gustu mitis. Lamellae adnatae, pallido-brunneae, deinde obscure brunneae, confertae, angustae. Stipes 4–9 cm longus, 3–6 mm crassus, supra coriaceus, infra brunneus, denique passim rubido-brunneus, leviter fibrillosus. Sporae 5.5–7 × 3.5–4 × 4–4.5 μ, ellipsoideae demum ovoideae, leves, truncatae. Pleurocystidia desunt; cheilocystidia (25)30–30 × 6–9 μ, cylindrica demum ventricosa. Cuticula ex hyphis brunnaceis repentibus composita. Caulocystidia desunt. Specimen typicum in Herb. Univ. Mich.; lectum prope Priest Lake, Idaho, 7 Juli, 1964, Smith 68254.

Pileus 1–2.5 (3) cm broad, sharply conic young, becoming conic-campanulate, margin fringed with fibrils at first and usually scarcely translucent striate, surface dry or subviscid to touch, ochraceous tawny to "buckthorn-brown" fading to "warm-buff." Context butterscotch-color, becoming pallid; taste mild, odor none. $FeSO_4$ and KOH no reaction.

Lamellae adnate, pallid brownish becoming concolorous with moist cap, crowded, narrow, thin, edges even.

Stipe 4–9 cm long, 3–6 mm thick, equal, fragile, darker rusty brown below, butterscotch near apex, finally reddish brown over all, very faintly fibrillose from remains of a thin veil.

Spores 5.5–7 × 3.5–4 × 4–4.5 μ, ovate to elliptic or rarely oblong in face view, in profile subelliptic to obscurely inequilateral, smooth, wall thickened to about 0.3 μ, tawny in KOH and a little more cinnamon in Melzer's reagent, apex slightly truncated from an apical pore.

Basidia 22–27 × 5–7 μ, 4-spored, clavate, hyaline in KOH, yellowish in Melzer's reagent. Pleurocystidia none. Cheilocystidia (25) 30–50 × 6–9 μ: 1) Subcylindric with obtuse to subcapitate apex and wall of shank flexuous, a few with one or more knoblike protuberances; 2) base somewhat ventricose and with a flexuous neck and obtuse apex; or 3) narrowly clavate, often rather irregular in outline; all types hyaline, thinwalled, with homogeneous content colorless in KOH, and most with a clamp at the septum. Caulocystidia present over apical region as scattered ends of tubular hyphae 3–5 μ diam.

Gill trama of inflated hyphae (9–18 μ) somewhat interwoven with cinnamon smooth, non-gelatinous walls as revived in KOH, hyphae near subhymenium narrower and more highly colored; subhymenium indistinct, not a gelatinous layer. Pileus epicutis a thin gelatinous layer of narrow (2.5–4 μ) hyaline thin-walled tubular hyphae; hypodermial region of hyphae 6–15 μ diam., cell walls thin and merely ochraceous to pallid in KOH, not structurally differentiated from context and at least in young material the hyphae about the same color. Clamp connections present. All hyphae inamyloid.

HABIT, HABITAT, AND DISTRIBUTION: Caespitose on conifer logs, Idaho, July, Smith 68254 (type) from Priest Lake.

OBSERVATIONS: The characters which mark this species include the sharply conic young pileus, the highly colored gill trama as revived in KOH, the cheilocystidia and the relatively small *Psilocybe*-like spores. *P. vernalis* is close but differs sharply in the features of the caulocystidia. It also has a more highly developed veil.

53. Pholiota subpapillata sp. nov.
Illustrations: Text figs. 489, 490, 492.

Pileus 1.5–3.5 cm latus, conico-campanulatus demum plano-umbonatus vel papillatus, viscidus, glaber, sordide cinnamomeus, deinde pallide ochraceous (hygrophanus). Contextus brunneolus demum pallidus; sapor mitis, cum "FeSO₄" concolor. Lamellae confertae, angustae, adnatae, brunneolae demum griseo-cacao color. Stipe 3–4 cm longus, 2–2.5 mm crassus, aequalis, cavus, cartilagineus, deorsum atrobrunneus, sursum griseo-brunneus, sericeus. Sporae 6–7 × 3–3.8 μ, truncatae. Pleurocystidia 28–42 × 8–13 μ, fusoide-ventricosa, obtusa. Specimen typicum in Herb. Univ. Mich. conservatum est; legit prope Cour d'Alene, Idaho. 2 Oct. 1966. Smith 73854.

Pileus 1.5–3.5 cm broad, conic-umbonate to obtusely umbonate at first, expanding to plano-umbonate or papillate, surface glabrous, viscid, hygrophanous, dingy cinnamon ("Sayal brown" more or less) and fading to pinkish buff, when old and wet grayish brown with a faintly striatulate margin. Context thin, watery brown fading to pallid, odor and taste none, FeSO₄ no reaction.

Lamellae crowded, narrow, adnate-seceding, dull brownish young, chocolate gray mature, horizontal, edges even.

Stipe 3–4 cm long, 2–2.5 mm thick, equal, hollow, cartilaginous-fragile, blackish brown below, paler purplish brown to grayish brown at the apex, naked or very thinly coated with silky grayish fibrils. Veil very rudimentary.

Spore deposit earth brown, when moisture has escaped dull "Sayal brown." Spores 6–7 × 3–3.8 μ, smooth, truncate from an apical pore, shape in face view subelliptic to ovate, in profile obscurely inequilateral, color in KOH dull cinnamon, in Melzer's about the same color; wall about 0.25 μ thick.

Basidia 4-spored, 18–24 × 6–7 μ, slightly clavate, hyaline or nearly so in KOH. Pleurocystidia 28–42 × 8–13 μ, fusoid ventricose to nearly utriform, hyaline in KOH, "empty," scattered to fairly abundant, smooth, thin-walled. Cheilocystidia similar to pleurocystidia but many with bumps near apex or short protuberances. Caulocystidia clavate, vesiculose or variously fusoid-ventricose and with obtuse projections or branches, mostly similar to cheilocystidia.

Gill trama of subparallel hyphae having short cells which become inflated to +15 μ and have pallid to brownish smooth walls in KOH, subhymenium a very narrow indistinct layer not gelatinous. Pileus cutis a thin gelatinous pellicle of narrow (2.5–4 μ) hyaline, smooth hyphae; hypodermium not differentiated. Context hyphae hyaline and thin-walled next to the cutis, near subhymenium with thicker ($\pm$ 1 μ) walls but hyaline, the region appearing parenchymatous in sections. Clamp connections present.

HABIT, HABITAT, AND DISTRIBUTION: Gregarious-caespitose on chip dirt, Couer-d'Alene. Idaho, Oct. 2, 1966. Smith 73854, type.

OBSERVATIONS: This species is very close to *P. vernalis* but is distinguished by the rudimentary veil all traces of which soon vanish, the chocolate colored gills which remind one of *Psilocybe,* and the presence of pleurocystidia. It is a more psilocyboid species than *P. vernalis* and again emphasizes that the two genera intergrade.

54. **Pholiota vernalis** (Pk.) comb. nov. f. vernalis.

Agaricus vernalis Peck, New York State Cab. Ann. Rept. 23: 91. 1872.
Agaricus lignicola Peck, New York State Cab. Ann. Rept. 23: 91. 1872.
Naucoria vernalis (Pk) Saccardo, Syll. Fung. 5: 838. 1887.
Naucoria lignicola (Pk.) Saccardo, Syll. Fung. 5: 838. 1887.
Naucoria praecox Murrill, North Amer. Fl. 10: 174. 1917.
Kuehneromyces vernalis (Pk.) Singer & Smith, Mycologia 38: 514. 1946.

Illustrations: Text figs. 153-154; pl. 19, 20.

Pileus 10–35 mm broad, when young with a conic umbo and a decurved inrolled margin, expanding to obtusely campanulate to convex or nearly plane, glabrous, margin frequently being decorated with veil remanants, viscid, when moist translucent over marginal area, when moist pale to dark butterscotch-color ("honey-yellow" to near "clay-color" or darker), hygrophanous, when faded pale yellow to (at times) almost pallid. Context watery pinkish-buff to cinnamon-buff, fairly pliant, thin, odor, and taste mild.

Lamellae crowded, narrow, (1.5–2 mm) bluntly adnate, seceding, pinkish buff young (pale dingy tan), becoming dark dull cinnamon, margins becoming crenulate to fimbriate at times.

Stipe (2) 3–6 cm long, 1.5–3 (5) mm thick, hollow, pliant, equal, at first covered over all by a fibrillose silky coating grayish to buff in color and with sparse patches or zones of veil remnants pale brownish in color below the evanescent annulus or annular zone, color beneath fibrils at first dingy butterscotch-color (dingy melleous) but soon stained dull rusty brown from base upward.

Spore print cinnamon-brown; spores 5.5–7 (7.5) × 3–4 (4.5) μ, smooth, obscurely truncate, dingy tawny in KOH, and scarcely darkening in Melzer's, ovate in face view, elliptic in profile, terete or very slightly compressed in cross section, wall less than 0.5 μ thick.

Basidia 16–20 (25) × 5–6 (7) μ, typically 4-spored, clavate, hyaline in KOH to somewhat ochraceous. Pleurocystidia none or a few seen near gill edge and similar to cheilocystidia. Cheilocystidia 24–46 × 4–9 μ, fusoid-ventricose to subfusoid, neck often elongated and flexuous, apex subacute to obtuse. Caulocystidia 34–104 × 7–18 μ, clavate, cylindric or ventricose, at times septate.

Gill trama of subparallel brown hyphae often with incrusted walls, cells 5–13 μ broad; subhymenium of nongelatinous often incrusted hyphae, and brown in KOH. Pileus with an epicutis of narrow gelatinous hyphae (2–4 μ diam.) mostly hyaline; hypodermium of brown radially disposed hyphae 6–12 μ in diam. Clamp connections present.

HABIT, HABITAT, AND DISTRIBUTION: Gregarious to caespitose on rotting wood, usually of conifers, but at times on hardwoods, typically vernal and abundant in our mountainous areas but throughout northern regions. It is one of the common species of the Rocky Mountain "snow bank flora."

OBSERVATIONS: The following material-studied list contains many collections on which complete data on macroscopic characters are lacking. Hence the listing is more to show the abundance of this complex than to sharply delimit its taxa. As a complex, it is one of the most difficult series of variants in *Pholiota,* particularly in the Rocky Mountains. A study in culture of this group would be most desirable.

MATERIAL EXAMINED: ALASKA: Wells, 7-4-64 #8 (S). CALIFORNIA: Cooke 18223, 30324, Siskiyou County (no number) (all MICH.); White 118, 122. COLORADO: Smith 51379, 53037, 53046, 53069, 53076, 53114, 53115, 53116, 53117, 53153. IDAHO: Cooke 20169, 21921; Gruber 22; Slipp 1498, 1513, 1591, V-2509; Smith 44157, 44160, 44161, 44248, 44729, 45257, 45305, 45375, 45380, 45478, 53219, 58617, 58687, 64900, 65093, 65116, 65117, 65176, 67870, 68030, 68251; Trueblood 104, 1048, 1077. MAINE: Bigelow 2931, 3145, 3182, 3224, 3347; Parlin 17115, 17138 (FH), 17783, 17784, 17816 (MICH). MASSACHUSETTS: Dadmun (FH). MICHIGAN: Bartelli 5-17-64; Charlton G-29 (MICH.); Kanouse 569, 5-30-45 (both MICH.); Kauffman 7-3-05; Nickell 11-18-45; Pennington 7-14-06; Otter 4444, 4473, 4540; Shaffer 1297, 1778; Smith 32150, 36332, 36438, 36813, 37006, 41601, 49584, 49673, 61025, 63925, 6647, 71508, 71510; Thiers 660, 2612, 2619, 3101, 3204, 3236, 3631. MONTANA: Cotner 55001, 570010, 570018, 570027. NEW MEXICO: Barrows 62, 211, 635, 641, 645, 648, 651, 662. NEW YORK: Peck (types of *A. lignicola,* and *A. vernalis*). NORTH CAROLINA: Hesler 17625, 20851.

OHIO: Cooke 33126, 33160. OREGON: Gruber 3, 763, 6-24-42 (MICH.) ;
Sipe 691, 893. TENNESSEE: Hesler 3873, 11395; Porter 11391; Hesler
& Smith 7340, 17034, 17625. VERMONT: Burt (as *N. lignicola*) (FH).
WASHINGTON: Brown 9-29-25; Imshaug 31, 32, 37, 42, 44, 53, 54, 55,
56, 57, 59, 61, 62, 63, 64, 65, 66, 103, 222, 227, 861, 1546; Simmons 1353;
Smith 12085, 13064, 13083, 13179, 13399, 13400, 13520, 13714, 13784,
13869, 28831, 29124, 29253, 29420, 29747, 30056, 41186, 47597, 47715,
48081; Smith & Digilio 7-6-48. UTAH: McKnight F318, F439, F1120
(All MICH). WYOMING: Arenberg 68, 8-2-38 (MICH.) ; Cronin 149
(MICH.) ; Smith 34370, 34377, 34378, 34384, 34417, 34807, 34888; Sol-
heim 3370, 3681, 3703, 3733, 3765, 3768, 3826, 3875, 3877, 3935, 4043,
4469, 4494, 4546, 4825, 4826, 4827, 4839, 4840, 4870, 5318; Thiers 129
(MICH.). CANADA (QUEBEC): Pomerleau 8-9-49. U.S.S.R.: Zinova
(LE) ; Vassilieva (LE, KAZ) .

55. Pholiota populicola sp. nov.
Illustrations: Text figs. 155-156.

*Pileus 1.5–3.5(4) cm latus, convexus deinde planus, "argus brown,"
denique margine "ochraceous tawny," denique "light buff," viscidus,
glabrous, striatulatus. Caro concolor; odore et gustu mitis. Lamellae depresso-adnatae, mox secedentes, stipatae," "tilleul buff," deinde "ochraceous tawny," planae vel leviter crenulatae. Stipes 7–9 cm longus, 3–4
mm crassus, supra albidus, ab imo sursum "Dresden-brown," pallido-coriaceus, conferte fibrillosus. Velum faciens crassum, superiorem, pallidum,
xylinum annulus. Sporae 5–7 × 4.5–4.8 × 4–4.5 μ, leves, truncatae, sub-
compressae. Pleurocystidia desunt; cheilocystidia 20–27 × 3–7 μ, ventricosa vel ventricoso-rostrata. Cuticula gelatinosa. Specimen typicum in
Herb. Univ. Mich. conservatum est; lectum prope Clearwater River,
Olympic Peninsula, Washington, May 9, 1939. Smith 13260.*

Pileus 1.5–3.5 (4) cm broad, convex becoming plane, at first "argus
brown" over all, becoming "ochraceous tawny" on the margin, fading to
"light buff" and finally dingy tawny, viscid when young, glabrous, striatulate. Context thin, concolorous with surface; odor and taste not distinctive.

Lamellae depressed adnate and soon seceding, crowded, more or less
30 reach the stipe, narrow (3–4 mm), 2–3 tiers of lamellulae, pallid
("tilleul-buff"), becoming "ochraceous-tawny," edges very thin and even
to slightly crenulate.

Stipe 7–9 cm long, 3–4 mm thick, whitish above, becoming "Dresden-
brown" from the base upward, tubular equal or slightly enlarged downward, at first densely fibrillose with a pale buff fibrillose coating, fibrillose-squamulose above the annulus, generally glabrescent. Annulus thick,
superior, pallid, and striate above, cottony and at times darker below,
often evanescent.

Spores 5–7 × 4.5–4.8 × 4–4.5 μ, smooth, distinctly truncate (truncation up to 1.5 μ broad), broadly ovate to elliptic-truncate in face view obscurely inequilateral to subelliptic in profile, pale cinnamon to pale tawny in KOH, paler in Melzer's reagent than in KOH, wall relatively thin (estimated at less than 0.25 μ).

Basidia 17–22 × 5–6 μ, narrowly clavate to subcylindric, 4-spored, hyaline to yellowish in KOH and Melzer's sol. Pleurocystidia none. Cheilocystidia 20–27 × 3–7 μ, ventricose-rostrate but small, varying to merely fusoid-ventricose or with odd shapes but apex obtuse, thin-walled, hyaline in KOH and Melzer's reagent, smooth, content homogeneous. Caulocystidia none located.

Gill trama of subparallel non-gelatinous hyphae with broad short to elongate cells, walls hyaline to yellowish in KOH and Melzer's reagent, and showing only a slight tendency to thickening (typically thin-walled); subhymenium narrow and indistinct. Pileus cutis a gelatinous layer of smooth hyaline hyphae 2–4 μ diam. appressed and the layer up to 8–12 hyphae deep (but usually thinner as seen in revived material); hypodermial region of yellowish to hyaline hyphae which are nongelatinous and cells distinctly inflated, the hyphal walls thin to slightly thickened but not measurable (less than 0.4 μ), yellowish in Melzer's reagent. Context hyphae yellowish to nearly hyaline in KOH and in Melzer's reagent; oleiferous hyphae rare. Clamp connections present.

HABIT, HABITAT, AND DISTRIBUTION: On rotton logs of *Populus trichocarpa*, Clearwater River, Olympic Mountains, Washington, May 9, 1939, Smith 13260 type.

OBSERVATIONS: The thick, superior, striate annulus collapses and disappears, but when present it is quite distinct from that of *P. vernalis*. The stipe below the annulus is not squamulose with recurved squamules as in *P. mutabilis* but rather is coated with pale buff veil fibrils or these aggregating into patches. These differences in addition to the habitat distinguish the species from *P. mutabilis*, but the aspect of the dried basidiocarps of these two is very similar.

Stirps Depauperata

This "stirps" may be more of an illusion than a reality as far as *Pholiota* is concerned since the dark gills suggest purple-brown spores. It is quite possible that the species belongs in *Psilocybe* but the data needed to justify making such a transfer are lacking. We do not know the color of the spore deposit.

56. Pholiota depauperata (Singer & Smith) comb. nov.

Kuehneromyces depauperatus Singer & Smith, Mycologia 38: 513. 1946.

Pileus about 17 mm broad, convex, subumbonate, strongly hygrophanous and almost subviscid, deeply sordid melleous when water-soaked, fading to pale pinkish buff and then becoming more ochraceous ("pale yellow-orange" to "light ochraceous-buff"), translucent-striate when moist. Context subconcolorous, watery and fleshy in the pileus, somewhat tougher in the stipe; odor none.

Lamellae adnexed to adnate, olive-fuscous at maturity, medium broad (2–2.5 mm), moderately close.

Stipe about 2.3 cm long, 2 mm thick, blackish fuscous, darkening from the base upward, nearly equal, tubular, base white-mycelioid, lower portion thinly fibrillose, nearly glabrous above.

Spores deep honey-color under the microscope, 6.2–6.8 × 3–4.4 μ, in face view elliptic to ovate varying to subrhombic, in profile convex on the ventral line (in optical section), wall smooth and double, apex truncate.

Basidia 14–20 × 5.8–6.3 μ, 4-spored. Pleurocystidia none. Cheilocystidia 27–29 × 6–7 μ, ventricose below, ampullaceous above, the neck 2–4 μ thick, sometimes cylindric to subconic above, rather uniform in size and distribution.

Gill trama of interwoven hyphae. Pileus cuticle gelatinous; hypodermium of brown-walled hyphae, not structurally differentiated. Clamp connections present.

HABIT, HABITAT, AND DISTRIBUTION: Solitary on decaying mossy trunk of hardwood tree, Florida, July. Singer F2992, type.

OBSERVATIONS: All the features of this species are typical of *Psilocybe,* especially the cheilocystidia, spore size and shape, and color of the mature gills. Ordinarily we would have simply relegated it to the excluded and doubtful category, but in view of what we now know about *Pholiota* it can be recognized as a species in this genus. Since the collector considered it brown spored, we follow this lead pending positive proof that this is wrong.

Section **Hemipholiota**

Pileus flesh moderately to very thick (1–2 cm as measured near the stipe apex) ; pleurocystidia absent; spores not dextrinoid; stipe typically 10 mm or more thick at the base.

Key to Stirpes

1. Spore deposit olive-yellow ("Isabella color") ; pileus with only scattered spotlike scales from the veil .... Stirps *Olivaceodisca*
1. Not as above 2
   2. Gill margins white-crenulate; spores 10–15 × 5–7.5 μ ....
   .... Stirps *Albocrenulata*

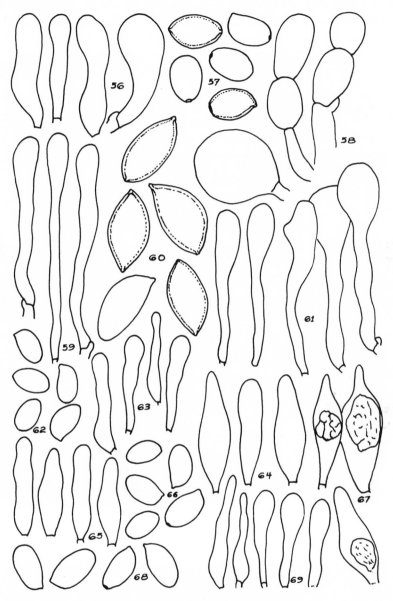

Text Fig. 4.

FIGS. 56, 57 & 58, cheilocystidia, spores and caulocystidia of *P. destruens;* 59-61, caulocystidia, spores and cheilocystidia of *P. albocrenulata;* 62-64, spores cheilocystidia and caulocystidia of *P. gummosa;* 65-66, cheilocystidia and spores of *P. burkei;* 67-69, pleurocystidia spores and cheilocystidia of *P. subcaerulea.*

2. Gill margins not conspicuously crenulate; spores 7–10 × 5–6.5 μ
.... Stirps *Destruens*

Stirps Destruens

1. Stipe not staining yellow when handled .... *P. destruens* var. *destruens*
1. Stipe readily staining yellow when handled ....
.... *P. destruens* var. *edmundii*

57. Pholiota destruens (Brond.) Gillet Champ Fr. p. 442. 1876.
Agaricus destruens Brondeau, Plant Crypt. Agen. pl. 6, 1828-30.
Dryophila destruens (Brond.) Quélet, Enchir. Fung. p. 67. 1886.
var. *destruens*
Illustrations: Text figs. 56-58; pls. 21-23.

Pileus (6) 8–16 (20) cm broad, convex when young, expanding to broadly convex, rarely umbonate, viscid, pallid to whitish, or creamy to ocher, at times gradually darkening on the disc throughout to avellaneous, wood-brown, or "Dresden brown" (dark yellow-brown), conspicuously decorated with the whitish to dingy buff remains of a copious veil in the form of floccose scales or patches which may become matted down in age or be washed off entirely, margin shaggy from the copious veil remnants. Context thick, firm, white; odor not distinctive (usually fungoid), taste slightly disagreeable but hardly distinctive.

Lamellae adnate to sinuate, broad, close, white when young but gradually becoming deep rusty cinnamon from the spores, edges even.

Stipe central to eccentric, 5–12 (18) cm long, 1–3 cm thick at apex, enlarged downward and (2) 5–7 cm thick at the base, clavate to equal, hard, solid, white at first, brownish at least below in age (especially if water-soaked), copiously decorated with the remains of the thick, white, floccose veil as scales or patches up to the floccose-cottony evanescent annulus, silky above.

Spore deposit "cinnamon-brown"; spores 7–9.5 × 4–5.5 μ, smooth, apex in some obscurely truncate from a distinct apical pore, near cinnamon brown as revived in KOH, paler in Melzer's reagent, wall appreciably thickened (up to 0.5 μ), in face view elliptic to ovate, in profile somewhat inequilateral to elliptic, apiculus not conspicuous.

Basidia 28–35 × 5–7 μ, mostly 4-spored, clavate, hyaline in KOH, faintly yellow in Melzer's reagent. Pleurocystidia none. Cheilocystidia 25–34 (66) × 4–9 μ, cylindric, narrowly clavate, or cylindric-capitate, walls smooth, hyaline and thin, content homogeneous. Caulocystidia abundant, vesiculose and up to 22 μ diam; clavate and up to 18 μ, and variable in length or as chains of broadly ellipsoid cells 10–15 μ diam., all elements hyaline in KOH, thin-walled and content homogeneous.

Gill trama of parallel hyphae 4–9 μ wide but cells becoming more inflated in age, hyaline in KOH, thin-walled, smooth, in Melzer's reagent ochraceous to reddish; subhymenium of parallel to somewhat interwoven narrow (2–3 μ) subgelatinous hyphae and base of basidium subgelatinous at times. Pileus with a poorly defined cuticular zone of subgelatinous hyphae 4–7 μ diam. hyaline in KOH and thin-walled, smooth; in Melzer's yellowish; hypodermium not differentiated by color or structure but hyphae the same size as in the context (7–20 μ diam.), hyaline, thin-walled, and smooth; in Melzer's reagent yellowish to orange-reddish in places. Clamp connections present.

HABIT, HABITAT, AND DISTRIBUTION: On logs and dead wood of *Populus*, especially cottonwood and balsam popular late in the fall, Michigan, Colorado, Wyoming, Idaho, Utah, Oregon, Washington and New Mexico, reported by Overholts (1927) from New York through the Central States to the Pacific and also known from Canada.

OBSERVATIONS: This is one of the most robust and striking species in the genus. It is most unfortunate that it has so little to recommend it for the table. It is to be expected during warm wet weather in late fall, especially in the irrigated regions of our western states. Young dried basidiocarps are pallid and show copious remains of the veil along the margin. Older basidiocarps tend to dry brownish. The veil remnants disappear slowly or may finally wash away. Lange (1938) described the odor as strong and somewhat aromatic. This feature was emphasized by Fries for *P. heteroclita*. We have one specimen from near Santa Fe, New Mexico collected by Barrows and Isaacs on *Populus* in which the stipe is 11 cm long and 1 cm thick. The veil is exceptionally cottony, thick and white, in fact the pileus is white from the evenly distributed velar remains. The spores measure 7–8.5 × 4.5–5.5 μ.

The Friesian descriptions of *A. destruens* cover our large late-fruiting species on *Populus* so well that there seems little doubt of its identity. We are not so sure of *P. heteroclita* and *P. comosa*, however, in fact at present we have not recognized them in our flora.

MATERIAL EXAMINED: COLORADO: Smith 52221. IDAHO: Smith 54193, 73484; Trueblood 704, 785. MICHIGAN: Bartelli 391; Davis 9-21-35; Dusseau 10-26-47; Harding 427, 439; Imshaug 4633; Potter 12171; Smith 51288, 64741, 64834, 66485, 71420. MINNESOTA: Kauffman 5-10-20. NEW MEXICO: Barrows 43a, 351, 908, 2089, 2710, Aug. 1961. NEW YORK: Kauffman 7-9-21; Stewart 5-10-26. OHIO: Harding 49. OREGON: Sipe 390; Smith Dec. 1941, 55352. SOUTH DAKOTA: Brenckle 50297. UTAH: McKnight F1153. Washington: Smith 10-18-52, 48918. WYOMING: Solheim 5484, 5485, 5486, 5487. Canada—ONTARIO: Cain 30814; Kelly 1736, 1816; Smith 4643.

57a. Pholiota destruens var. edmundii var. nov.

Pileus 3–5 cm latus, late umbonatus, albofibrillosus; odor fragrans; stipes albus, tactu luteus; sporae 8–10 × 4.5–5.5 μ. Specimen typicum in

Herb. Univ. Mich. conservatum est; legit prope Highlands Mich. 1 Oct. 1961, Smith 64509.

Pileus 3–5 cm broad, broadly umbonate with a decurved margin, surface at first decorated with scattered appressed fibrillose patches of veil material and the margin fringed or appendiculate with pieces of the submembranous veil, glabrous and subviscid over the disc and "cinnamon buff" (pale alutaceous), paler on the margin. Context thick, whitish, odor faintly fragrant, taste mild; $FeSO_4$ olive on context, KOH yellow to orange.

Lamellae pallid becoming dingy vinaceous cinnamon, narrow to moderately broad, close, adnexed, edges even and colored like the faces.

Stipe 8–14 cm long, about 1 cm thick, stuffed with a silky pith, becoming hollow, pallid in age, rusty ochraceous in the base, apex whitish and silky, with a fibrillose pallid evanescent superior ring, below the ring sheathed by a thin velar layer breaking up into appressed squamules and obscure zones, staining yellow when handled and stains finally rusty ochraceous.

Spores 8–10 × 4.5–5.5 μ, smooth, apical pore present; shape in face view oblong with blunt apex, in profile somewhat to distinctly bean-shaped; color in KOH ochraceous-rusty, in Melzer's dingy yellow-brown (as in *Psilocybe*); wall thin (about 0.25 μ).

Basidia 26–34 × 7–9 μ, 4-spored, hyaline in KOH. Pleurocystidia none. Cheilocystidia 18–30 × 5–7 μ, subcylindric to clavate (much like basidioles). Caulocystidia none.

Gill trama of a central hyaline strand of parallel hyphae with a gelatinous subhymenium diverging to the hymenium, all hyphae smooth and hyaline, cells all uninflated (but specimens young). Pileus cutis a subgelatinous pellicle of hyphae 3–5 μ wide, ochraceous in KOH, smooth and with distinct walls in the layer (slime secreted rather than resulting from breakdown of hyphal walls); no hypodermium differentiated, the context hyphae hyaline, thin-walled and closely interwoven; a few ochraceous oleiferous hyphae present. Clamp connections present.

HABIT, HABITAT, AND DISTRIBUTION: Solitary on hardwood logs, Highlands Recreation Area, Oakland County, Mich. Oct. 1, 1961. Smith 64509, collected by Edmund Golabiewski of the Michigan Botanical Club.

OBSERVATIONS: This is one of the variants around *P. destruens*. It has a faint but fragrant odor and mild taste, and the stipe stains yellow when handled. It has been found on wood other than that of *Populus* to date, but most collections were not retained or critically studied since at first Smith thought it was just an "off season" variation of *P. destruens*.

Stirps Albocrenulata

Characters as in the central and only species.

58. **Pholiota albocrenulata** (Pk.) Saccardo, Syll. Fung. 5: 760. 1887.
Agaricus albocrenulatus Peck, Buffalo Soc. Nat. Sci. 1: 49. 1873.
Hypodendrum albocrenulatum (Pk.) Overholts, North Amer. Flora 10: 281. 1932.
Hebeloma albocrenulata (Pk.) Singer, Rev. de Mycol. 4: 72. 1939.
Stropharia albocrenulata (Pk.) Kreisel, Fedes Repertorium 3: 212. 1964.
Pholiota fusca Quélet, Champ. Jura & Vosges 4th Suppl. 1876.
Illustrations: Text figs. 59-61; pls. 25a, 26, 27.

Pileus (2.5) 3–8 (12) cm broad, obtuse to broadly conic or convex, expanding to obtusely umbonate or nearly plane, surface glutinous to viscid, shining when dry, orange-fulvous to deep ferruginous and finally dark vinaceous-brown (near "Roods brown"), decorated with superficial brown fibrillose scales from remains of a veil, veil particles pallid on drying out, margin opaque and often decorated with remnants of the veil. Context thick, pallid; odor not distinctive, taste not recorded.

Lamellae adnate to subdecurrent or sinuate and with a decurrent tooth, at times rounded next to the stipe, close, very broad, whitish becoming grayish and at length rusty-umber, edge crenulate and beaded with white drops.

Stipe 3–10 (15) cm long, 5–15 mm thick, equal or nearly so, fibrous and firm, stuffed becoming hollow, pallid to grayish above, dark brown below, squarrose with brown scales up to the annulus, apex pruinose.

Spores 10–15 (18) × 5.5–7 (8.5) μ, smooth, with an apical discontinuity projecting only through the thick inner layer, wall at maturity 1–1.5 μ thick, in face view subfusoid, in profile more or less inequilateral or at least the ventral line straighter than the dorsal line, apiculate at base, in KOH dark cinnamon, in Melzer's reagent nearly tawny.

Basidia 4-spored, 30–36 × 7–9 μ, narrowly clavate, hyaline in KOH (hymenium hyaline) yellowish pallid in Melzer's reagent, projecting prominently when sporulating. Pleurocystidia none. (Occasional giant basidia present, some with one sterigma?). Cheilocystidia abundant, 43–75 × 4–9 μ, cylindric-clavate with pedicels flexuous, at times subcapitate, hyaline in KOH, wall thin and smooth, content homogeneous. Caulocystidia resembling the cheilocystidia but up to 100 μ or more long, content yellowish in KOH, homogeneous.

Gill trama of subparallel hyphae with greatly elongated wide (5–12 μ) cells; walls thin, smooth and perfectly hyaline in KOH, subhymenium a narrow hyaline gelatinous zone of narrow thin-walled hyphae. Pileus cutis a thick gelatinous layer (200 μ thick) of hyaline to yellowish narrow gelatinous hyphae appressed-interwoven; hypodermium not differentiated. Hyphae of context of inflated cells, hyaline in KOH, with somewhat thickened (about 0.5 μ) walls toward gill-trama, smooth, with small (3–6 μ) hyaline refractive oval to circular bodies numerous in the area above the gill trama (as revived in KOH). All hyphae inamyloid. Clamp connections present.

HABIT, HABITAT, AND DISTRIBUTION: Singly or in groups of two or three, on maple and perhaps other hardwood species, trunks, stumps, and logs, rarely on hemlock (Smith 50096); New Hampshire, New York, North Carolina, Tennessee, Michigan, Wisconsin, also Canada west to New Mexico; July to October; seldom abundant but not uncommon.

OBSERVATIONS: The apex of the spore in this species recalls the condition observed in *Agrocybe erebia,* but this is hardly sufficient reason for transferring the species to *Agrocybe.* Apparently there is a layer of colored hyphae below the gelatinous pellicle in old specimens but not in young well-dried material. The pleurocystidia, if they are not monosporous basidia, are rare and difficult to find. Although the spores are a very dark brown they are not violaceous, so there appears to be no good reason for transferring the species to *Stropharia* as was done by Kreisel.

Barrows and Isaacs collected this species in New Mexico on *Populus* (cottonwood), and also growing cespitose on stumps of *Pinus ponderosa.* The spores in the latter collection are small (10–12 μ long) but the specimens are immature. The stipes were exceptionally scaly. To say the least, pine is a most unusual host for this species.

MATERIAL EXAMINED: MICHIGAN: Harding 167, 234, 336, 383; Kauffman (no date), 8-4-05, 7-26-09, 10-13-26, 9-1906; Mains 32-528, 32-233; Pennington 8-30-06; Peters 1121; Smith 11116, 23483, 32957, 33789, 36655, 37286, 37485, 38028, 38375, 39308, 50096, 50447, 57354, 67435, 67372; Stuntz 7-31-49; Thiers 3267, 3902, 4269, 4374, 4405. NEW MEXICO: Isaacs 2708, 2695. NEW YORK: Type, North Elba; Smith 97, 130; NORTH CAROLINA: Sharp 20501; Smith 10703. Oregon: Smith 24716. TENNESSEE: Hesler 18040. CANADA—Nova Scotia: Wehmeyer 762; Ontario: Kelly 951, 1720; Smith 26465; Quebec: Smith 61713.

Stirps Olivaceodisca

59. Pholiota olivaceodisca sp. nov.
Illustrations: Text figs. 51-52.

Pileus 3–5 cm latus, convexus, viscidus, olivaceo-griseus, fibrillosus sparse squamulosus. Lamellae adnatae, pallide luteae, confertae, serrulatae. Stipes 4–6 cm longus, 5–10 mm crassus, luteo-fibrillosus, sursum albidus. Sporae in cumulo olivaceoluteae, 5.5–7 × 3.5–4 μ. Pleurocystidia desunt. Cheilocystidia 14–26 × 4–7 μ, fusoide ventricosa. Specimen typicum in Herb. Univ. Tenn. conservatum est; legit prope Claxton School, Anderson County, Tenn. 10 Nov. 1946. L. R. Hesler 17778.

Pileus 3–5 cm broad, convex, expanding, viscid, disc "deep olive-buff," elsewhere "olive-buff," fibrillose-appressed, with scattered spot-like scales, margin even. Context pale watery-white, medium thick; odor and taste mild.

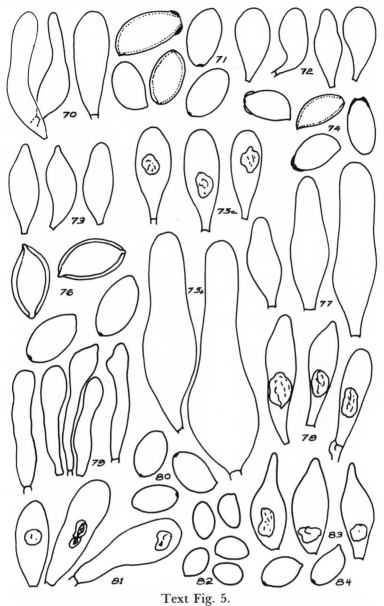

Text Fig. 5.

Figs: 70-71, cheilocystidia and spores of *P. serotina;* 72-74, cheilo-cystidia, pleurocystidia and spores of *P. kalmicola;* 75a, 75b, 76 & 77, two types of pleurocystidia spores and cheilocystidia of *P. sipei;* 78-80, pleurocystidia, cheilocystidia and spores of *P. albivelata;* 81-82, pleuro-cystidia and spores of *P. duroides;* 83-84, pleurocystidia and spores of *P. cubensis.*

Lamellae adnate to submarginate, "light buff" at maturity (yellowish), medium brown, rounded behind, crowded, edges serrulate.

Stipe 4–6 cm long, 5–10 mm thick, near apex yellowish fibrillose, below white and floccose-scaly, tapering downward, tubular.

Spore deposit "Isabella color" (olive-yellow). Spores 5.5–7 × 3.5–4 μ, smooth, apical pore minute but distinct, apex obscurely truncate in some; shape ovate to narrowly elliptic in face view, in profile somewhat inequilateral; pale cinnamon brown in KOH, in Melzer's reagent paler and buff colored; wall about 0.25 μ thick.

Basidia 18–24 × 5–6 μ, 4-spored, short-clavate, hyaline in KOH, yellowish in Melzer's reagent. Pleurocystidia none. Cheilocystidia 14–26 × 4–7 μ mostly fusoid-ventricose to ventricose-rostrate with rounded apex, varying to subcylindric and slightly capitate, smooth, thin-walled, content homogeneous. Caulocystidia 18–40 (60) × 3–7 μ, cylindric to subcapitate or somewhat utriform, some filamentose with various enlargements and constrictions varying to narrowly clavate.

Gill trama a central area of floccose hyphae parallel to subparallel, the cells 5–12 μ or more wide (becoming inflated), walls thin, smooth, somewhat ochraceous to hyaline in KOH; subhymenium of narrow hyaline gelatinous hyphae ± interwoven to subparallel. Pileus cutis of loosely tangled subgelatinous hyphae 2–3.5 μ diam. with smooth walls and ochraceous content; hypodermial zone more rusty brown fading to ochraceous, walls smooth and not gelatinous. Clamp connections present. All hyphae inamyloid.

HABIT, HABITAT, AND DISTRIBUTION: Caespitose on soil, in mixed conifer-hardwood woods, Tennessee, November, Hesler 17778, type.

OBSERVATIONS: The pileus colors are unique. The disc is deep olive-buff, elsewhere it is paler (olive-buff). When dried the pileus assumes a dingy olive-ocher color. The color of the spore deposit, the small spores and small cheilocystidia and lack of pleurocystidia are a distinctive set of characters.

Section **Variabilisporae** sect nov.

Sporae ad apicum multiporae. Typus *P. variabilispora.*

In the only species there is more than one germ pore near the spore apex in most spores.

60. **Pholiota variabilispora** sp. nov.
Illustrations: Text figs. 172-174.

Pileus 2–3 cm latus, convexus demum subplanus, glaber, viscidus, luteus demum argillaceus, ad marginem appendiculatus. Lamellae adnatae demum emarginatae, latae, confertae, pallidae demum sordide argillaceae. Stipes 3–4 cm longus, 3–4 mm crassus, subradicatus, pallide luteus, fibrillosus, sursum furfuraceus. Sporae (10) 11–15 × 7–10 μ, cum 2–3 poris. Pleurocystidia 30–38 × 10–15 μ, subcapitata. Specimen typicum in Herb. Mich. conservatum est; legit prope Echo Lake, Montana, C. H. Kauffman.

Pileus 2–3 cm broad, obtuse to convex, becoming broadly convex or nearly plane, surface glabrous and even, viscid when wet, "yellow ochre" to "ochraceous buff," becoming "clay-color" or darker when dried, margin at first appendiculate from fragments of the veil. Context whitish, thickish and pliant except along the margin, odor and taste not recorded.

Lamellae adnate, becoming emarginate to adnexed, broad (4–5 mm), close, pallid at first, finally "Dresden brown" (dark yellowish brown).

Stipe 3–4 cm long, 3–4 mm thick, base subrooting and with rhizomorphs, solid, pale yellow ("ochraceous buff"), fibrillose, apex furfuraceous, tubular; annulus not formed.

Spores (10) 11–15 × 7–10 μ, broadly ellipsoid to somewhat irregular, apex obscurely truncate or with 2–3 pores present near apex, dark tawny brown in KOH, thick-walled (0.5 μ), smooth.

Basidia two-spored, 22–26 × 7.5–9 μ, subclavate, hyaline in KOH. Pleurocystidia scattered, 30–38 × 10–15 μ, ventricose with subcapitate apex, dumbbell-shaped or simply fusoid-ventricose or apex subcapitate and below that equal to the base, hyaline, content homogeneous, thinwalled. Cheilocystidia 18–26 × 7–10 μ, fusoid-ventricose or apex subcapitate, thin-walled, hyaline in KOH.

Gill trama parallel to subparallel, subhymenium very thin, very slightly yellowish in KOH throughout, hyphae with inflated thin-walled cells. Pileus cutis a thin adnate gelatinous pellicle of appressed narrow hyphae hyaline in KOH but not different structurally from the context hyphae, the latter paler toward the gill trama. Clamp connections present.

HABIT, HABITAT, AND DISTRIBUTION: Gregarious in garden soil, Echo Lake, Montana, C. H. Kauffman, 1928. Known only from the type collection.

OBSERVATIONS: This species is likely to be mistaken for an *Agrocybe* in the field but the pileus cutis is not of inflated cells. Kauffman thought it was a *Stropharia* but the color of the spores is that of *Pholiota*. It is the only *Pholiota* known to us having spores with more than one germ pore on any of the spores. Some of the pleurocystidia are shaped like chrysocystidia but lacked the characteristic inclusion as revived in KOH.

Subg. **Phaeonaematoloma** (Singer) Singer, Lilloa 22: 517. 1951. Emended

The spores may or may not be truncate, but chrysocystidia are present. This latter feature was not emphasized in Singer's 1951 account, but his type species possesses them.

Key to Sections

1. Annulus conspicuous and distinct .... Sect. *Albivelatae*
1. Veil leaving a more or less evanscent zone ...... Sect. *Phaeonaematoloma*

Section **Albivelatae** sect, nov.

Annulus conspicuus, membranaceus vel floccosus; chrysocystidia adsunt. Typus *P. albivelata.*

Key to Species

1. Spores 9–12 × 4.5–6 μ .... *P. sipei*
1. Spores smaller 2
  2. Pileus pellicle well-developed; spores 7–9 × 4–5.5 μ ....
  .... *P. albivelata*
  2. Pileus lacking a gelatinous pellicle 3
3. Spores 4.5–6 × 3–4 μ .... *P. duroides*
3. Spores 6–8 × 4–5 μ 4
  4. Pleurocystidia 35–53 × 8–14 μ; spores with a germ pore ....
  .... *P. cubensis*
  4. Pleurocystidia 25–36 × 5–12 μ; spores without a pore ....
  .... *P. johnsoniana*

Stirps Albivelata

61. Pholiota sipei sp. nov.
Illustrations: Text figs. 75-77.

Pileus 2–4.5 latus, "light-drab," umbone "cinnamon-drab," viscidus, margine striatulatus. Lamellae sinuosae, concolores, confertae, mediolatae. Stipes 5–7 cm longus, 4–7 mm crassus, flexuosus, basi parvum bulbosus, supra planus, infra albus cum flavidis squamis. Velum album membraneum manifestum. Sporae 9–12 × 4.5–6 μ, ellipsoideae, truncatae. Pleurocystidia 41–64 × 10–18 μ, ampullacea, ventricosa vel clavata. Cheilocystidia 25–58 × 7–12 μ, ventricosa, clavata. Pilei trama stratosa, gelatinosa. Cuticula gelatinosa. Caulocystidia desunt. Specimen typicum in Herb. Univ. Mich.; lectum prope Williamette, Oregon, November 16, 1947, Sipe 1059.

Pileus 2–4.5 cm broad, glabrous, very viscid, margin finely striate, margin in some hung with fragments of the veil; color light drab over the marginal area and drab over the umbo (dull gray on disc and paler on margin, as dried marginal area olive grayish and disc dull fulvous).

Lamellae sinuate, close, moderately broad, pallid to avellaneous becoming cinnamon from the spores.

Stipe 5–7 cm long, 4–7 mm thick, flexuous, sometimes bulbous at base, smooth above the ring, white with yellowish floccose scales below the ring. Veil white to yellowish, membranous, leaving a distinct membranous annulus and at times pileus margin decorated with particles.

Spores 9–12 × 4.5–6 μ, elliptic in face view, mostly obscurely inequilateral in profile; smooth, thick-walled (1.5 μ ±), apex distinctly truncate from an obvious apical pore; dull tawny to pale bister in KOH, dull tawny in Melzer's reagent.

Basidia 26–33 × 7–9 μ, 4-spored, clavate, hyaline in KOH and yellowish in Melzer's reagent. Pleurocystidia of two types: 1) chrysocystidia 20–35 × 8–12 μ, clavate to mucronate, thin-walled, hyaline in KOH, with a highly refractive body or globule which in Melzer's reagent merely stains ochraceous; 2) giant leptocystidia 50–75 × 10–20 μ, fusoidventricose with rounded to obtuse apices, wall thin and delicate (readily collapsing and difficult to revive), content homogeneous. Cheilocystidia numerous, 26–58 × (7) 10–15 μ and broadly utriform, some giant cells like the hymenial leptocystidia also present. Caulocystidia none found.

Gill trama of hyaline thin-walled hyphae subparallel-interwoven, the cells tubular at first and 3–6 μ diam., inflating to 5–12 μ diam. at least near pileus trama, yellowish in Melzer's reagent; subhymenium narrow and indistinct to slightly gelatinous as revived in KOH. Pileus cutis with a thick gelatinous pellicle of loosely interwoven hyaline hyphae 3–4 μ diam., imbedded in slime, walls smooth and sharply defined as revived in KOH; hypodermium of pale tan non-gelatinous thin-walled hyphae the cells inflated to 12 μ or more, walls smooth but slightly colored. Context hyphae hyaline, 5–10 μ diam., or becoming more inflated, somewhat gelatinous in subhymenial area. All hyphae inamyloid. Clamp connections present.

HABIT, HABITAT, AND DISTRIBUTION: On soil under fir, near Willamette, Oregon, Nov. 16, 1947, Sipe 1059 type.

OBSERVATIONS: This is a very distinctive species closely related to *P. albivelata* but with larger spores. The basidiocarps are very similar in basic aspect, but there are major microscopic differences as is readily seen by comparing the descriptions. Sipe's notes clearly indicate the spores as cinnamon, and the gills as becoming cinnamon from the spores, otherwise one would immediately place the species in *Stropharia* where the combination of chrysocystidia and leptocystidia in the hymenium is by no means unique. The annulus is slightly more flocculose than that of *P. albivelata* and tends to be yellowish. We cannot state positively that caulocystidia are lacking, though we could find none on the material available for examination. We take pleasure in naming this species for the well known Oregon naturalist Dr. Frank P. Sipe, the collector.

62. Pholiota albivelata Murrill, Mycologia 4: 260. 1912.
Illustrations: Text figs. 78-80; pl. 24.

Pileus (2) 4–8 cm broad, broadly convex when young, expanding to broadly convex, or slightly umbonate, or plane, pale vinaceous brown to dark vinaceous brown ("army-brown" to "fawn-color"), the margin paler, the umbo slightly darker, viscid, smooth or somewhat papillate to rugulose from wrinkling of the pellicle, glabrous. Context thick on the disc, gradually thinner to the margin, white or whitish, soft and pliant; odor fungoid, taste mild.

Lamellae bluntly adnate, with a decurrent tooth, or slightly depressed around the stipe, white, becoming dark avellaneous ("wood-brown"), close or nearly so, moderately broad, edges white-crenate.

Stipe 5–10 cm long, 4–10 mm thick, white and appressed-fibrillose or floccose above the annulus, the lower portion discolored, or more rarely yellowish, conspicuously scurfy below the annulus but the base nearly glabrous, equal, hollow, usually the base with numerous white rhizomorphs. Veil forming a more or less median, broad, membranous, white, persistent annulus, which is striate on the upper surface and white floccose on the lower surface.

Spores "cinnamon-brown" in deposit (dark yellow-brown); 7–9 × 4–5.5 μ, elliptic to ovate in face view, in profile subelliptic to obscurely inequilateral, germ pore very minute (apex not truncate), in KOH dull cinnamon, in Melzer's reagent about the same.

Basidia 25–32 × 6–8 μ, 4-spored, clavate, hyaline in KOH, yellowish in Melzer's reagent. Pleurocystidia abundant, 30–50 (60) × 5–12 μ, clavate to mucronate, wall thin, smooth, and hyaline, content as revived in KOH coagulated into a refractive amorphous mass usually resting in upper third of cystidium, in Melzer's reagent this mass ochraceous to orange-brown to dull red. Cheilocystidia 20–56 × 3–7 μ, filamentose-subcapitate, pedicel flexuous, smooth, thin-walled, content homogeneous. Caulocystidia scattered to rare resembling cheilocystidia.

Gill trama parallel to somewhat interwoven, hyphae with smooth hyaline thin walls (revived in KOH), cells short to elongated and in age inflated; subhymenium cellular and narrow but in KOH subgelatinous. Pileus epicutis a thick (100 μ +) gelatinous layer of hyphae 1.5–3 μ diam. hyaline and smooth in KOH, interwoven; hymenopodium not differentiated structurally or by color or at most the hyphal cells in the region slightly more inflated. Context hyphae hyaline in KOH, floccose, with thin smooth walls, cells inflated in age. Clamp connections present. All hyphae non-amyloid.

HABIT, HABITAT, AND DISTRIBUTION: Solitary to scattered on debris, under conifers, Washington, Oregon and California, during the fall.

OBSERVATIONS: This species is closely related to *P. sipei*; for further comment see that species.

MATERIAL EXAMINED: CALIFORNIA: Smith 3625, 3911, 3914, 3943, 8235, 8372, 9383, 9444, 9476, 56087, 56543, 56913; OREGON: Gruber 14-4; Sipe 135; Smith 20122, 20239, 24540, 24642, 24692, 24738, 24872, 27336; 13651, 13717, 13949, 14436, 14793, 16220, 17369, 17542.

WASHINGTON: Imshaug 1086; Murrill 593 (type); Smith 13512,

Stirps Cubensis

63. Pholiota cubensis Earle, Inf. An. Estac. Centr. Agron. Cuba 1:
242. 1906.
Illustrations: Text figs. 83-84.

Pileus 3–12 cm broad, expanded, scattered or gregarious, dark tan,
"tawny" to "cinnamon-brown" in herbarium specimens, dry, flocoose-
scaly on the disc, margin areolate but not striate. Context yellowish, firm;
taste mild but somewhat unpleasant.

Lamellae sinuate with an adnate tooth, dark cinnamon, crowded,
3–7 mm broad.

Stipe 3–6 cm long, 3–10 mm thick, pale yellow, glabrous below,
floccose above, terete, solid, firm, base slightly enlarged, with a thick
cottony median annulus.

Spores 6–8 × 4–4.5 μ, smooth, apical pore very minute; subelliptic
to ovate in face view, in profile somewhat inequilateral (ventral line
straight to concave slightly, dorsal line humped to convex), color in KOH
bister to snuff brown, in Melzer's reagent paler and more tawny; wall
about 0.2 μ thick.

Basidia 15–18 × 4.5–6 μ, 4-spored, short and obese, yellowish in
KOH and Melzer's reagent. Pleurocystidia buried in hymenium, 26–35
× 8–12 μ, clavate, clavate-mucronate to ellipsoid, more rarely somewhat
fusoid-ventricose, with thin hyaline walls some with slight encrusting
material on midportion, many with some refractive internal coagulated
material rarely consolidated into a distinct body, these connected to
hyphae with similar content. Cheilocystidia (the only ones seen were
similar to the pleurocystidia, but gill edges were not favorable for study).
Caulocystidia 54–66 × 6–10 μ, more or less filamentous to narrowly subclavate, some narrowed to apex, thin-walled, hyaline.

Gill trama of very broad interwoven hyphae yellowish hyaline in
KOH, walls thin more or less; subhymenium a thin layer of narrow interwoven non-gelatinous hyphae. Pileus cutis a tangled layer but somewhat
oriented into fascicles of thin-walled hyphae with cells 8–20 μ diam.,
content yellowish in KOH, walls smooth, end cells somewhat cystidioid.
Context beneath of greatly enlarged thin-walled hyphae. Clamp connections present. All hyphae inamyloid.

HABIT, HABITAT, AND DISTRIBUTION: On soil, under a building and in
open fields. Cuba and Grenada. Type studied.

OBSERVATIONS: The general aspect of the basidiocarps reminds one
somewhat of *Agrocybe* but the minute scales on the disc are distinctive.
The annulus is apparently somewhat like that of *P. duroides*. Most of
the basidiocarps in the type collection at one time became infected with

an "imperfect." The hyphae of the latter may show rather prominent swellings, and are most numerous along the gills where the end-cells of some might be mistaken for cystidia. When a piece of the pileus was compressed between two sticks of pith for sectioning the pith stained orange from the expressed liquid, but in KOH no pigment pervaded the mount.

64. Pholiota duroides Peck, New York State Mus. Bull. 122: 148. 1908.
Flammula duroides (Peck) Singer, Mycologia 35: 162. 1943.
Illustrations: Text figs. 81-82.

Pileus 2.5–5 (9) cm broad, convex becoming nearly plane, creamy-white to ochraceous-buff, chamois, or cinnamon-buff or nearly ochraceous-orange, glabrous or slightly appressed-squamose or with spot-like scales or depressions in the center, dry, not hygrophanous, margin even. Context white; taste mild.

Lamellae adnexed or sinuate-adnate, sometimes with a decurrent tooth, whitish, becoming brown or rusty-brown, close, narrow (2–5 mm broad), edges white-crenulate.

Stipe 2.5–5 (10) cm long, 4–8 (15) mm thick, whitish, glabrous, equal or nearly so, stuffed or hollow, veil forming a superior white membranous, pendant or rolled, subpersistent annulus.

Spore deposit "bister" (dark yellow-brown) ; spores 4.5–6 × 3–4 × 4–4.5 μ, smooth, with a minute but distinct apical pore (but apex not truncate) ; shape in face view ovate to (rarely) elliptic, at times subtriangular (corners rounded), in profile more or less inequilateral to somewhat bean-shaped; in KOH dingy yellow-brown, somewhat more ochraceous in Melzer's reagent; wall thickened to about 0.3 μ.

Basidia 24–28 × 5–6 μ, 2- and 4-spored, clavate, hyaline in KOH, yellowish in Melzer's. Pleurocystidia 23–34 × 6–12 μ, clavate to (rarely) clavate-mucronate or with the mucro subcapitate, thin-walled, smooth, hyaline in KOH, with 1–2 refractive bodies merely yellowish in Melzer's reagent. Cheilocystidia similar to pleurocystidia, rare to scattered. Caulocystidia present only in the caulohymenium at stipe apex.

Gill trama of subparallel to interwoven floccose, hyaline to yellowish smooth thin-walled hyphae, the cells 3–8 μ diam., but inflating to twice that finally; subhymenium narrower, not sharply delimited from tramal body though in age somewhat cellular, non-gelatinous. Pileus cutis of hyphae smooth to slighty incrusted, hyphae thin-walled, in a loose arrangement and 4–9 μ diam., not gelatinous; hypodermium of rusty ochraceous hyphae with walls distinctly incrusted. Context hyphae interwoven, cells inflating, walls smooth to roughened, narrow, yellowish to hyaline in KOH, all hyphae inamyloid. Clamp connections present.

HABIT, HABITAT, AND DISTRIBUTION: On soil, especially in open woods, Massachusetts, Connecticut, New York, Pennsylvania, Virginia, Tennessee, and Missouri, summer. (Reported by Overholts). Material examined by us, the type by Hesler and 9081.

OBSERVATIONS: The description of microscopic characters above is based entirely on our study of the type. The gills are at first whitish, then become grayish, and finally rusty brown. Thus, some collections at least may suggest *Stropharia* or an annulate *Psilocybe*. As Overholts (1927) observed, Peck's attempt to relate it to *Pholiota dura* is confusing; the latter is an *Agrocybe*. *Pholiota albivelata* appears quite similar to this species in its *Stropharia*-like aspect but is readily distinct by the pileus having an epicutis of gelatinous hyphae. Actually *P. johnsoniana* is the most closely related species but differs in lacking incrusted hyphae in the hypodermial region of the pileus, a more gelatinous pileus cutis and slightly larger spores.

65. Pholiota johnsoniana (Pk.) Atkinson, Studies Amer. Fungi, p. 153. 1900.

Agaricus johnsonianus Peck, New York State Cab. Ann. Rept. 23: 98. 1872.

Stropharia johnsoniana (Pk.) Peck, New York State Mus. Ann. Rept. 41: 84. 1888.

Illustrations: Text figs. 484-485.

Pileus 3–10 cm broad, broadly convex or nearly plane, yellowish or ochraceous, or yellow in the center and white on the margin, glabrous or at times with small appressed squamules at the center, dry, sometimes purple stained, margin striatulate when moist. Context white, thick at the center, thin on the margin; taste agreeable, nutty.

Lamellae adnate or sinuate-adnate or nearly free, white then rusty-brown, close, narrow (2–5 mm broad).

Stipe 7–10 cm long, 8–15 mm thick, light colored, glabrous, apex slightly striate, equal. Veil forming a thick white, persistent cottony roll on the stipe, easily breaking and then disappearing.

Spores cocoa-color in deposit (type collection), 5.5–7.5 × 3.5–4 × 4–5 μ, smooth, many compressed slightly, apical pore minute and apex not truncate; shape in face view ovate to elliptic, many almost triangular-ovate; in profile varying from bean-shaped to somewhat inequilateral; color in KOH near ochraceous tawny to merely ochraceous, about the same color in Melzer's reagent; wall about 0.25 μ thick.

Basidia 4-spored, 20–25 × 5.5–7 μ, clavate, hyaline in KOH in Melzer's reagent ochraceous. Pleurocystidia abundant, 18–23 × 7–12 μ, clavate to clavate-mucronate, with a hyaline refractive inclusion usually near the apex (they are typical chrysocystidia) smooth, thin-walled, the refractive inclusion merely yellowish in Melzer's reagent. Cheilocystidia similar to pleurocystidia. Caulocystidia none except for those in caulohymenium at stipe apex and these similar to the pleurocystidia.

Gill trama of subparallel thin-walled smooth hyphae with cells 6–15 μ broad or more (when fully inflated), hyaline to yellowish in KOH and pale reddish brown in Melzer's reagent but soon fading to yellowish; subhymenium not sharply distinguished from the body of the gill trama (the hyphae merely narrower). Pileus cutis a pellicle of hyaline smooth thin-walled narrow (2–4 μ) subgelatinous hyphae; hypodermial region not showing distinct differentiation. Context hyphae hyaline to yellowish revived in KOH, thin-walled, interwoven the cells inflating to 15 μ, or more finally. All hyphae inamyloid. Clamp connections none.

HABIT, HABITAT, AND DISTRIBUTION: On soil, in pastures, and in leafmold in woods, New York, North Carolina and Michigan, September. (As reported in the literature). Type studied.

OBSERVATIONS: Singer (1963) preferred to place this species in *Stropharia* and indeed there is ample justification for this. The cocoa-colored spores can be used as a justification for placing this species in either *Pholiota* or *Stropharia,* however. This is an indication of the intermediate position of the species. We decided to place it in *Pholiota* because of the very minute apical germ pore of the spores. Also, its natural place in the classification of Agaricales appears to be here among the stropharioid *Pholiotae.*

Section **Phaeonaematoloma** (Singer) Singer, Lilloa 22: 517. 1951.

Flammula (Phaeonematoloma) Rev. Mycol. Paris. 2: 241. 1937.

Chrysocystidia or cells somewhat resembling them as to shape and content present in the hymenium; never with both the pileus and stipe distinctly scaly; spores not obviously truncate if the spore is less than 9 μ long; annulus not conspicuous.

Type species. *Pholiota myosotis.*

Key to Stirpes

1. Stipe viscid when young and fresh .... Stirps *Silvatica*
1. Stipe not viscid when young 2
 2. Pileus not viscid when young and fresh .... Stirps *Elongata*
 2. Pileus viscid when young and fresh 3
3. Spores typically 10 μ or more long and apex typically truncate ....
 .... Stirps *Myosotis*
3. Spores typically under 10 μ long and pileus viscid (or in a few species merely subviscid) .... Stirps *Subochracea*
 (See *P. caespitosa* and *P. tennessensis* also)

Stirps Silvatica

Key

1. Stipe with a fibrillose inner veil and a gelatinous outer veil; base

furnished with a pseudorhiza .... *P. silvatica*
1. Stipe not radicating and a double veil not evident .... *P. aberrans*

66. Pholiota silvatica (Smith) comb. nov.
Stropharia silvatica Smith, Contr. Univ. Mich. Herb. No. 5, p. 65, 1941.
Illustrations: Ibid, pl. 22.

Pileus 2–4 cm broad, obtuse, margin incurved slightly at first, becoming plane or with an obtuse umbo, the margin at first decorated with veil fragments, glabrous otherwise, viscid to glutinous, evenly "amber brown" to "argus brown" in buttons, soon fading to "amber yellow" along the margin and in age only the disc or umbo amber brown, the remainder "chamois" (pale yellow), not translucent striate at any time. Context concolorous with the surface, watery, moderately thin and pliant, odor and taste mild.

Lamellae adnate with a tooth and readily seceding, ventricose and broad (5–6 mm), close, 27–30 reach the stipe, 2–3 tiers of lamellulae, white when young, becoming "deep olive buff" and finally "Saccardo's umber" (dark yellow-brown) in age, edges even.

Stipe 8–16 cm long, 3–5 mm thick, equal above a long (4–6 cm) pseudorhiza, solid or with a narrow tubule, viscid over the lower two-thirds and sordid honey-yellow, upper part whitish but becoming pale yellow, a thin white inner fibrillose veil present beneath the glutinous veil; annular zone apical, evanescent; below the annular zone often more or less concentrically zoned from the drying gluten.

Spore deposit on stipe apex dull tawny; spores 10–13 × 5.5–7.5 μ, oval to elliptic in face view, in profile subelliptic to obscurely inequilateral, smooth, slightly truncate from a distinct apical germ pore, rusty cinnamon as revived in KOH, greenish-yellow in H_2O mounts fresh, pale tawny in Melzer's reagent, wall 0.25–0.4 μ thick (estimated).

Basidia 30–35 × 8–10 μ, subclavate to cylindric, 4-spored, yellowish-hyaline in KOH and in Melzer's reagent. Pleurocystidia abundant, 34–42 × 10–12 μ, clavate to broadly fusoid-ventricose to clavate-mucronate, apex subacute to obtuse, often with a highly refractive content in KOH (content typically yellowish and in lower half of cell—not an isolated clearly defined mass as in true chrysocystidia), some filamentose pseudocystidia 30–40 × 7–11 μ also present and with ochraceous content as revived in KOH. Cheilocystidia abundant, 28–36 × 10–14 μ, clavate to somewhat fusoid-ventricose, apex usually rounded, some with refractive content as revived in KOH. Caulocystidia abundant, often in clusters, 30–60 × 9–18 μ, utriform to clavate, hyaline in KOH, walls thin, content homogeneous; stipe hyphae hyaline in KOH and thin-walled, smooth.

Gill trama parallel to somewhat interwoven, non-gelatinous hyphae with tawny to ochraceous walls in KOH, walls thin and smooth; subhymenium a narrow region becoming gelatinous in KOH or remaining indistinct. Pileus cutis a gelatinous layer, the hyphae tangled loosely as in a collapsed trichodermium, 4–5 μ diam., mostly tubular, walls yellowish in KOH and incrusted; hypodermial layer of floccose hyphae rich tawny in KOH and cells 6–12 μ or more wide. Context hyphae interwoven, thin-walled, smooth, yellowish in KOH, inamyloid. Clamp connections present.

HABIT, HABITAT, AND DISTRIBUTION: Solitary under cedar and hemlock (*Thuja plicata* and *Tsuga heterophylla*, near Kalalock, Olympic Peninsula, Washington, May 1939, Smith 13509, type studied.

OBSERVATIONS: This species is closely related to *P. aberrans* in pigmentation and stature but differs in having a pseudorhiza, in having ventricose gills, and in the presence of a distinct veil of two layers.

67. Pholiota aberrans nom. nov. (not P. anomala Peck 1895).
Hypholoma anomalum Smith, Mycologia 33: 2. 1941.
Pholiota anomala (Smith) Singer, Sydowia 15: 70. 1961. (not *P. anomala* Peck 1895)
Naematoloma anomalum (Smith) Smith, Mycologia 43: 477. 1951.
Illustrations: Text figs. 168-171.

Pileus 2 cm broad, plane with an abrupt conic umbo and slightly decurved margin, surface glutinous, subrimose along margin beneath the gluten, appearing finely appressed-fibrillose under a lens, disc "rawsienna" the remainder "ochre-yellow" (bright brownish yellow to ochre-yellow), when dried tawny on disc and margin "amber brown." Context pale yellow, firm, odor and taste not distinctive.

Lamellae narrow, depressed-adnate, subdistant, equal, olivaceous yellow ("Isabella color"), edges even.

Stipe 4.5 cm long, 2.5 mm thick, equal, glutinous over lower two-thirds and orange-yellow, pale yellow and fibrillose scurfy above, soon dry and appearing agglutinated-fibrillose under a lens.

Spores 11–14 × 5.5–7 μ, rusty brown in deposit and pale cinnamon brown under microscope in KOH, with a distinct discontinuity and apex somewhat truncate or with a lens-shaped bulge, smooth as revived in KOH, in profile obscurely inequilateral, in face view ovate to nearly elliptic, in Melzer's reagent the wall pale to medium tawny.

Basidia 4-spored. Pleurocystidia 35–50 × 6–12 μ, imbedded or projecting, yellow in H₂O mounts of fresh material, rusty brown in KOH, usually with an amorphous highly refractive content revived in KOH. Cheilocystidia similar to pleurocystidia or mixed with these are saccate to fusoid-ventricose leptocystidia. Gill trama with numerous refractive oleiferous hyphae. Pileus with a cutis of hyphae 4–5 μ diam. with the free portions gelatinous (a collapsed trichodermium); hypodermium a layer differentiated by highly pigmented hyphal cells with pigment encrusted on the walls. Context hyphae yellowish in KOH. Clamp connections present.

HABIT, HABITAT, AND DISTRIBUTION: Solitary under rhododendrons,

Great Smoky Mountains National Park, September, known only from the type (Smith 10782).

OBSERVATIONS: The fungus when fresh reminds one of an *Inocybe* but the apical pore and viscid stipe are not features of that genus.

Stirps Myosotis

Stipe long and slender, growing in bogs or on peaty soil; pileus with a gelatinous pellicle.

Key to Species of Stirpes Elongata and Myosotis

1. Pileus with a gelatinous pellicle 2
1. Pileus lacking a gelatinous pellicle 3
   2. Pileus olivaceous; pellicle thick and tough .... *P. myosotis*
   2. Pileus orange-tawny to dull cinnamon; pellicle thin and easily obliterated .... *P. humidicola*
3. Stipe with a pseudorhiza; spores 6–8 × 4–5 μ .... *P. olympiana*
3. Stipe lacking a pseudorhiza; spores 8–11 × 5–6 μ .... *P. elongataipes*

68. Pholiota myosotis (Fr.) Singer.
Agaricus myosotis Fries, Syst. Myc. 1: 290. 1821.
Naucoria myosotis (Fr.) Kummer, Der Führer in die Pilzkunde p. 77. 1871.
Hyalophila myosotis (Fr.) Quélet, Enchir. Fung. p. 102. 1886.
Naematoloma myosotis (Fr.) Smith, Mycologia 42: 323. 1950.
Agaricus elatior Peck, Ann. Rep. N.Y. State Mus. 39: 41. 1887.
Naucoria elatior (Pk.) Saccardo, Syll. Fung. 9: 109. 1891.
Illustrations: Text figs. 157-159; pl. 28.

Pileus (10) 15–30 (40) mm broad, broadly conic to convex, glabrous except occasionally with scattered veil remnants along the margin, edge often appendiculate, viscid to glutinous, evenly olive to olive-green or olive-bronze ("medal bronze" to "citrine"), evenly colored, opaque when young but before fading becoming brownish and striatulate, near olive-buff when faded. Context olivaceous, pliant, odor and taste not distinctive.

Lamellae broad, adnate to shallowly adnexed, subdistant, becoming ventricose, whitish at first, then pale olivaceous and finally brown from the spores, edges minutely white-fimbriate and eroded.

Stipe (6) 10–15 (20) cm long, 2–5 (7) mm thick, very rigid, equal, hollow, covered to the line formed by the broken veil by white to olivaceous veil fibrils in patches or zones, densely pruinose above.

Spore deposit dull rusty brown; spores 14–17 × 7–9 μ, inequilateral in profile, ovate in face view, ochraceous tawny in KOH, smooth or a few faintly wrinkled as revived in KOH, apex not conspicuously truncate, wall thickened to 0.75–1 μ and pale tawny in Melzer's sol.

Basidia 4-spored, 26–34 × 9–11 μ, projecting when sporulating, hyaline to yellowish in KOH. Pleurocystidia present 35–50 × 10–15 μ, fusoid-ventricose to clavate-mucronate, beaked or with several protuberances over apical region, rarely ventricose with a broadly rounded apex, as revived in KOH with an amorphous highly refractive interior body or amorphous content variously disposed. Cheilocystidia abundant, 32–50 × 6–12 μ, a mixture of leptocystidia and chryosocystidia, fusoid-ventricose to clavate-mucronate. Caulocystidia merely hyphal ends 4–9 μ wide or these narrowly clavate, variable in length.

Gill trama hyphae subparallel, pale yellow revived in KOH, cells 5–15 μ broad, walls thin so slightly thickened and smooth; subhymenium cellular and hyphal walls not gelatinous. Pileus with a tough gelatinous pellicle of narrow 3–5 μ wide hyphae with walls smooth to slightly incrusted; hypodermium yellow in KOH, hyphal cells inflated (at times up to 20 μ or more), the walls thin and smooth to slightly roughened as revived in KOH. Clamp connections present.

HABIT, HABITAT, AND DISTRIBUTION: Gregarious in or along the edges of bogs or on boggy soil, typically northern, and often abundant during dry seasons. Material from New York, Michigan and Washington as well as Ontario in Canada has been examined.

OBSERVATIONS: This is a most distinctive species by virtue of the olive to olive-bronze viscid pileus, the dull cinnamon-brown spore deposit, large spores and whitish gills. The ornamentation of the spores is not a constant feature in this species and when present is best disregarded as a generic feature.

MATERIAL EXAMINED: MICHIGAN: Smith 33-788, 15483, 21157, 31890, 41657, 43906, 43907. NEW YORK: Smith 207, 334, 371, 553, 604; Peck's type of *Agaricus elatior*. WASHINGTON: Smith 2596, 16598, 40361, 40837, 40846. CANADA (ONTARIO) : Smith 4015.

69. Pholiota humidicola (Murr.) comb. nov.

Naucoria humidicola Murrill, North Amer. Fl. 10: 174. 1917.
Naematoloma humidicola (Murr.) Smith, Mycologia 40: 693. 1948.
Illustrations: Text figs. 160-161.

Pileus 10–20 mm broad, obtuse to convex and when young the margin incurved, expanding to broadly convex or plane, at times the margin remaining decurved, surface glabrous, moist, dull cinnamon to orange-tawny on disc ("Sayal-brown" to brighter), margin ochraceous and gradually becoming paler, in age more or less olivaceous ("Isabella-color" to more olive). Context thin, pliant, yellowish, odor none.

Lamellae broadly adnate and in age with a decurrent tooth, subdistant, very broad, pallid to dingy pale yellow, drying dingy tawny to clay color, edges white-fimbriate but even.

Stipe 4–6 cm long, 1.5–2.5 mm thick, equal, cartilaginous, pallid to sordid yellow above, soon dull rusty brown below, thinly appressed-fibrillose to glabrous, apex pruinose, base surrounded by white mycelium. Spores 9–11 × 5.5–6.3 μ, ovate to elliptic in face view, elliptic to slightly inequilateral in profile, smooth, pale tawny in KOH and very slightly redder in Melzer's, apical pore small and apex only obscurely truncate, wall about 0.5 μ thick.

Basidia 23–27 × 5–6.5 μ, 4-spored, clavate to subcylindric, hyaline to yellow in KOH. Pleurocystidia 44–58 (64) × 8–12 μ, scattered, fusoid-ventricose to narrowly clavate-mucronate, projecting beyond the basidia, usually with the refractive content of chrysocystidia. Cheilocystidia 24–32 × 5–8 μ, ventricose to subcylindric, hyaline, content homogeneous, thin-walled, abundant.

Gill trama subparallel, the cells equal in width throughout their length, pale yellow in KOH; subhymenium cellular but very thin and indistinct. Pileus epicutis a thin pellicle of narrow gelatinous hyphae 2.5–4 μ diam.; hypodermium of enlarged cells, yellow in KOH like hyphae of the context. Clamp connections present.

HABIT, HABITAT, AND DISTRIBUTION: Solitary to scattered on moss in conifer forests, New York, Idaho, Washington and Oregon: Smith 24133, 23160, and 24477 from Oregon, Smith 71086 from Idaho, and Imshaug 987 and 994 from Washington in addition to the type of *Naucoria humidicola* have been examined.

OBSERVATIONS: This species differs from *P. elongata* in having a gelatinous pellicle over the pileus and in the longer pleurocystidia, in fact the latter are unusually long for chrysocystidia.

Stirps Elongata

Pileus moist but not viscid, aspect of bog-inhabiting *Psilocybe* species (stipe long and slender).

70. Pholiota elongatipes (Pk.) comb. nov.

Agaricus udus var. *elongatus* Pers. ex Fries, Syst. Myc. 1: 292. 1821.
Hypholoma elongatum (Fr.) Ricken, Die Blätterpilze p. 250. 1912.
Naematoloma udum var. *elongatum* (Fr.) Karsten, Bdr. Finl. Nat. och
Folk 32: 497. 1879.
Naematoloma elongatum (Fr.) Konrad, Bull. Soc. Linnéenne Lyon, 8
annee, n. 18, p. 135. 1929.
Agaricus elongatipes Peck, Ann. Rep. N.Y. State Mus. 29: 40. 1878.
Hypholoma elongatipes (Pk.) Smith, Mycologia 33: 5. 1941. (Not *H.
elongatipes* Parker, Mycologia 25: 196. 1933)
Naucoria obtusissima Kauffman & Smith, Pap. Mich. Acad. Sci. Arts and
Letters 17: 188. 1933.
Illustrations: Text figs. 162-163; pl. 29a.

Pileus 6–20 mm broad, convex to obtuse, becoming broadly convex to nearly plane in age, surface glabrous and hygrophanous, margin faintly fringed with fibrils at the time the veil breaks, color pale to medium yellow with marginal area olivaceous in age when wet, paler yellow faded or often retaining an olive cast. Context thin, soft, pale yellow, odor and taste not distinctive.

Lamellae broad, adnate, subdistant, whitish to pallid yellowish at first, gradually becoming clay color to nearly wood-brown, edges at times whitish fimbriate.

Stipe 4–10 cm long, 1.5–2.5 mm thick, equal, tubular, strict to flexuous, fragile, pallid above at first but soon yellowish, silky above, with fibrillose flecs downward from the remains of the thin veil, becoming tawny from the base upward in aging.

Spores 8–11 (12) × 5–6 (7) μ, dull cinnamon brown in deposit, pale tawny in KOH under microscope and scarcely darker in Melzer's sol., smooth, apex obscurely truncate from an apical pore less than 1 μ wide, wall less than 0.5 μ thick, shape in face view ovate to subelliptic, in profile mostly elliptic.

Basidia 28–32 × 8–9 μ, 4-spored, clavate, yellow in KOH. Pleurocystidia of two types: 1) chrysocystidia 26–34 × 8–12 μ, and 2) leptocystidia 30–36 × 5–9 μ, fusoid-ventricose, apex obtuse. Caulocystidia none found on specimens examined.

Gill trama of parallel to subparallel non-gelatinous hyphae with yellow to rusty walls in KOH. Pileus with a poorly organized cutis of non-gelatinous hyphae 2.5–4 μ wide, hyphae yellow in KOH, smooth or obscurely asperulate; hypodermium of inflated hyphal cells up to 18 μ diam., walls yellow to pale fulvous in KOH and not or only very obscurely roughened. Context hyphae thin-walled, smooth, yellow in KOH. Clamp connections regularly present.

HABIT, HABITAT, AND DISTRIBUTION: Scattered to gregarious on *Sphagnum* during late summer and fall, across the continent wherever the proper habitat is found. We have examined specimens from Sweden as well as North America.

OBSERVATIONS: Smith (1951) placed this in *Naematoloma* but when one compares the population of North American *Pholiota* species with those of *Naematoloma* for the same region it is very clear that the only difference between the two genera is in the color of the spore deposit. Hence we have transferred this species to the group where people expect to find it.

MATERIAL EXAMINED: MICHIGAN: type of *Naucoria obtusissima;* Homola 1054; Kauffman 10-20-06, Rock River, 1929; Smith 33-778, 33-821, 33-989, 6123, 14942, 31898, 31899, 32020, 42207, NEW YORK: House, 1915; Smith 335, 372, 922. OREGON: Kauffman, 1922; Smith 27655, Oct. 1952. TENNESSEE: Hesler 14250, 17198. WASHINGTON: Smith 9-25-35, 12062, 14800, 39807, 40263, 40876, 40884, 48039. WEST VIRGINIA:

Walters 131. CANADA (ONTARIO): Smith 4612, 4779. SWEDEN: Lundell 23-9-1939. SCOTLAND: D. Reid 1955.

71. **Pholiota olympiana** (Smith) comb. nov.
Hypholoma olympianum Smith, Mycologia 36: 248. 1944.
Naematoloma olympianum (Smith) Smith, Mycologia 38: 502. 1946.
Illustrations: Text figs. 94-95.

Pileus 2.5–4 (6) cm broad, obtuse to convex and with an incurved margin at first, expanding to plane or retaining a slight obtuse umbo, surface at first canescent from a thin coating of whitish silky fibrils but soon glabrescent or fibrils more or less persistent toward the margin, moist, color pale tan to clay-color ("cinnamon-buff" to "clay-color") on disc and paler and yellower on margin (dingy honey-color). Context hard and thick in disc when fresh, abruptly thinner toward the margin, pallid but soon lutescent where cut or broken, odor not distinctive, taste quickly and decidedly bitter.

Lamellae close, about 33 reach the stipe, 3–4 tiers of lamellulae, narrow (3–4.5 mm), bluntly adnate but seceding, "cream-buff" (very pale yellow) young, dull yellow-brown in age ("buckthorn-brown") and often with dark rusty spots, edges even and pale yellowish.

Stipe 5–7 cm long, 3–6 mm thick, subfusoid to equal above a long tapered pseudorhiza, tubular to hollow, surface densely white-fibrillose from veil remnants, apex yellowish and pruinose, becoming yellowish where handled and finally dark sordid brown, in age more or less glabrescent.

Spore deposit cinnamon-brown; spores 6–7.5 (9) × 4–4.5 (5.5) μ, smooth, apex rounded and lacking a pore; shape in face view elliptic to ovate, in profile about the same; color dull yellow brown revived in KOH, in Melzer's reagent pale tawny; wall thin (about 0.25 μ).

Basidia 4-spored, 18–22 × 5–6 μ, projecting somewhat when sporulating. Pleurocystidia 22–36 × 9–15 μ, abundant, fusoid-ventricose to clavate-mucronate, with an irregular amorphous mass in the midportion as revived in KOH (hence they are chrysocystidia). Cheilocystidia 18–28 × 4–8 μ, narrowly clavate to subventricose, the apex rounded to obtuse, often yellow revived in KOH. Caulocystidia 18–28 × 4–10 μ, narrowly clavate to fusoid-ventricose, content homogeneous. Gill trama of non-gelatinous subparallel hyphae with yellowish to pale tawny walls in KOH; subhymenium of hyaline narrow hyphae not gelatinous. Pileus with an epicutis of narrow (1.5–2.5 μ), hyaline, non-gelatinous (to slightly gelatinous as revived in KOH) hyphae, smooth or practically so; hypodermium of brown-walled hyphae 5–12 × diam., and more highly colored than the hyphae of the context. Clamp connections present. All hyphae inamyloid.

HABIT, HABITAT, AND DISTRIBUTION: Gregarious to scattered around

Douglas fir stumps, Olympic National Park, Washington, Smith 18003, type.

OBSERVATIONS: This species is most closely related to *Naematoloma radicosum* from which it differs in the color of the spore deposit, and since the latter is yellow-brown the species is logically classified here. It is possible that some descriptions of the old *Flammula amara* apply to this species. Although the gills when mature in *N. radicosum* are dull rusty brown, the color of the spores in deposit is in the purple-brown spectrum.

Stirps Subochracea

Key

1. Pileus and stipe blue becoming olivaceous and fading to dingy buff
   .... *P. subcaerulea*
1. Not as above 2
   2. Pileus olivaceous on margin, gills yellow before spores mature; stipe coarsely fibrillose-squamulose near base .... *P. burkei*
   2. Not as above 3
3. Spores 5–6 × 2.5–3 μ .... *P. subochracea*
3. Spores 6–8 (9) × 3–5 μ 4
   4. Stipe with a distinct pseudorhiza; taste bitter ....
      .... *P. olympiana*
   4. Not as above 5
5. Stipe slender (up to 3.5 mm thick) 6
5. Stipe thicker (3–15 mm thick) 9
   6. Pileus dull reddish brown on disc, grayish brown over marginal area .... *P. subgelatinosa*
   6. Pileus ferruginous to ochraceous 7
7. Lamellae broad; subhymenium not gelatinous .... *P. parvula*
7. Lamellae narrow; subhymenium gelatinous 8
   8. Pileus with a prominent umbo; stipe lacking tawny mycelium around the base of the stipe .... see *P. prolixa*
   8. Pileus merely broadly convex; tawny mycelium present at stipe base .... *P. pusilla*
9. Pileus disc distinctly rosy brownish 10
9. Pileus not colored as above 11
   10. Lamellae narrow; stipe squamulose .... see *P. angustifolia*
   10. Lamellae broad; stipe merely fibrillose .... *P. ornatula*
11. Odor of honey; pileus honey-yellow .... *P. melliodora*
11. Not as above 12
   12. Pileus white to pallid when young, typically yellowing as it matures or in one variant becoming avellaneous 13
   12. Pileus more highly colored when young 14
13. Vesiculose-pedicellate pleurocystidia with bright ochraceous content

present .... *P. flavescens*
13. Chrysocystidia in hymenium fusoid-ventricose to clavate; no vesiculose-pedicellate cells present .... *P. lutescens*
14. Lamellae narrow; pleurocystidia as typical chrysocystidia .... *P. prolixa*
14. Lamellae broad 15
15. Pleurocystidia present as typical leptocystidia as to shape, but usually with an amorphous to granular content .... *P. californica*
15. Pleurocystidia inconspicuous but typical of chrysocystidia; cheilocystidia resembling those of *P. erinaceella* .... *P. contorta*

72. Pholiota subcaerulea sp. nov.
Illustrations: Text figs. 67-69; pl. 25b.

Pileus 2–4 cm latus, obtusus, demum explanato-umbonatus, glutinus, albo-squamulosus, caeruleus vel aerugineo-caeruleus, demum subargillaceo-maculatus. Lamellae pallide brunneae demum subcinnamomeae, confertae, latae, adnato-decurrentes. Stipe 3–6 cm longus, 1.5–4(8) mm crassus ad basin cum rhizomorphis albis, subcaeruleus, deorsum albofloccosus, sursum sericeus. Annulus membranaceus. Sporae 7–9 × 4–4.5 μ, leves. Pleuro-chrysocystidia 24–36 × 9–12 μ. Specimen typicum in Herb. Univ. Mich. conservatum est. legit. prope Portland, Oregon, 11 Nov. 1954, Ruth Oswald No. 2.

Pileus 2–4 cm broad, obtuse, with incurved margin, expanding to obtusely umbonate and the margin finally spreading, surface glutinous and dotted with white flecks of the remnants of a white veil, blue to greenish blue but gradually fading out to cinnamon-buff in blotches, often retaining the greenish blue color when dried; flesh thin, bluish, odor and taste none.

Lamellae pallid brownish becoming more or less sordid cinnamon brown at maturity (not truly purplish brown), close, moderately broad, adnexed to broadly adnate-decurrent, edges even.

Stipe 3–6 cm long, 1.5–4 (8) mm thick, equal or slightly enlarged at the base, base with numerous white rhizomorphs, lower portion with white floccose patches of veil tissue scattered over it, annulus white, single, median, often evanescent, silky to fibrillose above, concolorous with pileus over all or a little paler, dry.

Spores 7–9 × 4–4.5 μ, smooth, ovate to subelliptic in face view, elliptic to obscurely inequilateral in profile, apex with a minute germ pore but apex not truncate, wall relatively thin; spores on annulus pale cinnamon-brown, in KOH dingy tawny brown, and in Melzer's brighter colored but not dextrinoid.

Basidia 22–26 × 6–7 μ, 4-spored, hyaline in KOH, yellowish in Melzer's reagent. Pleurocystidia abundant, 24–36 × 9–12 μ, clavate, fusoid-ventricose to clavate-mucronate, thin-walled, hyaline in KOH and with a highly refractive hyaline amorphous body, in Melzer's reagent the refractive body bright red to bay red and very conspicuous. Cheilocystidia: 1) 30–52 × 2.5–4 × 5–8 μ, narrowly subcapitate-pedicellate to narrowly clavate, hyaline, thin-walled, content homogeneous; 2) some smaller fusoid-ventricose cells 20–28 × 4–7 μ also present; 3) some cells resembling pleurocystidia also present at times. Caulocystidia numerous, clavate to nearly filamentose, 4–6 μ diam. at apex, hyaline in KOH.

Gill trama of hyaline, parallel to somewhat interwoven, cells greatly inflated in age; subhymenium inconspicuous and somewhat gelatinous (including bases of basidia ?). Pileus cutis a thick gelatinous pellicle of interwoven hyphae, the hyphae 3–4.5 μ diam., hyaline, walls smooth and very delicate, inamyloid; hypodermial region colorless, hyphae nongelatinous and slightly more inflated than those of context. Clamp connections present, hyphal walls all inamyloid.

In small clusters in long grass under Douglas fir and dogwood, Portland, Ore. Nov. 11, 1954. Ruth Oswald No. 2.

Stropharia aeruginosa as we know that species has lamellae white to grayish and finally purplish brown. *P. subcaerulea,* which is closely related to it, is by generic definition relegated to *Pholiota* unless one wishes to go as far as to merge *Geophila* with *Pholiota.* The bright bay color of the inclusion in the pleurocystidia when mounted in Melzer's is a most striking feature and reminds one of the Melzer's reaction in the cystidia of many species of *Tylopilus. Pholiota ochrochlora* of Europe is related here, see Orton (1960). We have not found *P. ochrochlora* in North America.

MATERIAL EXAMINED: IDAHO: Smith 74017. OREGON: Ruth Oswald 2. WASHINGTON: Flett 170a, 11-15-41.

73. Pholiota burkei sp. nov.
Illustrations: Text figs. 65-66.

Pileus 3–5 cm latus, convexus demum late convexus, saepe obtuse umbonatus, hygrophanus, melleus, ad marginem olivaceus, glaber, striatulatus. Lamellae sinuatae, luteolae, angustae, confertae. Stipes 3–5 cm longus, 4–9 mm crassus, sursum pallide luteus; deorsum fibrillosus vel squamulosus et demum subfulvus. Sporae 5.5–7(7–9) × 3.5–4(4.5–5) μ, ovatae. Pleurocystidia 25–40 × 6–9(12) μ, ellipsoideo-mucronata vel ventricoso-rostrata. Caulocystidia 24–42 × 3–6 μ, cylindricato-capitata. Specimen typicum in Herb. Univ. Mich. conservatum est; legit prope Montgomery, Ala., R. P. Burke (AS) 29 Sept. 1942.

Pileus 3–5 cm broad, convex, expanding plane, at times with a low umbo, hygrophanous, when moist the central portion "honey-yellow," outer portion near "ecru-olive," when faded "deep colonial-buff," paler on the marginal portion, at times striatulate, glabrous, viscid. Context cream-color, unchanging; odor and taste mild.

Lamellae sinuate with a decurrent tooth, near "colonial buff" when young, becoming "honey-yellow" then "buckthorn-brown," five tiers of lamellulae present, narrow to moderately broad, close.

Stipe 3–5 cm long, 4–9 mm thick, apex "massicot-yellow" or paler, glabrous over the upper two-thirds, coarsely fibrillose-squamulose below, squamules reflexed, finally "buckthorn-brown," equal to enlarged above, at times compressed. Veil pallid, at first submembranous, finally subarachnoid, leaving a fringe on the pileus margin and an evanescent zone on the pileus.

Spores 5.5–7 (7–9) × 3.5–4 (4.5–5) μ, ovate to elliptic in face view, more or less inequilateral in profile, smooth, apical pore evident on all, on larger spores apex truncate (N.A. 1.4 lens), dull tawny in KOH, paler (ochraceous) in Melzer's sol. wall moderately thick ($\pm$ 0.3 μ).

Basidia 17–21 (20–25) × 4.5–6 (6–7.5) μ, 4-spored rarely 2-spored (only small ones were observed to be 2-spored), hyaline in KOH, yellowish in Melzer's reagent. Pleurocystidia scattered to rare, 25–40 × 6–9 (12) μ, two types observed; 1) elliptic-mucronate with thin hyaline walls and homogeneous content and 2) fusoid-ventricose to ventricose-elongate (neck filamentose), with a highly refractive amorphous body in ventricose part as revived in KOH, walls thin, smooth and hyaline, neck often drawn out into a filamentose extension, with walls flexuous. Caulocystidia rather numerous, 24–42 × 3–6 μ filamentose-subcapitate to narrowly fusoid-ventricose, apex subcapitate to acute, walls thin and hyaline, content homogeneous.

Gill trama a central area of subparallel hyphae, 6–15 μ broad (cells inflated in age), walls thin smooth and hyaline to yellowish in KOH, content homogeneous in KOH; subhymenium of narrow subparallel gelatinous colorless hyphae. Pileus cutis a thick gelatinous layer of narrow interwoven hyphae 2–3 μ diam., yellowish in KOH and walls smooth to asperulate (in age); hypodermium of ochraceous smooth-walled floccose hyphae 4–10 μ diam. Context hyphae 8–18 μ or more thick, (cells greatly inflated) walls smooth, thin colorless to yellowish in KOH; oleiferous hyphae present, yellow in KOH. All hyphae inamyloid. Clamp connections present.

HABIT, HABITAT, AND DISTRIBUTION: Caespitose on bare soil, in a road through a swamp, Alabama, collected by R. P. Burke (A.S.) Sept. 29, 1942.

OBSERVATIONS: This is a curious species in nearly all respects. The yellow colors, hygrophanous context, yellow gills and stipe when young, and scales at the stipe base make it a distinctive species in the field. Microscopically the tendency of the chrysocystidia to have a long filamentose neck is most unusual for this type of cystidium. The large spores are borne in 4's on the large basidia. No spores attached to two-spored basidia were seen. We are certain, however, that not all of the large spores seen are from 4-spored basidia. The fact that these larger spores in a fair number of individuals have a truncate apex is one reason for de-emphasizing the feature as a generic character.

74. **Pholiota lutescens** sp. nov.

Key to Varieties

1. Grayish squamules over pileus rather conspicuous ....
   .... *P. lutescens* var. *robusta*
1. Pileus glabrous or practically so .... *P. lutescens* var. *lutescens*

Var. lutescens

Illustrations: Text figs. 85-87; pl. 30.

Pileus 2–5(7) cm latus, convexus, viscidus, albus, tarde lutescens, ad marginem fibrillosus. Contextus albus demum luteus. Lamellae albae, demum luteae, adnatae, confertae, latae. Stipes 3–6 cm longus, 3–8 mm crassus, deorsum saepe attenuatus, albidus, tarde luteus, fibrillosus. Sporae 6.5–7.5(8.5) × 3.5–4(4.5) μ. Chrysocystidia 28–42 × 7–11 μ, clavato- mucronata vel fusoide ventricosa. Specimen typicum in Herb. Univ. Mich. conservatum est; legit prope Sharon Hollow (Manchester), Mich., 5 Nov. 1960, Smith 63406.

Pileus 2–5 (7) cm broad, convex with an incurved margin, pure white at first, gradually becoming lemon-yellow from disc out, margin at first fibrillose-appendiculate from remains of thin veil, glabrous over central part, fibrillose toward the margin, slightly viscid from a thin gelatinous pellicle. Context white, subcartilaginous; odor and taste not distinctive.

Lamellae adnate, white when young, becoming pale yellow and finally dull rusty brown from spores, close, moderately broad, tapered to cap margin, 2–3 tiers of lamellulae.

Stipe 3–6 cm long, 3–8 mm at apex, narrower downward or equal, white overall and fibrillose squamulose up to the faint apical zone left by fibrillose veil, gradually lemon-yellow overall, base near "Isabella color," finally rather cartilaginous-pliant.

Spores 6.5–7.5 (8.5) × 3.5–4 (4.8) μ, ovate to oblong in face view, in profile obscurely inequilateral to slightly bean-shaped; germ pore evident and apex tending to be slightly truncate; wall about 0.3 μ thick; in KOH rich tawny, in Melzer's reagent paler and more cinnamon.

Basidia 21–27 × 5–6 μ, 4-spored, clavate, hyaline to yellowish in KOH and dingy ochraceous in Melzer's reagent. Pleurocystidia 28–42 × 7–11 μ, clavate-mucronate to fusoid-ventricose, at times with a slender neck tapered to an acute apex, wall smooth thin and hyaline; content a highly refractive amorphous body yellowish in Melzer's reagent. Cheilocystidia 23–31 × 3–6 μ, cylindric with rounded to subcapitate apex or with a slight medial inflation in addition varying to fusoid-ventricose with obtuse apex. Caulocystidia present but not abundant, resembling those of var. *robusta* except that chrysocystidia were not observed.

Text Fig. 6.

Figs. 85-87, pleurocystidia, spores and cheilocystidia of *P. lutescens* var. *lutescens;* 88-91, spores, cheilocystidia, pleurocystidia and caulocystidia of. *P. lutescens* var. *robusta;* 92 & 93, spores and pleurocystidia of *P. subochracea;* 94 & 95, spores and pleurocystidia of *P. olympiana;* 96 & 97, pleurocystidia and cheilocystidia of *P. subgelatinosa;* 98-101, cheilocystidia, spores, caulocystidia and pleurocystidia of *P. parvula;* 102-104, tips of cheilocystidia, pleurocystidia and spores of *P. pusilla.*

Gill trama of a central strand of floccose hyphae with inflated cells 8–12 (16) μ broad, subparallel; walls thin smooth and yellow to pale tawny in KOH; subhymenium of gelatinous narrow hyaline hyphae somewhat interwoven. Pileus cutis a gelatinous layer of yellowish hyphae with smooth to asperulate walls, hyphae 2.5–5 μ diam.; hypodermium in KOH strongly ochraceous to pale rusty brown, hyphae smooth to asperulate, cells 5–12 μ diam. Context of greatly inflated hyphae with smooth ochraceous walls, non-gelatinous. All hyphae inamyloid but with a distinctly reddish tone. Clamp connections present.

HABIT, HABITAT AND DISTRIBUTION: Subcespitose around elm and on soil with chips etc. mixed in it, Nov. 5, 1960, near Sharon Hollow (Manchester), Michigan, Smith 63406 type, and 72896, 20896; also Bartelli 2334.

OBSERVATIONS: This is a white to pallid to yellow species with veil material present on the cap in varying amounts. The marked change in color from youth to old age is quite deceiving. For further comment see var. *robusta*.

74a. Var. **robusta** var. nov.

Pileus 3–7 cm latus, convexus, rare subumbonatus, viscidus, subsquamulosus, pallidus, demum avellaneus, lutescens. Lamellae pallidae, latae, subdistantes, subdecurrentes. Stipe 3–6 cm long, 4–8 mm crassus, pallidus, deorsum fulvescens. Sporae 5.5–6.5(7.5) × 3.3–4 μ. Chrysopleurocystidia 25–38(46) × 6–11(13) μ. Specimen typicum in Herb. Univ. Mich. conservatum est; legit prope Milford, Mich., 30 Sept. 1951, Smith 38863.

Illustrations: Text figs. 88-89.

Pileus 3–7 cm broad, broadly convex to plane or rarely with a slight umbo, surface viscid but soon dry, typically with minute slightly darker spotlike squamules around and over disc, pallid when young becoming avellaneous (grayish) and finally near snuff brown (dull yellow-brown), yellow tones dominant in dried material. Context pallid, thin, finally yellowish, odor and taste mild.

Lamellae pallid young, becoming near buckthorn brown and drying more ochraceous, more or less decurrent, broad, more or less subdistant, edges slightly fimbriate.

Stipe 3–6 cm long, 4–8 mm at apex, typically narrowed downward, pallid but soon dingy brown from base up though nearly evenly dingy buff as dried, with scattered minute scales below the veil-line, silky above.

Spores 5.5–6.5 (7) × 3.3–3.8 (4) μ, smooth, apical pore present, small but causing apex to appear obscurely truncate in many; shape in face view oblong to narrowly elliptic, in profile slightly bean-shaped to obscurely inequilateral; pale brownish revived in KOH, paler in Melzer's reagent; wall less than 0.25 μ thick.

Basidia 4-spored, 26–30 × 6–7.5 μ, clavate, hyaline in KOH, yellowish pallid in Melzer's reagent. Pleurocystidia abundant, 25–38 (46) × 6–11 (13) μ, clavate, mucronate to fusoid-ventricose, walls thin smooth and hyaline, content showing a highly refractive amorphous inclusion as revived in KOH, and merely yellowish in Melzer's reagent, or refractive material in more or less of a strand. Cheilocystidia abundant, 30–45 × 4–6 × 5–9 μ, filamentous-subcapitate, to capitate, varying to obtusely fusoid-ventricose, walls thin smooth and hyaline, content hyaline and homogeneous. Caulocystidia rare, as clavate hyaline end-cells of cortex hyphae projecting slightly and in width up to 16 μ, thin-walled.

Gill trama a somewhat interwoven strand of floccose hyphae with cells inflated to 12 μ or more and with "colloidal" content, bright red in Melzer's reagent fading slowly to ochraceous; subhymenium a well-defined gelatinous layer of narrow hyaline hyphae. Pileus cutis a gelatinous layer of hyphae 4–7.5 μ broad, hyaline to yellowish, smooth to asperulate, many with hyaline "granular" protoplasm as seen revived in KOH; hypodermial region not sharply distinct from context, the hyphae of both floccose and of inflated cells to 15 μ or more wide, yellowish smooth walls in KOH and content reddish in Melzer's reagent when first mounted, near the subhymenium the hyphal walls slightly thickened (appearing layered). Clamp connections present.

HABIT, HABITAT, AND DISTRIBUTION: Subcaespitose on soil at Proud Lake Recreation Area, Sept. 30, 1951, Oakland County, Mich. Smith 38863 type, and 21380.

OBSERVATIONS: The squamules over and around the disc are grayish and the pileus soon develops darker coloration overall than in var. *lutescens.*

75. Pholiota subochracea (Smith) comb. nov.

Hypholoma subochraceum Smith, Mycologia 36: 250. 1944.
Naematoloma subochraceum (Smith) Smith, Mycologia 38: 502. 1946.
Illustrations: Text figs. 92-93; pls. 31, 32, 86b.

Pileus 2–4 cm broad, convex with an inrolled margin and becoming broadly convex to plane, surface glabrous except for scattered fibrillose flecks along the margin from the broken veil, glutinous when wet, under a lens appearing somewhat appressed-fibrillose beneath the gluten, very pale ochraceous tawny on the disc, pale yellow ("massicot-yellow") over marginal area, when old more or less cinnamon-buff over all. Context thin, firm, equal, yellowish, unchanging, odor none, taste mild.

Lamellae close, about 35 reach the stipe, 2–3 tiers of lamellulae, equal, narrow to moderately broad, adnate becoming depressed-adnate, pale yellow ("marguerite-yellow") when young, dingy cinnamon when mature, edges even.

Stipe 5–9 cm long, 5–7 mm thick at apex, equal or slightly enlarged downward, tubular to hollow, surface over lower portion pale yellowish white from a thin coating of white fibrils extending to an evanescent zone left by broken veil, yellowish beneath the fibrils, apex yellow and silky, on aging becoming rusty brown from base upward and glabrescent.

Spore deposit yellow-brown ("snuff-brown"); spores 5–6 × 2.5–3 μ, smooth, elliptic to oblong in face view, in profile subelliptic to slightly bean-shaped; color pale ochraceous in KOH and Melzer's reagent; wall thin, apex blunt but not truncate, no apical pore visible.

Basidia 4-spored, 16–18 × 4–5 μ, yellowish in KOH. Pleurocystidia 32–47 × 10–15 μ, clavate-mucronate to fusoid-ventrocise, as revived in KOH with a highly refractive central body. Cheilocystidia mostly chryso-cystidia (like the pleurocystidia) but a few basidiole-like leptocystidia present also. Gill trama subparallel, hyphae non-gelatinous, walls yellow-ish to brownish revived in KOH; subhymenium scarcely distinct. Pileus epicutis a layer of appressed subgelatinous narrow (2–4 μ yellowish hyphae with smooth to faintly asperulate walls; hypodermium of inflated rusty ochraceous hyphae. Clamp connections present. All hyphae inamyloid.

HABIT, HABITAT, AND DISTRIBUTION: Caespitose to gregarious on decaying conifer logs, Pacific Northwest, in the fall, often late.

OBSERVATIONS: This species, like *P. astragalina,* is difficult to dry. It discolors badly if even slightly overheated. The pale ochraceous viscid pileus, numerous chrysocystidia and the fact that the spores are not truncate characterize it.

MATERIAL EXAMINED: IDAHO: Smith 73687, 74081. OREGON: Smith 19733, 19684, 19811, 19812, 19940, 20149, 20189, 24346. 24636, 24737, 24969, 27727, 27868, 26974, 28333. WASHINGTON: Smith 31573, 31681, 31766, 41178.

76. Pholiota subgelatinosa sp. nov.
Illustrations: Text figs. 96-97.

Pileus 1–2 cm latus, obtuse conicus demum campanulatus, glutinosus, obscure vinaceo-brunneus, ad marginem ligno-brunneus, appendiculatus. Lamellae adnatae, latae, confertae, pallidae demum olivaceo-luteae. Stipes 3–5 cm longus, 2–3 mm crassus, albidus, peronatus; velum ligno-brunneum. Sporae (4)5–6(7) × 3–3.5(4) μ. Pleuro-chrysocystidia 20–30 × 8–14 μ. Cheilocystidia 20–35(45) × 5–10 μ. Specimen typicum in Herb. Univ. Mich. conservatum est; legit prope. Lake Tahkenitch, Oregon, 23 Nov. 1935, Smith 3599.

Pileus 1–2 cm broad, obtusely conic to campanulate or convex in age, glutinous when wet, near "wood-brown" along the margin, disc darker and nearest "Verona-brown" (dull reddish-vinaceous brown), virgate with agglutinated fibrils, margin appendiculate with fibrillose patches. Context rather thick (4 mm), firm, watery brown; no odor, taste none.

Lamellae rounded adnate, broad, close, whitish becoming faintly "Isabella color," or remaining pale, edges even.

Stipe 3–5 cm long, 2–3 mm thick, white, covered to near the apex by a sheathing fibrillose-layer (near "wood-brown") which breaks into concentric annular patches (1 or 2 near apex at least), squamulose below, equal, tough, hollow, interior olive-ochraceous or sordid yellowish.

Spores (4.5) 5–6 (7) × 3–3.5 (4) μ smooth, apical pore distinct and apex obscurely truncate in many; shape oblong to elliptic or slightly ovate in face view, in profile elliptic to obscurely bean-shaped, wall thin (0.25 μ), color in KOH pale ochraceous to ochraceous tawny, in Melzer's about the same color.

Basidia 4-spored, 18–23 × 4.5–5 μ, narrowly clavate, hyaline in KOH, yellowish-hyaline in Melzer's reagent. Pleurocystidia clavate, 20–30 × 8–14 μ, smooth, thin-walled, content with a refractive, amorphous hyaline inclusion (in KOH). Cheilocystidia 20–35 (45) × 5–10 μ, versiform, clavate, cylindric, cylindric-subcapitate, fusoid-ventricose etc., smooth, thin-walled, hyaline in KOH, content homogeneous. Caulocystidia none.

Gill trama of a central area of floccose hyphae with thin, smooth ochraceous to hyaline walls, cells becoming inflated; subhymenium a gelatinous layer of narrow (2–3 μ) hyaline subparallel to interwoven hyphae. Pileus cutis, tangled and finally collapsing, the trichodermium of hyphae with encrusted (brownish) walls 5–10 μ diam., apical cells at times fusoid-ventricose, 30–50 × 10–15 μ, walls roughened, matrix translucent as if with gelatin between hyphae; hypodermial region of floccose rusty brown to ochraceous hyphae some with roughened walls. Context hyphae of inflated cells, thin walled, smooth and ochraceous to nearly hyaline in KOH. Clamp connections present. All hyphae inamyloid.

HABIT, HABITAT, AND DISTRIBUTION: On humus, Oregon, November.

OBSERVATIONS: This species is characterized by its gelatinous epicuticular hyphae which are agglutinated and give the pileus a virgate appearance, by clavate chrysocystidia, by its broad, close lamellae, and by small spores. The pileus is rather small and brown. It is near *P. pusilla*, which is pale-buff to yellow-ferruginous has narrow gills, and different cheilocystidia.

MATERIAL EXAMINED: OREGON: Smith 3599 (type, from Lake Tahkenitch, November 23, 1935).

77. Pholiota parvula sp. nov.
Illustrations: Text figs. 98-101; pl. 7c.

Pileus 1–2 cm latus, convexus demum planus, viscidus, pallide fulvus. Contextus albus. Lamellae adnato-sinuatae, confertae, pallidae, latae. Stipes 3–6 cm longus, 2.5–3.5 mm crassus, deorsum attenuatus, sparse fibrillosus vel squamulosus, glabrescens, sursum pallide luteus, deorsum tarde sordide brunneus. Sporae 6–7.5 × 3.5–4.5 μ, leves, subtruncatae. Pleurochrysocystidia 22–30 × 6–10 μ. Cheilocystidia 28–4J × 3–7 μ, subcylindrica vel fusoide ventricosa. Specimen typicum in Herb. Univ. Mich. conservatum est., legit prope Wilderness State Park, Mich. 24 Sept. 1953. Smith 43234.

Pileus 1–2 cm broad, convex, becoming plane, viscid, ochraceous tawny to near tawny on disc, margin pale cinnamon-buff to cinnamon-buff, in age the colors paler (near clay color), with veil remnants along the margin. Context white; odor and taste none.

Lamellae adnexed, close, broad, pallid, then pale cinnamon-brown, edges even.

Stipe 3–6 cm long, 2.5–3.5 mm thick at apex, narrowed downward, yellowish, faintly fibrillose to squamulose from the veil fibrils but these soon evanescent, in age becoming dark (more or less bister) from the base upward, apex naked or nearly so. Veil yellow, arachnoid.

Spores 6–7.5 × 3.5–4.5 μ smooth, apical pore distinct and apex in some slightly truncate, shape in face view elliptic to ovate, in profile slightly bean-shaped to obscurely inequilateral, dull cinnamon in KOH, slightly paler in Melzer's reagent, wall about 0.25 μ thick.

Basidia 20–24 × 5–6 μ, 4-spored, clavate, yellowish in KOH, the same in Melzer's reagent. Pleurocystidia numerous, 22–30 × 6–10 μ, oval, elliptic, clavate or slightly mucronate, with a large refractive inclusion yellow to orange-brown in Melzer's reagent; wall thin, smooth and hyaline. Cheilocystidia 28–40 × 3–7 μ, subcylindric to fusoid-ventricose, often irregular in outline; wall thin, smooth and hyaline, content homogeneous. Caulocystidia in the form of chrysocystidia 28–42 × 5–10 μ, elongate fusoid-ventricose with refractive inclusion varying to clavate ellipsoid etc., or homogeneous and resembling cheilocystidia.

Gill trama of parallel hyaline hyphae with rather short cells, walls thin and smooth, the cells 3–11 μ diam., inflated in age; subhymenium scarcely differentiated (not gelatinous). Pileus cutis a gelatinous layer of widely spaced ochraceous incrusted hyphae in KOH; hypodermium of dark rusty brown coarsely incrusted hyphae 4–10 μ diam. Context hyphae interwoven, with thin smooth yellowish walls (in KOH). Clamp connections present. All hyphae inamyloid.

HABIT, HABITAT, AND DISTRIBUTION: Caespitose to gregarious, on hardwood, Michigan, September.

OBSERVATIONS: This species is distinguished by its small size, white flesh, pallid gills, yellow veil, yellowish stipe, medium sized spores, and short, inconspicuous pleurocystidia in the form of chrysocystidia. The caulocystidia are in tufts.

MATERIAL EXAMINED: MICHIGAN: Smith 43158 (type), 43234, 50514, 50578, 50726, 51245.

78. Pholiota pusilla (Pk.) comb. nov.

Flammula pusilla Peck, New York State Mus. Bull. 67: 26. 1903.

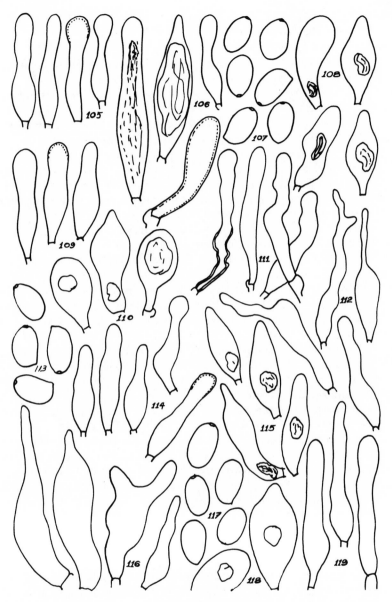

Text Fig. 7.

FIGS. 105 & 106, cheilocystidia and caulocystidia of *P. pusilla;* 107-109, spores, pleurocystidia and cheilocystidia of *P. ornatula;* 110-112, pleurocystidia, caulocystidia and cheilocystidia of *P. melliodora;* 113-116, spores, cheilocystidia, pleurocystidia and caulocystidia of *P. flavescens;* 117-119, spores, pleurocystidia, cheilocystidia of *P. prolixa.*

Illustration: Peck, N.Y. Mus. Bull. 67, pl. M., Figs. 35-41. Text figs. 102-104; 105-106.

Pileus 1.2–2.5 (3.5) cm broad, convex becoming nearly plane, pale buff or yellow-ferruginous, slightly viscid, glabrous. Context thin.

Lamellae adnate, whitish when young, brownish-ferruginous when mature, narrow, crowded.

Stipe 1.5–3 cm long, 2 mm thick, whitish, becoming ferruginous toward the slightly villose-strigose base, apex flocculent-pulverulent, equal, solid or stuffed. Veil slight, whitish to pale yellow.

Spores 6–7.5 × 3.5–4 μ, smooth, apical pore very minute but present; shape in face view oblong to narrowly elliptic, in profile slightly bean-shaped to suboblong, as revived in KOH rusty brown, merely ochraceous in Melzer's reagent; wall about 0.25 μ thick.

Basidia 17–23 × 4.5–6 μ, 4-spored (rarely 2-spored), subclavate hyaline in KOH, yellowish in Melzer's reagent. Pleurocystidia abundant, 26–35 × 10–20 μ, broadly fusoid to clavate-mucronate, with bright yellow coagulated content that adheres along wall preventing the cell from reviving in KOH, content orange to dull red in Melzer's reagent. Cheilo-cystidia 18–32 × 4–8 (9) μ, cylindric-capitate to narrowly fusoid-ventricose, walls thin, smooth and hyaline, content homogeneous, hyaline to yellowish. Caulocystidia 27–46 × 6–12 μ elongate clavate to fusoid-ventricose or irregularly fusoid, walls yellowish and often thickened slightly (0.5) μ, content a coagulated more or less wrinkled mass of amorphous material pale yellow to orange-brown in KOH, also cells similar to cheilocystidia at very apex.

Gill trama of a central area of floccose hyphae of elongate celled hyphae with smooth thin yellowish walls in KOH, cells (4) 5–12 μ diam. (more inflated in center area), subhymenium a broad and distinct gelatinous layer. Pileus cutis a collapsed trichodermium of nongelatinous loosely arranged rusty brown hyphae with encrusted walls, (usually heavily banded), the hyphae 4–9 μ wide and cells not greatly inflated; hypodermial zone bright rusty in KOH fading to ochraceous, almost pseudoparenchymatic in structure (cells inflated and closely packed), cell walls thickened (double) to about 0.5 μ. Context hyphae with walls like those of hypodermial area—refractive, smooth and showing a middle layer. Clamp connections present. All hyphae inamyloid.

HABIT, HABITAT, AND DISTRIBUTION: On roots, stumps and water-soaked wood in open places, Smithtown, Suffolk Co., New York. Type studied.

OBSERVATIONS: Kauffman in his study of the type noted the curious cells in the hymenium, which in the light of the present work are merely cystidia approaching the chrysocystidia type. Harding placed the species in synonomy with *Flammula carbonaria,* probably because Kauffman placed it in synonymy with *F. highlandensis,* and in an examination of a portion of the type Hesler found no pleurocystidia. Smith's observations were made on the specimens showing the tawny mycelium around the base (the appearance is like that of *Xeromphalina*) and his observations check with Kauffman's on microscopic features. Hence we interpret the species as having chrysocystidial-like cells in the hymenium. Kauffman thought the peculiar cells were foreign and reduced the species to synonymy with *F. highlandensis* from which it is readily distinct by obvious characters. The question of the viscidity of the pileus, a character mentioned by Peck, is more difficult to explain. The only explanation we can offer here is that the epicuticular hyphae in spite of being incrusted buckle and collapse as if the wall were very weak—much as in some other species known to be viscid to the touch. Hence Peck's observation, as usual, was undoubtedly an accurate one. The point is that the anatomical study shows the layer is not a gelatinous pellicle as in *P. highlandensis*. *Flammula ascophora* Pk may be a synonym of this species.

Because of the situation in regard to the type, our account here is based entirely on the original account of Peck and a study of specimens with the tawny mycelium at the base of the stipe. One is most apt to confuse this species in the field with *Pholiota vernalis*. *P. prolixa* is very slimy when fresh and wet.

79. Pholiota perniciosa sp. nov.
Illustrations: Text figs. 487, 488, 491.

Pileus 1.5–3 cm latus, convexus, glaber, glutinosus, sordid luteus, ad centrum subfulvosus, lamellae angustae, confertae, olivaceo-luteae; stipes 3–4 cm longus, 1.5–2.5 mm crassus, luteo-fibrillosus, sursum luteus; sporae 6.5–8 × 3.5–4.5 μ, subtruncatae, cum KOH ochraceo-fulvae; pleurocystidia fusoide ventricosa ut chrysocystidia; cheilocystidia ut chrysocystidia vel flexuosacapitata. Specimen typicum in Herb. Univ. Mich. conservatum est; legit prope Burt Lake, Mich. 23 Aug. 1953, M. Barr, (Smith 42322).

Pileus 1.5–3 cm broad, obtuse to broadly convex, glabrous, viscid to slimy, dingy yellow over all except the brownish disc, margin at first decorated with superficial particles of the veil. Context thin, yellowish pallid, odor and taste not recorded.

Lamellae close, narrow, bluntly adnate to slightly decurrent, yellowish to olive yellow becoming dingy yellowish brown, edges slightly fimbriate under a lens.

Stipe 3–4 cm long, 1.5–2.5 mm thick, equal, flexuous, thinly coated with yellowish veil fibrils to the evanescent veil line, yellowish and silky above, base becoming sordid but not darkened appreciably in dried specimens.

Spores dull cinnamon in deposit (on one cap) ; 6.5–8 × 3.5–4.5 μ, smooth, apical pore distinct and apex slightly truncate in many; shape in face view oblong to elliptic, in profile obscurely bean-shaped to elliptic; color in KOH bright ochraceous tawny fading to ochraceous, in

Melzer's sol. slightly more cinnamon (but not dextrinoid); wall less than 0.25 μ thick.

Basidia 4-spored, 18–24 × 6–7.5 μ subclavate, hyaline in KOH and merely yellowish in Melzer's reagent. Pleurocystidia 36–58 (65) × 6–12 (14) μ, versiform: 1) fusoid-ventricose with no pedicel and tapered to a point at apex; 2) narrowly fusoid-ventricose with a pedicel and the apex obtuse; 3) more or less clavate to clavate-mucronate; all thin-walled, smooth, and with the highly refractive content of chrysocystidia (an amorphous refractive body hyaline in KOH and orange red in Melzer's reagent). Cheilocystidia similar to pleurocystidia (as chrysocystidia) but mostly elongate, flexuous and subcapitate (much as in subgenus *Flavidula*) and usually slightly ventricose at base, 30–60 × 5–8 μ, walls smooth, thin or very slightly (–0.25 μ) thick, ochraceous in KOH. Caulocystidia more or less similar to both types of cheilocystidia, (some with refractive content), many ventricose and with 2–3 subapical prolongations.

Gill trama of a central strand of non-gelatinous hyaline to yellowish (in KOH) parallel hyphae with inflating cells, the walls thin and smooth; subhymenium a gelatinous band of narrow hyphae. Pileus cuticle a thick gelatinous pellicle the hypha 1.5–3 μ diam., and hyaline to yellowish; hypodermium bright ochraceous in KOH, hyphal walls smooth or nearly so in wider (6–12 μ) hyphae and incrusted on narrower (3–5 μ) ones. Context hyphae compactly interwoven, yellowish in KOH, smooth and thin-walled, ochraceous oleiferous hyphae also present. Clamp connections present.

Gregarious on debris in mixed conifer-hardwood swamp, Burt Lake, Mich. Aug. 23, 1953, M. Barr (Bigelow) collector. Smith 42322, type.

OBSERVATIONS: This species was mistaken in the field for *P. pulchella*. It is interesting because it combines truncate spores, gelatinous subhymenium, yellow-brown spore color, and projecting fusoid-ventricose pleurocystidia with the content of chrysocystidia along with cheilocystidia (some) of the *P. erinacella* type (fig. 486). In a sense the species makes a mockery not only of the use of cystidia to indicate different phylogeny in *Pholiota* but also of our definitions of cystidia. To us it simply emphasizes the point we have tried to emphasize in this work: Namely that each character in the *Pholiota* population is capable of being exchanged independently of other single characters, and that if you collect assiduously enough you will find species showing almost, or all, possible combinations. To us this is the best argument against recognizing genera in this group based on some of the combinations most frequently collected.

80. Pholiota ornatula (Murr.) comb. nov.
Gymnopilus ornatulus Murrill, Mycologia 4: 251. 1912.
Flammula ornatula Murrill, Mycologia 4: 262. 1912.
Illustrations: Text figs. 107-109.

Pileus caespitose, 3 cm broad, convex to nearly plane, gibbous or umbonate, slightly viscid when wet, fibrillose, flavo-melleous tinged with pale rose-brown, the latter color more conspicuous at the center.

Lamellae adnate, pallid when young, becoming pale-fulvous from the spores, plane, broad, of medium distance.

Stipe 5 cm long, 4 mm thick, smooth, glabrous and cremeous at the apex, subconcolorous and shaggy-fibrillose below.

Spores 5.5–7.5 × 3.5–4.5 μ, smooth, apical pore present and at times apex appearing slightly truncate, shape in face view elliptic to ovate, in profile obscurely inequilateral, pale tawny in KOH and only slightly paler in Melzer's reagent, walls 0.25 thick.

Basidia 18–22 × 5–6 μ, 4-spored, hyaline in KOH, yellowish in Melzer's reagent. Pleurocystidia present as imbedded chrysocystidia 18–25 × 6–10 μ, often 5–6 μ at basal septum, wall hyaline thin and smooth, content varying from a local area of granular-refractive material to the amorphous refractive mass characteristic of chrysocystidia and the inclusion merely yellowish in Melzer's reagent. Cheilocystidia 24–32 × 6–10 μ, subclavate to subcylindric or fusoid-ventricose. Gill trama a central floccose strand of hyaline hyphae 3–9 μ broad with thin, smooth walls; subhymenium gelatinous, structure not distinct but apparently divergent-interwoven. Pileus cutis a gelatinous pellicle. No other data on type reliable.

HABIT, HABITAT, AND DISTRIBUTION: On soil, roadside, California, November. Type studied.

OBSERVATIONS: This species is near *P. melliodora,* in which the pileus margin remains incurved for a long time, but the cheilocystidia are longer and more slender, the subhymenium more distinctly gelatinous, and the gills are crowded and at first yellow. The odor in *P. ornatula* is not recorded.

81. Pholiota melliodora sp. nov.
Illustrations: Text figs. 110-112.

Pileus 1–8 cm latus, convexus, melleus, viscidus, virgatus. Caro fragilis, mollis, lutea, odor fragrans. Lamellae adnatae, confertae, latissimae, luteae. Stipes 4–7 cm longus, 3–7 mm crassus, flexuosus, fibrillosus, luteus, deorsum subfulvus. Sporae 5.5–7.5 × 3.5–4 μ. Pleurocystidia 28–37 × 9–12 μ, ovata vell elliptico-pedicellata, ochracea. Caulocystidia 24–48 × 3–7 μ. Specimen typicum in Univ. Mich. Herb. conservatum est.; legit prope Portland, Ore., 2 Nov. 1957, R. Oswald.

Pileus 1–8 cm broad, convex, near honey-yellow, viscid, fibrillose, at first the margin appressed to stipe, finally expanding. Context brittle, soft, thick on disc, yellow; odor like honey.

Lamellae adnate, notched near stipe, yellow, up to 13 mm broad at broadest point, crowded, edges eroded.

Stipe 4–7 cm long, 3–7 mm thick, flexuous, fibrillose, yellow, darkening toward the base, apex enlarged.

Spores (5.5) 6–7.5 × 3.5–4 μ, smooth, apical pore distinct but apex not truncate; shape oblong in face view varying to elliptic, in profile obscurely inequilateral to subelliptic or obscurely bean-shaped; in KOH pale tawny and in Melzer's reagent paler.

Basidia 18–22 × 4.5–6 μ obese, 4-spored, yellowish to hyaline in KOH, yellowish in Melzer's reagent and with numerous yellowish globules. Pleurocystidia scattered, imbedded, 28–37 × 9–12 μ subglobose, ovate in optical section or elliptic, with a short pedicel; with granular-reticulate ochraceous content in KOH, thin-walled, some debris adhering on wall, the content darker (yellow-brown) in Melzer's than in KOH. Cheilocystidia versiform, 24–48 × 3–7 μ, contorted-filamentous, filamentous-capitate, narrowly fusoid-ventricose, or any of these shapes proliferating at apex (see figs.), walls thin to slightly thickened (–0.5 μ), yellowish in KOH, smooth, content homogeneous. Caulocystidia resembling the cheilocystidia or greatly elongate-subcylindric with a slight thickening of the wall at obtuse apex (50 × 5 μ ±), smooth, content homogeneous.

Gill trama of subparallel floccose hyphae with greatly elongated cells 5–12 μ wide; walls thin, yellowish in KOH, smooth; subhymenium a gelatinous zone of interwoven narrow (2–3 μ) hyaline hyphae. Pileus cutis a gelatinous pellicle of narrow ochraceous hyphae; hypodermial region of rusty to yellowish-tawny hyphae with smooth to slightly incrusted walls. Context hyphae interwoven, cells greatly inflated, walls smooth and yellowish in KOH. Clamp connections present. All hyphae inamyloid.

HABIT, HABITAT, AND DISTRIBUTION: Caespitose, on soil and near buried wood, Oregon, October—November.

OBSERVATIONS: This is distinguished by its honey odor and its pileus with an incurved margin. It is close to *P. ornatula,* which has smaller cheilocystidia and subdistant, pallid gills. The pleurocystidia are not typical chrysocystidia but because of their distinctive content would have to be classified there in a broad sense of the term. Apparently the cheilocystidia may proliferate more than once as several were seen in which it was thought that at least 3 stages could be seen.

MATERIAL EXAMINED: OREGON. Smith 68780, 68781 (type, from Portland, collected by Ruth Oswald, November 2, 1957).

82. Pholiota flavescens sp. nov.
Illustrations: Text figs. 113-116.

Pileus 1–4 cm latus, convexus, albidus demum pallide luteus, vel flavidus, saepe ad marginem luteo-olivaceus. Lamellae subdecurrentes, pallide luteae, confertae, latae. Stipes 2–4 cm longus, 2.5–4(8) mm cras-

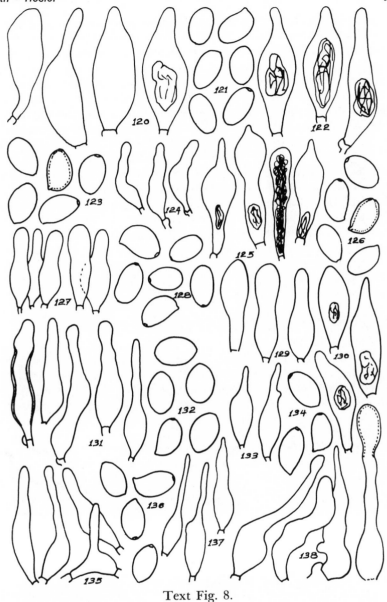

Text Fig. 8.

FIG. 120, pleurocystidia of *P. prolixa;* 121 & 122, spores and pleurocystidia of *P. californica;* 123 & 124, spores and cheilocystidia of *P.
mutabilis;* 125-127, pleurocystidia spores and cheilocystidia of *P. tennessensis,* 128-130, spores, cheilocystidia and pleurocystidia of *P. caespitosa;*
131 & 132, cheilocystidia and spores of *P. veris;* 133 & 134, cheilocystidia
and spores of *P. umbilicata;* 135-138, cheilocystidia, spores, pleurocystidia
and caulocystidia of *P. albo-olivascens.*

sus, sursum albidus, deorsum sordidus, fibrillosus. Sporae 5.5–7(7.5) × 3.5–4 μ. Chrysocystidia rara 22–30 × 5–8 μ. Caulocystidia versiformia. Specimen typicum in Herb. Univ. of Tenn. conservatum est; legit prope Gatlinburg, Tenn., 8 Nov. 1942. Hesler 13094.

Pileus 1–4 cm broad, convex, expanding broadly convex or nearly plane, at first whitish, becoming "ochraceous-buff" to "old-gold" or "olive-ochre," margin paler, appressed-fibrillose, fibrils brown, viscid, margin even. Context thin, thick on the disc, white; odor and taste mild.

Lamellae adnexed or subdecurrent, at first pale yellow, finally "clay-color" or darker, close, medium broad, edges even.

Stipe 2–4 cm long, 2.5–4 (8) mm thick, at times compressed, white above, dingy below, fibrillose, fibrils sometimes forming minute scales downward, dry, solid, equal. Veil arachnoid, white, leaving only a slight fugaceous ring.

Spore deposit dark yellow-brown ("Dresden-brown" to "snuff-brown") spores 5.5–7 (7.5) × 3.5–4 μ; ovate to elliptic in face view, obscurely inequilateral to elliptic in profile; wall about 0.2 μ thick, pale ochraceous tawny in KOH, in Melzer's about the same color, apex obscurely truncate in many.

Basidia 20–24 (27) × 5–6 μ, 4-spored, clavate, hyaline to yellowish in KOH, yellowish in Melzer's reagent. Pleurocystidia scattered to rare; 1) chrysocystidia 22–30 × 5–8 μ, fusoid, fusoid-ventricose to more or less fusoid or clavate-mucronate, with a highly refractive body of amorphous material in the lower part as revived in KOH, walls smooth thin and hyaline; 2) vesiculose-pedicellate cells 23–32 × 8–12 μ, content rich ochraceous in KOH and filling the cells, pedicel narrow. Cheilocystidia 22–33 (56) × 4–5 (8) μ, subcylindric, subclavate, or fusoid-ventricose to tibiiform, smooth, thin-walled, hyaline to yellowish in KOH. Caulocystidia (23) 36–54 × 5–14 (20) μ, clavate to irregular, fusoid-ventricose vesiculose, clavate-mucronate, etc., but none seen with a refractive amorphous body, thin-walled.

Gill trama of floccose hyaline to yellowish hyphae red-brown in Melzer's reagent, thin-walled, cells short to elongated and smooth; subhymenium a gelatinous, thin layer of narrow (2–3.5) μ hyaline, smooth hyphae subparallel in arrangement. Pileus cutis a gelatinous pellicle of appressed hyphae 2.5–3.5 μ wide, ochraceous in KOH, smooth or nearly so; hypodermial zone not differentiated. Context hyphae smooth, thin-walled becoming slightly thick-walled, cells becoming inflated, inamyloid. Clamp connections present.

HABIT, HABITAT, AND DISTRIBUTION: On soil, sometimes near sawdust and chips, Gatlinburg, Tenn. Nov. 8, 1942.

OBSERVATIONS: The chrysocystidia are imbedded in the hymenium and are best spotted in revived mounts by the refractive inclusion. In fresh material they are very difficult to spot. The vesiculose bodies are rare in the type but easily located because of their large diameter and

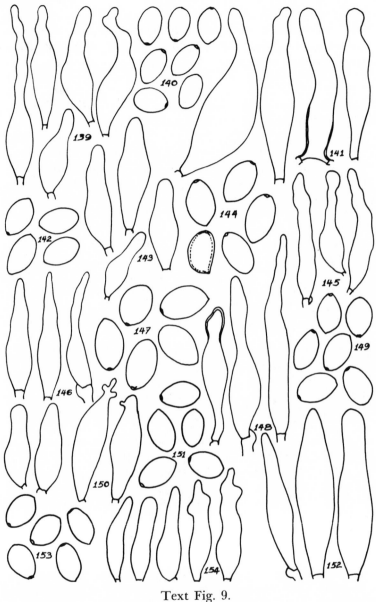

Text Fig. 9.

FIGS. 139 & 140, cheilocystidia and spores of *P. marginella;* 141-143, caulocystidia, spores and cheilocystidia of *P. bridgii;* 144 & 145, spores and cheilocystidia of *P. tahquamenonensis;* 146-148, cheilocystidia, spores and caulocystidia of *P. nigripes;* 149 & 150, spores and cheilocystidia of *P. pallida;* 151 & 152, spores and cheilocystidia of *P. atripes;* 153 & 154, spores and cheilocystidia of *P. vernalis.*

their color. The caulocystidia are remarkable for the variation in shape (fig. 116). It appears to be related to *P. caespitosa* and *P. lutescens.*

MATERIAL EXAMINED: TENNESSEE: Hesler 9641, 13094 (type), Gatlinburg, November 8, 1942.

83. Pholiota prolixa sp. nov.
Illustrations: Text figs. 117-119; 120; pls. 33, 70a.

Pileus 1.5–4(6) cm latus, obtusus demum convexus vel late umbonatus, viscidus, vel glutinosus, glaber, melleus vel ad centrum sordide argillaceus. Contextus cartilagineus, luteolus. Lamellae adnatae angustae, confertae, luteolae demum subcinnamomeae. Stipes 3–5 cm longus, 1.5–4 mm crassus, aequalis, luteolus, deorsum subfulvus, fibrillose squamulosus. Sporae 6–8 × 3–4(4.5) μ. Chrysocystidia 26–40 × 6–12(15) μ, fusoide ventricosa vel clavato-mucronata. Specimen typicum in Univ. of Mich. conservatum est; legit prope. Lakeland, Michigan, 4 Oct. 1936; Smith 5027.

Pileus (1.5) 2–4 (6) cm broad, broadly convex with an incurved margin, in age broadly convex-depressed with a decurved margin, "honey-yellow" to "yellow-ocher" over all when young, in age the margin paler and the disc "ochraceous-tawny," glabrous, glutinous, margin somewhat appendiculate from the submembranous veil, often appearing fibrillose-streaked beneath the gluten. Context cartilaginous tough, yellowish; odor not distinctive, taste slightly disagreeable.

Lamellae adnate, pale yellow to pallid, slowly becoming dull brownish with a slight chocolate shade, crowded, narrow (3 mm), tapering outward, edges becoming slightly eroded.

Stipe 3–5 cm long, 2–4 mm thick at apex, narrowed downward, hollow, rigid-fragile, yellowish over apical region, sordid tawny below, with scattered patches of fibrils to appressed fibrillose-squamulose below, annular zone interrupted and soon evanescent, punctate-fibrillose over apex.

Spores (5.5) 6.5–8 (9) × 3.5–4.5 (5) μ, smooth, apical pore very minute (under 1.4 NA ob.), shape in face view elliptic to ovate, in profile elliptic to obscurely inequilateral; yellowish tawny revived in KOH, merely ochraceous in Melzer's reagent; wall moderately thick (about 0.25–0.3 μ); apex not truncate.

Basidia 16–22 (26) × 4–5 (6) μ, 4-spored, clavate, yellowish in KOH and Melzer's reagent. Pleurocystidia of two types: 1) chrysocystidia 32–45 × 8–12 (15) μ, with a broad basal region, ventricose above and tapered to a subacute apex rarely merely clavate to elliptic with a pedicel, with a large amorphous highly refractive hyaline inclusion, the inclusion orange-brown to reddish in Melzer's reagent; 2) a few pedicellate-ellipsoid and completely filled with flavous homogeneous pigment, 26–35 × 7–11 μ. Cheilocystidia of two types; 1) similar to chrysocystidia on gill faces and 2) cylindric-obtuse to narrowly ventricose at base, 25–40 × 3.5–6 (8) μ, content homogeneous, hyaline to yellowish. Caulocystidia 28–47 × 5–15 μ versiform, some with coagulated content.

Gill trama of subparallel floccose hyphae ochraceous to tan as revived in KOH, walls thin, smooth; subhymenium a very thin layer of hyaline narrow subparallel gelatinous hyphae and gelatinization extending into the base of the hymenium. Pileus cutis a gelatinous layer of tangled hyphae 2–4 μ diam., with ochraceous to rusty incrustations; hypodermium of floccose heavily encrusted (ochraceous-rusty) hyphae grading into the paler context which is of greatly inflated (to 20 μ or more) hyphal cells with smooth ochraceous tawny or yellower walls. Clamp connections present. All hyphae inamyloid.

HABIT, HABITAT, AND DISTRIBUTION: Caespitose around stumps on soil in low swampy elm woods, late summer and fall, common, Ohio and Michigan.

OBSERVATIONS: This is a well characterized species in southeastern Michigan, both in the field and in the herbarium. It beings to fruit in August and builds up to a peak around the middle of September if the weather is moist.

OBSERVATIONS: We tried to recognize several species in this group but the combinations of characters were not constant. The veil is poorly developed on the small early season or very late season fruitings. At times some leptocystidia similar in shape to the slender cheilocystidia are seen but are not very constant. The diagnostic field features are narrow, close to crowded lamellae yellowish before maturity, fibrillose to submembranous veil on the stipe which in robust specimens leaves a weak annulus, the very numerous chrysocystidia with their refractive content changing to orange brown or nearly red in Melzer's reagent, and the slender cheilocystidia for the most part. In all of them clavate-pedicellate to elliptic-pedicellate pleurocystidia with flavous to tawny homogeneous to wrinkled content (revived in KOH) are usually readily demonstrated.

MATERIAL EXAMINED: OHIO: Walters 174. MICHIGAN: Harding 394, 418, 419, 421; Kauffman 11-7-19, 8-7-25 (type); Smith 33-1109, 20553, 50545, 50725, 50727, 72561, 72614, 73249, 73281, 9-28-33.

84. Pholiota contorta sp. nov.
Illustrations: Text figs. 53-55.

Pileus 3–6 cm latus, convexus, demum depressus, viscidus, sordide ochraceus vel ochraceo-brunneus, squamulosus, glabrescens. Lamellae latae, confertae, adnatae, sordide ochraceae. Stipes 1–6 cm longus, 3–8 mm crassus, subcontortus, fibrillosus, sordide ochraceus. Sporae 5–6 × 4–4.5 μ, (7–8.5 × 4.5–5.5 μ). Pleurocystidia ut chrysocystidia. Cheilocystidia 28–42 × 6–10 μ, capitata, ochracea. Specimen typicum in Herb. Univ. Mich. conservatum est; legit prope Cleveland, Ohio, 14 Oct 1948, M. B. Walters n. 169.

Pileus 3–6 cm broad, convex becoming broadly convex, surface viscid, color pale yellow-brown drying dull ochraceous, at first with minute squamules but becoming glabrous, margin slightly fringed at first.

Lamellae broad, thin, close, adnate-seceding, yellowish and drying yellowish, rather glaucous when fresh, edges minutely fimbriate.

Stipe 4–6 cm long, 3–8 mm thick, equal to contorted, some inflated at apex, dingy yellowish, fibrillose from remains of thin veil, as dried with yellow mycelium binding dirt at base.

Spores 5–6 × 4–4.5 μ (7–8.5 × 4.5–5.5 μ), elliptic to ovate in face view, elliptic to obscurely inequilateral in profile; apical pore very inconspicuous; walls relatively thin; color in KOH dingy ochraceous to pale ochraceous tawny, pale tawny in Melzer's reagent.

Basidia 4-spored, 18–23 × 5–6 μ, subcylindric with a broad central constriction when sporulating, hyaline in KOH and in Melzer's reagent. Pleurocystidia 25–36 × 5–11 (14) μ as chrysocystidia buried in the hymenium, ventricose-apiculate to fusoid-ventricose. Cheilocystidia 24–46 × 7–9 μ, resembling those of *P. erinaceella* but smaller, (capitate and narrowed irregularly to base), yellow in KOH from a homogeneous content, smooth, thin-walled. Caulocystidia 28–42 × 6–10 μ, clavate, fusoid-ventricose, or with a short apical projection, content homogeneous to coagulated and ochraceous as revived in KOH, walls thin and ochraceous in KOH, smooth.

Gill trama subparallel, of smooth non-gelatinous hyphae with very wide cells (some 20 μ or more), walls ochraceous and somewhat refractive in KOH, thin but visible as 2 lines each about 0.25 μ thick; subhymenium of gelatinous narrow hyphae, gelatinization extending to base of basidium. Pileus trama with a gelatinous cutis of encrusted yellowish hyphae 3–5 μ diam., which became rusty brown as they collapsed; hypodermium of wide rusty-brown encrusted hyphae 4–12 μ diam. Context hyphae very wide (20 μ in many), with smooth refractive walls most seen to be double in optical section. All hyphae inamyloid. Clamp connections present.

HABIT, HABITAT, AND DISTRIBUTION: Gregarious on soil in an old grassy road in a woods, Cleveland, Ohio, Oct. 14, 1948. Maurice B. Walters 169, type.

OBSERVATIONS: This species combines the gelatinous subhymenium with cheilocystidia of the *P. erinaceella* type and a viscid pileus. The basidiocarps remind one of a dingy *P. spumosa*. The pleurocystidia are easily overlooked. The cheilocystidia separate it at once from *P. prolixa* and *P. californica*.

85. Pholiota californica (Earle) comb. nov.

Flammula californica Earle, New York Bot. Gard. Bull. 2: 342. 1902.
Gymnopilus californicus (Earle) Murrill, Mycologia 4: 253. 1912.
Illustrations: Text figs. 121-122.

Pileus 4–7 cm broad, expanded, subumbonate, gregarious or caespi-

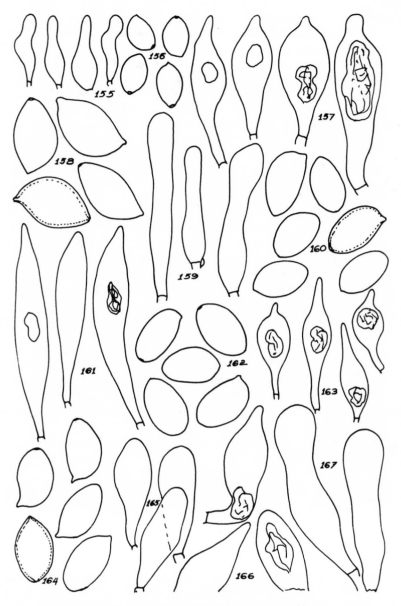

Text Fig. 10.

Figs. 155 & 156, cheilocystidia and spores of *P. populicola;* 157-159, pleurocystidia, spores and cheilocystidia of *P. myosotis;* 160 & 161, spores and pleurocystidia of *P. humidicola;* 162 & 163, spores and pleurocystidia of *P. elongata;* 164-167, spores, cheilocystidia, pleurocystidia and caulocystidia of *P. silvatica.*

tose, surface glabrous, viscid, subhygrophanous, pale ochraceaous-brown, often darker on the disc, margin entire. Context cream colored, unchanging; odor and taste mild.

Lamellae subsinuate-decurrent, pale ochraceous to fusco-ferruginous, heterophyllous, crowded, broad, subventricose.

Stipe 5–6 cm long, 3–4 mm thick, pale brown, yellowish white at the apex, subequal, slightly enlarged at the apex and base, glabrous above, brown-fibrillose below, solid, white-mycelioid at the base.

Spores (5.5) 6–7 (8) × 3.5–4 μ, smooth, apical pore distinct and apex obscurely truncate in some, shape in face view oblong to elliptic, in profile oblong to elliptic or obscurely inequilateral, pale dull tawny to ochraceous in KOH, paler in Melzer's reagent, wall less than 0.25 μ thick.

Basidia 18–23 (25) × 4.5–6 μ, 4-spored clavate, yellowish in KOH and in Melzer's reagent. Pleurocystidia scattered to abundant 25–37 (44) × 6–12 μ, clavate-mucronate or fusoid-ventricose; content distributed throughout the cell and amorphous-granular, in KOH it is bright ochraceous, in Melzer's amber-brown or darker; wall smooth thin and collapsing over the cell content and not readily reviving. Cheilocystidia 22–30 × 5–8 μ, subfusoid to fusoid-ventricose, wall thin and smooth, content hyaline to yellowish but not coarsely granular. Caulocystidia in tufts, 36–54 × 7–13 μ, versiform: cylindric to capitate, ventricose or irregular variously, walls smooth and thin content mostly "empty."

Gill trama reviving poorly but a gelatinous subhymenial layer present. Pileus cutis a gelatinous layer of narrow (2–5 μ) smooth to slightly incrusted hyphae yellow in KOH, hypodermial region rusty ochraceous in color but hyphal detail not clear. Clamp connections present. All hyphae inamyloid.

HABIT, HABITAT, AND DISTRIBUTION: Under trees, probably attached to buried wood, California, December. Type studied.

OBSERVATIONS: Although it was originally described as being dry, the pileus cuticle of the type shows a distinct zone of gelatinous hyphae. The species appears to be rare; no reports of it have appeared since the type was collected in 1901. The pleurocystidia are its most interesting feature in that they are not typical chrysocystidia but must be included in this category in a broad sense.

Subgenus **Flammula** (Fr.) Singer, Lilloa 22: 515. 1951 Emended

The dextrinoid, non-truncate spores combined with the absence of both leptocystidia and chrysocystidia in the hymenium, and the lack of a persistent membranous annulus distinguish this group. Young pilei are usually a bright yellow and the lower part of the stipe is strongly fulvescent. The spore deposit may have a stronger reddish tone than is typical for the genus as a whole.

Type: *P. flavida.*

Key

1. Taste distinctly bitter in fresh basidiocarps .... *P. alnicola*
1. Taste mild to nutty or fungoid 2
  2. Caulocystidia 30–80 (100) × 4–7 μ, subsetiform .... *P. abieticola*
  2. Caulocystidia not as above 3
3. Stipe with a thin coating of thick-walled hyphae .... *P. subvelutina*
3. Not as above 4
  4. Spores 6–9 (10) × 4–5 μ 5
  4. Spores 8–11 (12) × 4.5–5.5 μ 7
5. Odor heavy (as in some fats) .... *P. flavida* var. *graveolens*
5. Odor none to slightly fragrant 6
  6. Lamellae distant; hyphae of gill trama and pileus context orange-
    red in Melzer's reagent. .... *P. oregonensis*
  6. Lamellae close; hyphae of gill and pileus trama not as above (see
    (*P. aurantiflava* also) .... *P. flavida* var. *flavida*
7. Odor of freshly husked green corn; growing on wood of conifers ......
    .... *P. malicola* var. *macropoda*
7. Odor and taste not distinctive; on wood of hardwoods. ....
    .... *P. malicola* var. *malicola*

86. Pholiota alnicola (Fr.) Singer, Lilloa 22: 516. 1951.
Agaricus alnicola Fries, Syst. Myc. 1: 250. 1821.
Dryophila alnicola (Fr.) Quélet, Enchir. Fung., p. 71. 1886.
Flammula alnicola (Fr.) Kummer, Der Führer in die Pilzkunde, p. 82. 1871.
Gymnopilus alnicola (Fr.) Murrill, North Amer. Flora 10: 202. 1917.
Illustrations: Text figs. 177-178.

    Pileus 3–6 cm broad, convex then expanding, at times umbonate, caespitose or fasciculate, not hygrophanous, at first yellow, becoming deeper yellow or ferruginous in age, at times with a flush of olive-green toward the margin, disc at times reddish yellow (Moser), viscid, lubricous, sometimes merely moist, marginal portion fibrillose-subscaly, or appendiculate, glabrescent. Context pale yellow, thick on the disc; odor mild or fragrant to aromatic, taste bitter.
    Lamellae adnate or slightly rounded behind, at first pallid or pale straw-yellow, finally ferruginous to "ochraceous-tawny," broad, close.
    Stipe 4–8 (12) cm long, 4–12 mm thick, pale yellow above yellowish becoming brownish from the base up, flexuous, stuffed then hollow, fibrillose. Veil pallid or whitish, evanescent.
    Spores 8–10 × 4–5.5 μ smooth, apical pore present but inconspicuous; shape in face view subcymbiform to ovate or more rarely elliptic, in profile more or less inequilateral with a broad suprahilar depression, in KOH dark dull cinnamon, in Melzer's more rusty-cinnamon (darker and redder), wall about 0.3 μ thick.

Basidia 4-spored, 22–30 × (5) 6–8 μ, obscurely utriform to clavate, in KOH yellowish, in Melzer's yellowish. Pleurocystidia none. Cheilocystidia 22–46 × 3–6 μ, subutriform, fusoid-ventricose or clavate, wall thin smooth and hyaline, content hyaline and homogeneous. Caulocystidia resembling cheilocystidia but typically more elongated.

Gill trama of somewhat interwoven hyphae with elongated cells 5–15 μ diam. and nearly tubular, with colloidal content bright red to orange in Melzer's reagent but merely yellowish-hyaline in KOH, walls thin, smooth colorless; subhymenium of narrow (3–5 μ), yellowish, subparallel, non-gelatinous hyphae. Pileus cutis a pellicle of narrow (2–4 μ) subgelatinous (walls lacking sharp definition as revived in KOH), smooth to slightly roughened hyphae, the layer well developed; hypodermial region lacking differentiation from context. Context hyphae interwoven, nearly tubular, content "colloidal" and reddish to orange in Melzer's reagent. Clamp connections present.

HABIT, HABITAT, AND DISTRIBUTION: On hardwood trunks and stumps, at times on conifers, reported from New York (Peck 1898).

OBSERVATIONS: The pileus may be viscid, lubricous, or merely moist, depending on the weather conditions. There is also a possibility that the gelatinous surface hyphae of the pileus may slough away, and thus leave the surface "dry." Fries described the pileus as moist, not viscid, and several authors, following Fries, apparently have so characterized it. Our concept is based chiefly on a study of collections by Romell and Maas Geesteranus. Aside from the bitter taste the species is very similar to *P. malicola,* but since this appears to be such a variable group in North America we have recognized all populations with at least one distinctive character. We need a critical study of some American collections with a bitter taste. Our data are from European specimens.

The spores of a collection by Lars Romell (n. 9894) are as given in our description including the moderately strong dextrinoid reaction. The Romell specimen has a well-developed gelatinous pellicle over the pileus. Our disposition of this species is in a sense tentative since there is still a difference of opinion in Europe as to its exact characterization. Favre (1960) for instance, indicated the taste as not bitter.

87. Pholiota abieticola sp. nov.
Illustrations: Text figs. 189-191.

Pileus 2.5–4 cm latus, convexus, subviscidus, glaber, ochraceus. Lamellae adnatae demum subdecurrentes, pallide luteae, confertae, latae. Stipes 3–5 cm longus, 5–8 mm crassus, clavatus, siccus. Velum fibrillosum. Sporae 7–9(10) × 4.5–5.5(6) μ. Pleurocystidia desunt. Cheilocystidia clavata. Caulocystidia 30–80(100) × 4–7 μ. Specimen typicum in Herb. Univ. of Tenn. Conservatum est; legit G.S.M.N.P., 14 Sept. 1941. Hesler 1400.

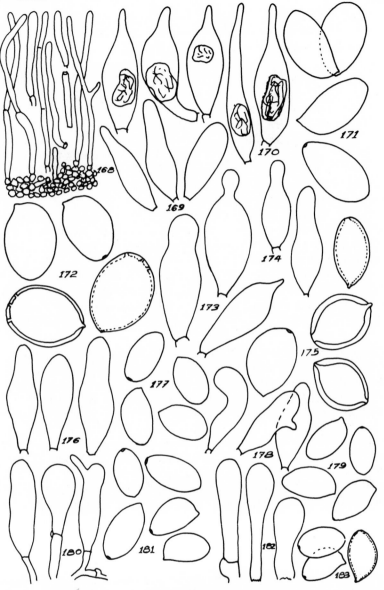

Text Fig. 11.

Figs. 168-171, pileus cuticle, cheilocystidia, pleurocystidia and spores of *P. abberans;* 172-174, spores, pleurocystidia and cheilocystidia of *P. variabilispora;* 175 & 176, spores and cheilocystidia of *P. subangularis;* 177 & 178, spores and cheilocystidia of *P. alnicola;* 179 & 180, spores and cheilocystidia of *P. subvelutina;* 181, spores of *P. oregonensis;* 182 & 183, cheilocystidia and spores of *P. flavida.*

Pileus 2.5–4 cm broad, convex, not fully expanding, viscid, soon dry, glabrous, ochraceous. Context yellow; odor and taste mild.

Lamellae adnate to subdecurrent, pale yellow, finally brown, close, rather broad.

Stipe 3–5 cm long, 5–8 mm thick, clavate-bulbous, dry concolorous. Veil arachnoid, white, copious, leaving an evanescent ring.

Spores 7–9 (10) × 4.5–5.5 (6) μ, elliptic to oval in face view, in profile elliptic to obscurely inequilateral, smooth, tawny in KOH but on standing become paler and more ochraceous, in Melzer's reagent slowly becoming dark reddish twany, wall (as measured in Melzer's reagent) 0.6–0.8 (1) μ thick, as measured in KOH (after mount stood for 2 hours or more) 1–1.8 μ thick, apical pore evident and in KOH mounts the apex obscurely truncated in some.

Basidia 4-spored, subcylindric to narrowly clavate, 26–30 × 6–7.5 μ, yellowish in Melzer's reagent, when first revived in KOH near lemon-yellow but fading to near hyaline. Pleurocystidia absent or present as contorted basidia (same size but more irregular in shape), irregular in occurrence. Cheilocystidia present merely as basidioles (edge seen with mostly fertile basidia). Caulocystidia slender, 30–80 (100) × 4–7 μ, flexuous-elongate to almost setiform, walls thickened slightly and ochraceous in KOH, smooth.

Gill trama of parallel thin-walled, non-gelatinous hyphae lemon-yellow to pale ochraceous in KOH, cells short and much inflated in central part, narrow to the cellular non-gelatinous inconspicuous subhymenium. No incrustations seen. Pileus cutis a gelatinous pellicle of narrow (2–4.5 μ) incrusted but nearly hyaline interwoven hyphae, collapsing, image not sharp (walls gelatinous); hypodermial area of floccose hyphae 4–9 μ diam. with tawny incrustations as revived in KOH (mostly as bands). Context hyphae inflated to 8–15 μ, thin-walled and yellowish to hyaline in KOH. Clamp connections present. All hyphae inamyloid.

HABIT, HABITAT, AND DISTRIBUTION: On dead fir (*Abies*), North Carolina, September, Hesler 1400, type.

OBSERVATIONS: This is a distinctive species on the basis of the thick-walled spores, lack of pleurocystidia (for all practical purposes) and the peculiar caulocystidia. It is clearly in the *P. alnicola-malicola* group. Here it's distinguishing features are the incrusted cuticular hyphae, the long flexuous often almost setiform caulocystidia with yellow walls in KOH, and lack of a distinctive odor or taste. In KOH the spores of *P. abieticola* are almost identical in color with those of *P. malicola*: a dark yellow brown, but in Melzer's both become somewhat dextrinoid (reddish tawny). Both have spore walls that swell appreciably in 2% KOH.

88. Pholiota subvelutina sp. nov.
Illustrations: Text figs. 179-180.

Pileus 6–12 cm latus, laete luteus, udus. Lamellae laete luteae, subdistantes. Stipes 8–10 cm longus, 8–17 mm crassus, sursum luteus, deorsum sordide brunneus. Sporae 7–10 × 4–5 μ. Pleurocystidia desunt. Velum hyphorum crassotunicatum. Specimen typicum in Herb. Univ. Mich. conservatum est; legit prope Florence, Ore., 22 Nov. 1934, Smith 3590.

Pileus 6–12 cm broad, convex to plane or the disc somewhat depressed, in age the margin elevated, surface with patches of converging fibrils particularly near the margin, glabrescent, viscid, "antimony-yellow" to "yellow-ochre," becoming darker ("cinnamon-brown") on the disc, margin faintly striate when moist, opaque after losing moisture. Context rather thin, tapering gradually to the margin, watery yellow, rather pliant; odor faintly fragrant, taste none.

Lamellae adnate or slightly adnexed, bright yellow, soon rusty (near ochraceous-tawny), narrow, subdistant to close, edges even.

Stipe 8–10 cm long, 8–17 mm thick, yellow above, dark sordid-brown below, appressed-fibrillose to subvelutinous, striate up to the fibrillose ring, equal or apex flattened, base clavate-enlarged.

Spores (7) 8–10 × 4–5 μ, smooth, germ pore at apex evident but apex not truncate; shape in face view ovate to subelliptic, in profile more or less distinctly inequilateral varying toward elliptic, apiculus small and inconspicuous; color in KOH golden-fulvous to fulvous, in Melzer's reagent distinctly tawny red (somewhat dextrinoid); wall about 0.3 μ thick.

Basidia 4-spored, 22–30 × 6.5–8 μ, subclavate to utriform, yellowish in KOH and in Melzer's reagent. Pleurocystidia none. Cheilocystidia 25–38 × 6.5–10 μ, irregularly clavate or apex with one or more apical to sublateral protuberances, utriform or fusoid-ventricose to inflated-pedicellate, walls thin but in some cells (of all types) with pale cinnamon walls as revived in KOH. Caulocystidia none.

Gill trama of floccose hyphae, cells broad (to 15 μ) and greatly elongated; walls thin, ochraceous to pallid in KOH, smooth; subhymenium a thin subcellular (cut ends of hyphae?) non-gelatinous layer pale yellow to pallid in KOH. Pileus cutis with 3 distinct features: 1) over the surface occurs a thin wheft of interwoven non-gelatinous hyphae 3–5 μ diam. with walls thin to slightly thickened (± 0.3 μ) and bright rusty brown in KOH, in Melzer's reagent merely yellowish. 2) a thick pellicle of gelatinous hyphae (their outline indistinct), yellowish, often encrusted, and 2–4 μ diam., the layer yellowish in KOH. 3) the hypodermial zone of compactly arranged ochraceous to ochraceous-rusty hyphae with walls non-gelatinous and smooth to encrusted. Context hyphae interwoven, the cells inflated; with smooth, ochraceous to paler, thin to slightly thickened walls. Surface of stipe with a dense covering of brown slender thick-walled hyphae with frequent clamps. All hyphae inamyloid.

HABIT, HABITAT, AND DISTRIBUTION: Caespitose or subcaespitose, on rotton log, Oregon, November, Smith 3590, type.

OBSERVATIONS: This is a moderately large fungus, with a fibrillose-subscaly, yellow pileus, with a slight fragrance, narrow gills, and large, yellowish, subvelutinous stipe which is clavate below. The colored thick-walled fibrils on the stipe are most unusual.

89. Pholiota oregonensis Murrill, Mycologia 4: 262. 1912.
Hypodendrum oregonense Murrill, Mycologia 4: 262. 1912.
Illustrations: Text fig. 181.

Pileus 5 cm or broader when mature, convex, obtuse, ochraceous-buff to ochraceous-tawny, glabrous, dry, margin strongly incurved. Context thin, cremeous; taste nutty or amygdaline in dried specimens.

Lamellae adnate, yellow or yellowish brown, becoming darker, medium-distant to distant, strongly interveined.

Stipe 6–10 cm long, 8–20 mm thick, yellowish above, fulvous below, with small, scattered, unicolorous, subfloccose, evanescent scales pointing upward, terete or compressed, equal or enlarged upward or downward, solid. Veil forming a superior or nearly apical, irregular, yellowish white annulus.

Spores 7.5–10 × 4–5 (6) μ, smooth, germ pore very minute; shape in face view more or less distinctly ovate, in profile inequilateral to obscurely so; color in KOH dull cinnamon, in Melzer's reagent dark reddish tawny (dextrinoid).

Basidia 25–34 × 5–7.5 μ, narrowly clavate, usually with a long narrow (2–3 μ) pedicel, 4-spored, hyaline to yellowish in KOH and Melzer's reagent. Pleurocystidia none. Cheilocystidia 23–33 × 3–9 μ, cylindric-flexuous to more or less clavate, hyaline, thin-walled, content not distinctive. Caulocystidia present as clavate end-cells of filamentous hyphae, not distinctive.

Gill trama of interwoven refractive hyphae with cinnabar to orange-yellow content in Melzer's reagent, "colloidal" in KOH, walls thin and smooth; subhymenium of narrow interwoven somewhat gelatinous hyphae. Pileus cuticle a well defined layer of subgelatinous refractive narrow hyphae 2–3 μ diam. hyaline to yellowish in KOH and Melzer's reagent; hypodermial region of ochraceous hyphae with colloidal-appearing content as revived in KOH, in Melzer's this layer and context hyphae with cinnabar to ochraceous or orange content. Clamp connections present.

HABIT, HABITAT, AND DISTRIBUTION: On a living willow, Oregon, November. Known from the type (Murrill, 754).

OBSERVATIONS: This species is likely to be mistaken in the field for *Gymnopilus spectabilis* but the latter is easily distinguished in the laboratory by the rough spores. Overholts (1928) pointed out the similarity. The dextrinoid spores, bright colors and lack of pleurocystidia place the species immediately in stirps *Alnicola*. The pleurocystidia observed by Overholts were more than likely immature basidia. The same situation as regards viscidity that applies to *P. flammans* and *P. alnicola* also applies here. The cuticle has all the features of one which becomes a gelatinous pellicle in wet weather.

For the time being at least we recognize both *P. malicola* var. *macropoda* and *P. oregonensis*. Both fruit in large clusters and both tend to have greatly enlarged stipes. In *P. malicola* var. *macropoda* the substrate is conifer wood whereas in *P. oregonensis* it is willow. This may not be significant taxonomically. *P. oregonensis* has distant gills and a scaly stipe with the scales pointing upward. We have not seen this in *P. malicola* var. *macropoda*. In the latter the pileus colors are apparently brighter, a faint though distinct odor is present when specimens are fresh, and the gills are typically close.

90. Pholiota flavida (Fr.) Singer, Lilloa 22: 516. 1949. (issued 1951) var. **flavida.**
Agaricus flavidus Fries, Syst. Myc. 1: 250. 1821.
Flammula flavida (Fr.) Quélet, Champ. Jura & Vosges 130. 1872.
Dryophila flavida (Fr.) Quélet, Enchir. Fung. p. 71. 1886.
Illustrations: Text figs. 182-183; pl. 34.

Pileus 3–7 cm broad, convex, expanding to broadly convex or nearly plane, margin incurved at first, surface thinly viscid and glabrous except for faint veil remnants variously arranged along the margin, yellow to watery dingy ochraceous-tawny, near "warm-buff" or brighter where faded, often with a watery zone along the margin. Context rather thick and firm, yellowish; odor faintly fragrant, taste mild.

Lamellae adnate to adnexed, close, narrow to moderately broad, pallid when young, pale rusty brown to "Sudan brown" in age, thin, edges even, no color change when bruised.

Stipe (4) 6–10 (12) cm long, 5–15 mm thick, equal or narrowed below, solid, pallid and silky above, with a faint evanescent zone of fibrils from the thin veil, lower part fibrillose-striate, becoming dark rust brown from base upward. Veil yellowish.

Spores 7–9 × 4–5 μ, smooth, apical pore distinct and apex in many appearing slightly truncate; shape ovate to subelliptic in face view, in profile somewhat inequilateral, with a slight apiculus and a faint suprahilar depression in some; color in KOH dull tawny fading to ochraceous on standing, in Melzer's reagent soon decidedly darker and redder (somewhat dextrinoid).

Basidia 4-spored, 24–32 × 5–7 μ, utriform (mostly slightly ventricose in midportion), yellowish in KOH and also in Melzer's reagent. Pleurocystidia none, cheilocystidia versiform, 26–40 × 3–9 μ, subclavate, subfusoid to near cylindric but outline mostly irregular, thin-walled, smooth, content homogeneous. Caulocystidia similar to cheilocystidia or longer and more versiform: 1) clavate and 15 × 9 μ (these rare); 2) elongate-subclavate 30–55 × 5–8 μ, outline irregular; 3) a few utriform-elongate,

34–47 × 7–10 μ walls thickened to about 1 μ and bright rusty brown, with or without encrusting material.

Gill trama of subparallel hyphae with thin, smooth, yellowish walls (in KOH) the cells elongate inflated 4–6 μ wide becoming up to 15 μ; subhymenium a very narrow non-gelatinous cellular zone (about 2 cells deep). Pileus cutis a thick gelatinous layer of hyphae 2.5–6 μ diam., dispersed loosely in the matrix, the hyphae ochraceous to hyaline and smooth to slightly incrusted; hypodermial zone not very distinct but slightly more colored than the context, hyphae smooth, 4–12 μ diam. Context hyphae with smooth, thin, pale greenish yellow walls in KOH, hyphal cells inflated, some orange-rufous oleiferous hyphae present. Clamp connections present. All hyphae inamyloid.

Habit, habitat, and distribution: Caespitose on logs and at the base of trees and stumps of conifers and hardwood, Maine, Idaho and Oregon, August-November.

Observations: The fragrant odor, pallid gills when young, small spores, and utriform basidia appear to distinguish it. In some caps the hypodermium is rusty orange but fades on standing. Odorless collections of this variety appear to be identical with a collection of *Flammula flavida* sensu Konrad & Maublanc from Josserand, Lyons, France. Fries described this species as having gills at first whitish, which fits our material. This is our common species on conifers in the Rocky Mountain area.

It will probably always be a rather hopeless problem to deal with the confusing literature on the "*P. alnicola*" problem on the one hand and the variation of the fungus in nature on the other. We have simply based our concept on excellent specimens from Europe which check with ours in all respects including the well developed gelatinous epicutis of the pileus which consists of a tangled mass of narrow yellowish to hyaline hyphae. Moser (1955) gives the spores as 6–7 × 4–4.5 μ; obviously this is not the same as Josserand's material. The odor in our specimens varies from none to faintly fragrant.

We have also studied a collection by Lundell from Sweden which Pilat annotated as *F. alnicola*. The following are our data on it. This apparently is a variant of the same species as Josserand's collection, but differing in the iodine reactions of the context hyphae and could possibly be our var. *graveolens*. In the Lundell collection we assume the taste was mild. There is no data on this character with the specimen:

Spores 7–9 × 4–5 μ smooth, apical pore present but minute, shape in face view ovate to elliptic, in profile somewhat inequilateral, color in KOH ochraceous-tawny to duller pale tawny, in Melzer's reagent rusty brown (dextrinoid); wall around 0.3 μ thick.

Basidia 4-spored, 22–26 × 6.5–8 μ, clavate, yellowish to hyaline in KOH, not changing appreciably in Melzer's reagent. Pleurocystidia none. Cheilocystidia mostly clavate, 26–34 × 7–10 μ, hyaline, smooth, content homogeneous. Caulocystidia 33–60 × 6–9 μ, cylindric to narrowly clavate, hyaline in KOH, thin-walled, content "empty."

Gill trama subparallel, of floccose-interwoven thin-walled hyphae; walls yellowish in KOH, smooth, content often orange-brown in Melzer's reagent. Subhymenium not a sharply defined layer, hyphae compactly interwoven, non-gelatinous (in sections the layer appearing more or less cellular). Pileus cutis a gelatinous pellicle of mostly ochraceous narrow (2–3 μ) gelatinous hyphae smooth to incrusted, hypodermial region of ochraceous, incrusted floccose hyphae 4–10 μ diam. Context hyphae interwoven, filled with "colloidal" content, becoming rusty reddish in Melzer's reagent. Clamp connections present.

90a. Pholiota flavida var. graveolens var. nov.
Illustrations: Pl. 35.

Pileus 5–7 cm latus, late convexus, viscidus, glaber, sordide luteus. Contextus luteolus; odor graveolens. Lamellae adnatae, latae confertae, luteae demum castaneae. Stipes 9–13 cm longus, 7–9 mm crassus, sursum luteolus, deorsum subcastaneus, sparse fibrillosus. Sporae 8–10 × 4.5–5 μ. Pleurocystidia desunt. Cheilocystidia 23–36 × 5–8 μ, subventricosis saepe irregularis. Specimen typicum in Herb. Univ. Mich. conservatum est; legit prope Priest Lake, Idaho. 26 Sept. 1964. Smith 70814.

Pileus 5–7 cm broad, plane with a decurved margin, viscid, glabrous, dingy honey-tan where not covered with spores, fading to dingy ochraceous (chestnut where covered with deposited spores in age). Context pliant; odor heavy and like some fats, taste mild; FeSO$_4$ no reaction, KOH no reaction.

Lamellae adnate-seceding, dingy yellow, becoming "auburn" from spores, horizontal, fairly broad, close, edges even.

Stipe 9–13 cm long, 7–9 mm thick, equal, yellowish pallid at apex, dark rusty chestnut from base up, thinly fibrillose from a very thin veil which leaves a few indistinct patches on the cap margin, cortex colored.

Spore deposit "chestnut" to "auburn" (with a strong red tinge). Spores 8–10 × 4.5–5 μ, smooth, apical pore distinct, wall thickened (0.3–0.4 μ); shape narrowly elliptic to ovate in face view, in profile somewhat inequilateral to subovate; dingy cinnamon or paler in KOH, more reddish cinnamon in Melzer's reagent.

Basidia 23–29 × 7–8 μ, 4-spored, yellowish in KOH or Melzer's. Pleurocystidia none; cheilocystidia 34–47 × 4–12 μ ventricose near base and with a crooked neck ending in an obtuse apex. Thin-walled. Gill trama with an indistinct cellular hymenium, central area of smooth inflated hyphae (to 25 μ). Pileus epicutis a pellicle of gelatinous hyphae 2.5–6 μ diam., yellow in KOH but fading; hypodermium yellow in KOH. Clamp connections present.

HABIT, HABITAT, AND DISTRIBUTION: Caespitose at base of a conifer stub, near Priest Lake, Idaho, Sept. 26, 1964. Smith 70814.

OBSERVATIONS: The color of the spore deposit is that of the type variety but the peculiar odor seems to distinguish it. The fresh specimens reminded one of *Pholiota mutabilis* except that the stipe was not scaly. The color of the spore deposit is a variation in the direction of the genus *Psilocybe*. The anatomy of the basidiocarps is that of the *P. alnicola* group.

91. Pholiota malicola (Kauff.) A. H. Smith Ann. Myc. 32: 480. 1934.
Flammula sulphurea Peck, New York State Mus. Bull. 157: 26. 1912. (non *F. sulphurea* Massee, 1902).
Flammula alnicola var. *marginalis* Peck, New York State Mus. Ann. Rept. 54: 167, 1901.
Flammula malicola Kauffman, Amer. Journ. Bot. 13: 24. 1926.
Illustrations: Text figs. 184-185; pls. 36, 37.

Var. *malicola*

Pileus, 3–6 (10–15) cm broad, evenly obtusely conic at first, remaining so in age or becoming conic campanulate, finally nearly plano-umbonate, viscid at first but soon dry and shining, at first decorated with thin patches of brownish fibrils from the veil, glabrescent, evenly "wax-yellow," "straw-yellow," "zinc-orange," or with a greenish tinge and then sulphur yellow, fading as though slightly hygrophanous, margin opaque. Context thick on disc, thin on margin, whitish; pliant, odor and taste not distinctive or rarely slightly alkaline.

Lamellae adnate to sinuate, narrow, tapered evenly outward, close to crowded, concolorous with pileus at first, finally "Kaiser-brown" (reddish cinnamon) from the spores, edges white-fimbriate or eroded.

Stipe 4–12 cm long, 4–12 mm thick, equal or base clavate-enlarged, fibrous, solid, pallid to yellowish within, surface at first concolorous with pileus or apical region whitish, darkening to tawny below, veil remnants yellowish to pallid, distributed as patches of fibrils below the superior annulus, or annular zone, and becoming tawny like the base; annulus fibrillose or submembranous, at times poorly formed and evanescent.

Spore deposit ferruginous ("hazel" or "cinnamon rufous" or "amber-brown"); spores 8.5–11 (12) × 4.5–5.5 (6) μ, in face view elliptic to ovate or a few obscurely fusoid, in profile obscurely to rather distinctly inequilateral, smooth, germ pore present but small, wall (in KOH) up to 0.8–1 μ thick, in Melzer's reagent 0.5–0.8 μ thick, as revived in KOH fairly dark dull yellow-brown (near "Dresden brown"), in Melzer's reagent reddish tawny.

Basidia 25–33 × 6–8 μ, 4-spored, clavate to subcylindric, yellowish in KOH and Melzer's reagent. Pleurocystidia none. Cheilocystidia 22–45 × 4–9 μ, fusoid-ventricose, utriform, or elongate-subcapitate, hyaline to yellow in KOH and Melzer's reagent, content homogeneous. Caulocystidia

25–52 (100) × 5–8 μ, clavate to subcylindric, thin-walled, hyaline in KOH, content homogeneous.

Gill trama parallel becoming somewhat interwoven, hyphae 3–6 (9) μ wide, at first but cells much more inflated in age, walls yellow in KOH, smooth, non-gelatinous; subhymenium a narrow zone of cellular structure (cells 3–7 μ diam.) non-gelatinous in KOH. Pileus cutis consisting of a well defined gelatinous pellicle of smooth narrow (2–4 μ) hyphae becoming irregular in outline in age or finally appearing somewhat roughened; hypodermial zone of more intensely ochraceous to rusty-ochraceous hyphae but not structurally differentiated. Context hyphae yellowish to hyaline in KOH, inflated to ± 15 μ in some, walls thin (near subhymenium some showing middle lamellae as revived in KOH). Clamp connections present. All hyphae inamyloid.

HABIT, HABITAT, AND DISTRIBUTION: Caespitose at the base of trees and stumps, or on debris of conifers and hardwoods, or attached to buried wood, New York, Pennsylvania, Michigan, and in Canada in Quebec and Ontario July—November.

OBSERVATIONS: Massee described *Flammula sulphurea* in 1902. Later, Peck (1912) used the same specific epithet for a different taxon. Finally, Kauffman (1926) proposed for Peck's agaric the name *Flammula malicola*. Peck's *F. alnicola* var. *marginata* appears to be the same as *P. malicola* var. *malicola*.

It seems likely from Orton's description that his *Pholiota aromatica* would also fall in this group. It should be carefully compared with *P. malicola*. We are inclined to regard with suspicion the terrestrial habitat of any caespitose *Pholiota* since we suspect that the vegetative mycelium of all of them lives on wood or lignicolous debris concentrated in the soil, and it must be remembered that Orton himself specified "on ground near oaks."

Flammula connisans Fr. sensu Kauffman (1926) is a variant of *P. malicola*. The subgenus *Flammula* as defined here is badly in need of studies in culture as well as further field studies. The pattern which Smith is encountering in his field work is that the characters of odor, spore color, pileus shape, etc. occur in all possible combinations so the question naturally arises as to whether we have many "species" or (and more probably) an extremely variable complex.

MATERIAL EXAMINED: MICHIGAN: Kauffman 9-22-24; Smith 32-508, 38240, 38241, 50622, 68798, 71448. NEW YORK: House 10-25-44. OHIO: Walters 12. PENNSYLVANIA: Overholts 16043. CANADA—ONTARIO: Groves 11923; Smith 4895. QUEBEC: Groves 9-9-54.

91a. Pholiota malicola var. **macropoda** var. nov.
Illustrations: Pls. 38, 39.

Pileus (3)4–12(15) cm latus, late convexus, viscidus vel subviscidus, glaber, luteus, olidus. Lamellae sublatae, confertae, adnatae, pallidae demum luteae. Stipes 6–10(18) cm longus, 4–10(25) mm crassus, sparse fibrillosus, sursum pallidus vel luteus, deorsum demum fulvus. Sporae 7.5–11 × 4.5–5.5 μ. Pleurocystidia nulla. Specimen typicum in Herb. Univ. Mich. conservatum est; legit prope Pen Basin, Landmark, Idaho, 5 Aug. 1958 Smith 59660.

Pileus (3) 4–12 (15) cm broad, convex, expanding to broadly convex or nearly plane, margin often wavy to lobed, viscid, glabrous except for faint veil remnants along the margin, disc orange-buff, pale yellow to watery dingy ochraceous-tawny, near "warm-buff" or brighter where faded, often with a watery zone along the incurved margin. Context rather thick and firm, yellowish; odor faintly fragrant, often suggestive of green corn; taste mild; with FeSO₄ bright green.

Lamellae close, adnate to adnexed, yellowish when young, pale rusty-brown in age, narrow to moderately broad, thin, edges even, color change when bruised none or at times slowly orange.

Stipe (4) 6–10 (18) cm long, 4–10 (25) mm thick, equal or narrowed below, solid, surface pallid to yellowish and silky above, with a faint evanescent zone of fibrils from the thin veil, lower part fibrillose-striate, becoming dark rusty brown from base upward, veil pallid to buff.

Spores 7.5–11 × 4.5–5.5 μ, smooth, apical pore distinct but apex not truncate; in shape narrowly ovate to nearly elliptic, in profile somewhat inequilateral to narrowly oval; in KOH dingy pale tawny becoming more ochraceous on standing, in Melzer's reagent moderately dextrinoid (tawny-red) wall about 0.3 μ thick.

Basidia 20–25 (30) × 5–6 μ, 4-spored, clavate, yellow in KOH and also in Melzer's reagent. Pleurocystidia none. Cheilocystidia (20) 30–41 × 6–9 μ, clavate to somewhat fusoid-ventricose but mostly irregular in outline, smooth, thin-walled, content homogeneous. Caulocystidia versiform, 25 × 10 μ, or 28–47 × 4–9 μ, some occasionally more elongate-subclavate, hyaline to yellowish in KOH, walls thin and smooth, content homogeneous.

Gill trama a central area of floccose subparallel hyphae with short cells becoming inflated in age or cells more elongate toward gill edge, walls thin, smooth and pale yellow in KOH; subhymenium cellular, 2–5 cells, deep, not gelatinous. Pileus cutis a gelatinous layer of yellowish hyphae 3–5 μ diam. and having incrustations of pigments over them, grading evenly into a zone of wider (5–10 μ) hyphae with smooth to heavily incrusted walls tawny in KOH and orange to red in Melzer's sol. Context hyphae of inflated cells with thin smooth pale yellowish walls in KOH. Clamp connections present. All hyphae inamyloid.

HABIT, HABITAT, AND DISTRIBUTION: Caespitose on conifer and hardwood trees, at the base of stumps or attached to buried wood, Michigan, Idaho, the Pacific Northwest and Northern California, August-November.

OBSERVATIONS: This resembles the type variety, but differs in its fragrant odor, its more yellowish flesh, and more poorly developed veil. The stipe tends to become greatly enlarged in age.

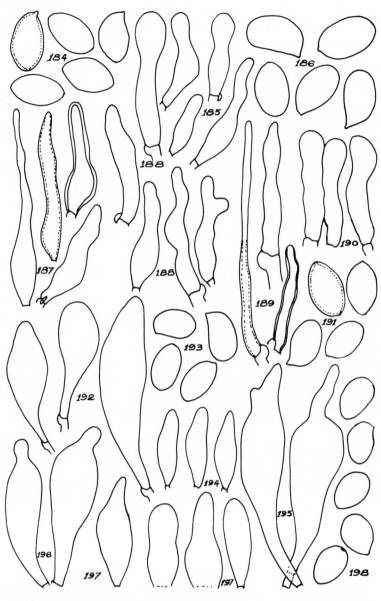

Text Fig. 12.

Figs. 184 & 185, spores and cheilocystidia of *P. malicola* var. *mali-cola;* 186-188, spores and cheilocystidia of *P. sola;* 189-191, caluocystidia, cheilocystidia and spores of *P. abieticola;* 192-195, pleurocystidia, spores, cheilocystidia and caulocystidia of *P. rigidipes;* 196-198, pleurocystidia, cheilocystidia and spores of *P. penningtoniana.*

MATERIAL EXAMINED: CALIFORNIA: White 551. IDAHO: Smith 59660 (type), 60741, 60742, 65989, 70146, 70887. OREGON: Smith 19458, 55877. WASHINGTON: Smith 3362.

Subgenus **Pholiota**

In keeping with the features of the type of the genus, the group is defined as containing species with both pileus and stipe distinctly scaly. It serves as a connecting link from species with no gelatinous layers in the subhymenium or pileus cuticle to those with a gelatinous sub-hymenium and slimy pileus surface. Obviously closely related species in which one or both of these features are somewhat reduced are also placed here. Chrysocystidia or very similar sterile cells are found in the hymenium of many of the species.

TYPE SPECIES: *Pholiota squarrosa*.

Section **Pholiota**

Key to Stirpes

1. Spores 7–10 (11) × 4.5–5.5 μ, very dark brown in KOH (*Agaricus*-like), and with a prominent apiculus .... Stirps *Fulvosquamosa*
1. Spores not as above 2
   2. Pileus and subhymenium both lacking any gelatinized layers; sub-hymenium more or less cellular .... Stirps *Schraderi*
   2. Not as above 3
3. Pileus cuticle lacking a gelatinous layer; subhymenium gelatinous ......
.... Stirps *Squarrosa*
3. Pileus with a gelatinous subcutis or pellicle 4
   4. Pileus with a gelatinous subcutis often obscured until near maturity by dry fibrillose-scaly epicutis .... Stirps *Squarrosoides*
   4. Pileus with a gelatinous cutis which is obvious at an early stage
.... Stirps *Adiposa*

Stirps Fulvosquamosa

It is questionable whether the central species actually belongs in *Pholiota* since the spores are typical of *Agaricus,* but we do not have data on fresh material. *Stropharia kauffmanii* appears to be the most closely related species, but it is not typical of *Stropharia* in many respects in spite of the color of the spore deposit.

92. **Pholiota fulvosquamosa** Peck, Bull. Torrey Club 30: 95. 1903. *Hypodendrum fulvosquamosum* (Pk.) Overholts, North Amer. Fl. 10; 281. 1932.

Pileus 6–12 cm broad, dry, convex becoming nearly plane, covered with a tawny fibrous cuticle of brownish fibrillose scales, the lighter colored flesh showing when the fibers separate into scales, sometimes concentrically cracked about the disc. Context thin, white, becoming brownish where cut; odor and taste of radish.

Lamellae adnate or joined to a narrow collar, narrow, attenuated near stipe, close, whitish becoming pinkish cinnamon then dark cinnamon, edges white-crenulate.

Stipe 5–8 cm long, 8–10 mm thick, covered below the ring with numerous erect, subfloccose, tawny scales, slightly floccose above the annulus, equal, stuffed or hollow. Veil forming an ample, membranous, persistent annulus, which is white above and tawny floccose-squamulose below.

Spores (6) 7–10 (11) × 4.5–5.5 μ, smooth, lacking an apical pore, in face view elliptic, in profile elliptic to obscurely inequilateral, as revived in KOH dark chocolate brown.

Basidia 25–28 × 7–8 μ, 4-spored, clavate. Pleurocystidia none. Cheliocystidia 20–28 × 7–9 μ, clavate-capitate, inconspicuous. Gill trama subparallel, hyphae 8–12 μ broad, floccose. Pileus trama interwoven. Pileus cuticle not sharply differentiated; surface bearing clumps of brownish hyphae (the scales). Clamp connections none. All tissues inamyloid.

Habit, habitat, and distribution: About the base of oak trees, Michigan, September. Type studied.

Observations: It is possible that we have here a distinct *Agaricus*-like genus comprising two species, Peck's and *Stropharia kauffmanii* Smith. The latter has dull violaceous drab gills when mature in contrast to Peck's species with dark cinnamon gills. Harper (1914, pl. 60) gives an excellent illustration of *P. fulvo-squamosa*. Harding (1952) thought it the same as *Agaricus subrufescens,* and Overholts (1927) commented that the scales on the pileus reminded him of those on *A. subrufescens.* The absence of clamp connections also seems to indicate a relationship to *Agaricus.*

Stirps Schraderi

The subhymenium is of cellular to filamentous structure but not gelatinous, the pileus is dry and lacks gelatinous layers. In these features the genus *Inocybe* comes to mind as a possibly related group, but the spores of *P. schraderi* and *P. scabella* have a minute pore. The group may seem artificial to some, but the species at least are united by basic characters. The basidiocarps of the three species do not closely resemble each other in aspect.

Key

1. Spores 8–10 × 4.5–5.5 μ .... *P. sola*

1. Spores smaller (6–8 × 4–4.5 μ) 2
  2. Pleurocystidia 38–78 × 10–14 μ .... *P. schraderi*
  2. Pleurocystidia smaller and at least some of them chrysocystidia ....
  .... *P. scabella*

93. Pholiota sola sp. nov.
Illustrations: Text figs. 186-188; pl. 40b.

Pileus 2–3 cm latus, obtusus demum obtuse campanulatus, vel sub-planus, fibrilloso-squamulosus; squamulae luteo-brunneae; contextus sub-spadiceus. Lamellae decurrentes, confertae, latae, pallide subluteae de-mum subfuscae. Stipes 6–8 cm longus, 7–8 mm crassus, intus subolivaceus, extus pallide luteus, deorsum squamosus; squamae recurvatae. Sporae 8–10.5 × 4.5–5.5 μ. Pleuro-pseudocystidia 3–9 μ latae. Cheilocystidia 35–56 × 6–8 × 2.5–3 μ fusoide-ventricosa et proliferata. Specimen typicum in Herb. Univ. Mich. conservatum est; legit prope Tahquamenon Falls State Park, 2 Aug. 1951. Smith 37424.

Pileus 2–3 cm broad, obtuse with an incurved margin, expanding to obtusely umbonate, or nearly plane and the umbo obsolete, surface appressed fibrillose-squamulose, the scales most distinct along the margin, ground color between avellaneous and cinnamon buff, squamules and fibrils "tawny-olive" to "cinnamon-brown." Context near "Saccardo's umber" (dark yellow-brown), fading; taste and odor none.

Lamellae decurrent, close, moderately broad, "cream-buff" when young, finally earth-brown from the spores.

Stipe 6–8 cm long, 7–8 mm thick, equal, tubular, dingy pale olive-yellowish inside, exterior near apex yellowish (paler than gills) yellow less evident toward the base, covered to the apical annular zone with scattered tawny-olive squamules concolorous with pileus over all except the apex.

Spores 8–10.5 × 4.5–5.5 μ, smooth, apical pore none, shape in face view oblong to elliptic, some obscurely angular, in profile more or less bean-shaped, in KOH tawny-cinnamon and about the same color in Melzer's reagent.

Basidia 30–54 × 6–9 μ, 4-spored, clavate, hyaline and homogeneous in KOH or some with granular pale ochraceous content, in Melzer's reagent a fair number with very dark yellow-brown to bister granular-amorphous content causing them to stand out prominently in mounts in Melzer's. Pleurocystidia present as crooked filaments with granular content, yellowish in KOH or in Melzer's with very dark yellow-brown granular to amorphous content and often seen connected to oleiferous hyphae with the same content, the cells 3–9 μ broad and length extremely variable. Cheilocystidia versiform: 1) subcylindric to subfusoid, walls often flexuous, 25–44 × 4–7 μ; 2) ventricose at base and proliferated into a narrow crooked neck, 35–56 × 6–8 × 2.5–3 μ; 3) fusoid-ventricose with wavy neck and obtuse apex, 24–35 × 5–8 μ; some cystidia branched at apex, walls hyaline or toward cap margin many with pale cinnamon brown walls in some part or overall. Caulocystidia 45–76 × 6–18 μ clavate to cylindric, walls brown, occurring in tufts.

Gill trama of parallel hyphae 4–10 μ broad, hyaline in KOH and thin-walled; subhymenium cellular. Pileus cutis with an epicutis in the form of a tangled turf of brown-walled hyphae smooth to slightly incrusted, ochraceous in KOH, dark red-brown in Melzer's reagent; arising from a layer of appressed yellow-brown hyphae. Content hyphae hyaline to yellowish in KOH, closely interwoven. Clamp connections present. Cutis hyphae weakly dextrinoid (reddish cinnamon).

HABIT, HABITAT, AND DISTRIBUTION: On humus, Michigan, August, Smith 37424, type.

OBSERVATIONS: This species is characterized by its avellaneous to cinnamon-buff colors, olive to brown fibrillose scales on the cap, twany-olive scales on the stipe, "pseudocystidia" and relatively large spores.

The features of this species are peculiar. The hyphae of the laticiferous system in some instances were seen to produce basidia—many of which were seen to bear immature spores; These basidia were often of indefinite length in that they could be traced back into the gill trama without finding a septum. The cheilocystidia are not typical of any *Inocybe* known to us though the spores and the anatomy of the pileus cutis suggest that genus. No cystidia were found over the basal or lower part of the stipe. Since the aspect of the basidiocarp is that of a *Pholiota* and the cheilocystidia are not out of line for that genus as far as shape is concerned, we describe the species here.

94. Pholiota schraderi (Pk.) Overholts, North Amer. Flora 10: 271. 1924.
Stropharia schaderi Peck, Bull. Torrey Bot. Club 32: 30. 1905.
Illustrations: Text figs. 493-496.

Pileus 5–8 cm broad, convex to nearly plane, pallid when young, ochraceous-buff when mature, dry, fibrillose, squamulose, or rimose-squamulose on the disc, squamules pale tawny in dried specimens. Context white; taste of radishes.

Lamellae adnate, whitish then brown, close, thin.

Stipe 2–4 cm long, 8–12 mm thick, squamulose and concolorous with the pileus below, white and mealy above, subequal. Veil forming a small white, lacerate, sometimes evanescent annulus.

Spores 6.5–8 (10) × 4–4.5 (5.5) μ, smooth, apical pore present but minute; shape in face view ovate to elliptic and many obscurely angular; in profile somewhat inequilateral to obscurely bean-shaped; color in KOH rather bright ochraceous to ochraceous tawny, in Melzer's reagent slightly duller; wall about 0.3 μ thick.

Basidia (21) 24–28 × 6–7.5 μ, 4-spored, when sporulating clavate or ventricose in lower half and cylindric above (obscurely urn-shaped), hyaline in KOH, in Melzer's reagent nearly hyaline. Pleurocystidia of two types: leptocystidia 40–60 (78) × 9–20 μ with a long narrow pedicel and clavate to utriform above or varying toward mucronate, content "empty," wall thin and smooth, or if thickened slightly then less than 0.5 μ thick; 2) chrysocystidia 28–44 × 7–12 μ, with refractive hyaline inclusion in KOH, in Melzer's the inclusion merely yellowish. Cheilocystidia 32–60 × 8–18 μ, similar to pleurocystidia (both types present). Caulocystidia present at stipe apex where a caulohymenium is present and both giant leptocystidia and chrysocystidia occur there as well as in the lamellar hymenium.

Gill trama of subparallel hyphae with colloidal content orange in Melzer's reagent, walls thin and hyaline, cells finally slightly inflated 3–8 μ or more diam.; subhymenium of non-gelatinous interwoven hyphae 3–5 μ diam., hyaline in KOH. Pileus context of inflated (8–15 μ) hyphae with thin smooth walls and "colloidal" content orange-red as revived in Melzer's reagent; cuticle of hyaline smooth narrow hyphae more or less appressed and no hypodermium differentiated; scales on pileus composed of fascicles of hyphae, the walls yellow in KOH, thin and smooth; cell content mostly "empty" but some with colloidal content; the cells in flated to sphaerocyst-like but varying in a single hypha to elongate. Clamp connections present. All hyphae inamyloid or dextrinoid as noted.

HABIT, HABITAT, AND DISTRIBUTION: On soil, District of Columbia, October. Type studied.

OBSERVATIONS: This species presents a problem in relationships because it is more closely related to *Stropharia hardii* and *S. caesiispora* than to any *Pholiota* known to us, yet it has bright ochraceous spores in KOH. Fresh spore deposits are needed to check the color. The deposit with the type collection is now near "snuff-brown" a yellow brown, but there is still a smoky tinge which could indicate that it was more purplish when fresh. In the light of the generic concept of *Pholiota* presented here we are forced to include the species as a *Pholiota* because of the spore features as described. It is related to *Stropharia kauffmanii* also, but in the latter the spores are definitely purplish. The germ pore of the spore in *P. schraderi* is clearly *Pholiota*-like.

95. Pholiota scabella Zeller, Mycologia 25: 386. 1933.

Pileus 6–10 cm broad, hemispheric to plano-expanded, dry, ochraceous, buff, to "Dresden brown," squamose to subsquarrose, shiny, cuticle separable. Context 8–12 mm thick, white to creamy; odor like certain green crushed stems (willow-like) ; taste bitterish acrid.

Lamellae adnate, with striate lines on the stipe (not a tooth) Saccardo's umber to sepia, narrow (4–5 mm broad), narrower in front than toward stipe, almost equal, close (not crowded), edges wavy.

Stipe 7–9 cm long, 15–20 mm thick, ivory-yellow and squarrose above, cream-buff and squamose scaly below annulus, staining ochraceous-buff or darker where bruised, almost equal, slightly tapering upward, solid and whitish within. Annulus membranous, persistent, 3–4 mm broad, median, deflexed, colored by the spores.

Spores 6–8.5 × 3.7–4.5 μ, elliptic to subovate, in profile slightly inequilateral; smooth, germ-pore minute.

Basidia 23–38 × 9–15 μ, 4-spored. Pleurocystidia of two kinds: 1) chrysocystidia 25–28 × 9–15 μ, clavate-mucronate to subfusoid, often with an amorphous content; 2) leptocystidia 50–54 × 10–17 μ, fusoid-ventricose to subcylindric, erratic in occurrence. Cheilocystidia 45–54 × 13–16 μ, fusoid-ventricose.

Gill trama slightly interwoven, hyphae 3–6 μ broad; subhymenium not distinctive. Pileus trama radial, somewhat interwoven. Cuticle not sharply differentiated, not viscid, the surface bearing some fascicles (the scales) of brown hyphae 6–12 μ broad and usually faintly incrusted. Clamp connections present.

HABIT, HABITAT, AND DISTRIBUTION: On soil, solitary, in dense coniferous forests, Oregon, October. Type studied.

OBSERVATIONS: We include this species with some reservations. A shiny pileus is not consistent with the scaly condition as described. It seems amply distinct as a species on macroscopic features, and the spores are certainly *Pholiota*-like.

Stirps Squarrosa

Key

1. Spores 6–8 μ long; some pleurocystidia hyaline in KOH and evenly refractive throughout .... *P. squarrosa*
1. Spores smaller (5–6.5 μ long) ; pleurocystidia not as above ....
.... *P. kodiakensis*

96. Pholiota squarrosa (Fr.) Kummer, Der Führer in die Pilzkunde, p. 84. 1871.

Agaricus squarrosus Fries, Syst. Myc. 1: 243. 1821.

Dryophila squarrosa (Fr.) Quélet, Enchir, Fung., p. 68. 1886.

Hypodendrum floccosum (Schaeff.) Overholts, North Amer. Fl. 10: 280. 1932.

Var. *squarrosa*

Illustrations: Pls. 41-43.

Pileus, 3–10 (12) cm broad, obtuse to convex when young, the margin incurved, becoming campanulate with a conic umbo to broadly convex or nearly plane, surface dry, cuticle broken up into numerous innate, recurved, or squarrose, scales, the margin at first conspicuously fringed with veil remnants, cuticle sometimes denuded along the edge leaving a glabrous margin, scales "cinnamon-buff" to "clay-color" and becoming dull tawny at maturity (light to dark yellowish brown), pale yellow between the scales, or in age pale greenish yellow along the margin. Context moderately thick and pliant, pale yellowish; odor none (or garlic in Smith 35793, 50928, 51814, 59711; of onion in Smith 51425, 51602, 52961), taste mild or slightly rancid.

Lamellae bluntly adnate to somewhat arcuate and with a decurrent line or tooth, close to crowded, narrow, pale yellowish when young, soon more or less sordid greenish yellow ("Isabella color"), and finally sordid rusty brown, edges even.

Stipe 4–10 (12) cm long, 4–12 (15) mm thick, equal or nearly so, at times tapered to a long strigose pointed base, solid, dry, yellowish within, surface covered with recurved pale tawny scales up to the annular zone, annulus often evanescent but sometimes membranous and persistent (and then pileus margin not conspicuously appendiculate).

Spores (5) 6–7.5 (8) × 3.8–4.5 μ, smooth, apical pore distinct but apex not truncate; shape in face view elliptic to ovate, in profile obscurely inequilateral to bean-shaped; dull tawny in KOH and near cinnamon in Melzer's reagent, wall about 0.25 μ thick.

Basidia (16) 20–25 × 5–7 μ, 4-spored, clavate, hyaline in KOH, yellowish in Melzer's reagent. Pleurocystidia present as chrysocystidia (26) 30–48 × (6) 8–16 μ, clavate to clavate-mucronate, apex papillate or drawn into a distinct projection, walls thin and smooth, refractive inclusion hyaline in KOH and dextrinoid in Melzer's reagent. Second type elliptic to oval-pedicellate or clavate, 30–45 × 9–14 μ, hyaline and evenly refractive throughout in KOH, yellowish in Melzer's reagent; walls thin and smooth. Cheilocystidia 18–43 × 5–15 μ, subfusoid, fusoid-ventricose, clavate or clavate-mucronate, some with highly refractive context. Caulocystidia present as filamentose-clavate cells 6–9 μ wide at apex, content homogeneous.

Gill trama of parallel floccose hyphae 5–8 μ broad or in age more inflated, walls thin smooth and hyaline, yellowish in KOH and Melzer's reagent; subhymenium of narrow (2–4 μ) gelatinous hyphae in a distinct layer. Pileus cutis a "collapsed" trichodermium of septate brown hyphae with smooth to incrusted walls, the terminal cell of a hypha clavate, subcylindric or fusoid-ventricose (cystidioid) 50–70 × 10–20 μ. Clamp connections present but not always abundant. All hyphae inamyloid.

HABIT, HABITAT, AND DISTRIBUTION: Caespitose on living conifer and hardwood trees, at the base of living or dead trees, or on logs and stumps, Michigan, Colorado, New Mexico, Idaho, Wyoming; also reported by Overholts (1927) from Maine, Massachusetts, New York, District of Columbia, Pennsylvania; and from Wisconsin by Harper (1913); and from Canada.

OBSERVATIONS: This is a showy, wood-inhabiting, conspicuously scaly *Pholiota*, with a dry pileus. The taste becomes more disagreeable as the basidiocarps age. The odor of garlic or onion reported for a number of collections however, as in Smith 59902 and 72388, is not dependent on the aging of the basidiocarps. The greenish gills in age will usually distinguish this species in the field from *P. squarrosoides*.

MATERIAL EXAMINED: COLORADO: Barrows 1418 (MICH); Smith 51425, 51602, 51814, 52435, 52961; IDAHO: Gruber P-23, P-53; Smith 15949, 46512, 47138, 53273, 59283, 59711, 59873, 60094, 60460, 60188, 66327, 69962; Solheim 5011; MICHIGAN: Shaffer 3787 (MICH); Smith 34135, 36093, 38316, 50156, 50928, 72388, 72691; Thiers 4426 (MICH); MINNESOTA: Kaplan 18; NEW MEXICO: Barrows 796, no number (1955); NEW YORK: Korf (no number) 1944; WYOMING: Smith 35409, 35793, 36239; Solheim 3094, 3561, 5083, 5160, 5161, 5214, 5220, 5327, 5444, 5959, 5990, 6259 (all MICH); Wehmeyer 4, 10 (MICH); CANADA: ONTARIO: Bell 4746 (TENN); Harper 9-1902 (MICH); Jackson 3711 (MICH); Smith 4561, 26545; AUSTRIA: Lowhag 1934 (MICH); FRANCE: Josserand 24-10-37; NETHERLANDS: Geestranus 9047; SWEDEN: Haglund 530; SWITZERLAND: Favre 2 colls. (MICH).

97. Pholiota kodiakensis sp. nov.
Illustrations: Text figs. 218-221.

Pileus 3.0–8.0 cm latus, late convexus, siccus, squamulosus; squamulae minutae; fulvus vel luteofulvus, ad marginem appendiculatus. Contextus pallidus, fragrans. Lamellae pallide luteae demum subfulvae, confertae, latae. Stipes 5.0–10.0 cm longus, 7–10 mm crassus, sursum subluteus et sericeus, deorsum squarroso-squamosus, intus pallide luteus. Sporae 5–6 × 3–3.5 µ. Pleuro-chrysocystidia 30–55 × 8–14 µ; pleuro-leptocystidia 23–40 × 5–11 µ, subclavata, vel subfusoide ventricosa. Specimen typicum in Herb. Univ. of Mich. conservatum est; legit prope Kodiak, Alaska, 27 Juli, 1964. Wells and Kempton no. 2.

Pileus 30–80 mm broad when expanded, convex at first with margin incurved, becoming nearly plane, surface dry and unpolished, with small squarrose scales overall in buttons, scales becoming separated and more appressed as pileus expands, in age often present only over the disc, margin at times decorated with veil remnants, colors tawny to orange ("raw sienna" to "raw umber"), becoming paler to nearly buff on margin at maturity. Context pallid to ivory, unchanging, thick in the disc, odor slight but fruity, taste mild.

Lamellae pale yellow in buttons, slowly becoming rusty brown, adnexed, close, moderately broad, (± 5 mm), edges concolorous and entire to slightly eroded.

Stipe 50–100 mm long, 7–10 mm broad at apex, equal, concolorous with pileus below, pale yellowish to tan at apex, silky fibrillose above veil line, squarrose scaly at first below. Veil material concolorous with scales on pileus; pale yellowish within above, paler downward at times. Annular zone on stipe from broken veil distinct.

Spore deposit rusty brown. Spores 5–6 × 3–3.5 μ, smooth, germ pore distinct and apex obscurely truncate in many; shape in face view ovate to elliptic, in profile slightly bean-shaped to subelliptic; in KOH ochraceous to tawny, paler in Melzer's reagent; wall about 0.3 μ thick.

Basidia 4-spored 18–26 × 3.5–5 μ, narrowly clavate, hyaline to ochraceous in KOH and Melzer's reagent. Pleurocystidia of two types: 1) clavate-mucronate to fusoid, 30–55 × 8–14 μ, wall thin, smooth, hyaline to yellowish, content with an inclusion of amorphous highly refractive material, hyaline to ochraceous in KOH and Melzer's reagent. 2) 23–40 × 5–11 μ, subclavate to subfusoid, thin-walled, smooth, content homogeneous (no refractive inclusion), both types intergrading in that some show refractive granular material not organized into a solid inclusion. Cheilocystidia 22–33 × 4–7 μ, similar to pleurocystidia (both types), some merely narrowly clavate to fusoid-ventricose, content yellowish to hyaline and homogeneous. Caulocystidia none found (from examination of dried material).

Gill trama with a central area of floccose hyphae with greatly inflated cells (to 25 μ), subparallel at first, then somewhat interwoven, hyphal walls thin smooth and ochraceous to hyaline; subhymenium a thin layer of interwoven somewhat gelatinous narrow hyphae, hyaline in KOH. Pileus cutis an interwoven layer of non-gelatinous hyphae 3–10 μ broad, smooth or incrusted and layer reddish fulvous in KOH. Context hyphae paler and ochraceous, smooth and thin-walled, cells greatly inflated. Clamp connections present and very prominent. All hyphae inamyloid.

HABIT, HABITAT, AND DISTRIBUTION: Caespitose on soil along a road among grasses, Wondy Island, Kodiak, Alaska. July 27, 1964. Wells and Kempton, no. 2.

OBSERVATIONS: The dry pileus, minute spores, prominent chrysocystidia and less conspicuous clavate hymenial cystidia with homogeneous content, scaly stipe and pale yellow lamellae are distinctive. The scales of both cap and stipe are very fine and do not show conspicuously on dried specimens as they do in *P. squarrosa* and *P. squarrosoides*.

Section **Adiposae** Konrad & Maublanc
Encyc. Myc. 15: 156. 1948

Stirps Squarrosoides

In aspect the species placed here more closely resemble *P. squarrosa* than any other because of the dense covering of dry squamules over the young pilei. However, a gelatinous subcutis is present which becomes noticeable chiefly in age. This stirps contains the best edible species in the genus.

Key

1. Spores 6–8 × 4–4.5 μ, oblong to elliptic in face view (see *P. angustipes* also) .... *P. rigidipes*
1. Spores smaller or more ovate in face view 2
  2. Spores 6–7.5 × 4–4.8 (5) μ, ovate in face view (see *P. simulans* also) .... *P. penningtoniana*
  2. Spores 4–6 × 2.5–4 μ 3
3. Pileus dark grayish brown to dark cinnamon; stipe with scales colored like those on pileus 3a
3. Not as above 4
    3a. Stipe not staining when handled .... *P. terrestris*
    3a. Stipe staining russet when handled .... *P. subcostanea*
  4. Pileus with coarse tawny scales 5
  4. Pileus with fine scales paler than in above choice 6
5. Inner veil yellow; pileus ground color ochraceous .... *P. barrowsii*
5. Inner veil white; pileus ground color pallid .... *P. squarrosoides*
  6. Spores 4–5 × 2.5–3 μ .... *P. romagnesiana*
  6. Spores 5–6.5 (7) × 3.5–4 (4.5) μ (see *P. simulans* also) ....
.... *P. angustifolia*

98. Pholiota rigidipes Peck, New York State Mus. Bull. 157: 31. 1912.
Illustrations. Text figs. 192-195.

Pileus 4–8 cm broad, broadly convex, sometimes slightly and broadly umbonate, pale yellow or buff, viscid; with obscure appressed fibrillose, brownish squamules which are more conspicuous in the center; obscurely striate when dried. Context thin, white, tinged yellow next to the lamellae; taste mild.

Lamellae adnexed or adnate, brownish ferruginous when mature, close, rather broad (3–6 mm), thin.

Stipe 5–9 cm long, 4–6 mm thick, white and pruinose at the apex, pallid and floccose-squamulose below, or nearly glabrous, rigid, flexuous, equal, stuffed or hollow. Veil leaving an evanescent annulus.

Spores 6–8 × 4–4.5 μ, smooth, apical pore distinct but apex not truncate; shape in face view oblong to elliptic, in profile much the same but a shade narrower, rarely slightly bean-shaped; color in KOH near pale ochraceous tawny, in Melzer's reagent paler and more ochraceous; wall about 0.25 μ thick.

Basidia 4-spored, 26–30 × 6–7 μ, ochraceous in KOH, paler in Melzer's reagent, narrowly clavate. Pleurocystidia 30–40 × 8–14 μ, clavate-mucronate to clavate, more rarely somewhat fusoid-ventricose, content tawny in KOH in most but some hyaline and evenly refractive, mostly buried in hymenium (no true chrysocystidia seen). Cheilocystidia small, 18–27 × 5–9 μ, obscurely fusoid-ventricose to suboblong-pedicellate to obtusely fusoid, walls smooth, thin, content hyaline to yellow. Caulo-cystidia 30–52 × 6–10 μ, clavate, capitate or mucronate, hyaline to yellow or pale tawny, walls smooth and thin.

Gill trama with a central strand of yellow subparallel floccose hyphae 3–9 μ diam., with walls smooth and swelling slightly in KOH, content not highly colored in Melzer's reagent; subhymenium a broad well defined gelatinous layer of narrow (2–3 μ) hyaline hyphae. Pileus trama with a zone of inflated hyphae (almost parenchyma-like in sections) walls in KOH 1.5–2 μ thick, and with a middle line showing as if two walls were fused, above this the cells with somewhat thickened walls, this type extending to the cuticular region and all hyphae ochraceous in KOH; cuticle a thick layer of subgelatinous hyphae 3–5 μ diam., smooth-walled, patches of tawny fibrils above this (from the veil) and these not gelatinous but some of the end-cells cystidioid and 42–56 × 6–12 μ. Clamp connections present. All hyphae inamyloid (none with orange to red content in Melzer's reagent).

HABIT, HABITAT, AND DISTRIBUTION: On the ground, probably on buried or exposed wood, New York, New Jersey and Missouri, September. Type studied.

OBSERVATIONS: Overholts (1924) reports it from the states named above. Peck (1912) states it is related to *Pholiota terrigena* Fr. from which he separated it because of its more slender habit, white flesh, adnexed lamellae, and more slender stipe. The dried specimens in the type collection remind one of those of our western form of *Pholiota squarrosa* more than any other species, but are not as scaly and there is gelatinization of the pileus cuticle. *P. penningtoniana* differs in the more ovate spores in face view. We regard this species as intermediate between stirps *Squarrosoides* and stirps *Adiposa*.

99. Pholiota penningtoniana sp. nov.

Illustrations: Text figs. 196-198.

Pileus 3–9 cm latus, convexus, squarroso-squamulosus, ad centrum fulvus, ad marginem subluteus (in siccatis). Lamellae confertae, angustae, subdecurrentes, luteae demum subfulvae; stipes 9–12 cm longus, 8–15 mm crassus, aequalis, squamosus, sursum subluteus, deorsum pallide fulvus. Sporae 6–7.5 × 4–4.8(5) μ, leves. Chryso-pleurocystidia 33–52(68) × 7–12 (15) μ, clavato-mucronata. Specimen typicum in Herb. Univ. of Mich. conservatum est; legit prope Marquette, Mich. 29 Aug. 1906. L. H. Penn-ington.

Pileus 3–9 cm broad, convex expanding to broadly umbonate, sur-face dry and recurved-squamulose as in *P. squarrosa,* possibly subviscid in age, color pale tawny on disc, yellowish over marginal area (as dried).

Lamellae crowded, narrow, subdecurrent, yellowish becoming sub-fulvous (as dried).

Stipe 9–12 cm long, 8–15 mm thick, equal, covered below the apical fibrillose annulus with recurved dry squamules, base of stipe pale tawny.

Spores 6–7.5 × 4–4.8 (5) μ, smooth, apical pore none or exceedingly small; shape in face view broadly ovate to elliptic, in profile obscurely bean-shaped to elliptic; wall thin (–0.25 μ) ; color in KOH dull cinnamon, paler to nearly the same color in Melzer's reagent.

Basidia 18–23 × 5.5–6.5 μ, clavate, yellowish in KOH and in Melzer's reagent. Pleurocystidia numerous and prominently projecting 33–52 (68) × 7–12 (15) μ, clavate, clavate-mucronate, or fusoid-ventricose, content *evenly* refractive as in *P. squarrosoides* (relatively few with a highly refractive inclusion and hence typical for chrysocystidia) ; color in Melzer's reagent evenly yellowish, in KOH refractive-hyaline or some with bright ochraceous content and connected to laticiferous elements with the same colored content, walls thin, smooth and hyaline. Cheilocystidia 28–37 × 6–11 μ, clavate, utriform, or fusoid-ventricose, with hyaline to yellow content in KOH, walls thin and smooth content, homogeneous. Caulocystidia scattered as clavate cells 29–48 × 8–12 μ, thin-walled, smooth, content homogeneous.

Gill trama with a floccose central area flanked on either side by a subgelatinous subhymenium. Pileus cutis with a subgelatinous layer (as a subcutis), the hyphae 3–5 μ and yellowish in KOH; hypodermium not differentiated. Context hyphae hyaline to yellowish in KOH, walls thin and becoming inflated. Clamp connections present. All hyphae inamyloid.

HABIT, HABITAT, AND DISTRIBUTION: Caespitose at base of tree, Marquette, Michigan. Aug. 29, 1906. L. H. Pennington, type.

OBSERVATIONS: The specimens were identified as *P. squarrosoides* by Kauffman, but as dried almost exactly resemble in color and markings those of *P. squarrosa*. The subcutis is merely subgelatinous—an intermediate state between the two species already mentioned. The spore shape, however is not typical of either. The pleurocystidia are much larger than in *P. rigidipes*.

100. Pholiota terrestris Overholts, North Amer. Fl. 10: 278. 1924.
Illustrations: Text figs. 199-201; pl. 44.

Pileus (1) 2–8 (10) cm broad, when young obtusely conic to convex, soon obtusely umbonate, at maturity expanded and with a slight umbo, at times nearly plane, usually covered with numerous fibrillose scales, or toward the margin merely fibrillose streaked, a gelatinous layer present beneath the scales and the latter consequently becoming rather readily weathered away, scales or fibrils "wood brown" along the margin, near "Verona brown" on the disc, when young the whole pileus evenly "warm sepia" because of the fibrillose covering, at times "Prout's brown" to "cinnamon-brown" when freshly matured, margin usually fibrillose-appendiculate. Context rather thick (more or less 4 mm), watery buff to brown, pliant and subcartilaginous; odor and taste mild.

Lamellae adnate, narrow, crowded, pallid becoming pale avellaneous and finally sometimes faintly tinged "Isabella color," pale cinnamon when dried, edges slightly uneven.

Stipe 3–8 (10) cm long, (2) 5–10 mm thick, equal or narrowed below, solid but soon hollowed, flesh grayish but with a strong tendency to stain yellow to brownish at base or around worm holes, occasionally staining where bruised or handled, surface covered to a superior annular zone or ring by dark avellaneous recurved scales, scales larger and more numerous upward, sheath at times merely becoming broken into zones or patches instead of scales, apical region fibrillose pruinose.

Spores 4.5–6.5 (7) × 3.5–4.5 μ, smooth, apical pore distinct but small, shape elliptic to broadly elliptic in face view, in profile subelliptic to slightly bean-shaped; in KOH dingy cinnamon, in Melzer's reagent paler; wall rather thin (–0.25 μ, estimated).

Basidia (20) 22–30 × 5–6.5 μ, 2- or 4-spored (mostly 4-spored), hyaline in KOH and only slightly yellowish in Melzer's reagent. Pleurocystidia 18–34 × (4) 5–10 (12) μ, clavate, clavate-mucronate, to fusoid ventricose, with the typical amorphous refractive inclusion of chrysocystidia, rarely with brown content, abundant but mostly scarcely projecting. Cheilocystidia 26–50 × 4–8 μ, numerous, cylindric, cylindric-subcapitate, sub-utriform to fusoid-ventricose, thin-walled, smooth, content homogeneous, hyaline in KOH. Caulocystidia (23) 47–88 × (94) 6–10 μ, cylindric-clavate, ventricose-capitate, to ventricose-rostrate, walls smooth, thin, yellowish in KOH.

Gill trama a central area of subparallel hyphae with hyphal cells 5–12 μ broad, walls thin, smooth, hyaline in KOH, in Melzer's reagent yellowish; subhymenium a well developed layer of narrow gelatinous interwoven hyphae. Pileus cutis with an epicutis of non-gelatinous brown hyphae with encrusted walls, the cells inflated to 12 μ at times, (these appearing to be in fascicles originating as a trichodermium, beneath this is an interwoven layer of gelatinizing brown incrusted hyphae (subcutis); hypodermium of compactly arranged mostly smooth dingy hyaline to brownish hyphae of variable diameter. Context hyphae interwoven, and with inflated cells smooth and thin-walled. Clamp connections present. All hyphae inamyloid.

HABIT, HABITAT, AND DISTRIBUTION: Caespitose on soil, roadsides, lawns, woods, more rarely on buried wood or even stumps, Michigan, Wisconsin, Idaho, Washington, Oregon, and California, June-January.

OBSERVATIONS: This is a characteristic road-side species in the Pacific Northwest, and most of the time appears to be terrestrial. However, we have collections from buried wood and from wood above ground. Mr. Bill Isaacs has found it lignicolous in Washington also. Hence the name is a bit deceiving. It is very close to *P. squarrosoides* in all features except color and habitat. Both have at first an essentially dry scaly pileus from the scaly outer layer. The chrysocystidia may often resemble basidioles in shape, but as revived in KOH have the characteristic inclusion.

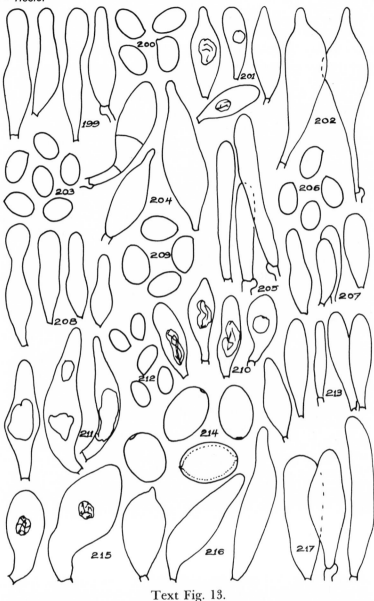

Text Fig. 13.

Figs. 199-201, cheilocystidia, spores and pleurocystidia of *P. terrestris;* 202 & 203, pleurocystidia and spores of *P. barrowsii;* 204-207, pleurocystidia, caulocystidia, spores, and cheilocystidia of *P. squarrosoides;* 208-210, cheilocystidia, spores and pleurocystidia of *P. angustifolia;* 211-213, pleurocystidia, spores and cheilocystidia of *P. flammans;* 214-217, spores, two types of pleurocystidia (214-216), and cheilocystidia of *P. aurivellioides.*

We have found it in large clusters with small pilei, large clusters with large pilei, small clusters with large pilei, and small pilei in small clusters, and hence cannot assume that the amount of available food material regularly determines the size of the basidiocarp as much, possibly, as it does the size of the cluster.

We have two collections from Cusick, Wash. Smith 73375 and 74152 (the latter collected by K. Harrison) which came up on dried mud in an old logging road. The caps were 1–3 cm broad, at first covered by wood-brown scales but as these become separated the dingy yellow ground color became evident and the older pilei are dingy yellowish as dried. Yellow tints also show in the stipes of both collections. Pending further collections of this depauperate "form" we merely mention its existence here and regard it as a dry weather variant.

MATERIAL EXAMINED: CALIFORNIA: Smith 3639, 3642, 8194, 56153; Thiers 8806; IDAHO: Trueblood 540c (MICH) ; Slipp 41FP 1969; Smith 569, 44149, 54030, 54489, 54814, 58500, 70478; MICHIGAN: Smith 34098; OREGON: Gruber 1946; La-1027 (MICH) ; Sipe 227, 232, 387; Smith 19347, 24677, 2852, 3604, 7861, 19359, 28120, 55354; WISCONSIN, Harper. WASHINGTON: E. Schmidt 2; Smith 16958, 17035, 39849, 68799; CANADA (BRITISH COLUMBIA): Waugh (Myc. Herb. Sci. Service 23958) .

100a. Pholiota subcastanea sp. nov.
Illustrations: Pl. 48.

Pileus 5–10 cm latus, plano-umbonatus, viscidus, squamosus, sub-castaneus, cartilagineus. Lamellae angustae, confertae, fulvo-cinnamomeae, demum maculatae. Stipes 6–12 cm longus, 6–12 mm crassus, durus, fibrosis, pallide argillaceus denum subcastaneo maculatus, squarroso-squamulosus. Annulus laceratus, cinnamomeus. Sporae 5–6 × 3.5–4 μ. Pleurocystidia mucronata. Specimen typicum in Herb. Univ. Mich. conservatum est; legit Sharon Hollow, Mich. 21, Sept. 1967, ad Juglans cinerea; Smith 75074.

Pileus 5–10 cm broad, obtuse, expanding to plano-umbonate or nearly so, surface viscid beneath a layer of squamules over disc, toward margin the squamules more or less triangular and appressed, color of scales dull reddish tawny to russet, ground color pallid becoming cinnamon buff. Context cartilaginous-pliant, pinkish buff to cinnamon buff, with a watery brown line above the gills; odor slightly pungent, taste not distinctive; $FeSO_4$ instantly green.

Lamellae narrow, close, adnexed, seceding, reddish cinnamon when mature and spotted russet where injured, edges even.

Stipe 6–12 cm long, 6–12 mm thick, equal to the slightly enlarged fused base, in consistency very hard and fibrous, yellowish to pinkish buff within but soon russet from the base upward, surface recurved-squamulose with cinnamon buff to "Verona brown" very fine but conspicuous lacterate often recurved scales from base to annulus; annulus ragged, underside separating into two layers and dingy cinnamon, upper layer cinnamon; apex of stipe dingy, ground color below ring pale dull cinnamon, becoming russet from base up where bruised.

Spore deposit "russet" moist, "Verona brown" when moisture has escaped. Spores 5–6 × 3.5–4 μ, wall smooth, scarcely thickened, ±0.25 μ, dull brown in KOH and Melzer's; elliptic in face view, nearly so in profile, no apical pore evident. Pleurocystidia as large chrysocystidia 36–47 × 9–15 μ, subclavate-mucronate, hyaline-refractive with even content (in KOH) or with a dark brown content more or less reticulate in some, scarcely projecting. Cheilocystidia 26–42 × 8–13 μ, obtusely fusoid ventricose to narrowly clavate but tapered slightly near apex in some, thin walled, lacking any distinctive content, walls faintly yellowish as first when revived in KOH but fading. Subhymenium gelatinous Pileus cutis a thick gelatinous layer, the hyphae narrow (2–4 μ) and with distinctly outlined walls as revived in KOH, hyaline to yellowish. Hypoderm orange-brown in KOH, of compactly arranged hyphae. Clamp connections present.

Habit, habitat, and distribution: Caespitose on a log of butternut (*Juglans cinerea*), Sharon Hollow, Mich. Sept. 2, 1967. Smith 75074.

This species is most similar to *P. terrestris* but is readily distinct by the colors, color changes and habitat. It is an intermediate between stirps *Adiposa* and stirps *Squarrosoides*.

101. Pholiota barrowsii sp. nov.
Illustrations: Text figs. 202-203.

Pileus 4–8 cm latus, late convexus, viscidus, squamosus, luteus; squamae subfulvae. Contextus pallidus demum pallide luteus. Lamellae latae, adnatae, confertae, pallide ochracea demum luteo brunneae. Stipes 4–9 cm longus, 5–12 mm crassus, solidus, deorsum fulvus et fibrillose squamosus vel flocculosus, sursum sericeus. Sporae 5–6.5 × 3–3.5 μ. Pleurocystidia 30–56(60) × 7–14 μ, clavata vel clavato-mucronata. Cheilocystidia 20–28 × 5–9 μ. Specimen typicum in Herb. Univ. of Mich. conservatum est; legit prope Santa Fe, New Mexico, Aug. 1957. Chas. Barrows 504.

Pileus 4–8 cm broad, convex becoming nearly plane, surface covered with coarse dry scales as in *P. squarrosa*, the scales dingy tawny brownish as dried, yellow ground color reminding one of *P. squarroso-adiposa* and near ochre yellow as dried, viscid in age as scales wear away from the thick gelatinous pellicle. Context pallid becoming yellowish and as dried pale buff, odor and taste mild.

Lamellae broad, bluntly adnate, in age adnexed, close, pallid ochraceous becoming near "buckthorn brown" (fairly dark clay-color), edges even.

Stipe 4–9 cm long, 5–12 mm thick, equal or nearly so, solid, becoming rusty brown over basal area, melleous above or paler, lower three fourths covered by copious shaggy floccose patches or zones of veil remnants terminating at an annular zone, paler and silky above, as dried the veil remnants yellowish.

Spores 5–6 (6.5) × 3–3.5 μ, smooth, apical pore not evident; shape in face view elliptic to ovate, in profile slightly bean-shaped to elliptic, in KOH about "cinnamon-buff" (pale clay-color), in Melzer's reagent, paler (nearly hyaline) : wall less than 0.25 μ thick.

Basidia 4-spored, 15–22 × 4–5 μ, clavate, hyaline in KOH, yellowish in Melzer's reagent. Pleurocystidia 35–56 (60) × 7–14 μ, clavate to clavate mucronate, with a long slender pedicel, wall thin and smooth; content homogeneous but opaque and somewhat refractive, in a few dark ochraceous. Cheilocystidia 1) clavate, 20–28 × 5–9 μ, hyaline, thin-walled smooth, content homogeneous; 2) similar to pleurocystidia. Caulocystidia (none observed on material available) .

Gill trama with a floccose interwoven central strand, the hyphal cells enlarged, smooth, in KOH yellowish to hyaline and wall slightly thickened (laminate) or thin; subhymenium a gelatinous layer of narrow 1.5–2.5 μ interwoven hyphae, giving off gelatinous branches ending in basidia and these also tending to cause hymenium to be almost trichodermium-like (composed of hyphal branches, not single cells in a palisade) . Pileus cutis an extremely thick layer of gelatinous narrow (1.5–3 μ) hyaline hyphae with walls lacking a sharp outline as revived in KOH; hypodermial region of dull ochraceous floccose hyphae 6–14 μ diam.; walls smooth, thin to slightly thickened, pigment present in the wall. Context hyphae of wide (8–18 μ) smooth hyphae with thin to slightly thickened (laminated) walls near subhymenium, yellow in KOH, reddish in Melzer's reagent when first mounted but soon fading to dull ochraceous. Clamp connections present.

HABIT, HABITAT, AND DISTRIBUTION: Caespitose on aspen, in the mountains near Santa Fe, N. Mexico 8000 ft. elevation. Aug. 1957. Chas. Barrows 504, type.

OBSERVATIONS: This species has the veil of *P. squarrosoides* but the veil is yellow, not whitish; it has the colors of *P. squarroso-adiposa* but the pileus is scaly as in *P. squarrosa*, for which it was mistaken in the field. It has a thick gelatinous pellicle over the pileus which of course excludes that species.

The conspicuous pleurocystidia are a striking feature of the species. Although they are of the characteristic shape of chrysocystidia (clavatemucronate) as revived in KOH they lack the amorphous-refractive inclusion. They closely resemble those of *P. squarrosoides* in all features except size. The scales of the pileus in both, as revived in KOH, have the hyphal cells rusty brown, and with thickened walls to about 1 μ, but in *P. barrowsii* the cells are elongate and mostly smooth, in *P. squarrosoids* more of the cells have incrustations on the walls and the cells tend to be isodiametric or nearly so. If one were given to speculation it would be a simple matter to visualize *P. barrowsii* as a hybrid between *P. squarroso-adiposa* and *P. squarrosoides*.

102. Pholiota squarrosoides (Pk.) Saccardo Syll. Fung. 5: 750. 1887.
Agaricus (Pholiota) squarrosoides Peck., New York State Mus. Ann. Rept. 31: 33. 1879.
Hypodendrum squarrosoides (Peck.) Overholts, North Amer. Fl. 10: 278. 1932.
Illustrations: Tex figs. 204-207; pls. 45-46.

> Atkinson, Stud. Amer. Fungi, 2nd ed., pl. 48.
> Harper, Wisconsin Acad. Sci. Arts & Letters 17, pls. 36, 37.
> Overholts, Annals Mo. Bot. Gard. 14, pl. 22.
> Peck, N. Y. State Mus. Ann. Rept. 54, pl. 73, figs. 6-15.

Pileus (2.5) 3–7 (11) cm broad, obtuse becoming broadly umbonate to convex, at times nearly plane, color white to whitish when fresh, becoming only slightly tinged with cinnamon in age, or remaining whitish, the margin often fringed with veil remnants, surface viscid beneath the scales, the scales dry, recurved to squarrose, pale tawny ("tawny" to "ochraceous-tawny"), scattered near the margin, often crowded over the disc. Context thick, whitish, rather pliant; odor and taste not distinctive.

Lamellae adnate but becoming sharply adnexed, close to crowded, moderately broad (more or less 5 mm), broadest at base and tapering toward the margin, whitish at first, slowly changing to dull rusty brown as the spores mature, sometimes with brighter rusty stains.

Stipe (4) 5–10 (14) cm long, 5–10 (15) mm thick, dry, fleshy-pliant, lower two-thirds covered by coarse, recurved, ochraceous tawny, persistent scales, tinged pale buff between the scales or with a tendency to stain rusty-brown near the base, ground color typically pallid, apical region whitish and silky, equal, stuffed or solid. Annulus superior, pallid, often more fibrillose than membranous, often evanescent.

Spores 4–5.5 (6) × (2.5) 3–3.5 μ, smooth, apical pore not evident; shape in face view ovate to broadly elliptic, in profile, subelliptic to obscurely inequilateral; in KOH pale dull cinnamon, in Melzer's reagent paler; wall less than 0.25 μ thick.

Basidia 17–22 (27) × 4–6 μ, 4-spored, narrowly clavate, hyaline in KOH and in Melzer's reagent scarcely colored. Pleurocystidia abundant, (25) 30–50 (65) × (6) 8–15 (18) μ, clavate, clavate-mucronate, fusoid-ventricose with an apical mucro or elongation, or wavy in outline and one of the above basic shapes; wall thin, smooth, hyaline in KOH; content homogeneous-opaque but hyaline or nearly so (no refractive inclusion), rarely secondarily septate, at times when poorly revived seen to have an ochraceous-brown content. Cheilocystidia 26–40 (50) × 5–11 (13) μ, clavate, fusoid-ventricose, or resembling the pleurocystidia in shape and then with similar content, none seen with a refractive-amorphous inclusion. Caulocystidia in scattered clusters, filamentose to narrowly clavate 26–55 × 5–8 μ, thin-walled, smooth, hyaline in KOH, content homogeneous.

Gill trama of a floccose central strand of more or less interwoven hyphae with inflated cells, walls smooth, thin, hyaline to ochraceous in KOH (hyaline in water mounts fresh); subhymenium a well defined gelatinous layer of narrow (1.5–3 μ) hyaline hyphae. Pileus cuticle with a gelatinous layer beneath the scales, the hyphae narrow and walls disintergrating to some extent; scales of more or less rusty brown encrusted to smooth hyphal cells often about as long as broad; hypodermial region of floccose ochraceous, brown, smooth to slightly encrusted hyphae. Context hyphae interwoven, inflated, thin-walled or wall thickened in the area near the subhymenium and then the wall "laminate." Clamp connections present. All hyphae inamyloid on standing but showing a tendency in sections to be reddish when first revived.

HABIT, HABITAT, AND DISTRIBUTION: Singly or caespitose, on trunks and stumps of hardwood trees, especially maple, birch, beech, basswood, and in the northwestern United States on alder. Known from Oontario and Nova Scotia in Canada and Maine, Vermont, Connecticut, New York, Pennsylvania, North Carolina, Tennessee, Michigan, Colorado, Oregon, and Washington in the United States. August to September.

OBSERVATIONS: The pleurocystidia of this species are not true chrysocystidia in that as revived in KOH the cell content is homogeneous instead of containing a highly refractive clearly delimited body. The shape and size of the cystidia varies greatly even in a single pileus. The caulocystidia are unusual in that they are simple as to morphology (elongate-clavate) and not like any of the lamellar cystidia.

The species differs from *P. squarrosa* in the gelatinous layer beneath the scales on the pileus. We have not been able to recognize var. *faginea* Pk. (1901: 183) on beech with smaller scales. The size of the clusters of basidiocarps is directly related to the amount of food available. This is a common species on the wood of red alder in the Pacific Northwest, and in the hardwood slashings of northern Michigan.

MATERIAL EXAMINED: COLORADO: Barrows 816 (MICH); IDAHO: Smith 70679, 70684; KENTUCKY: Kauffman 9-1-16; MAINE: Bigelow 4666; MARYLAND: Kelly 1700; MASSACHUSETTS: Harvard Forest (MICH); MICHIGAN: Bartelli 127, 128 (MICH); Harding 300, 344, 345, 364, Ex-70 (basidiocarp produced in culture); Harper 2251; Imshaug 3945, 4028; Kauffman 9-1905, 8-21-06, 8-29-06, 9-14-27, 10-5-27, 9-19-29; Povah 721, 7-30-14; Shaffer 201, 3746; Smith 32-597, 61, 25066, 37198, 37819, 38195, 39533, 64034, 67046, 67193, 68770; Thiers 1061; NEW HAMPSHIRE: Mains 4164; NEW YORK: Kauffman 9-8-03, 7-31-03, 8-31-03; Marsden 514 (MICH); Peck (type); NORTH CAROLINA: Hesler 15884; Smith 10185; OREGON: Smith 23832; 24369, 68771; TENNESSEE: Hesler 8324, 9388; Kauffman 9-11-16; Smith 10563; VERMONT: Shaffer 3394 (MICH); WASHINGTON: Kauffman 9-12-15;

Smith 16407, 16443, 16626, 17538 (dark colored), 19582, 31217, 31427, 31822, 47850, 49074; WYOMING: Kauffman 8-22-23, 8-24-23; CANADA: (Ontario): Beardslee 8-20-20; Cain 16024 (TENN); DAOM 33854 (MICH); Kelly 742, 1258, 1314, 1620; Smith 26380, 26467; NOVA SCOTIA: Wehmeyer 862.

103. Pholiota romagnesiana sp. nov.

Pileus 3–8 cm latus, obtusus demum campanulatus, sordide luteolus, squamulosus. Lamellae confertae, latae, adnatae, pallide luteae. Stipes 6–12 cm longus, 8–14 mm crassus, solidus, connato-cespitosus, squamulosus. Sporae 4–5 × 2.5–3 μ. Pleurocystidia 32–46 × 9–13 μ, clavata vel ellipticopedicellata. Specimen typicum in Herb. Univ. Mich. conservatum est; legit prope Santa Fe N. Mexico, Aug. 1964, Chas. Barrows 1739.

Pileus 3–8 cm broad, obtuse with an incurved margin, expanding to broadly campanulate or nearly plane but with a low obtuse umbo, ground color very pale dingy yellow (near cream color) and with small ochraceous tawny scales over the surface, scales most numerous over disc, scales recurved to appressed (reminding one of those of *P. squarrosa*). Context as in *P. squarrosa* but more pliant, taste pleasant, odor pleasant.

Lamellae close, moderately broad, adnate becoming slightly adnexed, cream-buff to slightly yellower (none completely colored by spores).

Stipe 6–12 cm long, about 8–14 mm thick, solid, equal, connate below, surface scaly as in *P. squarrosa* with dry recurved scales up to the ragged submembranous annulus or fibrillose veil-line, fibrillose-scurfy above the line, concolorous with pileus except for scales and only weakly fulvous at base as dried.

Spores 4–5 × 2.5–3 μ, smooth, no apical pore visible, elliptic to ovate in face view, obscurely bean-shaped to nearly oblong in profile, in KOH dingy ochraceous, in Melzer's reagent nearly hyaline.

Basidia 4-spored, 18 × 4 μ, hyaline to yellowish in KOH or Melzer's reagent. Pleurocystidia 32–46 × 9–13 μ, clavate to elliptic-pedicellate or clavate-mucronate, evenly refractive in KOH and Melzer's reagent, or some with an even dull brown content (not typical chrysocystidia). Cheilocystidia similar to pleurocystidia or clavate and thin-walled and up to 18 μ broad. Caulocystidia rare, present as fusoid end-cells of hyphae, 2–4 μ diam.

Gill trama with a gelatinous subhymenium and a hyaline floccose central strand of subparallel hyphae, walls hyaline and smooth. Pileus cutis a layer of narrow (2–4 μ) filaments interwoven, gelatinous and often with yellow content; hypodermial region of greatly inflated hyphal cells nearly colorless and with thin walls. Context hyphae with thickened "double" walls beneath the hypodermium, hyaline, walls smooth, cells mostly inflated. All hyphae inamyloid. Clamp connections present.

HABIT, HABITAT, AND DISTRIBUTION: Caespitose on a dead conifer stub,

Jemez Mountains near Santa Fe, New Mexico, August 1964, Chas. Barrows 1739, type.

OBSERVATIONS: This is a most interesting species identical in aspect with *P. squarrosa* as it occurs in New Mexico but lacking olive or green tones, lacking a garlic odor, and in having narrower spores than *P. squarrosoides*. Barrows considers it far superior to *P. squarrosa* as an edible species. No heliotrope stains were noted anywhere on the basidiocarps, it lacked a fruity odor and occured on conifer wood. Hence with the data available it cannot be properly referred to *Dryophila ochropallida* Romagnesi. However, we take pleasure in naming our species in his honor.

104. Pholiota angustifolia nom. nov.
Hebeloma appendiculatum Murrill, North Amer. Fl. 10: 220. 1917.
(non. *Pholiota appendiculata* Peck 1905).
Illustrations: Text figs. 208-210.

Pileus about 5 cm broad, convex, rather thick and fleshy and not fully expanding, slightly gibbous in some, surface viscid, silky and also finely imbricate-squamulose, rosy-isabelline (pinkish-cinnamon), cremeous on the disc, margin deflexed, concolorous, appendiculate with triangular fragments of the slight evanescent veil. Context white, thick at the center; taste nutty.

Lamellae sinuate, broad behind and tapering in front, narrow, arcuate, very crowded, pale cream-color and not darkening on drying, the edges pallid and distinctly crenate or dentate.

Stipe more or less 4 cm long, 1 cm thick, equal, spongy-stuffed, with creamy white pith, glabrous at apex, white above, concolorous below, revolute-squamulose.

Spores 5–6.5 (7) × 3.3–4 (4.5) μ, smooth, apical pore distinct but minute and apex not truncate, shape in face view ovate to elliptic or nearly oblong, in profile slightly bean-shaped to somewhat inequilateral; color revived in KOH ochraceous to cinnamon-buff, in Melzer's reagent about the same color; wall thin (–0.25 μ).

Basidia 15–20 (22) × 4.5–6 μ, 4-spored, obese, hyaline to yellowish in KOH and Melzer's reagent. Pleurocystidia numerous 20–28 × 6–12 μ, clavate-mucronate to fusoid-ventricose, apex obtuse, wall thin, smooth and hyaline; content refractive and reticulate or contracted into a more or less distinct refractive body, hyaline in KOH and merely yellowish in Melzer's reagent. Cheilocystidia (17) 25–40 (50) × 7–10 (15) μ, cylindric-capitate, ninepin-shaped, fusoid ventricose to utriform, smooth, thin-walled; content homogeneous and hyaline in KOH. Caulocystidia none.

Gill trama with central area of floccose subparallel hyphae hyaline to pale fulvous in KOH in sections, walls thin and smooth, cells 4–9 μ broad; subhymenium a distinct gelatinous zone. Pileus cutis a thin layer of hyaline subgelatinous hypha 3–5 μ diam. over the surface but no well organized typical gelatinous pellicle found; hypodermial region lacking differentiation as to color or structure. Context hyphae hyaline, interwoven, the cells inflated and with thin smooth walls. Clamp connections present but rare and difficult to demonstrate. All hyphae inamyloid.

HABIT, HABITAT, AND DISTRIBUTION: Caespitose on soil, at the base of a sugar maple, New York, September. Type studied.

OBSERVATIONS: In this species we again have a "stage" in the development of the typical chrysocystidium in that the content of the cell is not organized (as revived in KOH) into a sharply delimeted refractive inclusion but involves in most cells the shrunken coagulated total cell content. The spores and gelatinous subhymenium clearly remove the species from *Hebeloma* where it was described, and, along with the veil features, indicate *Pholiota* as the correct genus. It is very doubtful if the color of the spore deposit is purplish, but on this point we have no data. Under the microscope the color of the spores is more ochraceous than usual for a *Pholiota,* indicating that yellow tints probably would be prominent in a deposit.

MATERIAL EXAMINED: NEW YORK: Murrill (type, of *Hebeloma appendiculatum* on lawn, New York Botanical Garden, September 4, 1912).

Stirps Adiposa

The species with a gelatinous pellicle or subcutis and a gelatinous subhymenium are placed here but the gelatinous cutis is not obscured at first by a dense layer of squamules as in the previous stirps; however, the two intergrade.

Key

1. Spores 5–6 (8) μ wide 2
1. Spores mostly 2.5–5 μ wide 3
   2. Spores 6–8 μ wide .... *P. aurivelloides*
   2. Spores 4.5–6 μ wide .... *P. aurivella*
3. Spores 4–6 × 2.5–3.5 μ 4
3. Spores (5) 6–8 (9) μ long 5
   4. Pileus gills and stipe picric yellow; stipe with well-defined dry picric yellow recurved squamules .... *P. flammans*
   4. Pileus darker (ochre yellow); scales on stipe gelatinous ....
     .... *P. adiposa*
5. Taste bitter; some context hyphae with inclusions resembling those of chrysocystidia .... *P. lucifera*
5. Taste mild to fungoid or somewhat unpleasant; hyphae not as above
   6
   6. Stipe connate and pointed below; with a thin viscid layer over lower part of stipe .... *P. connata*
   6. Stipe not as above 7

7. Lamellae with pale yellow margins and pallid faces when young; stipe at first with scattered gelatinous scales below the annulus or annular zone .... *P. hiemalis*
7. Not as above 8
    8. Base of stipe surrounded by olive-yellow to tawny pubescence; pileus scales broad at base (± 3 mm) .... *P. subvelutipes*
    8. Not as above 9
9. Young lamellae distinctly yellow 10
9. Young lamellae pallid to white at first 12
    10. Pileus whitish; scales yellow .... see *P. caespitosa*
    10. Pileus rich yellow, scales fulvous 11
11. Some specimens in a cluster with a thick heavy subpersistent annulus; on wood of conifers .... *P. filamentosa*
11. Annulus never formed (veil-line merely a thin fibrillose zone); mostly on wood of hardwoods .... *P. squarroso-adiposa*
    12. Pileus covered with broad tawny scales; young gills pallid; stipe increasingly scaly downward from veil line; on wood of conifers .... *P. abietis*
    12. Not as above 13
13. Pileus squamulose with minute dotlike scales; stipe white to avellaneous 14
13. Not as above 15
    14. Fusoid chrysocystidia scattered to abundant in hymenium; some cheilocystidia capitate and head with thickened bright yellow walls revived in KOH .... *P. simulans*
    14. Cheilocystidia not as above; pleurocystidia clavate to filamentous .... *P. angustipes*
15. Hyphae of pileus context bright red in Melzer's .... *P. limonella*
15. Hyphae not as above .... see *P. rigidipes*

105. Pholiota flammans (Fr.) Kummer, Der Führer in die Pilzkunde p. 84. 1871.
Agaricus flammans Fries, Syst. Myc. 1: 244. 1821.
Hypodendrum flammans (Fr.) Murrill, Mycologia 4: 261. 1912.
Pholiota kauffmaniana Smith. Mycologia 36: 254. 1944.
Illustrations: Text figs. 211-213; pl. 47.

Pileus (3) 4–8 (10) cm broad, obtusely conic becoming broadly umbonate, at times the umbo obsolete, surface viscid beneath a covering of recurved fibrillose scales, glabrescent at times in age, the margin often fringed with veil remnants as a thin sheet or in patches, color a brilliant yellow ("picric-yellow") over all including the veil remnants, at times "lemon-chrome" to "deep-chrome" or "raw-sienna," disc at times tawny in age. Context firm, pliant, thick, yellow and with a greenish yellow line next to the gills; odor and taste mild.
Lamellae sharply adnexed, "picric-yellow," staining dingy brown

along the edges when rubbed, close to crowded, 3 tiers of lamellulae, moderately broad to broad in age, edges even.

Stipe (3) 5–10 (12) cm long, (3) 5–10 mm thick, equal or slightly enlarged at base, solid, stuffed to tubular, concolorous with pileus inside and out, darkening to cadmium yellow at base, covered up to the annulus with a dense coating of recurved yellow scales from the ruptured veil, silky fibrillose above the annulus. Veil forming an evanescent, superior zone of bright yellow fibrils or submembranous.

Spores 4–5 × 2.5–3 μ smooth, ochraceous in KOH and about the same color in Melzer's reagent, oblong to ellipsoid, smooth, wall thin, apical pore not evident.

Basidia 18–22 × 3.5–4.5 μ, narrowly clavate, 4-spored, hyaline in KOH, yellowish in Melzer's reagent. Pleurocystidia of two types; 1) 25–35 × 6–8 μ, clavate to mucronate and with a dark flavous homogeneous content as revived in KOH, in Melzer's reagent yellowish, walls smooth thin and hyaline; 2) chrysocystidia 26–40 × 6–9 μ fusoid ventricose to clavate-mucronate, content amorphous and granular-aggregated to forming folded (reticulate) masses cinnabar-color to orange-brown in Melzer's reagent. Cheilocystidia as in type 1 of pleurocystidia or small and cylindric (18–20 × 3 μ), the former abundant. Caulocystidia present only as filamentose end-cells of surface hyphae.

Gill trama of floccose subparallel hypha 4–8 μ broad, ochraceous in KOH and pigment diffusing into mount, masses of needle-like crystals forming in the mount; cell walls thin, smooth, yellowish; subhymenium of narrow hyaline somewhat interwoven gelatinous hyphae. Pileus cutis a thick layer (100 μ +) of narrow (2–4 μ) gelatinous hyphae yellowish in KOH; hypodermial region of ochraceous-brown hyphae, structurally continuous with context, the hyphae compactly interwoven, 4–12 μ diam., walls smooth thin and ochraceous to hyaline; oleiferous hyphae present. Clamp connections present. All hyphae inamyloid.

HABIT, HABITAT, AND DISTRIBUTION: On conifer logs and stumps, Maine, Michigan, Tennessee, North Carolina, Idaho, and Washington; August—October.

OBSERVATIONS: Kauffman, when collecting in the Olympic Mountains of Washington in 1925 described viscid specimens as a tentative new species. When Smith was working in the same area he found the same variation in the same condition and since a viscid as contrasted to a non-viscid pileus was an important feature in *Pholiota* he described the viscid variant naming it in honor of Kauffman. However, anatomical studies of this variant in comparison with material collected by Kauffman in Sweden and presumably checked by Romell, and material sent to Smith from France by Josserand are all so much alike microscopically that there appears to be no clear line of separation—particularly as applied to the pileus cutis. In addition, during the last twenty years Smith has observed the species in many areas of the United States and under variable weather conditions. He is now convinced that the problem is one of a pileus cutis which is of such a chemical composition that the hyphal walls slowly become subgelatinous in a highly humid atmosphere or from continuous rain, and that along the west coast these conditions are realized so regularly that we have a viscid variant of *P. flammans* in that area. During dry seasons, of course, the character will not show in the field, but is often very evident under a microscope where cuticular gelatinization in KOH is very distinct. In this respect this fungus is different from most species in the genus. When one encounters a gelatinizing cutis in this genus the hyphae are usually distinctly narrower than those of the context. This is not so clear as the two areas intergrade. The gelatinous subhymenium of *P. kauffmaniana* might seem to distinguish the latter from *P. flammans* but here again we are dealing with a character not often evident until maturity in *Pholiota,* and one found fairly inconstant in *Galerina* (Smith & Singer, 1964). Hence, we hesitate to place much emphasis on it here in particular since this feature is evident on the specimens from Josserand. The microscopic data on his specimen are identical with those of Smith 236 from New York which was used for our description. The chrysocystidia color typically in Melzer's, the gelatinous pellicle is thick and of hyphae narrower than those of the adjacent pileus context, the subhymenium is at least subgelatinous and the needle-like crystals form in KOH. The spores deposited on the cap average slightly larger (0.5 μ $\pm$) than in Smith 236 and the clavate pleurocystidia are slightly more orange in KOH. We do not regard the last two features mentioned as important taxonomically. The description of *P. flammuloides* Moser does not clarify the situation.

The outstanding features of this species are the thick pellicle of narrow gelatinous hyphae in sections revived in KOH, the chrysocystidia with content orange-brown to red in Melzer's reagent, the abundant more or less clavate pleurocystidia with homogeneous ochraceous content in KOH, the needle-like crystals often aggregated to a dendroid pattern which form in KOH mounts, and in the orange to yellow pigment diffusing in mounts of this medium. On anatomical grounds the species must be placed in the viscid group of subg. *Pholiota.*

MATERIAL EXAMINED: COLORADO: Kauffman 9-9-20; IDAHO: Smith 46285, 46833, 47020, 60222; MAINE: Bigelow 4546 (MICH); MICHIGAN: Bartelli 2110 (MICH); Harding 380, 37063, 38071; NEW YORK: Kauffman 9-15-14, 9-17-14; Smith 236; NORTH CAROLINA: Hesler 23386 (TENN); OREGON: Smith 19189, 20042, 24202, 26970, 27771; TENNESSEE: Hesler 10868, 21001 (GSMNP); Kauffman 9-16-16, 9-21-16, 9-20-16; Smith 10868; WASHINGTON: Kauffman 9-13-15, 10-23-15, 10-13-25, 10-31-25, 11-5-25; Smith 3167, 16161, 16186, 16268, (type, *P. Kauffmaniana*), 16339, 16549, 16854, 17317, 17342, 31113.

106. **Pholiota aurivelloides** Overholts, Annals Missouri Bot. Garden
      14: 151. 1927.

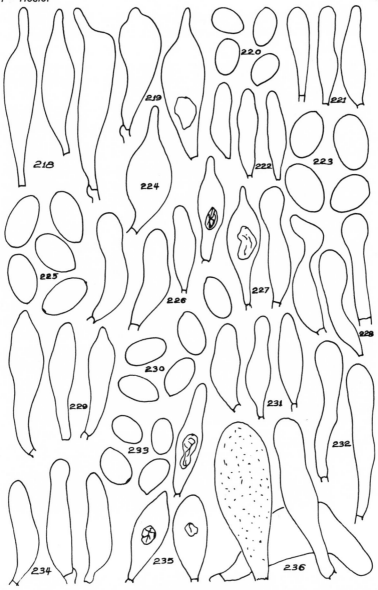

Text Fig. 14.

FIGS. 218-221, two types of pleurocystidia, spores and cheilocystidia of *P. kodiakensis;* 222-224, cheilocystidia, and spores of *P. aurivella;* 225-228, spores cheilocystidia, pleurocystidia and caulocystidia of *P. connata;* 229-232, pleurocystidia, spores, cheilocystidia and caulocystidia of *P. subvelutipes;* 233-236, spores, cheilocystidia, pleurocystidia and caulocystidia of *P. abietis.*

Hypodendrum aurivelloides Overholts, North Amer. Fl. 10: 281 1932.
Illustrations: Text figs. 214-217.

Pileus 5–8 cm broadly campanulate to convex, ferruginous to tawny, margin paler, slightly viscid, with a few spot-like or appressed scales. Context rather thick, yellow.

Lamellae sinuate-adnate or with a decurrent tooth, whitish then ochraceous-tawny or russet, medium close or slightly distant, broad (7–12 mm).

Stipe 4–8 cm long, 5–10 mm thick, yellowish or brownish, more or less scaly, the scales sometimes somewhat gelatinous, equal, solid.

Spores 8–11 (11.5) × 6–7 (8) μ, smooth, wall ± 0.3 μ thick, apical pore present and in larger spores often causing spore apex to appear somewhat truncate, elliptic in face view and also in profile or in profile varying to slightly bean-shaped, color in KOH yellowish-tawny, more cinnamon in Melzer's reagent.

Basidia 4-spored, 27–36 × 6–8 μ, clavate, hyaline to yellowish in KOH and in Melzer's reagent. Pleurocystidia abundant, 1) mostly clavate-mucronate, 25–36 × 8–12 μ, with thin smooth hyaline walls (in KOH), with a small highly refractive amorphous body not coloring in Melzer's reagent: 2) obtusely fusoid cells 30–48 × 6–11 μ and with brownish to ochraceous wrinkled content becoming dark amber-brown in Melzer's. Cheilocystidia 26–50 × 6–15 μ, versiform; clavate, subelliptic, inflated-vesiculose and at times capitate, or fusoid-ventricose, yellow to hyaline in KOH, walls typically thin and content homogeneous or resembling that of either type of pleurocystidia. Caulocystidia scattered, clavate up to 80 × 22 μ, and some with yellow to reddish homogeneous content in KOH.

Gill trama of floccose parallel hyphae with elongate thin-walled smooth inflated (finally) cells up to 15 μ diam., hyaline to yellowish in KOH, and many with highly refractive septa; subhymenium gelatinous-narrow and of interwoven narrow (2 μ) hyaline hyphae. Pileus cutis a thick gelatinous pellicle of hyphae 3–6 μ diam., walls thin smooth and hyaline, over this occur patches of amber-brown gelatinous hyphae 4–9 μ wide (representing the gelatinous scales); hypodermial region not distinct from content. Context hyphae inflated (6–15 μ ±), walls thin smooth, hyaline to yellowish. All hyphae inamyloid. Clamp connections present.

HABIT, HABITAT, AND DISTRIBUTION: On dead trees or from wounds in *Alnus, Salix* or *Betula,* Colorado, New Mexico, and Wyoming, late summer and fall. Type studied.

OBSERVATIONS: Our microscopic data in the above description are taken from Gruber 749, preserved at Michigan. The spores average broader than for *P. aurivella,* and there is a distinct difference in the pleurocystidia as described. Brown imbedded basidioles were not found in the type by us but were reported by Overholts, who was an accurate observer. Since these cells are generally present through the *P. adiposa* group in varying numbers even on basidiocarps in a single collection we are inclined not to give any taxonomic emphasis to their relative abundance in our treatment of this group.

MATERIAL EXAMINED: COLORADO: Bartholomew (type). NEW MEXICO: Barrows 791. UTAH: McKnight F-144. WYOMING: Overholts.

107. **Pholiota aurivella** (Fr.) Kummer, Der Führer in die Pilzkunde, p. 83. 1871.

Agaricus aurivellus Fries, Syst. Myc. 1: 242. 1821.

Hypodendrum aurivellum (Fr.) Overholts, North Amer. Fl. 10: 279. 1932.

Illustrations: Text figs. 222-224; pls. 49-50.

Pileus 4–16 cm broad, campanulate to convex, often broadly umbonate, when young more or less uniformly ochraceous orange to tawny, at maturity more uniformly tawny, at first covered with large appressed spot-like scales which may disappear and when wet may become more or less gelatinous, cuticle viscid or gelatinous. Context yellow, firm.

Lamellae adnate, sinuate-adnate, or emarginate, pale yellowish, becoming ferruginous brown, close.

Stipe 5–8 cm long, 5–15 mm thick, yellowish or yellowish brown, central or eccentric, floccose above the annulus, fibrillose below and increasingly scaly downward, the scales fibrillose and recurved, dry, equal, solid.

Spores 7–9.5 (11) × 4.5–6 μ, smooth, apical pore distinct but apex not truly truncate; in face view broadly elliptic, in profile broadly oblong to obscurely bean-shaped; in KOH dingy cinnamon-color, in Melzer's reagent darker reddish-tawny; wall about 0.25 μ thick.

Basidia 24–28 (30) × 4.5–6 μ, 4-spored, hyaline to yellowish in KOH and Melzer's reagent, narrowly clavate, some with hyaline refractive amorphous particles, some with rusty-brown content in KOH (clearing somewhat on standing) and some hyaline and homogeneous. Pleurocystidia 30–45 × 4–7 μ, mostly fusoid or branched once or twice near apex (rarely appearing as having 3-4 coarse sterigmata, 3-4 μ at base (but no spores ever seen attached); content hyaline to partially filled with solidified colloidal material or with refractive particles dark brown in Melzer's (but not with a characteristic refractive inclusion as in chrysocystidia). Cheilocystidia 26–35 × 5–10 μ, subfusoid with obtuse apex to fusoid-ventricose and obtuse, or versiform, wall at times thick enough to show as a double line. Caulocystidia none.

Gill trama of floccose subparallel hyphae of elongate cells 5–15 μ or more diam., thin-walled, smooth, hyaline to yellowish in KOH and Melzer's reagent; subhymenium of narrow hyaline gelatinous hyphae curving from a central strand to base of hymenium—very indistinct at best. Pileus cutis a thick gelatinous layer of interwoven yellowish to hyaline smooth hyphae 2–5 μ diam.; hypodermium of rusty brown hyphae (but color dissolving out and layer merely yellowish finally), hyphae 5–17 μ diam. Context hyphae hyaline and with "colloidal" content as revived in KOH, 6–15 μ diam., yellowish in Melzer's reagent, walls thin to slightly thickened and refractive in KOH. Clamp connections present.

HABIT, HABITAT, AND DISTRIBUTION: On trunks and logs of hardwood (maple, basswood, elm, sycamore, beech, birch) and conifers, New York, North Carolina, Tennessee, Michigan, Colorado, Idaho, Washington, Oregon, New Mexico; Canada (Ontario); Europe, England; also reported from California (Overholts 1927), and Illinois (Harper, 1911); June—November.

OBSERVATIONS: This species is marked by its viscid, yellowish to tawny pileus, with appressed spot-like scales, and a dry stipe with fibrillose, recurved scales which tend to be more numerous downward. The spores usually do not exceed 9.5 μ in length, only rarely reaching 10–11 μ. Generally, it is not found at the base of trunks and stumps, but on them.

Lange (1938) has proposed *P. aurivella* var. *cerifera* (Karsten) Lange for a variety which has a stipe with dense, recurved scales, which at first are whitish but soon brownish from the base upward. We have not distinguished this variant here in North America. *P. caespitosa* might appear close but it has yellow scales on the stipe and when young a whitish pileus. The brown bodies in the hymenium can be basidia, basidioles, or cystidia, so a distinction between cystidia and basidia on colored content is not made here. The pleurocystidia are a distinctive feature of the species, but revive poorly. Moser's (1950) report of *P. squarroso-adiposa,* to judge by the spore width, applies to *P. aurivella.*

The microscopic data given in the following account are from a specimen from Derek Reid, collected at Berkhamsted, England. Oct. 27, 1955.

Spores 7–10 (11) × 4.5–6 μ smooth, apical pore distinct but apex not truly truncate; shape in face view broadly elliptic, in profile broadly elliptic to obscurely bean-shaped, color in KOH dull tawny, in Melzer's reagent reddish cinnamon; wall about 0.4 μ thick.

Basidia 25–30 × 6–8 μ, 4-spored, clavate, hyaline in KOH and yellowish in Melzer's reagent. Pleurocystidia embedded, 26–34 × 7–12 μ, sharply fusoid to clavate mucronate, wall thin smooth and hyaline; content "empty" except for a small at times poorly formed refractive inclusion. Cheilocystidia 22–33 × 5–9 μ, subfusoid, subfilamentous or fusoid-ventricose; walls smooth, yellow to hyaline, thin; content homogeneous, yellow to hyaline. Caulocystidia in tufts (20) 33–65 × (8) 12–20 μ, clavate to vesiculose-pedicellate; walls smooth to roughened, yellowish to hyaline; content-"empty."

Gill trama of mostly floccose hyphae subparallel and with long greatly inflated (20+ μ) cells, walls smooth, slightly thickened and refractive; hyaline; subhymenium a poorly defined layer of subgelatinous hyphae (on mature gills). Pileus trama with a thick gelatinous pellicle of hyphae 2–8 μ diam., content ochraceous to brownish in KOH, the layer dull reddish cinnamon near surface, yellow to hyaline in midportion; hypodermial region not sharply distinct from context. Context hyphae interwoven, cells with slightly thickened to thin walls (2 double lines if thickened), smooth. Clamp connections present. All hyphae inamyloid.

It will be noted that no pleurocystidia with colored content (brown to red) were found in this specimen, but that typical chrysocystidia were, though in some the inclusion was not too sharply defined. In addition the caulocystidia were voluminous. If proved constant this combination of features may be indicative of an additional species. We refrain from describing another species at this time because we do not have sufficient data on the caulocystidia of the western American specimens and because we have seen both only in the dried condition.

MATERIAL EXAMINED: ALASKA: Baxter 8-1936; CALIFORNIA: Pusateri 25; COLORADO: Barrows 902, 1336, (MICH); IDAHO: Cooke 22069 (MICH); Smith 32030, 34208, 54694, 54695, 55258, 58331, 68714; Trueblood 270 (MICH); MAINE: Parlin 15260; MICHIGAN: Smith 3181, 21382, 71435, NORTH CAROLINA: Hesler 18170; NEW MEXICO: Barrows 105, 1498, 1498a (MICH); OREGON: Sipe 132, 224; Smith 19658; TENNESSEE: Hesler 9538, 9582, 12508; UTAH: McKnight F-144; WASHINGTON: Cooke 21922 (MICH); CANADA: BRITISH COLUMBIA: Tannhauser 10-26-48; ONTARIO: Bell (Tenn. 10274); QUEBEC: DAOM 45190; ENGLAND: Reid 27-10-1955; NETHERLANDS: Tenn. 23833; SWITZERLAND: Favre 9-10-48. Cultured basidiocarps: Arend 1935, Harding 4 specimens 1951-1952.

108. Pholiota connata sp. nov.
Illustrations: Text figs. 225-228.

Pileus 4–10 cm latus, late convexus, viscidus, luteus, squamis ad pressis. Contextus subluteus. Lamellae luteae demum subfulvae, confertae latae, adnatae, secedentes. Stipes 5–9 cm longus, 2–2.5 cm crassus, deorsum attenuatus, connato-caespitosus, deorsum luteus et subviscidus, demum subsquamulosus, sursum subsericeus. Vellum luteum, subcortinatum. Sporae 7–9 × 3.5–4.5 μ. Pleurocystidia 28–43 × 8–14 μ, clavata vel mucronata hyalina vel subbadia. Specimen typicum in Herb. Univ. Mich. conservatum est; legit Ann Arbor, Mich. 4 June 1966. Bill Isaacs (Smith 72927).

Pileus 4–10 cm broad, broadly convex, in age margin recurved, surface thinly viscid from a pale yellow pellicle (near "warm buff") over this, around disc are appressed fibrillose patches as squamules which darken to dingy brown, slowly the pellicle becoming darker yellow (near "ochre-yellow") and in age checking to produce minute squamules over the marginal area, edge at first appendiculate from veil remnants. Context thick, yellowish, odor and taste mild; $FeSO_4$ slowly olive-gray, KOH brownish (on pellicle orange-fulvous).

Lamellae near ochre-yellow young, dingy yellow-brown in age, broad, close, adnate, seceding, edges even.

Stipe 5–9 cm long, 2–2.5 cm at apex, narrowed to a point below (clusters as in *Clitocybe illudens*), solid, pale yellowish within, becoming lemon-yellow then rusty-brown in and over basal half, surface below veil line yellow like the pileus cutis but not as viscid and orange-fulvous in KOH, the layer breaking into minute squamules. Veil line soon evanescent, above it the surface pale yellowish and fibrillose pruinose to squamulose with very minute squamules.

Spore deposit cinnamon-brown. Spores 7–9 × 3.5–4.5 μ, smooth, apical pore evident but apex not truncate; shape in face view oblong to elliptic and varying slightly to ovate, in profile oblong to slightly bean-shaped; color near cinnamon-brown in KOH, paler reddish cinnamon in Melzer's reagent; wall about 0.25 μ thick.

Basidia 18–23 × 5.5–7 μ, 4-spored (rarely 2-spored), clavate to utriform, hyaline in KOH fresh, yellowish in Melzer's reagent. Pleurocystidia 28–43 × 8–14 μ, clavate to mucronate; wall thin, hyaline, and smooth; content dark rusty brown in Melzer's reagent (fresh material), in KOH some of them brownish and some hyaline. Cheilocystidia 25–36 × 5–10 μ, clavate, utriform, cylindric-subcapitate, or fusoid-ventricose; walls thin and smooth, hyaline in KOH; content homogeneous. Caulocystidia over apex of stipe in tufts, versiform; clavate, fusoid-ventricose, subcylindric, subfusoid (20) 30–60 × 8–20 μ, walls yellowish in KOH fresh and with tawny incrustations to smooth.

Gill trama of a central strand of floccose subparallel hyphae 4–12 μ diam., hyaline in KOH, and with colloidal-granular content; subhymenium a layer of narrow gelatinous hyphae. Pileus cutis a gelatinous pellicle of narrow ochraceous hyphae (in KOH); hypodermium not sharply differentiated. Context hyphae interwoven, hyaline with colloidal content. Clamp connections present.

HABIT, HABITAT, AND DISTRIBUTION: Caespitose on *Acer negundo* Ann Arbor, Mich., June 4, 1966, Mr. Bill Isaacs collector (Smith 72927 type). Also known from Maine, New York and Washington as well as Ontario in Canada.

OBSERVATIONS: This is one of the American species often confused with *P. adiposa*. Its features of distinction are: the connate fascicle of basidiocarps, the thin viscid layer over the stipe below the veil line, yellow pileus, and spores 7–9 × 3.5–4.5 μ. *P. adiposa* of Kühner & Romagnesi has spores under 7 μ long and should be very viscid or glutinous and with much more highly developed scales. The spores of *P. connata* are too narrow for *P. aurivella* (7–9 × 5–6 μ). This difference in spore width is significant in *Pholiota*. *P. cerifera* is said to have whitish recurved scales at first below the veil line of the stipe. Consequently it seems best to describe the American variant as distinct.

MATERIAL EXAMINED: MAINE: Shaffer 3779. MICHIGAN: Baxter 192k; Charlton G-390; Conrad & Langdon 8-11-1893; Harding 436; Imshaug 4786; Kauffman 9-30-07; 10-19-05; Potter 3181: Smith 21382, 32030, 34208, 34227, 50623, 58331, 64753, 64770, 72927 (type). NEW YORK: House 10-27-45; Kauffman 9-2-21; Shaffer 599. WASHINGTON: Smith 17886. CANADA—ONTARIO: Kelly 1235.

109. Pholiota hiemalis sp. nov.
Illustrations: Text figs. 497-499; pl. 51.

Pileus 4–11 cm latus, obtusus demum plano-umbonatus, glutinosus, squamulosus; squamulae gelatinosae, latae, agglutinatae; laete luteus. Contextus cartilagineus, cum "FeSO$_4$" olivaceo; sapor mitis. Lamellae pallidae demum luteae, acie laete luteae, confertae, latae. Stipes 4–9 cm longus, 6–12(15) mm crassus, luteus, squamulosus. Sporae 7–9(10) × 4–4.5 (5) μ; cheilocystidia fusoide ventricosa vel clavata, laete luteae. Specimen typicum in Herb. Univ. Mich. conservatum est; legit prope Upper Priest Lake, Boundary Co., Idaho. 13 Oct. 1966. Smith 74173.

Pileus 4–11 cm broad, obtusely conic when young, the margin incurved, expanding to plano-umbonate, the surface very slimy, at first with 1–3 rows of broad flattish pale dull fulvous gelatinous scales which soon become washed off in wet weather, ground color dull yellow ochre over disc, lemon-yellow near the margin. Context cartilaginous, watery yellowish, odor unpleasant but soon fading, taste mild, FeSO$_4$ slowly olive.

Lamellae pallid when young but with yellow margins, becoming dull yellow and finally dull cinnamon brown but edges remaining bright yellow, close, broad, adnate becoming adnexed, not staining when bruised.

Stipe 4–9 cm long, 6–12 (15) mm thick at apex, enlarged down to a flaring base, stuffed with a pallid pith, soon rusty brown in the base and over it, surface finely recurved-squamulose over basal area with dry fibrillose squamules, medial portion with at first scattered rusty brown gelatinous patches or scales similar to those on pileus, silky to silky fibrillose above from the remains of an inner cortinate veil, at times this veil leaving a fairly thick loosely fibrillose annulus or annular zone.

Spores dull rusty brown in deposit, 7–9 (10 × 4–4.5 (5) μ smooth; apex furnished with a small germ pore; shape in face view elliptic to ovate, in profile elliptic to obscurely bean-shaped; color in KOH pale dull tawny, in Melzer's sol. the same color or paler ochraceous, wall about 0.25 μ thick.

Basidia 17–22 × 4–5 μ, 4-spored, subcylindric to narrowly clavate, yellowish, hyaline in KOH and slightly more ochraceous in Melzer's sol. Pleurocystidia scattered, 30–50 × 8–15 μ, clavate-mucronate to clavate, content hyaline fresh but revived in KOH yellowish and wrinkled, in Melzer's the content in granules or irregular bodies and dull brown. (Not true chrysocystidia as far as content is concerned). Cheilocystidia versiform, clavate to vesiculose and 18–26 × 10–14 μ; narrowly clavate to fusoid-ventricose or utriform and 26–40 × 9–13 μ, some irregular or with one or two protuberances in upper part, with both a yellow content and wall (in KOH) when fresh, as revived with a distinctly yellow somewhat thickened wall in basal area or lower half, the upper part hyaline to yellowish and the wall thinner.

Gill trama with a central area of more or less parallel hyphae hyaline to yellowish in KOH and Melzer's, the hyphal cells inflating to 10–15 μ, the cells greatly elongated; subhymenium of gelatinous hyphae diverging to the hymenium and often with yellow content as revived in KOH, no incrusted hyphae noted. Pileus cutis a thick layer of gelatinized hyphae 3–7 μ diam., rather tangled in arrangement, the hyphal walls breaking down somewhat, the hyphae hyaline to ochraceous in KOH; hyphae of the gelatinous veil material breaking down almost completely (found as patches over the cutis); hypodermial region of hyphae with inflated cells (up to 20 μ) but walls hyaline to nearly so in KOH, in Melzer's the content of some cells ochraceous to orange. Context of hyaline hyphae with inflated cells hyaline in KOH and hyaline to dull ochraceous orange in Melzer's reagent, walls smooth and thin to slightly thickened in some ("double"). Clamp connections regularly present.

HABIT, HABITAT, AND DISTRIBUTION: Gregarious-caespitose on log of *Abies* (fir), Upper Priest River Boundary County, Idaho, Oct. 13, 1966. Smith 74173, type.

OBSERVATIONSS The distinguishing features of this species are its habitat on conifer logs, the large flat gelatinous scales on the pileus which finally disintegrate to dark brown discolorations which are not at all scale-like, the pallid young gills with their bright yellow margins, and the gelatinous as well as dry patches and squamules on the stipe. The spores are too large for *P. adiposa. P. abietis* appears to be closest and is abundant in the area, but does not have colored gill edges, and the scales on the pileus usually show as aggregations of appressed fibrils. In *P. abietis* the spores are 5.5–7 × 3.5–4 μ, i.e. slightly smaller.

P. hiemalis is a late-fruiting species, if one season is any indication. The type collection consisted of a log covered by the bright colored basidiocarps. Only a small amount of it was collected on Oct. 13th. That night a hard freeze came in the area, and I went back the next day to see what the remaining specimens were like. They were still frozen stiff at 10 o'clock in the morning. I gathered the remainder on the log and took them back to the laboratory. When set up for spore deposits they thawed out and deposited spores just as the unfrozen material had done from the day before. In the dried condition the frozen and unfrozen basidiocarps are indistinguishable. This is one reason for assuming that the fungus is a late fruiting species. It has apparently adjusted to freezing nights. Most other fungi in the woods had collapsed from the frost by noon that day.

Pholiota muelleri (Fr.) P. D. Orton is described as having gills with edges yellower than the faces at times, but Orton describes the scales of the pileus as being fibrillose rather than gelatinous. He also describes the spores as 5–7 × 3–4 μ.

110. Pholiota subvelutipes sp. nov.
Illustrations: Text figs. 229-232; pl. 52.

Pileus 4–7 cm latus, convexus demum planus, ad marginem appen- diculatus, luteus, glutinosus, squamosus. Contextus albus. Lamellae pal- lidae vel griseo-olivaceae, demum subfulvae, confertae latae, adnatae. Stipes 4–8 cm longus, 5–11 mm crassus, ad basim velutino-pubescens, deorsum squamosus, sursum pallidus demum pallide luteus. Velum luteum. Sporae 6.5–8(9) × 3–4 μ, leves, oblongae. Pleurocystidia 30–46 × 7–11 μ sordide brunnea. Cheilocystidia 23–35 × 4–9 μ. Specimen typicum in Herb. Univ. Mich. conservatum est., legit prope Rock River, Mich. 25 Sept. 1929. A. H. Smith.

Pileus 4–7 cm, broad, convex expanding to nearly plane, margin at first appendiculate with veil remnants, viscid to glutinous when young or wet, ground color bright pale yellow ("Pinard-yellow" to "empire- yellow") bruising to olivaceous ("sulphine-yellow") , on aging ferruginous from the center out, surface at first decorated with concentrically ar- ranged amber-brown ("amber-brown") scales about 3 mm in diameter and triangular near cap margin but subconic on the disc; margin even. Context white when young, flavescent moderately thick and pliant.

Lamellae adnate to adnate-emarginate with a tooth, 5–7 mm broad, crowded, when young pallid to "olive-buff," becoming avellaneous and finally clay-color, edges minutely floccose.

Stipe 4–8 cm long, 5–11 mm thick, equal to a flange-like enlargement at base and base surrounded by a radiating mass of olive-yellow to tawny pubescence, solid, whitish within at first, lutescent or finally fulvous below, the annular zone covered with closely set projecting yellow scales which became tawny in age, naked above the veil line. Veil pale yellow, almost cortinate.

Spores 6.5–8 (9) × 3–4 μ, smooth, apical pore present but minute, apex not truncate; shape in face view oblong to elliptic, in profile oblong to elliptic (often narrower by 0.3 μ in profile than in face view) ; color in KOH dull tawny, not much change in Melzer's reagent; wall about 0.25 μ thick.

Basidia 26–33 × 6–7.5 μ, 4-spored, narrowly clavate, hyaline in KOH in properly dried material, yellowish in Melzer's reagent. Pleurocystidia 30–46 × 7–11 μ, subclavate to narrowly ovate-pedicellate or nearer fusoid- ventricose; wall thin smooth and hyaline; content dark bister to very dull brown and filling the cell, coagulating in drying but not forming a distinctive body (inclusion) dark dingy brown as revived in Melzer's reagent; projecting 8–12 μ, some cells hyaline or only weakly colored. Cheilocystidia 23–35 × 4–9 μ, clavate, clavate-irregular, fusoid-ventricose, ventricose-capitate or merely subfusoid, wall thin smooth and hyaline, content homogeneous, typically hyaline. Caulocystidia as clavate end-cells of surface hyphae 30–75 × 4–7 μ, hyaline, thin-walled, smooth, content homogeneous.

Gill trama with a floccose central strand of subparallel hyphae hyaline to pale tan (in KOH), walls thin and smooth; subhymenium a rather wide gelatinous band of narrow hyaline interwoven hyphae. Pileus cutis a thick pellicle of gelatinous hyphae 2–5 μ diam., ochraceous to pale dingy brownish or hyaline in KOH; hypodermial layer scarcely differentiated. Context hyphae with slightly thickened refractive walls (in KOH) showing as a pair of double lines, smooth; hyphal cells considerably inflated. Clamp connections present. All hyphae inamyloid.

HABIT, HABITAT, AND DISTRIBUTION: Caespitose on log of *Betula lutea*, Rock River, Mich. Sept. 25, 1929. Coll. A. H. Smith (type).

OBSERVATIONS: This species was reported as *P. subsquarrosa* by Kauffman and Smith (1933). However, *P. subsquarrosa* is still not clearly defined by European authors, so at this time it appears best to report on the 1929 collection as a separate species. It is readily distinct from *P. squarroso-adiposa* by its narrower more oblong spores and velvety mycelium at the base of the stipe. In addition the gills are not yellow at first. It is at once distinguished from *P. connata* in the field by the scaly stipe and flanged stipe-base.

We have one collection, Smith 73596 on *Abies* wood from near Kellog, Idaho, which has the basal mycelium of *P. subvelutipes* but its gills are subdistant and when young yellow. This points up, again, the pattern of variability in the group and the various combinations of characters found to exist when large numbers of collections are studied. The Kellog collection may represent a distinct species but at present we do not care to describe it.

111. Pholiota abietis sp. nov.
Illustrations: Text figs. 233-236; pls. 53-54.

Pileus 4–9(15) cm latus, late convexus, glutinosus, squamosus luteus, squamis fulvis. Contextus subluteus. Lamellae pallidae demum cinnamomeae, adnatae, latae, confertae. Stipes 8–12 cm longus, 9–15 mm crassus, solidus, aequalis sed ad basin submarginatus, deorsum squamosus; squamis siccis. Sporae 5.5–7(7.5) × 3.5–4 μ, leves. Pleurocystidia: 1) 32–46 × 8–12 μ, clavata vel mucronata, subbadia. 2) Chrysocystidia 26–42 × 6–12 μ. Caulocystidia (20)30–70 × 6–12(20) μ, versiformia. Specimen typicum in Herb. Univ. Mich. conservatum est; legit prope Joyce, Wash. 24 Sept. 1935. Smith 2585.

Pileus 4–9 (15) cm broad, broadly convex with an incurved margin, in age nearly plane, more rarely with an obtuse umbo, surface slimy-viscid and covered by appressed spot-like tawny-brown scales arranged in concentric rows and causing the predominant tawny-fulvous color, lemon-yellow between the scales and on margin, margin at first appendiculate with veil fragments. Context pliant, moderately thick, pale dull yellow, odor and taste mild.

Lamellae when young *pallid* brownish (not yellow), becoming a dull cinnamon and when dried rusty-fulvous, moderately broad, close, tapering toward the cap margin, adnate to slightly adnexed or rounded as they meet the stipe.

Stipe 8–12 cm long, 9–15 mm thick, solid, equal to a slightly enlarged base, silky-pruinose to glabrous above the veil line and more densely scaly as one progresses down from the line, the scales fibrillose and dry, veil leaving an evanescent zone near apex (never a distinct annulus), ground color yellowish over all and not distinctly darker over basal area.

Spore print rusty cinnamon. Spores 5.5–7 (7.5) × 3.5–4 (4.5) μ, smooth, apical pore distinct but apex not truly truncate; shape in face view oblong to elliptic or more rarely obscurely ovate, in profile elliptic or nearly so varying to obscurely inequilateral, near cinnamon-brown in KOH and not much different (paler) in Melzer's reagent.

Basidia 18–23 × 5.5–7 μ, 4-spored, narrowly clavate, hyaline to yellowish in KOH or Melzer's reagent. Pleurocystidia 32–46 × 8–12 μ, clavate to clavate-mucronate and filled with dark reddish brown contracted wrinkled content (as revived in either KOH or Melzer's reagent), in addition chrysocystidia 26–42 × 6–12 μ present with hyaline thin smooth walls and a refractive inclusion, these clavate, fusoid or clavate-mucronate. Cheilocystidia (23) 32–56 × (4) 6–9 (11) μ, versiform but mostly varying around narrowly fusoid-ventricose to subcylindric-capitate, more rarely clavate or enlarged part irregular in outline, walls thin smooth and hyaline in KOH or in a few slightly thickened ($\pm$ 0.4 μ), hyaline (yellow to tawny if poorly dried), content typically hyaline and homogeneous. Caulocystidia numerous above veil line, (20) 30–70 × 6–12 (20) μ, elongate clavate, elongate-fusoid and of regular to irregular outline, filamentous-capitate with the capitellum lopsided at times, or fusoid-ventricose, walls hyaline to pale cinnamon and smooth to incrusted.

Gill trama of a central area of floccose hyphae subparallel and cells greatly elongated, 6–15 μ wide, walls hyaline and somewhat refractive as well as thickened slightly (showing as 2 double lines), smooth; subhymenium a gelatinous layer of closely packed hyaline hyphae 1.5–3 μ diam. Pileus cutis a thick gelatinous pellicle reddish in KOH, the hyphae 4–10 μ diam., appressed and walls gelatinizing, smooth to asperulate; hypodermial region not differentiated. Context hyphae yellowish to hyaline in KOH, smooth, walls thin, closely interwoven. Clamp connections present. All hyphae inamyloid.

HABIT, HABITAT, AND DISTRIBUTION: Caespitose-gregarious on *Abies*, dead trees, logs etc., Agate Beach, near Joyce Wash. Sept. 24, 1935. Smith 2585, type.

OBSERVATIONS: For years we have identified this species as *P. squarroso-adiposa* but Lange described the latter as having yellowish gills when young, and the stipe as having ferruginous-cinnamon scales. In ours the scales are not so dark colored and as dried the stipe is the same color over all, not darker below as in *P. connata* and as shown by Lange for *P. intermedia* (*squarroso-adiposa*). There is also the difference in habitat, one on conifer wood and the European species on that of *Juglans*, a deciduous species. In view of the fact that in North America there has been much confusion in the application of the names for taxa in this group we choose not to ignore the differences shown by American collections even though some may appear to be of minor importance. The spores in *P. aurivella* are larger but the stipe features of *P. abietis* remind one of that species.

112. **Pholiota limonella** (Pk.) Saccardo, Syll. Fung. 5: 753. 1887.
Agaricus (*Pholiota*) *limonellus* Peck, New York State Mus. Ann. Rept. 31: 33. 1879.
Hypodendrum limonellum (Pk.) Murrill, Mycologia 4: 261. 1912.
Illustrations: Text figs. 237-239.

Pileus 2.5–5 cm broad, convex or nearly plane, sometimes umbonate, lemon-yellow when fresh, with scattered reflexed or suberect fibrillose reddish or tawny scales, viscid. Context thin, yellow.

Lamellae sinuate-adnate or slightly adnexed, whitish, becoming ferruginous, narrow (2–4 mm broad), close.

Stipe 3–7 cm long, 3–5 mm thick, pallid or yellowish, with scattered, recurved yellow scales, smooth above the annulus, equal. Veil forming a floccose, evanescent yellow annulus.

Spores 6–7.5 × 4–5 μ, smooth, apical pore distinct causing apex to appear subtruncate in some; shape in face view ovate to elliptic, in profile obscurely bean-shaped to obscurely inequilateral, color in KOH dull tawny to ochraceous tawny, in Melzer's reagent more ochraceous on standing; wall about 0.3 μ thick.

Basidia 4-spored, 18–24 × 6–7.5 μ at apex, about 2 μ in the pedicel, hyaline in KOH, nearly so in Melzer's reagent. Pleurocystidia 23–40 × 7–12 μ, long-pedicellate and clavate-mucronate to subclavate above, with a hyaline refractive inclusion as revived in KOH or containing evenly ochraceous to rusty brown homogeneous material, smooth, thin-walled. Cheilocystidia 23–30 × 5–9 μ, clavate, fusoid, or subcylindric, content usually ochraceous, thin-walled, smooth. Caulocystidia rare, resembling the cheilocystidia.

Gill trama of a central area of interwoven hyaline hyphae reddish orange in Melzer's reagent as revived, walls thin and smooth; subhymenium of gelatinous narrow hyphae. Pileus cuticle a gelatinous pellicle of

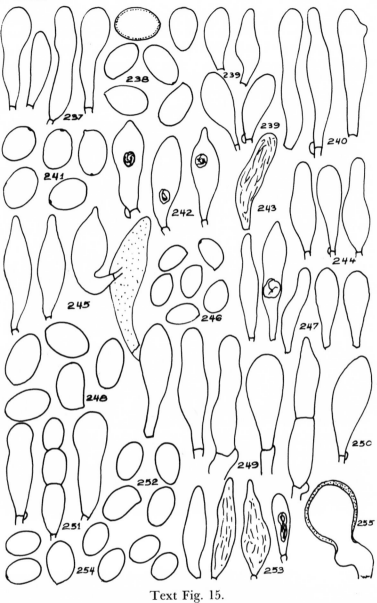

Text Fig. 15.

FIGS. 237-239, pleurocystidia, spores and cheilocystidia of *P. limo-nella;* 240-244, caulocystidia, spores, pleurocystidia, and cheilocystidia of *P. squarroso-adiposa;* 245-247, pleurocystidia, spores and cheilocystidia of *P. adiposa;* 248-250, spores, cheilocystidia and caulocystidia of *P. lucifer;* 251-253, cheilocystidia, spores and pleurocystidia of *P. angustipes;* 254 & 255, spores and cheilocystidium of *P. simulans.*

hyphae 2–4 μ diam. with colloidal content and red in Melzer's but fading to paler on standing; below this a region of wider (5–12 μ) hyphae with colloidal content dark red in Melzer's fading to orange-reddish. Clamp connections present.

HABIT, HABITAT, AND DISTRIBUTION: On prostrate beech trunks, New York, September. Type studied.

OBSERVATIONS: Our data are all taken from the type or original description. *P. limonella* is distinguished from *P. flammans* by larger spores. It is very close to *P. squarroso-adiposa,* so close we thought for a time the two were identical, and they may well be. However, the Melzer's reaction of the pileus context appears to separate them. In addition, by comparison, the basidiocarps of *P. limonella* are more delicate. The figure (pl. 45) in Icones Farlowianae is very likely some other species. *Pholiota subsquarrosa* Fr. sensu Soehner (1922) is very close to this species but has bright yellow gills when young. Fries' illustration shows a species very close to *P. limonella* but again the gills are yellow when young.

113. **Pholiota squarroso-adiposa** Lange, Flora Danica 5: 101. 1940. *Pholiota intermedia* Lange, Flora Agar. Danica 3: 55. 1938.

(non. *P. intermedia* Smith 1932 or *P. intermedia* Singer 1928) Illustrations: Text figs. 240-244; pl. 55.

Pileus 3–6 (8) cm broad, obtusely conic to convex, when young the margin incurved, becoming broadly conic to nearly plane but with a broad low umbo or more rarely merely convex, surface slimy viscid and at first covered with flat strap-shaped to triangular recurved scales 3–4 mm long on young caps and about 3 mm broad at base, in age the scales disappearing or becoming agglutinated and spot-like, young buttons dark rusty brown ("russet" to "Mars-brown"), becoming paler ("ochraceous tawny), and marginal area pale bright yellow ("antimony-yellow") and this color gradually becoming dominant as velar layer disappears. Context thick and pliant, yellow ("massicot-yellow") or pallid, often with a watery green line next to the gills, odor and taste not distinctive.

Lamellae pale yellow ("cream-buff") becoming more or less rusty from the spores, close, narrow (3–4 mm), adnate, equal in width, about 3 tiers of lamellulae, edges even.

Stipe 4–7 cm long, 8–10 mm thick, equal above an abrupt flanged or bulbous base, solid, becoming hollowed, pale yellow ("massicot yellow") within or fading to whitish, surface up to apical fibrillose zone covered with recurved straw yellow to ochraceous tawny scales which are floccose (perfectly dry); veil pale yellow fading to pallid, leaving an evanescent apical zone when it breaks.

Spore deposit near cinnamon-brown; spores 6–7.5 × 4.3–4.8 μ, smooth, apical pore present but inconspicuous; shape in face view broadly ellipsoid varying to subovate, in profile, subelliptic, cinnamon-brown in KOH and about the same in Melzer's reagent, wall about 0.25 μ thick.

Basidia 24–30 × 5.5–7 μ, 4-spored, clavate, yellowish to hyaline in KOH, yellowish in Melzer's reagent. Pleurocystidia abundant to scattered, 26–35 × 7–11 μ, clavate to oval-pedicellate, usually with a highly refractive inclusion which is hyaline to yellowish in Melzer's reagent, also present are scattered cells 33–48 × 9–13 μ with contracted wrinkled dark reddish-brown content in KOH and in Melzer's. Cheilocystidia 24–35 × 5–9 μ, clavate, fusoid, to fusoid-ventricose, apex obtuse; walls thin, yellowish to hyaline, smooth; content homogeneous and hyaline to yellowish, a few similar to the dark brown pleurocystidia also occurring. Caulocystidia versiform and size very variable; clavate, subcylindric, narrowly fusoid-ventricose, 25–55 × 6–9 μ; 20–40 × 5–6; 30–65 × 7–11 μ or 26–35 × 6–10 μ; some elongate subellipsoid and up to 12–16 μ diam. with walls slightly incrusted.

Gill trama when properly revived of hyaline subparallel hyphae with elongate cells having smooth thin to slightly thickened hyaline walls (as revived in KOH) ; subhymenium a narrow gelatinous layer of compactly arranged narrow (2–5 μ ±) hyaline hyphae. Pileus cutis a thick gelatinous pellicle of narrow (1.5–4.5 μ) ochraceous to nearly hyaline hyphae (in KOH) ; over this occur the remains of scales composed of reddish tawny hyphae with short cells (1:w was 2:1 compared to 3-8:1) , with smooth to roughened walls, the hyphae parallel in arrangement; hypodermial region of rusty cinnamon somewhat incrusted floccose hyphae 4–8 μ diam. Context hyphae interwoven, cells inflated, smooth-walled, walls thin to thickened slightly and showing as a pair of double lines. Clamp connections present. All hyphae inamyloid.

HABIT, HABITAT, AND DISTRIBUTION: Caespitose in large masses on alder and maple logs in the Pacific Northwest. Description from Smith 16892 Baker Lake, Wash., Sept. 12, 1941.

OBSERVATION: This material is the closest we have found in North America to Lange's *P. squarroso-adiposa*. It has the short rather broad spores, the yellowish young gills and the scaly cap and stipe exactly as Lange illustrates it. Also, in the cited collections the stipe usually dries darker at the base than at the apex.

114. **Pholiota filamentosa** (Fr.) Herpel, Hedwigia 49: 160. 1910.
Illustrations: Text figs. 498, 500, 501; pls. 56-57.

Pileus 5–16 cm broad, convex with an incurved margin, viscid, lemon yellow to ochre yellow, covered with rusty brown spot-like scales, in age these appearing as rusty stains and with remains of the inner veil as appressed triangular patches of fibrils agglutinated and at the tips feathered out slightly; margin undulating and when young often fringed. Context whitish, around larval tunnels becoming yellow and finally yellow-brown; odor and taste not distinctive; color with $FeSO_4$ olivaceous, with Guaiac—O; KOH on pileus cutis rusty brown.
Lamellae yellow when young, becoming rusty brown at maturity,

broad, close, adnexed, edges even and pallid to concolor with faces.

Stipe 4–8 cm long, 1–2 cm thick, equal to a flanged base, yellowish within, apex yellowish and silky fibrillose, lower down with distinct tawny appressed fibrillose scales and entire base showing ochraceous tawny or darker in age; annulus subpersistent, heavy, thick and fibrillose in texture, with tawny patches on under side similar to scales on pileus or their outlines not as clear, gelatinous, often broken as cap expands and remains clinging to pileus margin.

Spore deposit dull rusty brown; spores 6–7.5 (8) × 3.8–4.2 μ, smooth, apical pore minute; shape in face view mostly elliptic varying to slightly ovate, in profile mostly elliptic to obscurely bean-shaped; color in KOH dull cinnamon, in Melzer's sol. slightly paler; wall about 0.25 μ thick.

Basidia 26–32 × 5–7.5 μ, clavate, 4-spored, hyaline to yellowish in KOH, content orange-buff in Melzer's sol. Pleurocystidia 25–40 × 6–13 μ, narrowly clavate-mucronate to broadly so and with a long pedicel, content like that of chrysocystidia to merely reticulate (in KOH) and hyaline to rusty brown, in Melzer's reagent the content brownish to hyaline. Cheilocystidia 18–32 × 5–11 μ, clavate to ventricose or fusoid-ventricose, some rather irregular in outline, content ochraceous in KOH, walls thin or very slightly thickened near base. Caulocystidia 30–65 × 5–11 μ, rarely 30–40 × 9–13 μ, abundant, narrowly clavate, hyaline to weakly yellowish in KOH, roughened by adhering small plates (readily visible as thickened areas in optical section) .

Gill trama of parallel hypha 6–15 μ wide and with long cells having hyaline to yellowish walls in KOH, the walls thin for the most part; subhymenium not gelatinous in young to freshly matured specimens and only slightly so in age, of hyphae 2–3 μ diam. and closely interwoven. Pileus cutis a gelatinous pellicle of hyphae 3–6 μ diam., hyaline to yellowish in KOH, the walls finally disintegrating, hypodermium of inflated non-gelatinous hyphae 10–25 μ diam., hyaline to brownish in KOH, content of some dull orange in Melzer's sol. Clamp connections present.

HABIT, HABITAT, AND DISTRIBUTION: Caespitose on a Douglas fir (*Pseudotsuga*) log, Newport, Wash. Sept. 23, 1966, coll. Kenneth Harrison. (Smith 73615) , description taken from this collection.

OBSERVATIONS: We have used the Friesian name for this species because his fungus is described as growing on conifer wood and has floccose-radiate annulus and concentric scales on the pileus. *P. abietis* differs in having pallid brownish gills when young, in lacking an annulus, and in having a truly gelatinous subhymenium. *P. fallax* has yellow marginate gills and glutinous gelatinous scales on the stipe. Both this species and *P. aurivella* attain exceptionally large size in the Pacific Northwest. To this extent our material does not fit the Friesian concept.

115. Pholiota adiposa (Fr.) Kummer, Der Führer in die Pilzkunde, p. 83. 1871.

Agaricus adiposus Fries, Syst. Myc. 1: 242. 1821.

Hypodendrum adiposum (Fr.) Overholts, North Amer. Fl. 10: 279. 1932.
Illustrations: Text figs. 245-247.

Pileus caespitose, 6–9 (16) cm broad, convex, then plane, yellow to dark-yellow, viscid or glutinous, with ferruginous-brown, more or less concentric scales, which dry down to resemble cherry-gum. Context yellow.

Lamellae adnate to sinuate, at first yellow or straw-yellow, becoming ferruginous, close, broad.

Stipe 5–12 cm long, 6–15 mm thick, viscid or glutinous, yellow above, becoming ferruginous brown downward, base enlarged, with numerous, glutinous, superficial squarrose or recurved scales up to the apical ring. Inner veil yellowish, subfloccose, forming an evanescent annulus.

Spores 5–6 × 3–4 μ, smooth, with a minute apical pore; shape in face view ovate to elliptic, in profile subelliptic to slightly bean-shaped; color in KOH pale tawny to clay-color, in Melzer's merely ochraceous; wall thin (–0.25 μ).

Basidia 16–20 × 3.5–5 μ, 4-spored, narrowly clavate, hyaline in KOH, weakly yellowish in Melzer's reagent. Pleurocystidia of two types: 1) 25–40 × 5–10 μ, subfusoid, walls thin smooth and hyaline, content coagulated and shrunken away from the walls, wrinkled, dark brown in KOH and in Melzer's reagent: 2) chrysocystidia 18–28 (33) × 6–9 (13) μ fusoid to somewhat fusoid-ventricose; walls thin, smooth and hyaline; inclusion small, hyaline in KOH and Melzer's reagent, usually well defined. Caulocystidia none except for those in the caulohymenium at very apex of the stipe and resembling hymenial cystidia.

Gill trama a floccose central area of somewhat interwoven hyphae hyaline in KOH, the cell walls thin and smooth; subhymenium a thin gelatinous layer of very narrow hyphae. Pileus cutis a very thick gelatinous pellicle of yellow to cinnamon-colored hyphae 2–5 μ diam., collapsing, walls mostly smooth. Clamp connections present. All hyphae inamyloid.

HABIT, HABITAT, AND DISTRIBUTION: On hardwood logs, British Columbia. September.

OBSERVATIONS: This species has been misinterpreted by some European mycologists, and even to a greater extent in North America. We are following the concepts of Lange, Ricken, Kühner & Romagnesi, Moser and Reid, all of whom appear to agree that its distinctive characters are a viscid or slimy pileus yellow to dark yellow with brown scales which become cherry-gum-like, viscid or slimy scales on the stipe, and spores 5–6 × 3–4 μ. This species has obviously been confused with *P. aurivella,* which also has broad gills, but has a dry stipe, and larger spores than *P. adiposa.* Many of the North American collections, in various herbaria, are filed erroneously under one of these names. The true *P. adiposa* appears to be rare in North America. The microscopic data given in our description are taken from a collection by Derek Reid at Oldbury,

England. Sept. 22, 1951. The reliable characters of distinction are the very small pale colored spores, glutinous scales on the stipe, and yellowish young gills. The macroscopic features even to the glutinous scales apply to more than one taxon here in this group in North America.

MATERIAL EXAMINED: BRITISH COLUMBIA; SLOVAKIA: Kmet, Prencow, Aug. 6, 1891 (STOCKHOLM). ENGLAND: Reid.

116. Pholiota lucifera (Lasch) Quélet, Champ. Jura & Vosg., p. 249. 1872.

Agaricus lucifera Lasch, Linnaea 3: 408. 1828.
Dryophila lucifera (Lasch) Quélet, Enchir. Fung., p. 68. 1886.
Illustrations: Text figs. 248-250.

Pileus 3–6 cm broad, convex, becoming more or less plane, at length umbonate, yellow, the disc somewhat ferruginous, viscid; with small, ferruginous-fulvous, adpressed, drop-like scales; margin appendiculate from veil remnants. Context whitish to yellowish, or yellow under the cuticle; taste bitter.

Lamellae adnate, yellow then bright rusty or ferruginous, close or crowded, rather narrow, edges at first white-crenulate.

Stipe 2–5 cm long, 3–8 mm thick, yellowish above, brownish and fibrillose-squamulose below the peronate-fibrillose fugacious ring, equal, solid.

Spores 6.5–9 $\times$ 4.5–5.5 μ, smooth, no germ pore evident; shape in face view ovate to elliptic, in profile obscurely inequilateral to bean-shaped; color rusty cinnamon in KOH, in Melzer's reagent slightly redder, wall thin (–0.25 μ).

Basidia 26–32 $\times$ 6–7 μ, 4-spored, narrowly clavate, yellowish in KOH and Melzer's reagent. Pleurocystidia rare and inconspicuous, 27–42 $\times$ 5–7 μ clavate-mucronate, (possibly merely basidioles). Cheilocystidia abundant, 28–60 $\times$ 5–12 μ, elongate-clavate to capitate, rarely somewhat fusoid-ventricose or septate, hyaline thin-walled, smooth, yellowish in Melzer's reagent. Caulocystidia present as a few clavate end-cells arising from surface hyphae over apex.

Gill trama of subparallel-interwoven hyphae 4–15 (20) μ diam., cells often short, thin-walled, yellowish to hyaline in KOH, smooth, content colloidal and $\pm$ hyaline in KOH causing hyphae to stand out boldly, in Melzer's reagent the content cinnabar-red to reddish orange; sub-hymenium of narrow (3–4 μ) subgelatinous closely packed hyphae hyaline in KOH and yellowish in Melzer's reagent. Pileus cutis of subgelatinous mostly ochraceous hyphae (in KOH) 2.5–4 μ broad and more or less radially disposed (not in a compact pellicle), hypodermial region not distinct from context. Context hyphae (in KOH) with colloidal content, scattered hyphal cells with a refractive metallic body (crystal?) resembling the inclusion in typical chrysocystidia (in KOH), hyphal walls thin, smooth and nearly hyaline, in Melzer's reagent the cell content red to orange-red or more ochraceous. Clamp connections present.

HABIT, HABITAT, AND DISTRIBUTION: On wood and woody debris, Europe, Summer—Fall.

OBSERVATIONS: This species is characterized by the drop-like appressed scales on the pileus, the stipe fibrillose-squamulose below the evanescent ring, and bitter taste. Its spores are distinctly larger than in *P. flammans*. We have not, as yet, seen any North American collections of *P. lucifera*. The Melzer's reactions remind one of those obtained from some collections of *Macowanites americanus*. They are most unusual in *Pholiota*. The impression one receives from the dried basidiocarps is that they are conspecific with *P. multifolia*, but this is not substantiated by the microscopic features. The iodine reaction of the context hyphae reminds of *P. limonella* but the larger spores and bitter taste distinguish it immediately. It is the only species we have encountered in which at least some of the cells of the context hyphae have a refractive inclusion resembling that of chrysocystidia.

MATERIAL EXAMINED: FRANCE: Josserand, from near Lyon, November 14, 1932 (MICH); SWEDEN: Lundell, August 27, 1946.

117. Pholiota angustipes (Pk.) Saccardo, Syll. Fung. 5: 740. 1887.

Agaricus (Pholiota) angustipes Peck, New York State Mus. Ann. Rept. 30: 40. 1878.

Hypodendrum angustipes (Pk.) Overholts, North Amer. Fl. 10: 280. 1932.

Illustrations: Harper, Wisc. Acad. Sci. Arts & Letters 17, p. 34. Text figs. 251-253.

Pileus 2–8 cm broad, hemispheric then convex or nearly plane, at first brown, then fading to ochraceous brown or subalutaceous, drying to tawny, squamulose with minute dotlike appressed scales, only slightly viscid when wet. Context fleshy thin, yellowish or whitish; taste unpleasant.

Lamellae adnate, sinuate-adnate or subdecurrent, whitish or dull cream-color, becoming tawny or cinnamon-buff, in dried basidiocarps cinnamon, close, narrowed outward, medium broad at stipe.

Stipe 3–7.5 cm long, 4–10 mm thick, white to grayish or avellaneous, slightly squamulose, the scales darker or fibrillose, equal or tapering downward, stuffed or hollow. Veil fibrillose, buff whitish, forming an evanescent annulus.

Spores 6–7.5 × 4–4.5 μ, smooth, germ pore at apex distinct; shape in face view elliptic, in profile subelliptic to obscurely bean-shaped; color in KOH ochraceous to pale clay color, in Melzer's reagent paler ochraceous; wall thin (–0.25 μ).

Basidia 4-spored, 18–24 × 5–6 μ, clavate, hyaline in KOH and nearly so in Melzer's reagent. Pleurocystidia scattered 16–30 × 5–8 μ, fusoid to clavate or filamentous, content in some golden yellow in KOH (possibly pseudocystidia), some (mostly the fusoid cells) with wrinkled-refractive content extending the length of the cell. Cheilocystidia versi-form: some in chains and the cells 2–3 in numbber, 6–9 μ diam. and about as long; some pear-shaped and 26–32 × 9–12 μ; some fusoid ventri-cose with acute apex; nearly all with thin hyaline walls, content hyaline or in a few bright yellow (in KOH). Caulocystidia at extreme apex of stipe and resembling the cheilocystidia but often larger, some with yellow content, 30–50 (67) × 4–9 μ.

Gill trama with a central area of somewhat interwoven hyaline floccose hyphae with thin smooth walls, the hyphae with narrow (4–6 μ) or more inflated cells; subhymenium becoming gelatinous in KOH, of interwoven hyphae tightly packed (in sections appearing cellular). Pileus cutis a poorly formed layer of somewhat gelatinous hyphae 3–6 μ diam., thin-walled, hyaline in KOH, smooth; hypodermial region of interwoven floccose hyaline hyphae more or less like those of context. Context hyphae hyaline in KOH, thin-walled, cells inflating. Clamp connections present. All hyphae inamyloid.

HABIT, HABITAT, AND DISTRIBUTION: On soil, in pastures, near stumps, New York, Michigan and in Canada, Ontario; also reported from Ohio (Overholts 1927) and from Wisconsin (Harper 1913), July to October. Type studied.

OBSERVATIONS: This species is distinguished by its small dot-like scales on a brown fading pileus. Overholts (1927) reports that in an Ohio collection, some pilei were glabrous among the typically scaly ones. Cystidia are present in the hymenium of the type but they revived poorly and are most readily discovered by their refractive inclusion in mounts revived in KOH.

118. Pholiota simulans sp. nov.
Illustrations: Text figs. 254-255; 256-258.

Pileus circa 8 cm latus, planus, squamulosus, subviscidus, griseo-brunneus, sublutescens. Lamellae confertae, angustae, adnatae demum subdecurrentes. Stipes circa 8 cm longus, 9 mm crassus, subsquamulosus. Sporae 5–6 × 4–4.8 μ, leves, obscure truncatae. Pleurocystidia 36–54 × 8–13 μ, numerosa, fusoide ventricosa, ut chrysocystidia. Specimen typicum in Herb. Univ. Mich. conservatum est; legit prope Pontiac, Mich. 17 Sept. 1965, Simth 72658.

Pileus about 8 cm broad, plane with a decurved margin, or margin uplifted in age, surface covered by very fine appressed fibrillose squamules more numerous and less distinct over disc, squamules dull ochraceous tawny and disc this color from dense arrangement of squamules, becom-ing rimose toward margin, ground color with a yellowish tinge (more accentuated on drying), surface beneath the scales subviscid and soon dry. Context thin, buff, FeSO₄ olivaceous; taste slight and not distinctive, odor none.

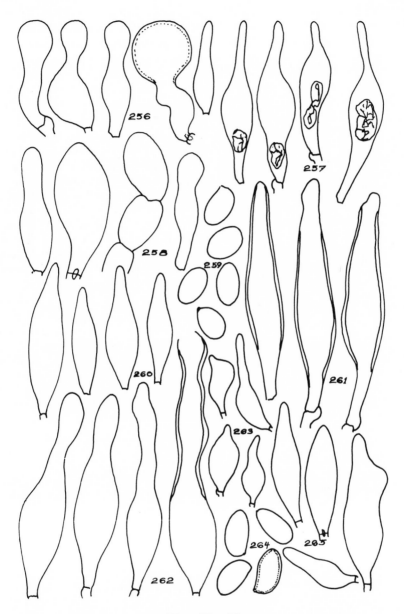

Text Fig. 16.

Figs. 256-258, cheilocystidia, pleurocystidia and caulocystidia of *P. simulans;* 259-261, spores, cheilocystidia and pleurocystidia of *P. virgata;* 262-265, pleurocystidia (largest type) pleurocystidia (small type), spores and cheilocystidia of *P. castanea.*

Stipe about 8 cm long, 9 mm thick, solid, equal, pale dingy greenish yellow with base dull clay-color, surface below veil-line decorated by fibrillose squamules or lacerate-fibrillose, pruinose above veil-line.

Spores 5–6 × 4–4.8 μ, smooth, apical pore distinct and larger spores obscurely truncate, in face view elliptic to subglobose, in profile about the same, pale dull tawny in KOH, paler in Melzer's reagent, wall about 0.25 μ thick.

Basidia 4-spored, 18–25 × 5–6.5 μ, subcylindric, pale ochraceous as revived in KOH or hyaline, appearing as if subgelatinous as revived in KOH (wall outline soon less distinct than walls of tramal hyphae). Pleurocystidia 36–54 × 8–13 μ, fusoid to fusoid-ventricose, the neck often drawn out to a crooked filamentose projection with a subacute apex; walls thin, smooth, hyaline; content showing a refractive-amorphous inclusion of various shapes and orange-brown in Melzer's reagent, sometimes the refractive body extending the length of the cell. Cheilocystidia versiform variable in size, the capitate cells with a head up to 12–15 μ and with the wall yellow as well as slightly thickened, otherwise thin-walled, hyaline and smooth. Caulocystidia numerous, versiform and variable in size, the large vesiculose cells up to 20 μ in diam., mostly with smooth hyaline thin walls; content homogeneous.

Gill trama of parallel smooth-walled hyphae the walls thin to slightly thickened, cells becoming inflated and greatly elongated; subhymenium cellular, of hyaline non-gelatinous hyphae. Pileus cutis with a thin pellicle of gelatinous to subgelatinous hyphae 2–4 μ diam. and hyaline to yellowish in KOH, walls with incrusting plates of pale yellowish pigment; hypodermial region of floccose hyphae with some cells having slightly thickened walls but region not highly colored. Context of voluminous hyphal cells (12–30 μ) with "colloidal" content in KOH and bright orange in Melzer's reagent. Clamp connections present.

HABIT, HABITAT, AND DISTRIBUTION: Solitary on an old hardwood stump near Pontiac, Mich. Sept. 17, 1965, Smith 72658, type.

OBSERVATIONS: The fusoid chrysocystidia and the yellow-capitate cheilocystidia are an unusual set of features sufficient to distinguish a species. In the type of P. angustipes the cystidia are difficult to find and when found vary more to the clavate or filamentose condition. Overholts failed to note them.

Subgenus **Flammuloides** Subg. nov.

Pileus viscidus vel glutinosus, glaber vel floccoso-squamulosus. Stipes glaber vel fibrillosus vel subsquamosus. Pleurocystidia conspicua. Subhymenium gelatinosum vel subgelatinosum, rare non-gelatinosum.
Typus: *Pholiota subfulva.*

Pileus viscid to glutinous from a gelatinous layer in the cuticle, hyphal walls usually gelatinizing, glabrous to merely virgate with fibrils, or rarely at first squamulose from superficial veil remnants; margin sometimes appendiculate; stipe very seldom conspicuously scaly but often decorated with colored zones or patches of veil material; pleurocystidia prominent and conspicuously projecting; subhymenium typically gelatinous.

Section **Flammuloides**

The diagnostic features of the section are: The viscid to glutinous pileus, typically gelatinous subhymenium, very prominent pleurocystidia, and the walls of the latter in many of the cystidia in a hymenophore thick enough to measure (about 0.5 μ or more) as revived in KOH or in Melzer's reagent. It remains to be seen how much of this thickening shows on fresh material, but from our experience so far it appears that the feature is a reliable one. In addition to the species formally placed in this section *P. baptistii, P. spinulifera, P. haerenosa, P. innocua, P. stratosa* and *P. pseudopulchella* show a tendency toward wall thickenings in the cystidia, and in *P. innocua* thick-walled cheilocystidia are numerous enough to cause one to wonder if eventually some thick-walled pleurocystidia will be found.

Key to Stirpes of Section Flammuloides

1. Subhymenium cellular and not gelatinous ...... Stirps *Olivaceophylla*
1. Subhymenium gelatinized by maturity 2
  2. Spores 7–9 (10) × 3.7–4.5 (6) μ .... Stirps *Condensa*
  2. Spores smaller than above 3
3. Pileus pallid to yellowish on disc at first, but many become olivaceous over marginal area .... Stirps *Adirondakensis*
3. Pileus with different coloration 4
  4. Pileus dark vinaceous brown on disc at first or very dull red-brown .... Stirps *Decorata*
  4. Not colored as above 5
5. Pileus ferruginous, bay, hazel etc. (see *P. sublubrica* also) .... Stirps *Ferruginea*
5. Pileus with cinnamon to russet or olive brown colors 6
  6. Pileus on disc at first russet, cinnamon, tan or clay color .... Stirps *Occidentalis*
  6. Pileus olive to olive-brown or tawny-olive .... Stirps *Virgata*

Key to Sections

1. At least some pleurocystidia with walls thickened to 0.5 μ (or much thicker), the wall thickening should be observed at the base of the neck or in the ventricose portion .... Section *Flammuloides*
1. Pleurocystidia consistently thin-walled 2

2. Always fruiting on burned ground around charcoal ....
.... Section *Carbonicolae*
2. Not as above, but habitat typically lignicolous, more rarely on
soil or humus 3
3. Spores 7–10 × 5–6 μ but if 7–9 × 4–5 μ try this choice also ....
.... Section *Spumosae*
3. Spores smaller 5–7.5 (8) × 3–4.5 (5) μ .... Section *Lubricae*

Stirps Virgata

The characteristic olive tones are evident in both the fresh material
and the dried specimens. Aside from the color and streaked appearance
of the pileus the stirps is very close to stirps Occidentalis. As yet the
stirps contains only the type species and *P. pseudograreolens,* which
has a strong odor.

119. Pholiota virgata sp. nov.
Illustrations: Text figs. 259-261.

*Pileus 3–10 cm, latus, demum late convexus, viscidus, glaber, luteo
brunneus. Contextus pallidus. Lamellae confertae, latae, adnatae, pallidae
bubalinae. Stipes 4–5.5 cm longus, 6–10(12) mm crassus, pallidus subfibrillosus. Sporae (5.5)6–7(7.5) × 3.5–4(4.5) μ. Pleurocystidia 48–67 × 10–14 μ,
fusoide-ventricosa; tunica 0.5–0.75 μ crassa. Specimen typicum in Herb.
Univ. Mich. conservatum est; legit prope Santa Fe, New Mexico. Aug.
1957. Chas. Barrows 542.*

Pileus 3–10 cm broad, convex, expanding more or less wavy, buffy
brown to near tawny-olive, margin paler (yellowish-brown), virgate,
slimy to viscid, margin even. Context pallid; taste insipid.

Lamellae adnate then emarginate, pale-buff to deep-buff then dull
yellow-brown, close, medium broad.

Stipe 4–5.5 cm long, 6–10 (12) mm thick, more or less equal or enlarged at base, dingy-pallid, becoming darker below, striate, with scattered
fibrils, becoming hollow. Veil white, arachnoid.

Spores (5.5) 6–7 (7.5) × 3.5–4 (4.5) μ, smooth, apical pore present
but minute; shape in face view elliptic to ovate, in profile elliptic to
very obscurely inequilateral, in KOH dull cinnamon, in Melzer's reagent
paler; wall about 0.25 μ thick.

Basidia 21–25 × 5–6 μ, 4-spored, narrowly clavate, hyaline in KOH
and nearly so in Melzer's reagent. Pleurocystidia 48–67 × 10–14 μ, fusoid
ventricose to subfusoid, rarely obclavate, apex subacute to subcapitate,
surface smooth, wall thickened to 0.5–0.75 μ, content homogeneous and
hyaline to ochraceous. Cheilocystidia 28–45 (60) × 6–12 μ, similar to
pleurocystidia or smaller and subfusoid to obclavate, walls smooth and
thin to slightly thickened, content homogeneous. Caulocystidia 40–70 ×

7–15 μ, elongate-ellipsoid to subfusoid, thin-walled, smooth, content homogeneous.

Gill trama a central area of floccose hyphae more or less parallel in arrangement becoming more interwoven finally and cells often greatly inflated (+ 15 μ), walls thin, smooth, ochraceous to nearly hyaline in KOH; subhymenium a gelatinous layer of hyaline, narrow hyphae (2–3 μ diam.), subparallel or diverging to basidia. Pileus cutis a gelatinous pellicle of narrow pale ochraceous smooth to asperulate hyphae interwoven loosely in the gelatinous matrix; hypodermial zone of amber-brown (in KOH) floccose smooth to incrusted hyphae of various diameters (cells inflated in many). Context hyphae with smooth thin ochraceous to hyaline walls, cells inflated. Clamp connections present. All hyphae not amyloid.

HABIT, HABITAT, AND DISTRIBUTION: On soil or rotten logs, New Mexico, August, Barrows 763.

OBSERVATIONS: This species is related to *P. lubrica,* in which the cystidia have thin walls. It dries to a tawny-olive tint, and is very dingy in appearance.

120. Pholiota pseudograveolens sp. nov.
Illustrations: Text figs. 508-510; pl. 58.

Pileus 6–7.5 cm crassus, late convexus demum planus, subviscidus, ad centrum sordide luteo-brunneus, ad marginem laete citrinus, glaber. Contextus crassus, firmus, laete citrinus demum olivaceo-brunneus; sapor mitis; odor fragrans. Caum "FeSO$_4$," olivaceus, "Guaiac" deinde caeruleus. Lamellae laete luteae demum subfulvae, adnatae, late, confertae. Stipes 4–6 cm longus, 9–12 mm crassus, deorsum sordide luteo-brunneus, sursum citrinus. Sporae 6–8 × 3.5–4 μ. Pleurocystidia crassotunicata. Specimen typicum in Herb. Univ. of Mich. conservatum est; legit prope Proud Lake Recreation Area, Oakland Co., Michigan. Sept. 3, 1966, Smith 73302.

Pileus 6–7.5 cm broad, expanded plane at maturity, broadly convex when young, glabrous, subviscid when fresh but soon dry, color near "bister" on disc or dull "tawny," (dull to brighter yellow brown), near the margin lemon yellow, opaque when moist or faded. Context thick and firm, lemon chrome near margin, near olive to olive-brownish in disc, odor strongly fragrant as in *Cortinarius percomis,* taste mild, with FeSO$_4$ olive, with Guaiac quickly blue.

Lamellae bright yellow, slowly becoming buckthorn brown from spores, broadly adnate, tapered to margin of pileus, broad, close, edges crenulate.

Stipe 4–6 cm long, 9–12 mm thick, equal, chrome yellow within above, becoming bister in cortex over the base and finally over all; surface thinly fibrillose, upper part lemon yellow, basal mycelium orange in age.

Spores 6–8 × 3.2–3.8 (4) μ, smooth, with a minute but distinct apical pore, shape in face view ovate to nearly elliptic, in profile somewhat narrowly inequilateral; color in KOH dull cinnamon and about the same in Melzer's reagent; wall about 0.25 μ thick.

Basidia 4-spored, 18–22 × 5–6.5 μ, narrowly clavate, yellowish in KOH, dull ochraceous orange in Melzer's reagent. Pleurocystidia 38–65 (76) × 9–15 μ basically fusoid-ventricose but neck elongate and with swellings and constrictions, apex typically obtuse; smooth; wall thin at first but soon thickened to 0.6–1.2 μ at upper portion of ventricose part and in adjacent part of neck, content of some cystidia yellow and coagulated even in fresh specimens, coagulated content in revived sections (in KOH) orange brown but soon fading to yellowish, in Melzer's reagent the content nearly colorless, many originating from the parallel hyphae of the gill trama. Cheilocystidia 28–40 × 7–12 μ, clavate to fusoid ventricose but the necks short, walls thin, smooth, yellowish in KOH. Caulocystidia present merely as the occasional more or less appressed clavate end-cell of a surface hypha, walls yellowish in KOH.

Gill trama consisting of a broad band of parallel hyphae with more or less inflated elongate hyphal cells having thin to scarcely thickened walls yellowish to hyaline in KOH as revived, walls smooth; subhymenium a gelatinous band of narrow (2–3 μ) much branched hyphae. Pileus cutis of interwoven narrow (2–4 μ) hyphae yellow to hyaline in KOH, outline distinct but imbedded in a gelatinous matrix, hypodermium of rusty to orange-brown hyphae with inflated cells to 12–20 μ diam., walls smooth to incrusted. Context hyphae yellow in KOH (fresh or revived specimens), typically thin walled, closely interwoven and hyphal cells inflated. Clamp connections present.

HABIT, HABITAT, AND DISTRIBUTION: Gregarious on decaying aspen log, Proud Lake Recreation Area, Sept. 3, 1966. Smith 73302, type.

OBSERVATIONS: This species may be more closely related to *P. graveolens* than any other species, but the thick-walled cystidia separate it at once. The strong odor, tendency of the cystidia to develop thickened walls, the orange mycelium at the base of the stipe on old bsidiocarps, and the dull brown pileus disc compared to the bright yellow margin are a distinctive set of features.

Stirps Olivaceophylla

This stirps is placed here because a few of the pleurocystidia develop walls up to around 0.5 μ thick, but it is to be regarded as borderline. In all features save the lack of gelatinization of the subhymenium it appears to be a group typical of subg. *Flammuloides*. Both of the species included here need further critical study based on ample collections.

Key

1. Lamellae white when young; pileus chestnut to bister in color from

youth to age .... *P. castanea*
1. Lamellae olivaceous young; pileus yellowish tan to whitish ....
.... *P. olivaceophylla*

121. Pholiota castanea sp. nov.

Illustrations: Text figs. 262-265; pl. 59a.

Pileus 3–5 cm latus, convexus, demum late-convexus vel depressus, glaber, viscidus, subcastaneus. Contextus albidus. Lamellae emarginatae, latae, confertae, albidae demum luteae. Stipes 4–6 cm longus, 4–6 mm crassus, pallidus, fibrillosus. Sporae 6–7.5(8) × 3.5–4 μ. Pleurocystidia dimorpha: 1) 45–72 × 10–14 μ, fusoide-ventricosa. 2) 12–18 × 4–6 μ, ventricosa, rostrata vel fusoide ventricosa vel elliptica. Specimen typicum in Herb. Univ. Tenn. conservatum est; legit prope Knoxville, Tenn. Hesler 20269.

Pileus 3–5 cm broad, convex, finally expanded-convex, in age at times depressed-concave, glabrous, viscid, "chestnut-brown" to "bister," paler when young (near "tawny"), margin even. Context thin, firm, white; odor and taste mild.

Lamellae emarginate, white when young, finally "tawny-olive" or slightly darker, close or crowded, rather broad, edges slightly eroded.

Stipe 4–6 cm long, 4–6 mm thick, tapering downward, pallid then dingy, fibrillose, solid or somewhat stuffed. Veil webby, yellowish, evanescent, leaving an evanescent ring.

Spores 6–7.5 (8) × 3.5–4 μ, oblong to elliptic in face view, oblong to slightly bean-shaped in profile, smooth, dull cinnamon in KOH, paler cinnamon in Melzer's sol., wall slightly thickened (± 0.3 μ), apical pore distinct but apex not truncate.

Basidia 18–24 (27) × 5–6 μ, 4-spored, ochraceous in KOH on sections of hymenium (in mass), in Melzer's reagent yellowish. Pleurocystidia: 1) 45–72 × 10–14 μ, basically fusoid-ventricose but neck with distinct constrictions and often thick-walled in the constriction, apex obtuse to knobbed or with one or more bulgy proliferations, walls thin (except as noted above), surface smooth, content homogeneous and in KOH hyaline to ochraceous. 2) 12–18 × 4–6 μ, ventricose-rostrate to fusoid ventricose to elliptic and then about 18 × 8 μ, hyaline thin-walled, smooth, content homogeneous, buried in hymenium. Cheilocystidia 26–38 × 6–9 μ (12) μ, subfusoid, to fusoid-ventricose, thin-walled, yellow in KOH mostly, and content homogeneous. Caulocystidia in agglutinated tufts, 18–35 × 4–9 μ, versiform, (basidium-like, contorted, subfusoid, or filamentose), yellow in KOH, walls smooth.

Gill trama of filamentose subparallel to interwoven hyphae with elongate cells 8–20 μ broad, walls slightly thickened (middle-lamella evident), refractive, smooth and ochraceous in KOH; subhymenium cellular; cells 3–6 μ diam. and walls not gelatinous. Pileus cutis a thick gelatinous layer of narrow (2–3 μ) ochraceous smooth hyphae easily torn away in sectioning; hypodermium orange-rusty in KOH from floccose encrusted hyphae 8–18 μ or more broad, walls thin to slightly thickened. Context hyphae smooth, inflated, walls slightly thickened (0.5 μ ±) as revived in KOH and somewhat refractive. All hyphae inamyloid. Clamp connections present.

HABIT, HABITAT, AND DISTRIBUTION: On soil and rotten wood, near Knoxville, Tenn. Dec. 11, 1951. A. J. Sharp, (Hesler 20269, type).

OBSERVATIONS: This species and P. olivaceophylla lack the gelatinous subhymenium featuring most species with the prominent pleurocystidia. In the dried state the gills are decidedly yellowish. The aspect of the basidiocarps is that of a dingy P. spumosa but the subhymenium of the latter distinguishes it. The very small and very large pleurocystidia is an interesting combination. The cheilocystidia should be re-studied from fresh material.

122. **Pholiota olivaceophylla** sp. nov.
Illustrations: Text figs. 266-267.

Pileus 6–11 cm latus, late convexus, pallide luteus, viscosus, contextus albus. Lamellae olivaceae, confertae, latae. Stipes 6–12 cm longus, 10–15 mm crassus, fibrillosus, anguste clavatus. Sporae 6–8 × 3.4–4.5 μ. Pleurocystidia 40–70 × 9–12 μ, fusoide ventricosa, rare crassitunicata. Specimen typicum in Herb. Univ. Mich. conservatum est; legit Wm. B. Cooke 29502, Mt. Shasta, Calif. June 1954.

Pileus 6–11 cm broad, expanding to nearly plane, yellowish tan to whitish, with a yellowish slimy covering. Context white; odor somewhat nutty, taste none.

Lamellae adnate, at first olive, then brown, close, broad (10 mm more or less).

Stipe 6–12 cm long, 10–15 mm thick, fibrillose, inflated below to 25 mm, with conspicuous white rhizomorphs.

Spores 6–8 × 3.5–4.5 μ, smooth, apical pore minute, ovate to elliptic in face view, in profile obscurely inequilateral to slightly bean-shaped, tawny in KOH, about the same color or paler revived in Melzer's reagent, wall thin (± 0.3 μ).

Basidia 20–25 (28) × 5–7 μ, 4-spored, narrowly clavate, yellowish in KOH and Melzer's reagent. Pleurocystidia abundant, 45–70 × 9–20 μ yellow to hyaline in KOH, content homogeneous, thin-walled or rarely the wall up to 0.5 μ thick, fusoid-ventricose to ventricose-rostrate with the neck narrowest at the apex of the ventricose part, neck usually filled with a homogeneous "colloidal" substance, smooth, apex obtuse. Cheilocystidia 43–52 × 12–17 μ, fusoid-ventricose to subellipsoid-pedicellate, yellow to hyaline in KOH, content homogeneous, at times the neck short and apex somewhat capitate, a few seen with particles of debris adhering. Caulocystidia none.

Gill trama a central area of greatly inflated hyphae more or less

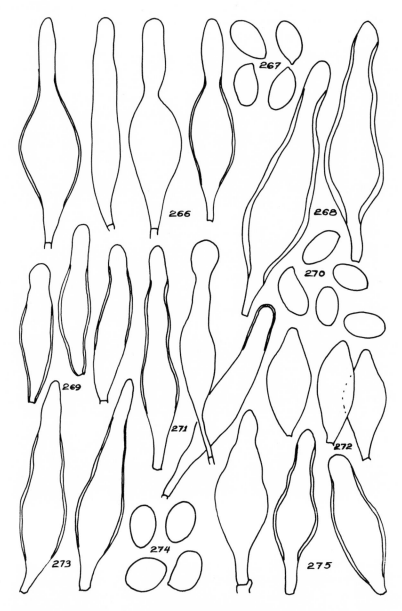

Text Fig. 17.

FIG. 266 & 267, pleurocystidia and spores of *P. olivaceophylla;* 268-270, pleurocystidia, cheilocystidia and spores of *P. adirondackensis;* 271, pleurocystidia of *P. agglutinata;* 272-274, cheilocystidia, pleurocystidia and spores of *P. velaglutinosa;* 275, pleurocystidia of *P. alabamensis.*

interwoven, the walls thin, smooth and yellowish to hyaline in KOH; subhymenium cellular and not gelatinous in freshly matured specimens, cells small (4–7 μ) and the layer inconspicuous. Pileus cutis an exceedingly thick layer of hyaline gelatinous hyphae 2–5 μ diam. with smooth walls disintegrating almost completely; hypodermium a layer of smooth bright ochraceous hyphae the walls thickened slightly and refractive (in KOH) but not incrusted. Context hyphae smooth, yellowish to hyaline in KOH, cells 8–15 μ diam., inflated. Clamp connections present. All hyphae inamyloid.

HABIT, HABITAT, AND DISTRIBUTION: On and near very rotten Shasta fir log, Mt. Shasta, Calif. June 1954. Wm. B. Cooke 29502, type.

OBSERVATIONS: This species is unusual because of the hymenium which is cellular and not gelatinous, though on standing in KOH it becomes rather transparent and possibly subgelatinous. It is in sharp contrast, however, to the branched-filamentous hyphal structure typical of subg. *Flammuloides*. The pleurocystidia vary from narrowly to broadly ventricose, and in a few the wall may be seen to measure up to 1.5 μ thick, but most remain thin-walled. It is the manner in which the neck is constricted just at the apex of the ventricose part in many of the cystidia which is distinctive. It has the stature of *P. sublubrica*. The colors are much paler fresh than in *P. castanea*, but the two are related by the nongelatinous subhymenium.

Stirps Adirondackensis

Here we have three essentially pale yellow species all on wood of conifers; two from Idaho and one from New York. The type species has very thick cystidial walls, in *P. flavopallida* they are relatively thin, and in *P. agglutinata* they are intermediate.

Key

1. Odor rather strong and penetrating; young lamellae olive-yellow young
.... *P. adirondackensis*
1. Odor not distinctive; lamellae white to pallid when young 2
 2. Pleurocystidia 40–56 × 12–17 μ .... *P. flavopallida*
 2. Pleurocystidia 55–80 × 8–15 μ .... *P. agglutinata*

123. Pholiota adirondackensis sp. nov.
Illustrations: Text figs. 268-270.

Pileus 3–9 cm latus, companulatus vel convexus, demum plano-umbonatus, viscidus, pallide luteus demum olivaceo-luteus, ad marginem appendiculatus. Contextus luteus, odor pungens. Lamellae olivaceo-luteae, angustae, confertae. Stipes 4–9 cm longus, 5–9 mm crassus, aequalis, luteus, deorsum demum fulvus. Sporae 6–7.5 × 3.2–4 μ. Pleurocystidia 50–75 × 9–18 μ, fusoide-ventricosa, crassounicata. Specimen *typicum in Herb. Univ. Mich. conservatum est; legit prope Lake Placid, New York C. H. Kauffman, 2 Sept. 1914.*

Pileus 3–9 cm broad, companulate-convex expanding to plano-umbonate, glabrous except for a zone of veil remnants near or along the margin, viscid, color at first evenly pale yellow ("wax-yellow") becoming olive-yellow ("olive-ochre" to "olive-lake"), the disc in age dull tawny. Context concolor with surface (yellow), thin, soft, odor rather strong in age (earthy to radish-like), penetrating; taste slight.

Lamellae at first olive-yellowish soon "olive-ochre" and then rusty brown ("Sudan-brown"), close, narrow, adnate to sinuate or in age subdecurrent, thin, edges yellow.

Stipe 4–9 cm long, 5–9 mm thick, equal or tapered downward, stuffed becoming hollow, pale yellow when young, soon dingy ferruginous below, naked at apex, thinly fibrillose elsewhere, no persistent annular zone.

Spores 6–7.5 × 3.2–4 μ, smooth, germ pore very minute, pale tawny in KOH and slightly duller in Melzer's reagent; in face view oblong, elliptic or ovate, in profile bean-shaped to narrowly elliptic, apiculus scarcely evident.

Basidia 4-spored, narrowly clavate, 17–23 × 5–6 μ, hyaline to ochraceous in KOH or in Melzer's reagent. Pleurocystidia abundant, 50–75 × 9–18 μ, fusoid-ventricose with obtuse apex, smooth or with amorphous debris adhering variously around apex, thick-walled (both in Melzer's reagent and in KOH), at times the wall 3–4 μ thick, content hyaline to ochraceous in KOH and usually granular-colloidal. Cheilocystidia similar to pleurocystidia or smaller. Caulocystidia none.

Gill trama of somewhat interwoven elongate floccose hyphae 8–20 μ wide with pale tan to ochraceous smooth thin walls; subhymenium a broad gelatinous zone of narrow branched filaments, the layer pale ochraceous in KOH. Pileus cutis a gelatinous layer of nongelatinous-walled hyphae 2–4 μ diam. with fine incrustations over surface, the hyphae appressed-interwoven; hypodermium of broader (5–12 μ) more heavily incrusted rusty brown hyphae. Context hyphae 9–20 μ diam., smooth, walls thin and pale tan to greenish hyaline revived in KOH. Clamp connections present. All hyphae inamyloid.

Habit, habitat, and distribution: On mossy decayed spruce log, Lake Placid, Adirondack Mts., New York, Sept. 2, 1914. C. H. Kauffman, type.

Observations: This species was identified as *Flammula lubrica* by Kauffman and part of his description (Kauffman 1926), was drawn from his notes on it. It obviously cannot be *Agaricus (Flammula) lubrica* Fries as the colors are "wrong." That it is a distinct species in its own right can scarcely be disputed. The wax-yellow pileus becoming olivaceous, the yellow context, olive-yellow gills, yellow stipe which stains ferruginous and the large thick-walled pleurocystidia are outstanding.

It differs from *P. olivaceophylla* in having a yellow instead of a white pileus context, narrow gills, and cystidia with much thicker walls. Also, no rhizomorphs were noted for *P. adirondackensis. P. flavopallida* has white lamellae when young and a white stipe at first. It perhaps is closest to *P. alabamensis* but the type of that species has distinctly shorter (33–50 μ long) pleurocystidia.

124. Pholiota agglutinata sp. nov.
Illustrations: Text figs. 271.

Pileus 1–4 cm latus, late conicus vel plano-umbonatus, pallide fulvus, ad marginem pallide subluteus et appendiculatus. Lamellae adnatae, confertae, latae, albidae demum subfulvae. Stipes 2–4 cm longus, 3–5 mm crassus, aequalis, solidus, intus pallidus, extus fibrillosus, deorsum demum fulvus. Sporae 5.5–6.5(7) × 3.5–4 μ. Pleurocystidia et cheilocystidia 55–80 × 8–12(15) μ, ad apicem latae; sub-crassotunicata. Specimen typicum in Herb. niv. Mich. conservatum est; legit prope Black Lee Creek, Payette National Forest, 31 Aug. 1958. Smith 60691.

Pileus 1–4 cm broad, obtuse with an incurved margin, expanding to broadly conic, or finally plano-umbonate, ochraceous tawny to rusty brown over disc, pale cartridge-buff to whitish toward the margin, viscid, variously virgate-streaked with agglutinated fibrils, margin fringed at first with veil remnants. Context cartilaginous, pallid; odor and taste mild; rusty brown around worm holes, instantly malachite green in $FeSO_4$; context yellow with KOH.

Lamellae squarely adnate, whitish becoming dull rusty brown, close, broad, edges even.

Stipe 2–4 cm long, 3–5 mm thick, equal, solid, pallid within, pith green in $FeSO_4$, fibrillose streaked from veil fibrils over surface, whitish but soon rusty brown in basal area, apex white and silky, scarcely a fibrillose zone left by white veil.

Spores 5.5–6.5 (7) × 3.5–4 μ, smooth, apical pore minute; shape oblong, narrowly elliptic or slightly ovate in face view, in profile sub-elliptic to obscurely inequilateral; in KOH pale tawny, in Melzer's reagent slightly paler; wall relatively thin (0.25 μ ±).

Basidia 21–24 × 5–6 μ, 2-, and 4-spored, clavate, hyaline to yellowish in KOH or in Melzer's reagent. Pleurocystidia abundant, 55–80 × 8–12 (15) μ, narrowly ventricose to subcylindric, with a long flexuous neck 5–7 μ diam. ending in a rounded to obtuse apex, sometimes capitate, wall in neck thickened (0.5–1 μ thick), hyaline to yellowish in KOH, smooth, with a long narrow pedicel. Cheilocystidia similar to pleurocystidia but mostly slightly smaller and neck more often with yellow content. Caulocystidia none.

Gill trama with a floccose central strand of subparallel, thin-walled smooth hyaline to yellowish hyphae, the cells short or greatly elongated, hyphae 3–9 μ wide but in age the cells more inflated; subhymenium of narrow (2–3 μ) gelatinous-interwoven hyphae. Pileus cutis a thick gelatinous layer of hyphae 2–4.5 (5.5) μ diam. with hyaline smooth walls revived in KOH) ; hypodermium of narrow (3–6 μ) , smooth, interwoven, ochraceous to orange-ochraceous hyphae nongelatinous in KOH, the walls thickened slightly (0.5 μ or more) . Context hyphae 8–15 μ diam., cells inflated, walls smooth to slightly thickened, hyaline to yellowish in KOH. All hyphae inamyloid. Clamp connections present.

HABIT, HABITAT, AND DISTRIBUTION: Scattered on a mossy bank, under spruce. Payette National Forest, Idaho, Black Lee Creek, Aug. 31, 1958. Smith 60691 (type) , 60706, 60707.

OBSERVATIONS: The narrowly ventricose, greatly elongated pleuro-cystidia are one of its distinctive features. The virgate pileus, whitish gills when young, sharp $FeSO_4$ reaction of the context, white veil and whitish stipe apex are distinctive field characters along with the terrestrial habitat.

125. Pholiota flavopallida sp. nov.

Pileus 2–5.5 cm latus, plano-umbonatus, glutinosus, glaber, pallide flavus vel luteolus ad centrum subfulvus. Contextus luteolus. Lamellae angustae, confertae adnatae demum decurrentes, pallidae demum luteae demum brunneae. Stipes 3–4 cm longus, 3–5 mm crassus, aequalis, fibrillosus, deorsum subfulvus, sursum pallidus; velum album, fibrillosum. Sporae 5–6(7) × 3–3.5 μ. Pleurocystidia 40–56 × 12–17 μ, fusoide ventricosa vel subfusoidea, tenuitunicata vel rare subcrassotunicata (± 0.5 μ). Specimen typicum in Herb. Univ. Mich. conservatum est; legit prope Nordman, Idaho. 11 Nov. 1956. Smith 54485.

Pileus 2–5.5 cm broad, convex to plano-umbonate, glutinous, glabrous, marginal area pale yellow ("pale pinkish-buff" to "ivory-yellow") , disc clay-color to dingy pale tawny, margin lacerate at times. Context pallid becoming yellowish, green in $FeSO_4$, odor not distinctive, taste mild.

Lamellae narrow, close, adnate to short decurrent, whitish becoming yellowish and finally dingy cinnamon to brown ("Verona-brown") .

Stipe 3–4 cm long, 3–5 mm thick, white above, clay-color to rusty brown below, equal or base enlarged somewhat, thinly fibrillose from the poorly developed veil. Apex silky to silky-pruinose.

Spores 5–6 (7) × 3–3.5 μ, ochraceous to pale tan in KOH and merely tinged cinnamon in Melzer's reagent, smooth, apical pore exceedingly minute, wall thin (scarcely visible as a double line) , in face view oblong to narrowly elliptic, in profile slightly bean-shaped to oblong.

Basidia 16–20 × 4–5 μ, mostly 4-spored, narrowly clavate, yellowish in KOH and in Melzer's sol. Pleurocystidia 40–56 × 12–17 μ fusoid-ventricose to subfusoid, obese, thin-walled or with wall up to 0.5 μ thick, smooth, apex rounded to obtuse, content often yellow in KOH when first revived. Cheilocystidia 27–45 × 7–12 μ, fusoid-ventricose to subfusoid, often with yellow homogeneous content in KOH, walls thin and smooth.

Caulocystidia 48–76 × 10–20 μ, cylindric to clavate or capitate, rarely mucronate, thin-walled and smooth, wall hyaline to ochraceous. Stipe hyphae yellowish-hyaline in KOH.

Gill trama of parallel to slightly interwoven floccose hyphae with short or long inflated cells 8–20 μ diam., and thin smooth ochraceous to lemon-yellow or hyaline walls; subhymenium of gelatinous hyaline narrow (3 μ) hyphae. Pileus cutis a thick gelatinous layer of interwoven narrow hyphae 2–3 μ diam., hyaline to yellowish in KOH, and walls smooth or nearly so; hypodermium of floccose smooth-walled hyphae, rusty orange to ochraceous in KOH, and 4–12 μ diam. Context of interwoven hyphae with inflated cells, thin-walled, smooth, walls pale lemon-yellow to hyaline in KOH. Clamp connections present. All hyphae inamyloid.

HABIT, HABITAT, AND DISTRIBUTION: On conifer wood, Idaho, Smith 54485, type and Smith nos. 70998 and 71217.

OBSERVATIONS: The narrow crowded whitish gills, very small spores, and almost utriform cystidia are distinctive. The caulocystidia are versiform. This species at once reminds one of *P. subochracea,* but the cystidia distinguish them at once. Caulocystidia are present in both collections but less abundant on Smith 70998. The pileus gills and stipe are pale yellow as dried. When the stipe darkens in the fresh material this usually shows on the dried specimens.

Stirps Condensa

Like the previous stirps, this one is questionably placed in this section because of the variation in the wall thickness of the pleurocystidia. If the thickening in the walls of some cystidia is disregarded, then the species would fall in stirps *Spumosa.*

Key

1. Basidiocarps obviously lingnicolous 2
1. Basidiocarps appearing terrestrial 3
   2. Pileus glabrous; on oak wood; spores 5–6 μ broad ...... *P. subminor*
   2. Pileus decorated with veil remnants; on wood of conifers; spores 4–5 μ wide .... *P. bakerensis*
3. Spores 5–6 μ wide .... *P. iterata*
3. Spores 3.5–5 μ 4
   4. Pileus with a thick gelatinous pellicle; growing under *Sequoia* in northern California .... *P. sequoiae*
   4. Not as above 4
5. Pleurocystidia 33–50 × 9–15 μ .... *P. alabamensis*
5. Pleurocystidia 48–72 × 7–14 μ .... *P. condensa*

126. **Pholiota bakerensis** sp. nov.
Illustrations: Pl. 60a.

Pileus 2–5 cm latus, obtusus demum convexus, deinde planus vel leviter depressus, "ochraceous-tawny," margine paene "avellaneous," viscidus, ordines agglutinatarum squamularum circum idem centrum gerens. Caro pallido-"avellaneous"; gustus mitis, odor leviter fragrans. Lamellae adnatae, "tawny-olive," confertae. Stipes 3–5 cm longus, 3–5 mm crassus, pallidus, fibrillosus, infra "clay-color." Sporae 7–9 × 4–5 μ, ellipsoideae demum ovoideae, leves. Pleurocystidia 50–70 × 9–14 μ. Cheilocystidia 30–40 × 9–12 μ, fusoide ventricosa demum subellipsoideo-pedicellata. Cuticula gelatinosa. Specimen typicum in Herb. Univ. Mich. conservatum; lectum prope Mt. Baker, Washington, 8 Sept. 1941, Smith 16727.

Pileus 2–5 cm broad, obtuse to broadly convex young, plane or disc broadly and shallowly depressed in age, the margin usually arched, surface viscid, opaque, "ochraceous-tawny" on disc, near "avellaneous" over marginal area, with one or more concentric rows of agglutinated fibrillose squamules. Context thin and pliant, pale watery avellaneous; taste mild, odor faintly fragrant.

Lamellae adnate, short decurrent by a tooth, "tawny-olive" 3–4 mm broad, about equal, close, about 32 reach the stipe and 2 tiers of lamellulae between each, edges serrulate.

Stipe 3–5 cm long, 3–5 mm thick, equal, solid or hollowed by worms, fleshy-pliant, surface pallid from a thin coating of pale buff fibrils, with an evanescent apical fibrillose zone, more or less glabrescent and thin, "clay-color" at least over lower part.

Spores 7–9 × 4–5 μ, elliptic to obscurely ovate in face view, obscurely inequilateral to obscurely bean-shaped in profile, dull tawny in KOH, smooth, apical pore minute.

Basidia 4-spored, 18–20 × 6–7 μ, yellow in KOH in sections of hymenium. Pleurocystidia 50–70 × 9–14 μ, abundant, fusoid-ventricose, apices obtuse and often with refractive particles in the neck and apex, yellow in KOH from the pale colored wall which is very slightly thickened in lower neck and upper ventricose portion. Cheilocystidia 30–40 × 9–12 μ, fusoid-ventricose to nearly elliptic-pedicellate, some with refractive content (as in chrysocystidia), pale yellow in KOH, or some similar to pleurocystidia in size or shape.

Gill trama with a floccose central strand flanked by a very narrow subgelatinous subhymenial layer as revived in KOH (not evident on all sections). Pileus trama floccose-interwoven and hyaline to yellowish in KOH, no distinct hypoderm showing as a colored layer. Cuticle gelatinous, of appressed interwoven yellow (in KOH) incrusted hyphae, 4–6 μ in diameter. Clamp connections present.

HABIT, HABITAT, AND DISTRIBUTION: Scattered on conifer sticks, Washington, September, Smith 16727, type.

OBSERVATIONS: The lack of a colored hypoderm, the very weak development of the gelatinous subhymenium, and the thin coating of buff fibrils on the stipe appear distinctive along with spores which are up to 9 μ long.

127. Pholiota subminor sp. nov.
Illustrations: Text figs. 504-505; 507.

Pileus 2–3 cm latus, convexus, viscidus, glaber, ad centrum vinaceobrunneus, ad marginem subluteus; contextus subluteus, sapor mitis, inodorus; lamellae confertae latae, adnatae, luteolae demum subfulvae; stipes 2–3 cm longus, 2–3.5 mm crassus, sursum subluteus, deorsum sordide brunneus; sporae 7–9 × 5–6 μ, leves, ovatae; pleurocystidia 55–80 × 9–15 μ fusoide ventricosa, saepe crassotunicata. Specimen typicum in Herb. Univ. Mich. conservatum est; legit in querci, Oregon Caves Road, prope Cave Junction, Ore., 1 Dec. 1937. Smith 9294.

Pileus 2–3 cm broad, convex expanding to plane, surface slimy viscid (slime layer thin), glabrous, on the disc dingy to bright vinaceous brown, more yellowish to the margin (pallid in sporulating basidocarps, sulphur yellow in sterile ones). Context pallid to yellowish, odor and taste not distinctive.

Lamellae close, broad adnate, yellowish becoming dingy ochraceous tawny but sulphur yellow in sterile caps, edges even.

Stipe 2–3 cm longus, 2–3.5 mm thick, yellowish above veil line, soon dingy yellowish-brown below, brighter yellow if gills were sterile, veil yellowish, cortinate, leaving an apical evanescent zone.

Spores 7–9 × 5–6 μ, smooth, apical pore distinct but apex not truncate; shape in face view ovate to elliptic; in profile mostly subelliptic, color in KOH rather bright ochraceous tawny, in Melzer's reagent about the same; wall about 0.25 μ thick.

Basidia 4-spored, 17–20 × 6.5–8 μ, subclavate, many ochraceous in KOH (content colored). Pleurocystidia 55–80 × 9–15 μ, fusoid ventricose, the neck with walls up to 1.5 μ + thick in some, apex 4–6 μ broad, obtuse, content coagulated and ochraceous in KOH, or hyaline and homogeneous, smooth; cheilocystidia similar to pleurocystidia and with thinner walls (± 0.5 μ thick). Caulocystidia present only near stipe apex and similar to cheilocystidia.

Gill trama of subparallel hyphae with cells inflated to 10–20 μ, walls thin and smooth, yellow to hyaline in KOH; subhymenium a gelatinous zone of branched narrow hyphae. Pileus cutis a gelatinous pellicle of loosely arranged yellowish hyphae with disintegrating walls in KOH, hyphae 2–4.5 μ diam., hypodermium of interwoven non-gelatinous hyphae with ochraceous incrusted walls, the cells inflated to 15 μ(±). Context hyphae interwoven, smooth, yellow in KOH, cells inflated. Clamp connections present.

HABIT, HABITAT, AND DISTRIBUTION: Gregarious on an oak log, near Oregon Caves, Ore. Dec. 1, 1937. Smith 9294, type.

OBSERVATIONS: In its wide spores, broad gills, coloration and yellow veil the species is close to *P. pulchella* especially var. *brevipes*, but is readily distinct by its thick walled pleurocystidia, and habitat on oak. It was mistaken at first for *P. velaglutinosa* with "reduced" veil and filed as a variant of that species. The spores, habitat and lack of a gelatinous veil readily distinguish it.

128. Pholiota iterata sp. nov.
Illustrations: Text figs. 502-503; 506.

Pileus 3–7 cm latus, late convexus vel obtuse umbonatus, ad centrum vinaceo brunneus, ad marginem subluteus, glutinosus; stipes 3–7 cm longus, 3–8 mm crassus, luteo fibrillosus. Vellum siccum, luteum; sporae 7–9 × 5–6 μ; pleurocystidia 60–85 × 9–18 μ fusoide ventricosa, crasso tunicata. Specimen typicum in Herb. Univ. Mich. conservatum est; legit prope Cave Junction, Ore., 1 Dec. 1937. Smith 9318, in pinetis.

Pileus 3–7 cm broad, obtuse to convex, expanding to broadly convex or with a slight umbo, margin inrolled at first, margin at first decorated by superficial remains of the veil, glabrescent, slimy viscid; colors dull to vinaceous brown over the disc and pale ochraceous to pallid brownish on margin, marginal area yellowish in dried specimens. Context pliant, yellowish in age, odor and taste not recorded.

Lamellae close, adnate or with a decurrent tooth moderately close to subdistant, yellowish pallid young, soon olivaceous-yellow and then dull rusty brown, edges even.

Stipe 3–7 cm long, 3–8 mm thick, equal, apex yellowish and silky-fibrillose, fibrillose downward from the annular fibrillose zone left by the broken veil, veil fibrils pale yellow, veil dry or with a thin layer of slime over exterior which extends from the cap margin a short distance; stipe dry below veil line, not appreciably discolored below—merely dingy brownish.

Spores dark rusty brown (near russet in deposits on stipe) in mass, 7–9 × 5–6 μ, smooth, apical pore distinct but minute, shape in face view broadly ovate to broadly elliptic, in profile broadly elliptic to very obscurely inequilateral; color in KOH dull tawny, fading to pale ochraceous, slightly paler in Melzer's reagent; wall about 0.25 μ thick.

Basidia 4-spored, 18–25 × 6.5–9 μ, broadly clavate, many with ochraceous content in KOH; pleurocystidia 60–85 × 9–18 μ fusoid-ventricose, neck greatly elongated, apex 4–6 μ broad, obtuse to subacute, wall 1–3 μ thick in ventricose part; content yellowish to hyaline in KOH and homogeneous or as a colloidal plug of material in the neck, content scarcely colored in Melzer's reagent. Cheilocystidia subclavate to ventricose and 30–55 × 8–12 μ or 40–60 × 9–15, and fusoid-ventricose, mostly thin-walled and with yellow content in KOH (with some encrusting material variously over exterior in some—possibly paraffin from waxed paper). Caulocystidia none observed except for a few semi-erect clavate ends of cortical hyphae.

Gill trama of a wide central area of subparallel hyphae yellowish to hyaline in KOH, walls thin and smooth, cells short to long and becoming inflated; subhymenium poorly developed as a narrow somewhat gelatinous zone of hyaline narrow (3–4 μ) hyphae. Pileus cutis a thick gelatinous pellicle of hyphae 2–4 μ diam., loosely interwoven, yellowish in KOH and some with incrusted walls; hypodermium a zone of non-gelatinous more or less inflated hyphae with heavy ochraceous incrustations as revived in KOH; context hyphae yellow in KOH, thin walled, interwoven, and cells greatly inflated. Clamp connections present.

HABIT, HABITAT, AND DISTRIBUTION: Gregarious on needle carpet under pine, Cave Junction, Ore., Dec. 1, 1937. Smith 9318, type.

OBSERVATIONS: This species is obviously very close to *P. subminor* in cystidial and spore features. It differs in growing on duff under conifers instead of on oak logs, in the stature of the basidiocarps, and in the weaker development of the gelatinous subhymenium. From *P. velaglutinosa* it is readily distinct in its larger spores and less gelatinous veil.

129. **Pholiota sequoiae** sp. nov.
Illustrations: Text figs. 474-476.

Pileus 4–7 cm latus, conicus demum conico-umbonatus, glutinosus, squamulosus, (squamis superficialibus), ad centrum obscure fulvus, ad marginem pallidus. Contextus pallide luteus. Lamellae latae, adnatae confertae, subdecurrentes, pallide vel pallide luteae, demum avellaneae vel lignobrunneae. Stipes 6–8 cm longus, 6–9 mm crassus, subcartilagineus, intus luteus, ad apicam furfuraceo-sericeus et albidus, deorsum fulvus. Sporae (6)7–8(9) × 4–4.5(5) μ. Pleurocystidia anguste fusoide ventricosa, 40–80 × 9–15 μ; subcrassotunicata (0.4–1 μ). Specimen typicum in Herb. Univ. Mich. conservatum est; legit prope Orick, Calif., Dec. 5, 1935. Smith 3789.

Pileus 4–7 cm broad, conic-campanulate to expanded and with a sharp conic umbo, glutinous when young and in age with patches of brownish gluten along the margin, extreme edge with fibrillose squamules from the broken veil, disc at first covered by appressed, buff colored fibrillose squamules, glabrous in age, "russett" to "cinnamon-brown" on the disc (rusty brown to pale fulvous) near "ochraceous-tawny" toward the whitish margin; flesh thick in the disc, tapering evenly, pale watery yellow, rather tough, odor and taste not distinctive.

Lamellae close, moderately broad (6–7 mm), equal, adnate, with a slight decurrent tooth, whitish to pale yellow becoming avellaneous to wood-brown.

Stipe 6–8 cm long, 6–9 mm equal, hollow, fairly tough, yellowish within, apex fibrillose-scurfy, below the faint fibrillose zone fibrillose with yellowish appressed fibrils, whitish above, base becoming dingy rusty brown.

Spores (6) 7–8 (9) × 4–4.5 (5) μ, smooth, apical pore very minute, shape elliptic to subovate in face view, in profile elliptic to obscurely inequilateral, rusty cinnamon to more ochraceous tawny in KOH, in Melzer's more ochraceous, wall moderately thick (about 0.3 μ).

Basidia 18–24 × 5–8 μ, rather obese to clavate, 4-spored, yellowish in Melzer's reagent, hyaline to yellowish in KOH. Pleurocystidia abundant, 40–80 × 9–15 μ, subcylindric to narrowly fusoid-ventricose, apex obtuse to capitate, smooth, wall slightly thickened (0.4–1 μ), content ochraceous in KOH at least in neck but leaching out on standing, walls hyaline to yellowish-hyaline in KOH and Melzer's, at times with refractive particles in neck near apex. Cheilocystidia similar to pleurocystidia but smaller and varying to subfusoid, walls often thinner and apex merely obtuse. Caulocystidia none.

Gill trama a central area of floccose subparallel hyphae flanked on either side by a gelatinous subhymenial layer of narrow (2 μ ±) branched hyphae. Pileus cutis a thick gelatinous layer of narrow (3–5 μ) pale ochraceous (in KOH) hyphae some having encrusting material, loosely arranged in the matrix of slime; hypodermial region of broader 4–10 μ hyphae rusty-brown in KOH and incrusted. Context hyphae smooth, thin-walled, interwoven, cells inflated to 15 μ +, walls ochraceous to hyaline. All hyphae inamyloid. Clamp connections present.

HABIT, HABITAT, AND DISTRIBUTION: Gregarious on redwood sticks and debris, Orick, Calif. Dec. 5, 1935. Smith 3789, type.

OBSERVATIONS: The outstanding features of this species are the glutinous pileus with superficial squamules of veil remnants at first, the rusty brown disc and whitish pileus margin, pale watery yellow flesh, whitish to pale yellow gills when young, whitish stipe apex and stipe base becoming rusty brown, the large pleurocystidia with slightly thickened walls, and medium sized spores. It is close to *P. agglutinata* especially in colors and cystidial features but the latter has spores 5.5–6.5 (7) × 3.5–4 μ and grew on a mossy bank.

130. Pholiota alabamensis (Murr.) comb. nov.

Gymnopilus alabamensis Murrill, North Amer. Fl. 10: 199. 1917.
Illustrations: Text figs. 275; 276-278.

Pileus gregarious to subcespitose, 2–5 cm broad, convex to expanded, slightly umbonate, pale brownish yellow, disc reddish brown, viscid, margin entire. Context yellow, thin; taste mild.

Lamellae adnate, tawny-yellow, becoming darker, rather narrow, subdistant to distant, edges entire and concolorous.

Stipe 5–10 cm long, 3–6 mm thick, yellow above, fulvous below, glabrous, equal.

Spores 6–8.5 × 3.8–4.5 μ, elliptic or at times oblong-elliptic to subovate in face view, obscurely inequilateral in profile, smooth, germ-pore present.

Basidia 24–30 × 5–6 μ, 4-spored. Pleurocystidia 33–50 × 9–15 μ, flask-shaped to ventricose, apex at times crystallate, sometimes with a brown pigment, walls thickened. Cheilocystidia 37–50 × 7–10 μ, ventricose and similar to pleurocystidia, at times with a brown pigment. Caulocystidia none.

Gill trama with a central area of narrow (2–4 μ), subparallel hyphae, flanked by a gelatinous subhymenium. Pileus trama radial. Cuticle a gelatinous zone of narrow, brownish hyphae, some of which are slightly incrusted, these resting on an hypodermium of brown hyphae. Clamp connections present.

HABIT, HABITAT, AND DISTRIBUTION: On soil, clay bank, possibly attached to buried sticks or roots, Alabama, December. Type studied.

OBSERVATIONS: The description of microscopic characters is based on a study of the type. This species is near *P. gregariformis,* in which, however, the lamellae are close, the spores slightly longer and broader, and caulocystidia similar to the pleurocystidia are present.

131. Pholiota condensa (Pk.) comb. nov.

Flammula condensa Peck., Bull. Torrey Club 33: 217. 1906.
Gymnopilus condensus (Pk.) Murrill, North Amer. Fl. 10: 198. 1917.
Illustrations: Text figs. 279-280.

Pileus 2–3 cm broad, convex or nearly plane, often irregular from its densely caespitose mode of growth, usually umbonate, brownish yellow, the umbo reddish brown or chestnut colored, viscid when fresh. Context white, often tinged with yellow.

Lamellae adnate or slightly decurrent, yellowish becoming brownish ferruginous, moderately broad, subdistant, sometimes rugosely wrinkled.

Stipe 2–4 cm long, 2–3.5 mm thick, apex yellowish, pallid or brownish toward the base, equal, hollow.

Spores 7–9 (10) × (3.7) 4–5 μ, smooth, apical pore distinct but apex not truncate; shape subelliptic to ovate (rarely obscurely angular) in face view, varying from obscurely bean-shaped to obscurely inequilateral in profile, tawny to ochraceous-tawny in KOH, in Melzer's slightly more cinnamon-color, wall about 0.3 μ thick.

Basidia 20–25 × 5.5–7.5 μ, 4-spored, clavate, yellowish in KOH and in Melzer's reagent. Pleurocystidia 48–72 × 7–14 μ, fusoid-ventricose, apex usually obtuse, neck undulating, walls smooth or coated with amber-brown amorphous coating, thin-walled or wall up to 0.4 μ thick, content often amber-brown in KOH but fading to yellowish on standing, rarely with any inclusions such as rod-like particles but colloidal material evenly dispersed and evident in the neck of many. Cheilocystidia 30–50 × 6–12 μ, fusoid to fusoid-ventricose, otherwise similar to pleurocystidia.

Text Fig. 18.

Figs. 276-278, pleurocystidia, cheilocystidia and spores of *P. ala-bamensis;* 279 & 280, spores and pleurocystidia of *P. condensa;* 281-284, cheilocystidia, pleurocystidia, caulocystidia and spores of *P. humii;* 285 & 286, cheilocystidia and caulocystidia of *P. decorata.*

Caulocystidia none except at apex where hymenium extends for a short distance on the stipe and cells there similar to hymenial cystidia.

Gill trama of a central area of yellowish floccose hyphae as revived in KOH, and a distinct gelatinous subhymenium. Pileus cutis a gelatinous pellicle 3–6 hyphae deep, the hyphae 2–3.5 μ with walls gelatinizing, yellowish in KOH; hypodermial region of highly colored floccose compactly arranged hyphae either smooth or with incrustations on the wall. Clamp connections present. All hyphae inamyloid.

HABIT, HABITAT, AND DISTRIBUTION: Cespitose, in pine clearings and on stony hills, District of Columbia, December, type studied.

OBSERVATIONS: Peck (1906) stated that the pileus is viscid and we have demonstrated a typical gelatinous pellicle on some of the specimens in the type collection. Since the material even though appearing to be fairly well dried revives poorly, negative results in demonstrating the pellicle are to be expected by ordinary techniques—the pellicle may be torn off or simply not revive. By heating sections in KOH (2.5 %) however, we demonstrated its presence conclusively. The species has all the features of the *P. spumosa group,* and indeed, has spores the size of European material of *P. spumosa.* The only discordent anatomical feature is the rather thin pellicle. Because of the terrestrial habitat the thin pellicle, and cystidia with slightly thickened walls, we recognize this species in this Section.

MATERIAL EXAMINED: Peck (type, from near Washington, D. C., December, collected by F. J. Braendle).

Stirps Decorata

This is a rather distinct group of dingy reddish species found in our western states on rotting conifer wood or on conifer duff.

Key

1. Pleurocystidia with walls 1.3–3 μ thick 2
1. Pleurocystidia rarely with walls over 1.5 μ thick 3
   2. Odor fragrant; caulocystidia present; pleurocystidia 45–75 × 9–17 μ .... *P. humii*
   2. Odor lacking; caulocystidia lacking (?); pleurocystidia 60–115 × 10–17 μ .... *P. vinaceobrunnea*
3. Veil glutinous and leaving an evanescent glutinous annulus .... *P. velaglutinosa*
3. Veil floccose (dry) and fibrillose 4
   4. Odor not distinctive; stipe below the veil-line with brownish squamules at first, in age the squamules mostly whitish .... *P. decorata*
   4. Odor fragrant; veil remnants pallid to yellow below the veil-line .... *P. rubronigra*

132. **Pholiota humii** sp. nov.
Illustrations: Text figs. 281-284.

Pileus 1–3 cm latus convexus, viscidus, glaber, vinaceo-brunneus. Contextus pallidus, graveolens. Lamellae adnatae demum subdecurrentes, pallidae demum luteae, confertae, subangustae. Stipes 2.5–4 cm longus, (1.5)2–5 mm crassus, aequalis deorsum vinaceo-brunneus, sursum pallidus demum luteus. Sporae 5.5–7 × 4–4.5(5) μ. Pleurocystidia 45–75 × 9–17 μ, fusoide ventricosa, obtusa, crassotunicata. Specimen typicum in Herb. Univ. Mich. conservatum est; legit prope "Heaven's Gate, Seven Devils Mts.," Idaho, 5 Juli, 1958, Smith 58633.

Pileus 1–3 cm broad, convex, expanding, viscid, when young dark vinaceous brown ("natal-brown" to "Verona-brown"), later the disc "army-brown," finally reddish tawny, the margin paler brown, glabrous, even. Context pallid; odor fragrant (like green corn), taste slight; $FeSO_4$ —bright green.

Lamellae adnate to subdecurrent, at first whitish, then brown, close, medium narrow.

Stipe 2.5–4 cm long, (1.5) 2–5 mm thick, with scattered fibrils, pallid or pale tawny, base dull vinaceous brown ("army-brown"), equal. Veil arachnoid, yellowish.

Spores 5.5–7 × 4–4.5 (5) μ, in face view ovate to elliptic, in profile somewhat bean-shaped to subelliptic, wall relatively thin (± 0.2 μ) and apical pore a very minute spot (under 1.4 NA ob.). In KOH dingy ochraceous tawny, in Melzer's reagent paler but more cinnamon.

Basidia 19–24 × 6–7.5 μ, 4-spored, yellow in KOH or in Melzer's reagent, narrowly clavate. Pleurocystidia 45–75 × 9–17 μ, abundant, fusoid-ventricose with obtuse apex, wall up to 3 μ thick in ventricose part, thin-walled at obtuse apex; content ochre-yellow when first revived in KOH, slowly fading, homogeneous; wall in neck somewhat flexuous; surface smooth. Cheilocystidia 30–45 × 9–14 μ, broadly subfusoid, subelliptic-pedicellate, or fusoid-ventricose with obtuse apices, both thin-walled and thick-walled cells intermingled. Caulocystidia abundant, broadly fusoid, 35–70 × 10–20 μ, thin-walled or wall thickened (0.4–1 μ), hyaline, content homogeneous.

Gill trama with short- to long-celled hyphae more or less in parallel arrangement, the cells becoming inflated in age, 6–12 (20) μ broad; walls thin, hyaline to yellowish in KOH, smooth; subhymenium of narrow (–3 μ) gelatinous interwoven smooth-walled hyphae, hyaline in KOH, near gill edge the zone at times so broad as to nearly obscure the floccose central strand. Pileus cutis a gelatinous layer of appressed-interwoven narrow (2–5 μ) yellowish hyphae, those near the hypodermium conspicuously incrusted (not so at upper edge of layer); hypodermium of floccose hyphae 5–12 μ diam. with coarse dark rusty brown pigment incrustations. Context hyphae yellowish to hyaline in KOH, cells inflated to 15 μ or more, thin-walled and smooth. All hyphae inamyloid. Clamp connections present.

HABIT, HABITAT, AND DISTRIBUTION: Gregarious to scattered on or around rotten conifer logs. July and August, Idaho, Smith 58633, type.

OBSERVATIONS: This species is characterized by the vinaceous brown pileus, truly thick-walled pleurocystidia, whitish gills at first (but they soon become yellow) and fragrant odor. *P. vinaceobrunnea* has much longer pleurocystidia, lacks a fragrant odor and has well-developed whitish veil. We found caulocystidia on the stipe of *P. humii* but not on *P. vinaceobrunnea* but the comparison was made from dried specimens and we have some reservations concerning it.

MATERIAL EXAMINED: IDAHO Smith 38633, 73893, 59054, 60696.

133. **Pholiota vinaceobrunnea** sp. nov.
Illustrations: Pl. 61.

Pileus 2–5.5 cm latus, umbonatus, subviscidus ad marginem fibrilloso-squamlosus, glabrescens, sordide vinaceo-brunneus. Lamellae albidae demum ligno-brunneae, adnatae, angustae, confertae. Stipes 3–7 cm longus, 4–8 mm crassus, aequalis, solidus, sursum pallidus, deorsum vinaceo-brunneus, fibrillosus, sursum fibrilloso-zonatatus. Sporae 5.5–7 × 4–5 μ. Pleurocystidia 60–115 × 10–17 μ, crassotunicata. Specimen typicum in Herb. Univ. Mich. conservatum est; legit prope McCall, Idaho. 6 Aug. 1964. Paul Miller (Smith 68927).

Pileus 2–5.5 cm broad, obtusely umbonate expanding to plane or with a slight umbo, thinly viscid fresh but soon dry; color dark dull vinaceous-brown ("warm-sepia" to "Verona-brown") over the disc, dingy pale pinkish buff over marginal area but dingy tawny in between, at first decorated with 1–2 zones of veil fibrils or the fibrils occurring in scattered patches, glabrous in age or merely obscurely spotted. Context thin, fleshy-cartilaginous, with $FeSO_4$ bluish olive, taste mild, odor none.

Lamellae whitish becoming wood-brown and finally dull pale cinnamon-brown, adnate, narrow, close, not becoming spotted, edges even.

Stipe 3–7 cm long, 4–8 mm thick, equal, solid, surface pallid above, soon more or less "Verona-brown" (dingy vinaceous-brown) at base, fibrillose from the thin pallid cortinate veil, rarely with a persistent zone of veil elements near apex.

Spore deposit cinnamon-brown; spores 5.5–7 × 4–5 μ, smooth, apical pore not evident, shape in face view subovate to elliptic, somewhat bean-shaped; color ochraceous tawny in KOH, pale tawny brown in Melzer's reagent.

Basidia 4-spored, 17–22 × 5–6 μ, yellowish in KOH, slightly more so in Melzer's. Pleurocystidia abundant 60–115 × 10–17 μ, fusoid-ventricose, apex obtuse or sometimes abruptly tapered to a spicule of a point, thick-walled (at least in the ventricose portion, 2–3 μ thick), arising deep in the subhymenium, content in neck portion often coagulated and dingy ochraceous in KOH and also in Melzer's; thickened walls hyaline in Melzer's. Cheilocystidia similar to pleurocystidia but smaller. Caulocystidia none found.

Gill trama of a parallel stratum of hyphae ochraceous in KOH and with smooth walls; subhymenium of gelatinous narrow (2–3 μ) interwoven hyphae in a gelatinous matrix, the hyphae with walls ochraceous and mostly with banded to spiral incrustations; beneath this a band of floccose hyphae 4–12 μ diam. with rusty colored patches of incrusted material (a hypodermium). Context hyphae pale ochraceous, smooth and cells 5–15 μ diam., walls scarcely darker in Melzer's reagent. Clamps regularly present.

HABIT, HABITAT, AND DISTRIBUTION: Scattered on conifer logs, summer and fall Idaho and Washington.

OBSERVATIONS: For a comparison with *P. humii* see that species. *P. vinaceobrunnea* is closest to *P. decorata* but differs in the thicker-walled pleurocystidia. However, it is to be regarded as part of the *P. decorata* complex.

MATERIAL EXAMINED: IDAHO: Smith 68927 (type), 71217, 73869. WASHINGTON: Smith 40486, 40494.

134. **Pholiota velaglutinosa** sp. nov.
Illustrations: Text figs. 272-274; pl. 62.

Pileus 3–6 cm latus, convexus, demum explanatus, glutinosus, ad marginem appendiculatus, sordide vinaceo-brunneus. Lamellae adnatae, latae, confertae, avellaneae demum ligno-brunneae. Stipes 3–6 cm longus, 4–8 mm crassus, sursum sericeus et olivaceoluteus; deorsum fulvus. Annulus gelatinosus. Sporae 6–7.5 × 3.7–4.5 μ. Pleurocystidia 55–82 × 9–15 (20) μ, fusoide ventricosa. Cheilocystidia 30–55(60) × 10–15(20) μ, utriformia vel subfusoidia. Specimen typicum in Herb. Univ. of Mich. conservatum est; legit prope Cave Junction, Oregon, 29 November, 1937, Smith 9285.

Pileus 3–6 cm broad, convex becoming plane or the margin elevated and wavy, glutinous to viscid, the marginal area decorated with the thin patches of fibrils, and often more or less appendiculate from the remains of the glutinous partial veil, color bright to dingy vinaceous brown ("cameo-brown") over all but becoming "sorghum-brown" or finally nearly "wood-brown" on the margin) appearing finely fibrillose-streaked beneath the pellicle. Context pliant, greenish yellow, buff colored in age; odor and taste not distinctive.

Lamellae adnate and with a slight decurrent tooth, near avellaneous but becoming "wood-brown" at maturity, broad, close, edges even.

Stipe 3–6 cm long, 4–8 mm thick, equal, hollow, with an apical glutinous evanescent annulus, silky and greenish yellow above, coated with appressed buff-yellow fibrillose patches or concentric zones below annulus, becoming rusty stained where handled, and dark brown below in age.

Spores 6–7.5 × 3.7–4.5 μ, smooth, germ pore present as a minute hyaline spot under highest magnification; dull cinnamon in KOH, slightly paler in Melzer's reagent, in face view elliptic to broadly elliptic or ovate; in profile subovate to slightly bean-shaped; wall relatively thin. Basidia 4-spored, 20–25 × 6–7.5 μ, hyaline in KOH, yellowish in Melzer's reagent, clavate. Pleurocystidia abundant, 55–82 × 9–15 (20) μ, fusoid-ventricose with the apex subacute to obtuse, smooth, content often colloidal and ochraceous in the neck, ventricose portion with wall 0.5–1.5 μ thick, wall of neck often flexuous. Cheilocystidia 30–55 (60) × 10–15 (20) μ, utriform to subfusoid with apex obtuse, thin-walled, content often ochraceous, smooth. Caulocystidia 42–60 × 7–20 μ fusoid-ventricose to subfusoid, similar to cheilocystidia and often with ochraceous content.

Gill trama of a central area of parallel to subparallel hyphae with hyaline to yellowish thin smooth walls, the cells long or short and 4–9 μ diam., but inflating in age; subhymenium gelatinous, hyaline, of interwoven narrow hyphae. Pileus cutis a gelatinous layer usually over 100 μ thick, of narrow (2–3 μ) mostly incrusted tubular hyphae hyaline to yellowish in KOH; hypodermium a dark rusty brown (in KOH) layer of floccose heavily incrusted hyphae with cells 4–15 μ diam. Context hyphae interwoven, the cells greatly inflated, thin or with slightly thickened walls, hyaline to yellowish in KOH. All hyphae inamyloid. Clamp connections present.

HABIT, HABITAT, AND DISTRIBUTION: Scattered on humus under pine, Oregon and California.

OBSERVATIONS: This species differs from *P. ferrugineo-lutescens* in the more bean-shaped spores in profile view, and in more of the pleurocystidia having subacute to obtuse apices. In the dried specimens the veil dries to resemble a thin-sheet of plastic over the gill cavity. For further comment see *P. ferrugineo-lutescens*.

MATERIAL EXAMINED: CALIFORNIA: Lanphere 18. OREGON: Smith 3560, 9218, 9285 (type).

135. Pholiota decorata (Murr.) comb. nov.

Gymnopilus decoratus Murrill, Mycologia 4: 251. 1912.
Flammula decorata (Murr.) Murrill, Mycologia 4: 262. 1912.
Illustrations: Text figs. 287-288; pls. 63-64, 79b.

Var. *decorata*

Pileus 3–7 (9) cm broad, obtuse to convex when young, expanding to umbonate with a spreading margin, or nearly plane, disc dark vinaceous brown ("natal-brown," "army-brown" to "cameo-brown" at first, fading to near "fawn-color") the margin pallid to avellaneous, in age often "Isabella-color," surface glutinous to viscid, with numerous to scattered rows of concentrically arranged fibrillose scales above the gela-

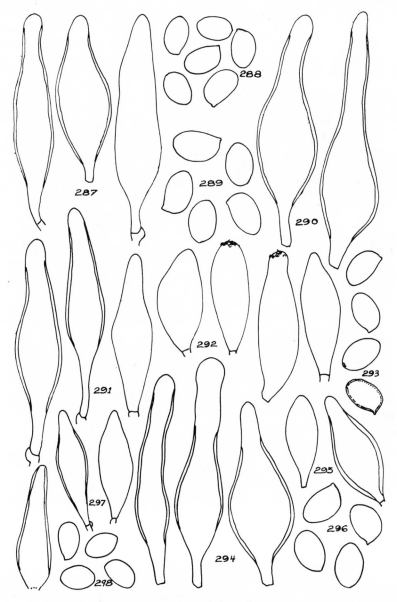

Text Fig. 19.

Figs. 287 & 288, pleurocystidia and spores of *P. decorata* var. *decorata;* 289 & 290, spores and pleurocystidia of *P. sienna;* 291-293, pleurocystidia, cheilocystidia and spores of *P. ferrugineo-lutescens;* 294-296, pleuro-cystidia, cheilocystidia and spores of *P. hypholomoides;* 297 & 298, cheilo-cystidia and spores of *P. ferruginea.*

tinous layer, scales frequently disappearing before maturity, in age often glabrous and appearing fibrillose-streaked beneath the gluten, margin usually fringed with fibrils when young. Context moderately thick, watery cartilaginous to soft and pliant, white to (in age) yellowish; odor faintly fragrant or lacking, taste mild or nearly so.

Lamellae adnate to sinuate, sometimes merely depressed, close, moderately broad, thin, white to yellowish ("ivory-yellow"), becoming avellaneous and finally dingy clay-color, edges even or nearly so.

Stipe 4–8 (11) cm long, 3–8 (10) mm thick, solid but becoming hollow, equal above a subbulbous base or base not enlarged, cortex brownish in base, yellowish to pallid above, surface over lower portion covered by dingy vinaceous brown floccose-fibrillose scales or patches from a ruptured sheath which at first extends to the annular zone or scales mostly whitish, apex silky and pale greenish yellow to pallid.

Spores (5.5) 6–7.5 (8.5) × 3.5–4.5 μ, smooth, apical pore minute, ochraceous rusty-brown to ochraceous-tawny in KOH, paler ochraceous in Melzer's reagent; wall about 0.25–0.3 μ thick, shape in face view ovate to elliptic with some obscurely wedge-shaped, in profile obscurely inequilateral to somewhat bean-shaped.

Basidia (19) 23–27 × 5–7 μ, 4-spored, clavate, hyaline to yellowish in KOH, yellowish in Melzer's reagent. Pleurocystidia 50–90 × (6) 9–18 μ, fusoid-ventricose with obtuse apex, with a slender basal stalk in many extending from below the subhymenium, thick- to thin-walled (on the same pileus) but some thick-walled individuals seen in every mount, wall 1–1.5 or up to 2 μ thick in neck but thin at apex, smooth, hyaline to yellow in KOH (pigment mostly in content and fading). Cheilocystidia 36–55 × 8–12 μ, subfusoid to nearly clavate or more or less fusoid-ventricose, yellow to hyaline in KOH, mostly thin-walled, smooth in KOH. Caulocystidia versiform, 1) clavate to vesiculose, 15–40 × 12–30 μ, walls smooth, thin to slightly thickened and yellowish to hyaline in KOH; 2) subfusiform, 40–60 × 9–14 μ with slightly thickened (0.5 μ) walls, content homogeneous, occurring both types together in a cluster.

Gill trama a floccose cetnral strand of non-gelatinous thin-walled subparallel hyphae that are smooth and ochraceous to hyaline in KOH, inamyloid. Pileus cutis a gelatinous layer of widely separated narrow hyphae (± 2.5 μ) diam., smooth, and thin-walled; hypodermium of ochraceous slightly roughened floccose hyphae 4–8 μ diam. Context hyphae greatly inflated, smooth, walls thin, inamyloid. Clamp connections present.

HABIT, HABITAT, AND DISTRIBUTION: Single to scattered on fallen conifer branches and debris, July to November in Washington, Oregon, California, Idaho, and Colorado; in Canada known from British Columbia.

OBSERVATIONS: As Kauffman (1926) points out, the measurements of cystidia given by Murrill (1912) are incorrect. Kauffman also adds that the taste is slowly bitter and somewhat nauseous. In an Oregon collection (No. 3560), Smith detected a slight fragrant odor. It appears to prefer a conifer habitat, but in Smith 47205, from Idaho, it grew on birch. This is one of the characteristic species on conifer slash in the Pacific Northwest, and will be found to vary in color depending on whether it fruits during relatively dry or very wet weather. It is generally paler under the latter condition. Smith has encountered numerous collections in which the gills gradually become bright yellow and few spores were ever found on them. Since this same feature is a very common one during good seasons in species of *Naematoloma,* a closely related genus, no particular significance was ascribed to it in the field and no collections were saved in which it was specifically noted. However, sterility or partial sterility in species of the Strophariaceae is sufficiently common to deserve detailed study—particularly the accompanying change in the pigment features of the basidiocarp.

The pleurocystidia were described as thin-walled by Kauffman in his notes on the type and his identified collections under this name show such cystidia but in addition thick-walled cystidia also are present. In many of Smith's collections most of the cystidia are thick-walled. Apparently in fresh specimens the cystidia all appear thin-walled, at least Smith made no notation of thick walled elements in the hymenium at the time the material was fresh. The character needs further observation on fresh specimens and then these same specimens dried and the cystidia rechecked in KOH.

In the type this same condition prevails. Cystidia with walls 1.5 μ thick or more are not uncommon but there are as many or more with thin walls. The species concept here put forth is consistent with the microscopic characters of the type.

MATERIAL EXAMINED: CALIFORNIA: 3569, 3659, 3734, 3872, 3916, 8198, 56109, 56119; COLORADO: Smith 51386, 52373, 52485, 58599; IDAHO: 47205, 53662, 54770, 69700, 70180, 70259, 70481, 70577, 70844, 71104; OREGON: Gruber 32, 18-8; Kauffman 10-16-22; Smith 3286, 3591, 7899, 8074, 19663, 20165, 24388, 24696, 24697, 28138, 28209, 55417; WASHINGTON: Murrill 553 (type); Kauffman 9-21-15, 10-19-15, 10-28-25, 11-5-25; Smith 16986, 17017, 17047, 17107, 17227, 68744. CANADA (BRITISH COLUMBIA) Buckland 71 (MICH).

136. **Pholiota rubronigra** sp. nov.
Illustrations: Pl. 65a.

Pileus 3–8 cm latus, late convexus vel planus, viscidus, fibrilloso-squamulosus, glabrescens, badius. Contextus albus, fragrans. Lamellae adnatae demum subdecurrentes, latae, confertae, pallidae demum cinna-momeo-brunneae. Stipes 4–6 cm longus, 3–7 mm crassus, ad basin compacte myceliosus, sursum luteus, deorsum fulvus et squamulosus, velum fibrillosum. Sporae 6–8.5 × 4–5 μ. Pleurocystidia 45–75 × 10–15 μ fusoide ventricosa tenuitunicata vel crassotunicata (1.5 μ). Specimen typi-

cum in Herb. Univ. of Mich. conservatum est; legit prope Trinidad, California, 3 Dec. 1956, Smith 56192.

Pileus 3–8 cm broad, convex, expanding to plane, margin incurved and often appendiculate with veil fragments, color dark vinaceous brown ("Natal-brown") young, in age bay on disc and paler reddish brown on margin, viscid, at first decorated with concentric zones of pallid to yellowish-pallid veil remnants. Context white to pallid; odor distinctly fragrant, taste mild, no color changes observed.

Lamellae adnate becoming subdecurrent, pallid young, dull cinnamon-brown in age, close, only moderately broad, edges even.

Stipe 4–6 cm long, 3–7 mm thick, equal, bulbous from white mycelium at base, apex yellowish to the fibrillose annulus, pallid to grayish fibrillose or subscaly below to the base which darkens to rusty brown within, cortex pallid below at very first. Veil heavy, fibrillose, leaving a semi-persistent ring.

Spores 6–8.5 × 4–5 μ smooth, apical pore present but apex not truncate, shape in face view elliptic to ovate, in profile, slightly bean-shaped to obscurely inequilateral, dull rusty brown in KOH, slowly fading to ochraceous tawny, in Melzer's reagent merely slightly more cinnamon, wall about 0.25 μ thick.

Basidia 25–30 × 6–7 μ, 4-spored, clavate, hyaline to yellowish in Melzer's reagent. Pleurocystidia 45–75 × 10–15 μ, fusoid-ventricose, apex subacute to obtuse and showing a tendency to proliferate, walls thin to 1.5 μ thick in upper part of ventricose portion; content yellowish or rarely dingy amber-brown, colloidal; wall smooth, colorless (somewhat greenish-hyaline) in KOH. Cheilocystidia 33–52 × 8–12 μ, obtusely fusoid to fusoid-ventricose, mostly thin-walled throughout and content similar to that of pleurocystidia. Caulocystidia 34–71 × 10–20 μ, clavate, subpyriform, fusoid or fusoid-ventricose, utriform, etc., thin-walled or wall up to 1.5 (2) μ thick; content homogeneous.

Gill trama a central area of floccose subparallel to interwoven hyphae with long or short cells, the cells (3) 5–15 μ diam., or more (as they inflate) ; walls thin, smooth, hyaline in KOH; subhymenium a gelatinous layer of somewhat divergent hyphae 2–3 μ diam. and hyaline in KOH. Pileus cutis a thick gelatinous pellicle of narrow (2–3 μ) hyaline gelatinous hyphae; hypodermium of dark rusty brown hyphae with heavy incrustations of pigment, cells 4–10 μ diam. Context hyphae inflated, walls thin, smooth, hyaline in KOH. Clamp connections absent. All hyphae inamyloid.

HABIT, HABITAT, AND DISTRIBUTION: On pine and redwood logs, Idaho and California, November-December.

OBSERVATIONS: Among the species with thick-walled cystidia *P. rubronigra* can be recognized by its fragrant odor, some pleurocystidia with walls up to 1.5 μ thick, very dark reddish brown color over the disc of the pileus as dried, and lack of brown squamules over the lower part of the stipe. In the dried state the whole basidiocarp of *P. decorata* is much paler in color and when fresh its stipe has brown squamules of veil remnants, and it typically lacks a fragrant odor. Both show variation from thin to thick-walled pleurocystidia.

P. vinaceobrunnea lacks a fragrant odor, has pleurocystidia with walls 2–3 μ thick, and no caulocystidia were found in an examination of dried material. Also its cystidia measure 60–115 μ long. *P. humii* with pleurocystidia having walls to 3 μ thick, has a fragrant odor, and a veil so poorly developed as to scarcely leave a zone of fibrils where it breaks. Also it appears to be a more slender species.

This stirps, with the exception of *P. velaglutinosa* appears to be a "collective" species, and as indicated in other similar situations, comparative studies in culture are badly needed.

MATERIAL EXAMINED: CALIFORNIA: Smith 56059, 56192 (type), 56583, 56647. IDAHO: Smith 69534.

Stirps Ferruginea

As indicated, the species with bright rusty red, orange, and variations of these colors over the disc of the young pileus are placed here. The colors may fade and then the species may resemble those of stirps *Occidentalis.* If only old material is available for identification try both stirpes to obtain an identification. This stirps might be further divided on the color of the gills at maturity: one group with dull colored gills and the other with yellow-brown gills. Presumably there would be a difference in the color of the spore print but this remains to be checked.

Key

1. Spores mostly 6–7 × 4–5 μ; gills with wood brown to fuscous tones when mature and fresh 2
1. Spores usually narrower in relation to length; gills yellow brown 4
   2. Odor strong (of iodiform or Inocybe-like) ; pileus "burnt sienna" fresh .... *P. sienna*
   2. Odor not distinctive; pileus ferruginous at first 3
3. Stipe readily staining yellow .... *P. ferrugineo-lutescens*
3. Stipe not staining as above .... *P. hypholomoides*
   4. Pleurocystidia with walls 1.5–4 μ thick .... *P. ferruginea*
   4. Pleurocystidia with walls thinner (0.5–2 μ) ....
      .... see *P. lubrica* var. *luteifolia, P. rufodisca* and *P. abruptibulba*

137. Pholiota sienna (Kauff.) comb. nov.
Stropharia sienna Kauffman, Pap. Mich. Acad. Sci. Arts, Papers and
   Letters 11: 207. 1930.
Illustrations: Text figs. 289-290.

The following description is adopted from Kauffman's original account and maintains his wording to a great extent.

Pileus 4–8 cm broad, fleshy, campanulate-expanded to almost plane, obtuse or obsoletely umbonate, center colored with "burnt sienna" (R), tawny-olive or paler on margin, with a glutinous toughish separable pellicle when wet, at first with veil remnants near the membranous and even margin. Context avellaneous, 2–4 mm thick, odor strong, *Inocybe*-like or of iodiform; taste tardily disagreeable.

Lamellae adnate with decurrent tooth, becoming slightly decurrent in age, broad, narrowed in front, subventricose, close to crowded, "clay-color" (R) with fuscous tints when mature, edge entire, concolorous.

Stipe 5–7 cm long, 5–8 mm thick, rather slender, curved or flexuous, equal or only slightly enlarged at base, peronate by an appressed fibrillose, rufescent-tinged veil to near apex, with an evanescently fibrillose annulus, apex faintly yellowish, at first stuffed then hollow, whitish to faintly yellowish within.

Spores 6–7 (8) × 4–5 μ, elliptic to oval (almost corn-kernel shaped in one view), fuscous in mass, pale fuscous-purplish under microscope, smooth. Cystidia abundant on side and edges of gills, lanceolate, subventricose below, neck tapering to obtuse apex, hyaline, thin-walled, 60–65 × 9–16 μ; basidia short, 16–18 × 4–5 μ, 4-spored.

Type collected under oak and Douglas fir, Takilma, Oregon, December 2, 1925, C. H. Kauffman.

The type specimens now have dark dull ochraceous tawny gills much as in other species of subg. *Flammuloides*. The pileus is darker yellow-brown over the disc than over the margin and the latter is not at all virgate—as is true for *P. decorata*. The spore print described by Kauffman is not with the specimen, in fact we suspect that he observed the color of the spore deposit either on the stipe apex or on spores deposited on a second cap. If such is actually the case this might account for the fuscous color as described by Kauffman. Certainly the basidiocarps now in the type collection belong in *Pholiota*. Smith's study of the microscopic features of the type follows:

Spores 6–7.5 (8) × 4–5 μ smooth, lacking a distinct apical pore (possibly a minute pore present); shape in face view ovate or varying to elliptic, in profile obscurely inequilateral to slightly bean-shaped; color ochraceous tawny in KOH, paler in Melzer's reagent; wall about 0.25 μ thick.

Basidia 18–20 × 6–7 μ, 4-spored, short-clavate, hyaline in KOH, yellowish in Melzer's reagent. Pleurocystidia 56–70 × 10–14 μ, fusoid-ventricose, with subacute apex, walls often thickened to 1.5 μ ventricose part and smooth, content as revived in KOH, yellowish-brown and granular-amorphous (not a solid inclusion as in chrysocystidia). Cheilocystidia similar to pleurocystidia or shorter and walls often thin. Caulocystidia none found.

Gill trama with a central strand of subparallel hyphae hyaline to pale yellow in KOH and the hyphae 4–7 μ or more in diam., cells with smooth thin non-gelatinous walls; subhymenium a distinct gelatinous layer of narrow interwoven hyphae. Pileus cutis a thick gelatinous pellicle of narrow (1.5–3 μ) yellowish hyphae more or less appressed; hypodermial zone of hyphae 5–10 μ or more diam. with heavily pigmented walls from rusty brown incrustations. Context hyphae loosely interwoven and floccose, nearly hyaline in KOH, walls thin and smooth. Clamp connections present.

OBSERVATIONS: This species is close to *P. avellaneifolia* but the latter has grayish gills when young, a yellowish veil, and the context stains pinkish buff when cut.

138. Pholiota ferrugineo-lutescens sp. nov.
Illustrations: Text figs. 291-293.

Pileus 3–7 cm latus, convexus, ferrugineus demum fulvus, ad marginem luteus, glutinosus. Lamellae adnatae, albidae demum lignobrunneae, confertae, angustae. Stipes 6–8 cm longus, 10–15 mm crassus, fibrillosus, fibrillis luteis, deorsum fulvus. Sporae 5.5–7 × 4–4.5 μ. Pleurocystidia 50–75 × 9–16 μ, fusoide ventricosa. Cheilocystidia 30–50 × 8–14 μ, ad apicem rotundata. Specimen typicum in Herb. Univ. Mich. conservatum est; legit prope Orick, Calif. 4 Dec. 1937, Smith 9393.

Pileus 3–7 cm broad, obtuse to convex, the margin incurved, expanding to plane or with a slight broad umbo, at first between "hazel" and "ochraceous-tawny" (somewhat ferruginous), disc remaining yellowish tawny, but the margin finally pale yellow, glutinous-viscid, with radial fibrillose streaks beneath the gluten, glabrous except for veil-remnants adhering along the margin. Context thick, cartilaginous-pliant, whitish to watery yellowish; odor and taste mild.

Lamellae slightly adnexed, whitish at first, soon dull brown ("woodbrown"), close to crowded, narrow, equal, thin, edges even.

Stipe 6–8 cm long, 10–15 mm thick, equal, stuffed, becoming tubular, surface fibrillose over lower portion from the pale yellowish veil remnants, with an apical fibrillose zone from the ample fibrillose to submembranous veil, white to whitish over all, soon stained yellow where handled and cortex yellow when cut, in age sordid rusty brown below (inside and out); base with dense, radiating, white hairs.

Spores 5.5–7 × 4–4.5 μ, pale tawny in KOH, about the same color in Melzer's reagent, smooth, in face view elliptic to slightly ovate, in profile elliptic to very obscurely inequilateral, pore apical but minute, wall somewhat thickened.

Basidia 4-spored, 26–34 × 6–8 μ, hyaline in KOH and slightly yellowish in Melzer's sol. clavate. Pleurocystidia abundant, 50–75 × 9–16 μ, fusoid-ventricose, apex rounded to obtuse, stalk slender and often curved, surface smooth or rarely with some debris adhering around apex, wall thin to thickened (in the ventricose part 0.4–1.5 μ thick and yellow-refractive in KOH), content homogeneous or in some ochraceous-colloidal or merely not reviving well and both ochraceous and reticulate. Cheilocystidia 30–50 × 8–14 μ, utriform to subfusoid, thin-walled, smooth except for crystals and debris around apex in some, content yellowish to hyaline, (in either KOH or Melzer's sol.). Caulocystidia none.

Gill trama a floccose central area of parallel to subparallel hyaline to yellowish hyphae (in KOH) with short to elongated thin-walled colorless to smooth walls, the cells short or elongated; subhymenium of interwoven hyphae, gelatinous in KOH. Pileus epicutis a gelatinous layer of appressed-interwoven ochraceous-incrusted hyphae 3–5 μ diam.; hypodermium of floccose hyphae 4–10 μ diam. with heavy, orange-rusty incrustations producing a highly pigmented region. Context hyphae ochraceous-pallid in KOH, hyphae 5–14 μ diam., cells inflated, walls mostly smooth and thin to slightly thickened (swelling slightly in KOH), inamyloid. Clamp connections present.

HABIT, HABITAT, AND DISTRIBUTION: On debris around redwood logs, Orick, Calif. Dec. 14, 1937, Smith 9393, type. IDAHO: On conifer wood, Smith 54021.

OBSERVATIONS: The walls of the pleurocystidia vary from thin to over 1 μ thick, so the species is placed in this section. It's outstanding field characters are the ferruginous color at first, white gills becoming wood brown, and the stipe readily staining yellow. It is very close to *P. velaglutinosa* but that species has a greenish yellow context, and greenish yellow stipe apex in addition to the gelatinous outer veil.

139. Pholiota hypholomoides (Murr.) comb. nov.
Gymnopilus hypholomoides Murrill, Mycologia 5: 26. 1913.
Flammula hypholomoides Murrill, Mycologia 5: 36. 1913.
Illustrations: Text figs. 294-296.

Pileus 3–6 cm broad, convex to expanded, viscid (Murrill says dry), subfibrillose, pale-fuscous, ferruginous in the center, margin thin, somewhat folded and uneven, not striate. Context thin, yellowish; of mawkish flavor.

Lamellae sinuate, tawny-yellow to pale-fuscous, inserted, crowded, rather narrow.

Stipe 4–6 cm long, 2–4 mm thick, concolorous, cylindric, curved, fibrillose, solid, tough.

Spores 5.5–7.5 × 4–5 μ, smooth, apical pore present but minute, shape in face view mostly ovate but a few subelliptic, in profile somewhat inequilateral, color in KOH dark tawny, paler in Melzer's reagent, wall about 0.25 μ thick.

Basidia 17–21 (25) × 5–7.5 μ, mostly 4-spored, obese to subutriform, yellow in KOH and Melzer's reagent. Pleurocystidia 45–80 × 6–12 (rarely shorter) and up to 20 μ broad, fusoid-ventricose, apex obtuse, wall smooth or with some solidified gelatinous material adhering in places, wall thin to distinctly thickened (up to 1.5 μ in ventricose part, content colloidal, reticulate or diffuse and amber-brown to yellow in KOH fading to nearly hyaline, with rods and particles of solid material often in upper end of neck. Cheilocystidia 34–68 × 7–14 μ, small and subfusoid, to fusoid-ventricose like pleurocystidia but usually wall thin, or thickened from above pedicel to apex (where it is thin). Caulocystidia none found, (only dried material examined).

Gill trama a central area of floccose hyphae subparallel in arrangement, the hyphal cells 4–9 μ diam. and inflating to 16 μ or more in age, walls thin, smooth and yellowish in KOH; subhymenium a distinct gelatinous layer of interwoven hyaline hyphae 2–3 μ diam. more or less intricately branched. Pileus cutis a gelatinous pellicle of narrow hyphae over a hypodermium of dark rusty brown (in KOH) floccose heavily incrusted hyphae. Context hyphae interwoven, walls yellowish in KOH (not reviving well in type). Clamp connections present. All hyphae inamyloid.

HABIT, HABITAT, AND DISTRIBUTION: On soil, apparently attached to buried wood, Jamaica, October, type studied.

OBSERVATIONS: Murrill (1913) states that the pileus surface resembles *Hypholoma* (*Naematoloma*) *sublateritium*. Murrill also describes the pileus as dry, but sections of the type reveal a distinct gelatinous cutis and a hypodermial layer. The pleurocystidia distinguish it at once from the common brick-cap. The color of the mature gills, however, suggests purple brown spores. In the dried material, however, the gill color is that of the *P. spumosa* group generally. Because of the gelatinous pellicle of the pileus, the large pleurocystidia and the gelatinous subhymenium, the species is unquestionably a *Pholiota*.

140. Pholiota ferruginea sp. nov.
Illustrations: Text figs. 297-298.

Pileus 4–8 cm latus, obtusus demum obtuse umbonatus, viscidus, ferrugineus, ad marginem aurantio-ochraceus. Contextus luteus. Lamellae latae, confertae, demum subdecurrentes. Stipes 5–8 cm longus, 3–8 mm crassus, aequalis, farctus, subluteus, sursum sericeus, deorsum fibrillosus et demum fulvus. Velum fibrillosum copiosum. Sporae 6–7 × 3.5–4 μ. Pleurocystidia 45–65 × 9–14 μ fusoide ventricosa crasso-tunicata (1.5–4 μ). Specimen typicum in Herb. Univ. of Mich. conservatum est; legit prope Port Angeles, Wash., 21 Sept. 1941. Smith 17092.

Pileus 4–8 cm broad, obtuse with a curved in margin when young, expanding to broadly umbonate with a decurved margin, surface viscid, ferruginous, gradually becoming more orange to ochraceous along the margin and disc ferruginous-brown. Context yellowish, odor and taste not recorded.

Lamellae moderately broad, close, adnate, developing a decurrent tooth, pale yellow or very soon becoming so, finally dull tawny from the spores, edges even.

Stipe 5–8 cm long, 3–8 mm thick, equal, stuffed, pallid yellowish above, silky above the veil line, appressed fibrillose lower down and becoming dark rusty brown from base up. Veil copious, fibrillose, yellowish, leaving an evanescent zone where it breaks.

Spores 6–7 × 3.5–4 μ, smooth, apical pore very minute, in face view elliptic to oval, rarely slightly constricted in mid-portion, in profile slightly bean-shaped to obscurely inequilateral, in KOH pale tawny, merely slightly duller in Melzer's reagent, wall thin (± 0.25 μ).

Basidia 18–22 × 5–6 μ clavate, 4-spored, hyaline to ochraceous in KOH and Melzer's reagent. Pleurocystidia abundant 45–65 × 9–14 μ, fusoid-ventricose, with walls 1.5–4 μ thick, apex obtuse, content homogeneous to yellow to hyaline in KOH, smooth or with some amorphous debris around apex, usually with a distinct narrow pedicel, wall hyaline throughout. Cheilocystidia similar to pleurocystidia or shorter and with thinner walls. Caulocystidia none observed.

Gill trama of floccose subparallel hyphae of long and short cells finally inflated, hyaline to yellowish in KOH; subhymenium gelatinous, of narrow hyaline smooth hyphae. Pileus cutis a gelatinous pellicle of ochraceous or paler hyphae, with yellowish to tan incrustations, interwoven, 3–5 μ diam.; hypodermium of bright rusty cinnamon (in KOH) hyphae 5–12 μ diam. with conspicuous incrustations. Context hyphae smooth, cells inflated, walls thin and hyaline to yellowish in KOH. Clamp connections present. All hyphae inamyloid.

HABIT, HABITAT, AND DISTRIBUTION: Gregarious on debris under conifers, summer and falls, Idaho, Washington and Oregon.

OBSERVATIONS: This species closely resembles *P. ferrugineo-lutescens* but the pleurocystidia have conspicuously thickened walls, and the stipe did not stain yellow when handled.

MATERIAL EXAMINED: IDAHO: Smith 54461, 69534, 70601. OREGON: Smith 19647, 24022, 24445, 24583. WASHINGTON: Smith 17092 (type), 17344, 17768, 40566, 49042.

141. **Pholiota rufodisca** sp. nov.
Illustrations: Text figs. 299-301.

Pileus (1)3–6 cm latus, convexus vel obtuse-umbonatus, fulvo-aurantiacus, rufo brunneus vel ad marginem luteo-avellaneus, glaber, viscidus. Contextus luteus, tenuis. Lamellae adnatae vel subdecurrentes, angustae demum latae, confertae, pallide luteae demum luteo-brunneae. Stipes 3–6(8) cm longus, (2)3–6(8) mm crassus, deorsum subfulvus, sursum luteus, velum fibrillosum, luteum. Sporae 5–7 × 3.5–4.5 μ. Pleurocystidia 50–73 × 11–17 μ, fusoide ventricosa, crassotunicata. Specimen typicum in Herb. Univ. Mich. conservatum est. legit prope Payette Lakes, Idaho. 31 Aug. 1954. Smith 47146.

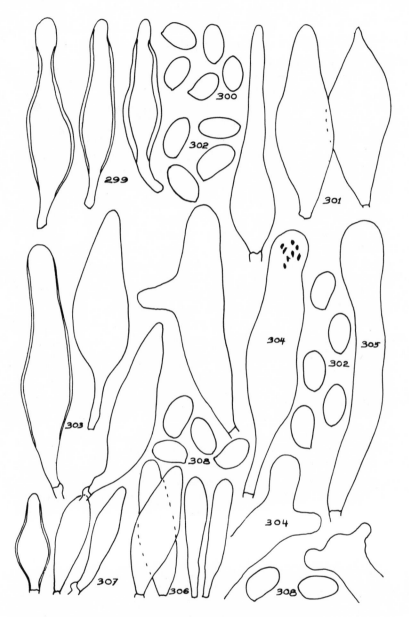

Text Fig. 20.

Figs. 299-301, pleurocystidia, spores and caulocystidia of *P. rufodisca;* 302-306, spores, pleurocystidia (303 & 304), caulocystidia and cheilocystidia of *P. abruptibulba;* 307 & 308, cheilocystidia and spores of *P. verna.*

Pileus (1) 3–6 cm broad, convex, expanding, at times more or less umbonate, disc rusty orange to dark reddish brown, blackish when dried at times, marginal portion buff to yellowish gray, glabrous, viscid, margin incurved, even. Context thin, yellow.

Lamellae adnate or subdecurrent, yellowish when young, "buckthorn brown" at maturity, narrow to medium broad to broad, close.

Stipe 3–6 (8) cm long, (2) 3–6 (8) mm thick, yellowish and pruinose above, dingy downward, basal portion rusty brownish, equal, slightly fibrillose, glabrescent, stuffed then hollow. Veil yellowish, arachnoid.

Spores 5–7 × 3.5–4 μ, smooth, apical pore distinct and apex obscurely truncate in some, in shape elliptic to ovate, in profile obscurely inequilateral, dull tawny in KOH, paler in Melzer's reagent, wall thin (–0.25 μ).

Basidia 4-spored, 20–27 × 5–6 μ clavate, yellowish to hyaline in KOH, yellowish in Melzer's reagent. Pleurocystidia 50–73 × 11–17 μ fusoid-ventricose, apex obtuse; wall smooth and 1.5–2.5 μ thick, hyaline-refractive in KOH, content hyaline to yellow and homogeneous. Cheilocystidia 30–56 × 6–14 μ similar to pleurocystidia. Caulocystidia versiform, 40–80 × 12–25 μ, clavate, fusoid-ventricose, or fusoid, thin-walled, smooth, content "empty."

Gill trama a central area of floccose hyphae 4–12 μ broad; walls thin, yellowish to hyaline in KOH, smooth; subhymenium a gelatinous layer of narrow hyaline hyphae. Pileus cutis a thick gelatinous pellicle of narrow (2–3 μ) hyaline to yellowish hyphae, those near hypodermium incrusted; hypodermium a layer of floccose hyphae 4–8 (12) μ with heavy incrustations, fulvous in KOH. Context hyphae yellowish hyaline in KOH, cells inflated, walls thin, smooth. Clamp connections present. All hyphae inamyloid.

HABIT, HABITAT, AND DISTRIBUTION: On conifer wood and debris, Idaho, Oregon and Washington, August—October.

OBSERVATIONS: *P. rufodisca* is close to *P. brunneodisca* which Peck (1913) stated was slightly viscid. In our study of the type, however, we found no gelatinous pellicle. *P. ferruginea* lacks caulocystidia as far as our observations indicate. There is a difference in the degree to which the veil is developed also.

MATERIAL EXAMINED: IDAHO: Smith 47146 (type), 47033, 70858, 71113. NEW MEXICO: Barrows 925, 141. OREGON: Smith 24733. WASHINGTON: Smith 47594, 47650, 48240.

Stirps Occidentalis

Species with cinnamon, tan, russet to clay-colored pilei are placed here. Some in other stirpes fade out to the above colors hence fresh young or barely mature pilei are needed for correct disposition of a collection.

Key

1. Stipe 10–20 mm thick 2
1. Stipe thinner, usually 3–8 mm diam. 3
   2. Pileus glabrous and glutinous .... *P. abruptibulba*
   2. Pileus soon with spotlike or appressed squamules from the break-
      ing up of the cuticle .... *P. verna*
3. Pileus at maturity rivulose .... *P. rivulosa*
3. Pileus not as above 4
   4. Pileus evenly dull cinnamon; typically on hardwood —*Alnus and
      Acer* .... *P. occidentalis*
   4. Pileus paler on margin; on conifer debris 5
5. Spores 7–9 × 4–5 μ .... see stirps *Condensa*
5. Spores smaller 6
   6. Pleurocystidia with walls up to 0.5 μ thick .... *P. fulvodisca*
   6. Pleurocystidia with walls about 2 μ thick .... *P. subfulva*

142. Pholiota abruptibulba sp. nov.
Illustrations: Text figs. 302-306.

*Pileus (4)7–9 cm latus, demum late convexus, glutinosus, fulvus. Con-
textus pallide luteus. Lamellae subdecurrentes, pallide luteae, confertae,
latae. Stipes 5–9 cm longus, 10–18 mm crassus, solidus demum cavus,
tactu subfulvus, abruptibulbus. Sporae 5.5–7.5 × 3.5–4 μ. Pleurocystidia
50–92 × 10–18 μ. Caulocystidia voluminosa. Specimen typicum in Herb.
Univ. Mich. conservatum est; legit prope Larch Mt. Oregon, 30 Oct.
1947. Wm. B. Gruber (Smith 28421).*

Pileus (4) 7–9 cm broad, convex with an inrolled margin, becoming
broadly expanded with a decurved margin, disc "ochraceous-tawny," or
a little darker, "pinkish-buff" on the margin, very glutinous, glabrous
except for scattered remains of veil near margin. Context pallid yellowish,
thick; odor and taste not distinctive. (Color of flesh after standing becoming near pinkish buff or paler).

Lamellae broadly adnate-subdecurrent, in age short-decurrent, pale
yellowish, (near "cartridge-buff"), gradually paler and dull brownish,
close to only moderately close, broad, edges soon eroded.

Stipe 5–9 cm long, 10–18 mm thick, equal, solid, becoming hollow,
base with a small abrupt bulb, surface whitish or pale yellowish, stained
a sordid pale-tawny where handled, slightly fibrillose from a thin, pallid
veil.

Spores 5.5–7 (7.5) × 3.5–4 μ, smooth, with a minute pore (under a
1.4 NA obj., in face view oblong to narrowly elliptic, in profile slightly
bean-shaped to nearly oblong, pale cinnamon in KOH, paler and more
ochraceous in Melzer's reagent.

Basidia small, 15–20 × 5–6 μ, 4-spored, narrowly clavate, hyaline to
yellowish in KOH and Melzer's reagent. Pleurocystidia 50–92 × 10–18 μ,

versiform, varying from elliptic-pedicellate (in optical section) to sub-fusoid to utriform or fusoid-ventricose, with yellowish content at least in the broad neck as revived in KOH and near the apex often with rod-shaped to granular-amorphous bodies irregularly distributed, these bodies apparently soluble in Melzer's reagent, content pale yellowish and homo-geneous in Melzer's; the wall thin to slightly thickened (0.5–1 μ) as revived in KOH, but many of them long remaining collapsed, thin-walled as seen in Melzer's sol.; many cystidia are seen to have lateral protrusions or knobs or the cell at times forked. Cheilocystidia 30–50 × 6–12 μ, sub-fusoid to fusoid-ventricose, thin-walled, content homogeneous and color-less in KOH. Caulocystidia scattered, elongate-clavate, 55–90 (110) × 8–20 (25) μ, thin-walled, content homogenous in KOH.

Gill trama a floccose central strand of parallel to somewhat inter-woven hyphae, 4–12 μ broad, the cells short to elongated, thin-walled, yellowish in KOH and smooth, in age the cells considerably in-flated; subhymenium a broad gelatinous zone of interwoven, narrow (2–3 μ) smooth hyaline hyphae. Pileus cutis a thick gelatinous pellicle of narrow gelatinizing hyphae 2–5 μ broad and yellow to hyaline in KOH, walls smooth to incrusted and in age very wrinkled; hypodermium of incrusted ochraceous hyphae (in KOH) with the cells not greatly inflated. Context hyphae broad 8–15 μ, yellow in KOH, walls smooth and thin to only slightly thickened. Clamp connections present. All hyphae in-amyloid.

HABIT, HABITAT, AND DISTRIBUTION: Gregarious beside a conifer log, coll. Wm. B. Gruber (Smith 28421, type) near Larch Mountain, Oregon. Oct. 30, 1947.

OBSERVATIONS: The distinctive features of this species are the small mostly oblong spores, the very small basidia in relation to the giant pleurocystidia, stipe staining pale tawny where handled, and the abruptly bulbous stipe-base. The pleurocystidia are branched frequently enough to suggest that this will eventually probably also be found to be a dis-tinguishing character. An interesting feature is that apparently the cystidial wall swells somewhat on standing in KOH and appears quite pliant, at least many bent cystidia are seen in mounts as compared to no broken ones.

143. Pholiota verna sp. nov.
Illustrations: Text figs. 307-308; 309-310; pl. 66.

Pileus 6–12 cm latus, late convexus, virgatus, viscidus, demum sub-squamulosus, fulvus, ad marginem subluteus. Contextus albus. Lamellae confertae latae, adnatae, albidae demum subfulvae. Stipes 4–6 cm longus, 10–12 mm crassus, aequalis, farctus demum cavus, albidus, deorsum de-mum sordide luteo-brunneus, sursum sericeus. Velum fibrillosum. Sporae 6–7 × 3.5–4 μ. Pleurocystidia crassotunicata, 60–85 × 9–14 μ, flexuosa. Specimen typicum in Herb. Univ. Mich. conservatum est; legit prope

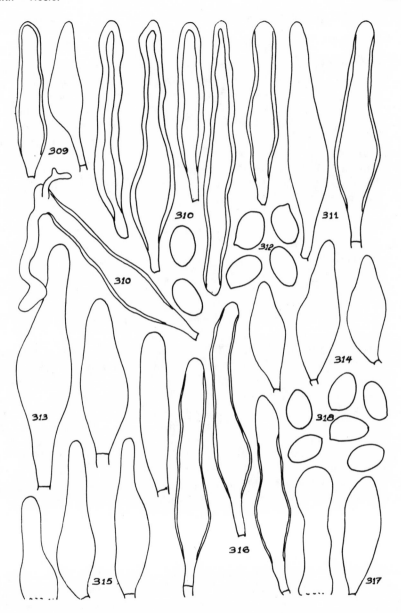

Text Fig. 21.

FIGS. 309 & 310, cheilocystidia and pleurocystidia of *P. verna;* 311-314, pleurocystidia, spores, caulocystidia and cheilocystidia of *P. occidentalis;* 315-318, cheilocystidia, pleurocystidia, cheilocystidia (317) and spores of *P. fulvodisca.*

Oil City, Hoh River, Olympic National Forest, Wash. 7 Mai 1939, Smith 13176.

Pileus 6–12 cm broad, broadly convex becoming plane or with a somewhat wavy turned up margin at maturity, surface virgate beneath a thin gelatinus pellicle, in age the margin often with agglutinated spot-like scales from the broken cuticle (not from veil remnants) color "tawny" on disc (fulvous), paler to the margin, at times whitish at first and decorated with inconspicuous patches of veil remnants. Context thick (5–6 mm near disc), whitish with a watery line above the gills, firm, odor and taste none.

Lamellae close (67–78 reach stipe), broad (8–10 mm), adnate or slightly adnexed, toothed, 2–3 tiers of lamellulae, white when young, near "tawny-olive" (yellow-brown) at maturity, edges even.

Stipe 4–6 cm long, 10–12 mm thick, equal, stuffed, becoming hollow, fleshy, surface white and at first fibrillose from veil, becoming dingy yellowish to bister from the base upward on aging, apex silky and remaining whitish. Annular fibrillose zone left by veil soon evanescent.

Spores 6–7 × 3.5–4 μ, oblong, or ovate or narrowly elliptic in face view, in profile mostly slightly bean-shaped to elliptic, apical pore extremely minute, color in KOH pale tawny, in Melzer's pale tawny but dull and some giving impression of being faintly amyloid, in H_2O mounts when fresh distinctly reddish, wall thin (0.25 μ ±).

Basidia 4-spored, 25–32 × 6–8 μ, clavate, hyaline to ochraceous revived in KOH and in Melzer's sol. Pleurocystidia abundant, 1) 36–50 × 8–12 μ and elliptic to ovate-pedicellate, walls 1–2 μ thick as revived in KOH, content usually yellowish and colloidal. 2) 60–85 × 9–14 μ almost subcylindric-flexuous or somewhat ventricose above the long narrow pedicel, walls as revived in KOH 1–2 μ thick but thickening generally irregular, apex subacute to obtuse, content colloidal and homogeneous, hyaline to ochraceous in KOH, surface smooth or a slight amount of debris adhering. Amyloid debris scattered in a few places along hymenium. Cheilocystidia resembling pleurocystidia but smaller and some enlarged basidioles (?) present. Caulocystidia none.

Gill trama of parallel to slightly interwoven hyphae with cells finally enlarged to 10–20 μ diam., and mostly greatly elongated; walls pale tan to greenish yellow or hyaline as revived in KOH, thin, smooth, rather refractive; subhymenium a conspicuous broad gelatinous band of narrow hyaline branched hyphae. Pileus cutis a pellicle (gelatinous), the hyphae appressed, ochraceous in KOH and more or less incrusted, the cross walls highly refractive in KOH; hypodermial region of floccose more heavily incrusted hyphae 5–12 μ diam. and bright fulvous to orange-fulvous in KOH. Context hyphae, mostly smooth, interwoven, yellowish to yellowish-hyaline in KOH, cells greatly inflated, walls at times up to 1 μ thick in area beneath hypodermium. All hyphae inamyloid. Clamp connections present.

HABIT, HABITAT, AND DISTRIBUTION: Gregarious on debris of *Populus trichocarpa,* Hoh River, Olympic National Forest, Wash., May 7, 1939. Smith 13176, type.

OBSERVATIONS: The greatly elongated flexuous cystidia which are thick-walled as revived in KOH are a most peculiar feature, and exclude the species from *P. lubrica* with which it had been identified in the field. Cystidial features also exclude it from *P. avellaneifolia* and *P. sublubrica* which have generally the same aspect.

In Smith 14692 from the same area the cystidia are less flexuous and more are fusoid-ventricose. It was also collected on debris of cottonwood. When first mounted in KOH most of the cystidia are collapsed and were thin-walled but on standing ten to fifteen minutes they assume their typical shape and show a wall at least thick enough to measure accurately. Many of the cystidia had debris adhering on or around the apex.

144. **Pholiota occidentalis** sp. nov. var. **occidentalis.**
Illustrations: Text figs. 311-314; pl. 67b.

Pileus (2)2.5–6.5 cm latus, late umbonatus, cinnamomeus, viscidus. Lamellae adnatae, angustae, subdistantes, pallidae demum argillaceae. Stipes 3–4 cm longus, 4–8 mm crassus, albidus, deorsum subfulvus. Sporae 5.5–7 × 4–4.5 μ. Pleurocystidia 44–87 × 9–15 μ. Specimen typicum in Herb. Univ. Mich. conservatum est; legit prope Mt. Hood. Ore., 2 Oct. 1944. Smith 19388.

Pileus (2) 2.5–6.5 cm broad, obtuse becoming broadly umbonate, "cinnamon" when young, becoming "pale cinnamon-buff" along the margin, in age often more or less avellaneous over the water-soaked marginal area, glutinous, with fibrillose remains of the veil scattered along the margin, fibrils beneath the gluten finally becoming aggregated to form appressed fascicles. Context thick in the disc, pallid to pale watery buff; odor and taste not distinctive.

Lamellae broadly adnate to almost arcuate or slightly decurrent, white, finally becoming pale clay-color, nearly close to subdistant, 1–2 tiers of lamellae, narrow, broadest near stipe (3–4 mm), edges even.

Stipe 3–4 cm long, 4–8 mm thick, equal, solid, whitish, in age with a cinnamon tinge, more or less silky-fibrillose from the remains of the thin fibrillose veil, in age slightly darker at base (dark sordid brown). Veil white, arachnoid.

Spores 5.5–7 × 4–4.5 μ, smooth, apical pore small but distinct, shape elliptic to subovate in face view, in profile obscurely bean-shaped varying to obscurely inequilateral, color in KOH ochraceous tawny, in Melzer's reagent paler ochraceous; wall thin (about 0.2 μ).

Basidia 18–24 × 5–7 (8) μ, 4-spored, subclavate, hyaline to yellowish in KOH, yellowish in Melzer's sol. Pleurocystidia 44–87 × 9–15 μ, fusoid-ventricose, apex obtuse to subacute, smooth, wall thin or up to 1 μ thick (rarely thicker), content homogeneous, lemon yellow revived in KOH but soon fading, neck often filled with homogeneous colloidal content.

Cheilocystidia 30–50 × 7–14 μ, obtusely fusoid to fusoid-ventricose, varying to subclavate, lemon-yellow in KOH, wall thin and smooth. Caulocystidia 28–80 × (4) 6–14 (18) μ, versiform (cylindric, fusoid, fusoid-
ventricose or subclavate) smooth, walls thin to slightly thickened, yellowish in KOH to nearly hyaline, content homogeneous.

Gill trama of a central region of parallel hyphae, or in age somewhat
interwoven, the cells becoming inflated, walls smooth, thin, pale yellow
in KOH; subhymenium gelatinous, of narrow (2–3 μ) hyphae in subparallel to interwoven arrangement. Pileus cutis a thick gelatinous
pellicle with narrow (2–2.5 μ) yellowish hyphae dispersed widely in it,
the hyphal walls smooth to slightly encrusted, in age many reticulated
or creased transversely; hypodermial zone of floccose narrow hyphae 3–8
μ with rusty brown walls smooth or with slight incrustations. Context
hyphae inflated, with smooth thin yellowish to greenish-yellow walls.
Clamp connections present. All hyphae inamyloid.

HABIT, HABITAT, AND DISTRIBUTION: On alder branches and debris
but also on conifer wood, Pacific Northwest, September—October.

OBSERVATIONS: This is a small pale cinnamon species very common
on the remains of alder and other hardwoods in the Pacific Northwest.
The flesh is pallid, and the lamellae, veil, and stipe are white. It appears
related to P. subfulva and P. decorata. The color (ochraceous tawny) of
the spores in KOH is unusual in this group, and the pleurocystidia often
have the thickened wall almost obscured by the content of the cell which
has about the same index of refraction. Broken cystidia with the content
escaped are best for measuring wall thickness.

MATERIAL EXAMINED: (on alder): OREGON: Smith 19239, 19239a,
19388 (type). On conifer wood); IDAHO: Smith 23531, 44311, 44340,
44341, 44485, 46594, 47117, 47117a, 53886, 55223, 58470, 58521, 58631,
58690, 68820, 69620, 70091, 70261, 73316, 73582, 73588, 73662, 73959,
73977, 74070. OREGON: Smith 23669, 23916, 23975, 24005, 27374.
WASHINGTON: Smith 16727, 30627, 30731.

144a. Pholiota occidentalis var. luteifolia var. nov.

*Pileus 2.5(6) cm latus, convexus, viscidus, minute squamulosus
glabrescens, cinnamomeus. Lamellae pallide luteae latae, adnatae, confertae vel subdistantes. Stipes 2.5–6 cm longus, 3–6 mm crassus, sursum
pallidus, deorsum fulvus. Vellum pallidum. Sporae 6–7 × 3.5–4 μ. Specimen typicum in Herb. Univ. of Mich. conservatum est; legit prope Upper
Priest Lake, Boundary Co., Idaho. 13 Oct. 1966. Smith 74169.*

Pileus 2–5 (6) cm broad, convex with an incurved margin, expanding to plane or slightly depressed, thinly slimy and at first with minute
squamules of veil remnants which are soon removed, at times finally
more or less areolate, tawny cinnamon on disc, pallid to yellowish pallid
on margin in age, margin at first fringed with pallid fibrils from the veil.

Context pliant, watery brownish, odor and taste not distinctive, $FeSO_4$ slowly olivaceous.

Lamellae pale yellow when immature, dull cinnamon when mature, close to nearly subdistant, broad, broadly adnate to short decurrent, thin, edges even.

Stipe 2.5–6 cm long, 3–6 mm thick, stuffed, equal, pallid above, becoming rusty cinnamon from the base upward, veil thin, fibrillose, pallid, leaving scattered fibrils on the stipe.

Spores 6–7 × 3.5–4 μ, smooth, with scarcely any sign of an apical pore (very minute); shape in face view elliptic to ovate, in profile obscurely bean-shaped to obscurely inequilateral, wall about 0.25 μ thick; pale dull cinnamon in KOH, in Melzer's reagent no appreciable change.

Basidia 16–25 × 6–7.5 μ, 4-spored, clavate many yellow in KOH from a colored content. Pleurocystidia 50–70 × 10–16 μ fusoid-ventricose, content as revived in KOH yellow, walls up to 1 μ thick in ventricose part in many of the individuals, some with adhering material near the base of the neck. Cheilocystidia similar to the pleurocystidia but shorter. Caulocystidia up to 20 μ broad, clavate to vesiculose or fusoid-ventricose, yellow to hyaline, walls thin or some with thickened walls in pedicel, content hyaline to yellowish, granular in apex in some.

Gill trama with a central area of parallel to subparallel hyphae with thin smooth walls hyaline in KOH, cells finally considerably inflated; subhymenium gelatinous, of narrow, branched hyphae. Pileus cutis a gelatinous pellicle of ochraceous encrusted hyphae 3–5 μ diam. with outlines very distinct; hypodermium of bright ochraceous fulvous hyphae in KOH, the walls somewhat roughened and cells more or less enlarged. Context hyphae hyaline to greenish-hyaline in KOH, closely arranged, walls thin and smooth. Clamp connections present.

HABIT, HABITAT, AND DISTRIBUTION: On conifer slash, Upper Priest River, Boundary County, Idaho. Oct. 13, 1966. Smith 74169, type.

OBSERVATIONS: This poses a problem recurring throughout the subgenera *Flammuloides* and *Pholiota*: Namely variants distinguished by the presence of yellow pigment in some part of the basidiocarp in species not normally having it. This situation caused confusion between *P. lenta* and *P. gummosa* in North America. We found it in *P. terrestris* in 1947 and 1966, in *P. occidentalis* as described here, and the degree to which yellow is evident in the *P. spumosa* complex causes confusion there. Its development may also be associated with partial sterility as we have noted many times in *Naematoloma*.

145. Pholiota rivulosa sp. nov.

Pileus 2–5 cm latus ,convexus, glaber, viscidus, demum rivulosus, cinnamomeus; lamellae pallide luteae, latae, subdistantes; stipes 2–4 cm longus, 3–6 mm crassus, pallidus, deorsum demum subcinnamomeus, sporae 6–7.5 × 3.5–4.2 μ; pleurocystidia 54–78 × 8–12(15) μ, crassotuni-

cata, anguste fusoide ventricosa. Specimen typicum in Herb. Univ. Mich. conservatum est; legit prope Payette Lakes, Idaho. 6 June 1954. Smith 44318.

Pileus 2–5 cm broad, convex becoming broadly convex, glabrous, viscid to thinly glutinous, dark to pale cinnamon color, the margin near pale pinkish buff, on aging the entire surface rivulose to rimulose but this not showing in the dried specimens. Context thin, pliant, pallid, odor and taste not distinctive.

Lamellae broad, adnate, subdistant, yellowish when young, dingy tawny as spores mature, edges even.

Stipe short, 2–4 cm long, 3–6 mm thick, equal pallid over all at first but soon dingy cinnamon from the base up in age (finally colored to some extent over all), as dried dingy yellowish to pallid over all, veil thin and fibrillose.

Spores 6–7.5 × 3.5–4.2 μ, smooth, apical pore not visible in most spores, shape in face view ovate to elliptic, in profile obscurely inequilateral to subelliptic; color in KOH dull cinnamon, paler in Melzer's sol.; wall less than 0.25 μ thick.

Basidia 4-spored, 17–20 × 6–7 μ, clavate, hyaline in KOH. Pleurocystidia abundant, 54–78 × 8–12 (15) μ, narrowly fusoid-ventricose with a long neck and subacute to obtuse apex, smooth, wall thickened to 1–2 μ in the neck, content yellow in KOH (or hyaline) and typically homogeneous throughout. Cheilocystidia similar to pleurocystidia but smaller (walls often ± 1 μ thick).

Gill trama of a central strand of parallel hyphae with smooth refractive walls up to 0.5 μ thick, the cells elongate and inflated mostly near the septa, pale ochraceous brown to nearly hyaline as revived in KOH; subhymenium a gelatinous layer of hyphae 3–5 μ diam., smooth and hyaline in KOH. Pileus cutis a pellicle of narrow (2–4 μ) hyphae with distinct outlines but in a gelatinous matrix, walls of hyphae incrusted; hypodermium of dull rusty to cinnamon non-gelatinous hyphae smooth or with incrustations. Context of closely arranged yellowish-hyaline (in KOH) hyphae with smooth walls, the cells inflated to 10–15 μ at maturity. Clamp connections present.

HABIT, HABITAT, AND DISTRIBUTION: Gregarious to caespitose on conifer duff and rotten conifer logs, Pacific Northwest. Type: Smith 44313, type, also 23552, 23526.

OBSERVATIONS: Old specimens are immediately recognizable because of the rivulose pileus, an unusual feature in *Pholiota*. Young specimens, can be distinguished from *P. occidentalis* var. *occidentalis* by the pale yellow gills.

P. occidentalis var. *luteifolia* has pleurocystidia with thinner walls and conspicuous caulocystidia.

146. Pholiota fulvodisca sp. nov.

Illustrations: Text figs. 315–318.

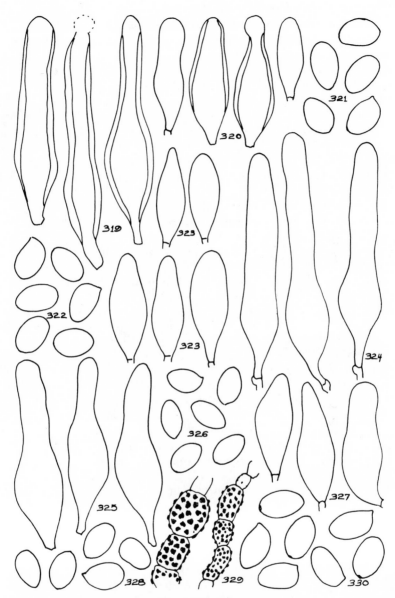

Text Fig. 22.

Figs. 319-321, pleurocystidia, cheilocystidia and spores of *P. subfulva;* 322-324, spores, cheilocystidia and pleurocystidia of *P. carbonaria;* 325-327, pleurocystidia, spores, and cheilocystidia of *P. brunnescens;* 328 & 329, spores and cells from hypodermium of pileus of *P. fulvozonata;* 330, spores of *P. highlandensis.*

Pileus 2–4 cm latus, demum late convexus, viscidulus saepe virgatus, ad centrum sordide argillaceus, ad marginem pallide subluteus. Contextus albus. Lamellae adnato-emarginatae, pallidae demum subcinnamomeae, latae, confertae. Stipes 2–4 cm longus, 7–12 mm crassus, aequalis, solidus, deorsum fulvus, sursum pallidus, deorsum fibrillosus vel subsquamulosus. Sporae 5.5–7(7.5) × 3.5–4.5 μ leves. Pleurocystidia 50–72 × 8–16 μ, fusoide ventricosa. Specimen typicum in Herb. Univ. Mich. conservatum est; legit prope McCall, Idaho, 13 Aug. 1912. Smith 65898.

Pileus 2–4 cm broad, convex, expanding to plane or nearly so, disc clay-color to pale tawny, margin near "cartridge-buff" (pale yellow) slightly viscid but soon dry, more or less fibrillose streaked (virgate) with tawny fibrils and at first the margin fringed with remains of the whitish fibrillose veil. Context white, firm, thick; odor and taste not distinctive. FeSO$_4$ instantly bright green.

Lamellae adnate becoming adnexed, pallid, finally becoming pale dingy cinnamon, broad, close, edges even.

Stipe 2–4 cm long, 7–12 mm thick, equal, solid to tubular, fleshy, dingy rusty brown in base, whitish above, surface whitish and silky above, brownish and fibrillose to subsquamulose below. Veil arachnoid, white.

Spores 5.5–7 (7.5) × 3.5–4.5 μ, smooth, apical pore minute; shape in face view ovate to elliptic, in profile obscurely inequilateral to subelliptic; color in KOH, rusty cinnamon becoming paler on standing, in Melzer's reagent soon dingy ochraceous, wall about 0.25 μ thick.

Basidia 20–26 × 5–6.5 μ, 4-spored, clavate, hyaline to yellowish in KOH and in Melzer's more yellowish. Pleurocystidia 50–72 × 8–16 μ, fusoid-ventricose to (rarely) rather narrowly ventricose, neck often flexuous, apex subacute to (rarely) capitate, wall thin or up to 0.5 μ thick, content ochraceous in KOH becoming paler on standing, often with rod-like particles in interior near apex. Cheilocystidia smaller than pleurocystidia and more often capitate (at times ninepine-shaped), usually ochraceous in KOH. Caulocystidia none.

Gill trama with a central floccose strand of hyaline to ochraceous or pale tan hyphae parallel and with thin smooth walls, cells short to elongated and 5–10 μ broad before inflation; subhymenium of hyaline gelatinous hyphae subparallel in arrangement, 3–5 μ diam., walls smooth. Pileus cutis a thin layer of hyphae imbedded in a gelatinous matrix, hyphae 3–5 μ diam., pale yellow to hyaline revived in KOH, wall smooth to asperulate; hypodermium of ochraceous to rusty floccose hyphae 4–10 μ diam., with encrusted walls. Content hyphae with cells inflated to 20 μ or more, walls thin smooth and weakly yellowish in KOH. All hyphae inamyloid. Clamp connections present.

HABIT, HABITAT, AND DISTRIBUTION: On conifer duff, near McCall, Idaho, Aug. 13, 1962, Smith 65898, type.

OBSERVATIONS: This species is close to *P. spumosa* but lacks caulocystidia, grew on duff, has a thinner pellicle covering the pileus, and pallid gills when young. It is closest to *P. subfulva* but the pleurocystidia have thinner walls, the $FeSO_4$ reaction is bright green rather than dark olive, and its spores are a darker brown in KOH.

147. Pholiota subfulva (Pk.) comb. nov.

Flammula subfulva Peck, New York State Mus. Ann. Rept. 41: 68. 1888.
Gymnopilus subfulvus (Pk.) Murrill, North Amer. Flora 10: 204. 1917.
Illustrations: Text figs. 319-321.

Pileus 3–6.5 cm broad, convex, sordid tawny to rusty, marginal portion pallid or yellowish and appressed-scaly, the scales darker, viscid, fibrillose with fugacious veil-remnants on the margin. Context grayish white; odor and taste not distinctive.

Lamellae adnate, white or pallid, becoming brownish ochraceous, close, thin, medium broad.

Stipe 5–7.5 cm long, 4–8 mm thick, whitish to pale yellowish, apex pruinose, the base staining rusty in age, more or less fibrillose-scaly, solid. Veil buff or yellowish white, copious, forming an evanescent fibrillose ring.

Spores 6–7.5 × 4–4.5 μ, smooth, apical pore absent to very minute. Shape in face view elliptic to ovate, in profile obscurely bean-shaped to somewhat inequilateral, color revived in KOH pale golden tawny to ochraceous tawny, in Melzer's reagent paler ochraceous tawny to dull pale ochraceous; wall about 0.25 μ thick.

Basidia 4-spored, 18–24 × 5–6.5 μ, narrowly clavate, yellowish in KOH and in Melzer's reagent. Pleurocystidia abundant 50–75 × 8–12 (15) μ, fusoid-ventricose with obtuse apex, outline of neck often flexuous to almost contorted, smooth or with some adhering gelatinous material, wall thick in ventricose portion ($\pm$ 2 μ), thinning out in neck, neck filled with a plug of hyaline to ochraceous homogeneous material, some of this in some cells extruded in the form of a cap over apex of the cell, walls hyaline to yellowish in KOH. Cheilocystidia subcylindric to fusoid ventricose, 28–46 (55) × 7–12 μ, walls thickened in most, with mucilaginous adhering material in many and content mostly ochraceous in KOH. Caulocystidia present at apex of stipe, 40–60 × 10–16 μ, scattered, elliptic-pedicellate to fusoid-ventricose, walls thin to somewhat thickened. Cheilocystidium-like cells also present in the cauohymenium.

Gill trama with a central strand of floccose-interwoven hyphae yellowish in KOH, thin-walled, smooth and hyphal cells greatly inflated; subhymenium a gelatinous layer of narrow interwoven hyphae hyaline to faintly yellowish revived in KOH. Pileus cutis a gelatinous pellicle of narrow (2–5 μ) encrusted hyphae, in age the collapsing hyphae transversely crinkled or creased; hypodermial region of tawny floccose hyphae 4–12 μ (or more) in diam., the incrustations as annular zones, plates etc., and ochraceous tawny in KOH. Context hyphae thin-walled mostly smooth, walls hyaline to yellowish in KOH, cells greatly inflated at times. Clamp connections present. All hyphae inamyloid.

HABIT, HABITAT, AND DISTRIBUTION: More or less caespitose, around the base of trees, or on rotten wood (logs etc.) New York. Type studied; one collection on conifer duff known from Idaho.

OBSERVATIONS: This species, based on our study of the type, has distinctly thick-walled pleurocystidia, pale ochraceous tawny to ochraceous spores as revived in KOH, distinctly incrusted pellicular hyphae, hypodermial hyphae distinctly incrusted and floccose (not gelatinous), and a pileus with appressed squamules. *P. fulvodisca* has the spores rusty cinnamon in KOH, pleurocystidia thin-walled or walls up to about 0.5 μ thick, and particles of refractive debris (as rods or granules) in the neck near the apex of the pleurocystidium. Smith 70261 is from conifer duff. French Creek Grade, Salmon River, Idaho, Sept. 6, 1964. It has the flexuous thick-walled (1–2 μ thick) pleurocystidia of the type. This is evidence to extend the range of the species westward and associate it clearly with a coniferous substratum.

Sect. **Carbonicola** sect. nov.

Ad terram adustam, carbones etc.; pileus viscidus; pleurocystidia conspicua.

Typus *P. fulvozonata.*

This is an ecological grouping of species very similar morphologically. It is now thought that species with this habitat require a high concentration of minerals to induce fruiting—such as released from burned wood. The characters of the section are the habitat in addition to those defining the subgenus. Singer (1963) placed *P. carbonaria* Smith, which has a red veil, in his section *Subflammentes* but for this section described the veil as pale colored "not rusty brown, ochraceous brown nor bright yellow, red etc." We do not know his type species, *P. subflammans* (Speg.) Singer, but assume it does not have a colored veil. We exclude from section *Subflammantes P. carbonaria* Smith. Sect. *Subflammantes* is probably identical with Sect. *Adiposae* of our work. We have not studied the type.

Key

1. Veil in young specimens red to rusty brown or cinnamon 2
1. Veil bright yellow, pallid or absent 4
    2. Veil ferruginous red .... *P. carbonaria*
    2. Veil russet to cinnamon 3
3. Taste mild; veil russet .... *P. fulvozonata*
3. Taste very disagreeable; veil pale cinnamon .... *P. subsaponacea*
    4. Lamellae ochre yellow; pileus bay red both when fresh and when dried .... *P. luteobadia*
    4. Not as above 5
5. Stipe 5–10 mm thick 6

5. Stipe 1.5–4 (5) mm thick; veil pallid at first .... *P. highlandensis*
6. Pileus pale buff young; veil orange brown on aging .... *P. molesta*
6. Pileus dark yellow-brown; veil lemon yellow young ....
.... *P. brunnescens*

148. **Pholiota carbonaria** A. H. Smith, Mycologia 36: 253. 1944.
Pholiota carbonicola Singer, Agar. Mod. Tax. p. 543. 1963.
Illustrations: Text figs. 322-324; pl. 68.

Pileus 2–4 cm broad, convex with an incurved margin beautifully appendiculate with remains of the veil, expanding to plane or with slight umbo, rarely the disc slightly depressed, "warm-buff" to "antimony-yellow" young, becoming darker and finally nearly cinnamon-brown in age on the disc, the margin remaining paler, surface viscid, covered at first by concentric rows of small nearly "hazel" or "ferruginous" fibrillose scales, more or less glabrescent. Context watery brown, thick in the disc; odor and taste not distinctive.

Lamellae bluntly adnate, narrow, crowded, equal, white to grayish when young, becoming nearly snuff-brown at maturity, edges slightly crenulate.

Stipe 3–6 cm long, 4–6 mm thick, equal, somewhat compressed or terete, fibrous, dingy watery yellowish within, solid, becoming tubular at least in apical region, surface covered by small "hazel" to "ferruginous" fibrillose squamules from the remains of the veil, squamules often recurved, ground yellowish but darkening slightly below, apex pruinose.

Spores (5) 6–7 (8) × 3.5–4 (4.5) μ, smooth, apical pore present but apex not truncate; shape in face view elliptic to ovate, in profile sub-elliptic to obscurely inequilateral; color tawny in H_2O mounts fresh, revived in KOH cinnamon-brown, in Melzer's reagent paler cinnamon; wall about 0.3 μ thick.

Basidia 18–23 × 6–7 μ, 4-spored, clavate, yellowish to hyaline in KOH or Melzer's reagent. Pleurocystidia abundant, 50–88 × 9–14 μ, fusoid ventricose with obtuse or rarely subcapitate apices, when fresh some with adhering amorphous material around the apex, smooth in KOH, hyaline or with yellowish content in the neck or throughout, thin-walled, rarely the apex forked (in Smith 54261) ; cheilocystidia abundant, 25–47 × 7–13 μ, clavate to subfusoid or obscurely fusoid ventricose, walls ochraceous in KOH, smooth or some slightly incrusted. Caulocystidia none.

Gill trama hyaline, interwoven, floccose, some sections showing a slight gelatinization of the subhymenium. Pileus trama floccose-interwoven and yellowish hyaline in KOH. Hypodermium rusty brown. Cuticle gelatinous, hyaline to yellowish, of interwoven hyphae 2–3.5 μ in diameter. Clamp connections present. All hyphae inamyloid.

HABIT, HABITAT, AND DISTRIBUTION: On burned soil and exposed roots, rarely on manure-heaps, Washington, Oregon, California, and Idaho, summer, autumn, and early winter.

OBSERVATIONS: The distinctive mark of this species is the fiery red or ferruginous veil, which, in age, fades to ochraceous, leaves fibrillose squamules on the stipe, and is appendiculate on the pileus margin. The lamellae are narrow and whitish to grayish when young.

A collection from England by Smith (63165, MICH) is close; in it the veil-remnants form orange-tawny squamules on the stipe. Further collections of it might prove it to be a form of *P. carbonaria*. The name *P. carbonicola* Singer was based on conversations Singer had with Smith who admitted that he had first intended to publish the species as *P. carbonicola*. It is doubtful, in a strict interpretation of the International Rules, if the change to *carbonicola* from *carbonaria*, as finally published by Singer, is now justifiable. At any rate, Peck's species epithet *highlandensis* is available for the fungus commonly known in the past as *Flammula carbonaria*.

MATERIAL EXAMINED: CALIFORNIA: White 575 (MICH); Smith 3638, 3773, 9003, 9386, 9446, 9500, (type). IDAHO: Smith 44428, 44458, 44906, 45336, 45485, 46021, 46022, 53888, 54261, 55314, 68196; OREGON: Sipe 918 (MICH); Smith 3406, 3418, 3616, 9342; WASHINGTON: Smith 17998, 18019, 48364, 48449. Stuntz and Isaacs (Stuntz 1587).

149. Pholiota fulvozonata sp. nov.
Illustrations: Text figs. 328-329; 331.

Pileus 1–2 cm crassus, conicus demum late conicus vel convexus, saepe-umbonatus, viscidus, fulvo-squamulosus, ad centrum pallide fulvus, ad marginem pallidus. Contextus pallidus, cartilagineus, cum FeSO$_4$ viridis; sapor mitis. Lamellae pallidae, confertae adnatae. Stipes 1–2 cm longus, 3–4 mm crassus, deorsum attenuatus, pallidus, conspicue fulvozonatus. Sporae 6–7 × 4–4.5 μ. Pleurocystidia 33–46 × 9–16 μ conspicua, fusoide ventricosa. Specimen typicum legit prope Upper Priest Lake, Boundary County, Idaho, Oct. 3, 1966. Smith 73887 (Mich).

Pileus 1–2 cm broad, conic expanding to broadly conic or conic campanulate, surface tawny on disc and pallid on margin, viscid pellicle tough and separable, surface covered with superficial dark russet squamules representing the remains of the outer veil, slowly glabrescent. Context pallid, pliant, odor and taste not distinctive, with FeSO$_4$ quickly green.

Lamellae pallid becoming dull cinnamon, crowded, broadly adnate, edges even and pallid.

Stipe 1–2 cm long, 3–4 mm thick, narrowed downward, solid, ground color pallid but so densely covered by concentric zones of dark russet veil material as to almost obscure the ground color except at apex.

Spores 6–7.5 × 4–4.5 μ, with a minute apical pore; shape in face view ovate to elliptic, in profile elliptic to obscurely inequilateral; color

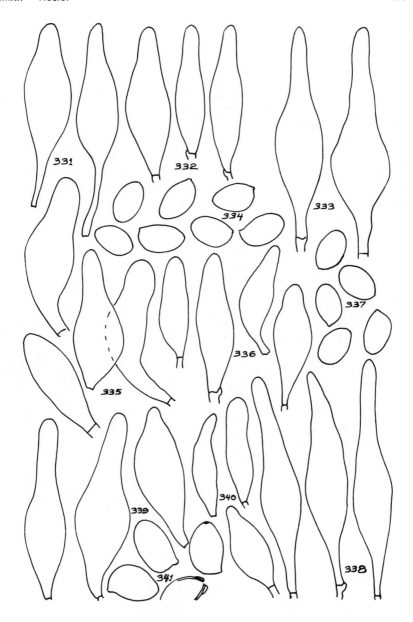

Text Fig. 23.

Figs. 331, pleurocystidia of *P. fulvozonata;* 332-335, cheilocystidia, pleurocystidia, spores and caulocystidia of *P. highlandensis;* 336-338, cheilocystidia, spores and pleurocystidia of *P. saponacea;* 339-341, pleurocystidia, cheilocystidia and spores of *P. sphagnicola.*

in KOH cinnamon brown, paler and brighter rusty brown in Melzer's reagent, wall about 0.25 μ thick.

Basidia 4-spored, 18–24 × 5–7 μ, clavate, hyaline to pale yellow in KOH. Pleurocystidia abundant, 33–46 × 9–16 μ, fusoid-ventricose to utriform (apex rounded in some), thin-walled, yellowish in KOH, content "colloidal" but merely yellowish in Melzer's reagent, hyaline when fresh, smooth. Cheilocystidia similar to pleurocystidia. Caulocystidia scattered near stipe apex, similar to pleurocystidia or larger.

Gill trama of a central area of parallel hyaline hyphae (in KOH) with elongated cells, walls of hyphae smooth and thin; subhymenium of gelatinous hyphae 2–3 μ diam. in a rather interwoven arrangement. Pileus cutis a tangled mass of loosely arranged narrow (2–3 μ) hyaline to yellowish hyphae imbedded in slime, at the surface the hyphae more appressed, more highly ochraceous and somewhat incrusted; hypodermium of bright orange-brown (in KOH) interwoven hyphae, walls rough or smooth, conspicuously ornamented where intergrading with the cutis. Context hyphae yellow to hyaline in KOH, closely interwoven. Veil hyphae with brown to ochraceous walls in KOH, often encrusted, many hyphae consisting of chains of short to subglobose cells—but not sphaerocyst-like. Clamp connections present.

HABIT, HABITAT, AND DISTRIBUTION: Gregarious on burned (partially) chip dirt. Upper Priest Lake, Boundary County, Idaho. Oct. 3, 1966. Smith 73887, type.

OBSERVATIONS: This species is closely related to *P. carbonaria* Smith but differs in the veil being russet instead of red, and the pileus darker in color.

One collection by Kauffman, Lake Quinault, Washington, Nov. 4, 1925, probably belongs here. He identified it as *P. terrestris*. As dried the fruit bodies have the stature of *P. carbonaria* Smith i.e., stipe 2–5 cm long and 2–2.5 mm thick. The pilei are pale tan on the disc and pale yellow on the margin, and a few show minute patches of fulvous veil material. The gills are broad, close, adnate and yellowish as dried. The stipe is yellowish above and dingy pale tan below but clearly shows the fulvous particles or patches that are the remnants of the veil. The spores are cinnamon in KOH, 6–7.5 × 4–4.5 μ and oval in face view, with a very minute pore. The pleurocystidia are 55–75 × 9–15 μ, and vary from utriform (with rounded, broad apex), to merely obtuse or subcapitate, tapered to a blunt point at the tip of the swollen portion. The pellicle is of the slimy type, thick and with hyphae widely dispersed in a gelatinous matrix. It was found on soil at the base of a stump.

In the type, the specimens were from chip dirt partly burned. On Kauffman's collection there is no charred material. Hence the species is keyed both ways in this work.

150. Pholiota subsaponacea sp. nov.
Illustrations: Text figs. 336-338; pl. 69b.

Pileus 1–3 cm latus, late convexus, demum planus vel subdepressus, glutinosus, glaber, subbadius. Contextus cartilagineus, brunneolus; odor nullus, sapor subsaponaceo-farinaceus, cum FeSO₄ olivaceo. Lamellae albae demum cinnamomeae, confertae, latae, adnatae. Stipes 1.5–3 cm longus, 3–6 mm crassus, equalis, cavus, dersum demum fulvus, sursum albus et pruinosus. Vellum sordide pallide cinnamomeum. Sporae 6–7.5 × 3.5–4.2 μ. Pleurocystidia 54–70 × 9–14 μ, fusoide ventricosa. Specimen typicum in Herb. Mich. conservatum est., legit prope Upper Priest Lake, Boundary Co., Idaho, 11 Oct. 1966. Smith 74095.

Pileus 1–3 cm broad, broadly convex with an inrolled margin, expanding to plane or slightly depressed, surface glutinous, glabrous, bay brown (pale to dark). Context pliant, watery brownish, odor none; taste very disagreeable (somewhat soapy farinaceous), with $FeSO_4$ olivaceus.

Lamellae whitish becoming dull cinnamon, close to crowded, moderately broad, thin, adnate becoming adnexed; edges even, pallid.

Stipe 1.5–3 cm long, 3–6 mm thick, equal, hollow, soon rusty over the base (but not within), coated up to the apical veil zone with a dull cinnamon sheath which breaks up into patches, apex whitish and pruinose.

Spores 6–7.5 × 3.5–4.2 μ, minute pore present at apex; shape in face view elliptic to slightly ovate, some nearly oblong, in profile elliptic to obscurely inequilateral; dull cinnamon brown in both KOH and Melzer's sol.; wall about 0.25 μ thick.

Basidia 4-spored, 20–36 × 5–6 (7) μ, narrowly clavate, hyaline in KOH. Pleurocystidia abundant, 54–70 × 9–14 μ, fusoid-ventricose with long narrow pedicels, content hyaline to yellowish in KOH, coagulated content not distinctively colored, walls thin and hyaline. Cheilocystidia 26–38 × 8–12 μ, mostly fusoid-ventricose with obtuse apex, content colloidal but not distinctively colored in KOH or Melzer's, walls thin and hyaline. Caulocystidia 55–70 × 9–12 μ scattered, hyaline, thin-walled, smooth, apex obtuse to slightly rounded.

Gill trama, an area of hyaline thin walled narrow parallel hyphae with some oleiferous hyphae scattered through it; subhymenium a gelatinous layer of narrow hyphae 2–4 μ diam. Pileus cutis a thick layer of widely spaced narrow (2–3 μ) hyphae with yellow slightly incrusted walls as revived in KOH (possibly a trichodermium in very young material); area next to hypodermium of narrow non-gelatinous hyphae with rather coarse incrustations; hypodermium proper of closely packed orange-brown (in KOH) incrusted hyphae with some cells up to 12 μ or more in diam. Context yellow to hyaline in FeSO₄, closely arranged and with thin smooth walls. Clamp connections present.

HABIT, HABITAT, AND DISTRIBUTION: Gregarious on burned areas, Upper Priest Lake region, Boundary County, Idaho. 11 Oct. 1966. Smith 74095, type.

OBSERVATIONS: The very disagreeable persistent taste along with the dull cinnamon veil distinguish it from *P. fulvozonata, P. brunnescens,* and *P. highlandensis.*

151. Pholiota luteobadia sp. nov.

Pileus 8–20 mm latus, late convexus, glaber, glutinosus, badiorubrus; contextus luteus; lamellae luteae, angustae, confertae; stipes 1–2.5 cm longus, 1–1.5 mm crassus, luteus, subfibrillosus. Sporae 6–7.5 × 3.8–4.2 μ; pleurocystidia 48–75 × 10–15 μ subacuta; cheilocystidia 33–55 × 8–16 μ, clavata, submucronata vel fusoide ventricosa et ad apicem obtusa. Specimen typicum in Herb. Univ. Mich. conservatum est; legit prope Wilderness Point State Park, Emmet Co., Mich. 24 Sept. 1953. Smith 43222.

Pileus 8–20 mm broad, broadly convex with an inrolled margin, surface glabrous, slimy, dark bay red over all and remaining this color in drying. Context yellowish, thin, pliant, odor and taste not recorded.

Lamellae narrow close, adnate, ochre yellow and retaining much of this color in drying.

Stipe 1–2.5 cm long, 1–1.5 mm thick, equal, yellowish and drying with a yellow tone, veil rudimentary, stipe surface at maturity merely with a thin coating of fibrils, darkening only slightly at the base.

Spores 6–7.5 × 3.8–4.2 μ, smooth, apical pore minute; shape in face view elliptic to narrowly ovate, in profile elliptic to oblong; color in KOH dark cinnamon, in Melzer's reagent paler; wall about 0.25 μ thick.

Basidia 16–20 × 5–6 μ, yellow in KOH, fading to hyaline, 4-spored, clavate. Pleurocystidia abundant, 48–64 (75) × 10–15 μ, fusoid ventricose with subacute to obtuse apex, rarely branched, walls thin, content homogeneous and yellow to hyaline. Cheilocystidia abundant, 33–55 × 8–16 μ clavate to utriform or merely fusoid-ventricose.

Gill trama of a central area of parallel non-gelatinous smooth hyphae yellowish in KOH becoming hyaline, the walls smooth and the cells not greatly inflated (all young) ; subhymenium a very narrow subcellar zone of hyphal cells (1–2 deep) possibly subgelatinous (very slightly refractive in KOH). Pileus cutis a very thick pellicle of gelatinous ochraceous often incrusted hyphae 2–3 μ diam., loosely interwoven; hypodermium bright ferruginous, the hyphae heavily incrusted but hyphae not (yet) greatly enlarged. Context of yellowish then hyaline thin-walled closely interwoven hyphae. Clamp connections present.

HABIT, HABITAT, AND DISTRIBUTION: Gregarious in a burned area, Wilderness Park, Mich., Emmet Co., Sept. 24, 1953. Smith 43222, type.

OBSERVATIONS: This is a distinctive species both in the field and in the herbarium by virtue of the dark red pileus and yellow gills and stipe. Of the microscopic features the very weak development of a subhymenium appears significant, but old specimens have not been available for study.

152. Pholiota molesta sp. nov.
Illustrations: Pls. 7a, 70b.

Pileus 2–4 cm latus, late convexus, pallide luteolus ("pale pinkish-buff"), viscidus. Lamellae pallidae angustae, confertae. Stipes 3–7 cm longus, 5–10 mm crassus, subalbidus, fibrillosus. Sporae 5.5–6.5(7.5) × 3.5–4 μ. Pleurocystidia 45–66(70) × 8–12(16) μ in ligno semiusto. Specimen typicum in Herb. Univ. Mich. conservatum est; legit prope McCall, Idaho. 23 Juni 1962, Smith 65008.

Pileus 2–4 cm broad, broadly convex with an incurved margin which for a time is fringed with a thin layer of veil remnants, "pale pinkish-buff" overall (young), developing a reddish or brownish flush in age, thinly glutinous, glabrous except for minute veil particles or fibrils near margin, somewhat virgate. Context white; odor mild, taste fungoid. KOH slowly orange-yellowish, $FeSO_4$—no reaction.

Lamellae adnate, pallid like pileus, becoming cinnamon-buff to wood-brown, crowded, narrow, edges even and concolorous.

Stipe 3–7 cm long, 5–10 mm thick, surface at first whitish-fibrillose overall and whitish beneath the fibrils, equal or narrowed downward, solid, watery pallid within, cortex whitish, not discoloring below, the fibrillose (veil) layer separating into zones or patches and becoming a dingy brownish orange, terminating as a faint annular zone, white and silky above the zone.

Spores 5.5–6.5 (7.5) × 3.5–4 μ, smooth, no apical pore present, in face view elliptic to ovate, in profile somewhat inequilateral, ventral line nearly straight as seen in optical section, dorsal line humped toward apiculate end or merely convex, wall about 0.3 μ thick, color in KOH dull cinnamon to dull tawny, in Melzer's reagent pale tawny.

Basidia 4-spored, 24–30 × 4.5–6 μ, hyaline in KOH, pale yellowish in Melzer's reagent. Pleurocystidia abundant, 45–66 (70) × 8–12 (16) μ, fusoid-ventricose with subacute to obtuse apex, wall thin smooth and hyaline, content homogeneous and hyaline, rarely with yellow to brown content. Cheilocystidia 28–45 × 8–15 μ, clavate to subfusoid or fusoid-ventricose, walls thin smooth and hyaline, content homogeneous and hyaline. Caulocystidia none found.

Gill trama of a central area of more or less parallel floccose hyphae hyaline or nearly so in KOH; hyphae 4–6 μ broad before cells inflate, walls thin to slightly thickened ("double"); subhymenium a distinctly differentiated layer of gelatinous hyphae. Pileus cuticle a thick gelatinous pellicle of hyphae 2–5 μ diam. walls smooth to roughened, hyaline to yellowish in KOH; hypodermium a layer of floccose hyphae with bright orange-rusty walls in KOH, walls mostly smooth. Context hyphae with thin to slightly thickened "double" walls, smooth, cells inflated. Clamp connections present. All hyphae inamyloid.

HABIT, HABITAT, AND DISTRIBUTION: On burned area, Idaho, June. Smith 65008, type.

OBSERVATIONS: The distinctive characters of this species include the pale pinkish-buff young pileus which develops a reddish or brownish flush, the short thick stipe the white veil which becomes dingy brownish orange, and the separation of the veil into zones or patches on the stipe. These features distinguish it from other carbon-inhabiting species. The pale pileus of immature basidiocarps is the best feature for distinguishing the species from *P. highlandensis* in the field, and the lack of caulocystidia will distinguish it in the herbarium. Since in most *Pholiota* species the stipe darkens at the base we believe more observations on this non-darkening species are desirable.

153. Pholiota brunnescens sp. nov.

Illustrations: Text figs. 325-327; 447-450; pls. 40a, 71.

Pileus 2–7 cm latus, convexus demum late convexus vel obtuse umbonatus, glutinosus, squamulosus, glabrescens, sordide luteo-brunneus, subhygrophanus. Lamellae adnatae, angustae, confertae, albidae demum cinnamomeae. Stipes 4–6(9) cm longus, (4)8–10 mm crassus, aequalis, albidus demum pallide luteus, tactu brunneus, luteo-fibrilloso-cingulatus. Sporae 6–7 × 4–4.5 μ. Pleurocystidia 48–70 × 9–16 μ, fusoide ventricosa, saepe bifurcata. Caulocystidia 40–120 × 15–40 μ versiformia. Specimen typicum in Herb. Univ. Mich. conservatum est; legit prope Lake Tahkenitch, Ore., Nov. 18, 1935, Smith 3525.

Pileus 2–7 cm broad, convex with an incurved margin, expanding to plane or retaining a low umbo, at times slightly depressed around the umbo, viscid to glutinous, at first sparsely decorated with small, whitish veil remnants forming evanescent fibrillose squamules, "Prout's-brown," "chestnut-brown," "tawny-olive," or "snuff-brown" (dark yellow-brown) margin at times fading to "apricot-orange." Context rather thick, dingy watery brown; odor and taste mild or slightly disagreeable.

Lamellae adnate to adnexed, at first whitish, becoming dull cinnamon, narrow, crowded, edges even or nearly so.

Stipe 4–6 (9) cm long, (4) 8–10 mm thick, equal, whitish to ivory-yellow, with numerous concentric fibrillose zones of citrine-yellow veil remnants, the surface staining tawny in age or where handled.

Spores 6–7 × 4–4.5 μ ovate to subelliptic in face view, obscurely inequilateral to elliptic in profile, smooth, wall slightly thickened (± 0.3 μ), apex with an extremely minute pore (1.4), pale to medium tawny in KOH, pale tawny to ochraceous in Melzer's reagent.

Basidia 18–22 × 5–6 μ, 4-spored, hyaline in KOH, yellowish in Melzer's reagent. Pleurocystidia 48–70 × 9–16 μ, abundant, fusoid-ventricose, apex obtuse, wall thin and hyaline, content homogeneous or with coagulated ochraceous content in neck as revived in KOH, in Melzer's reagent the coagulated material rather rusty-ochraceous to dingy orange-brown, many forked (with 2 necks). Cheilocystidia 32–47 × 9–14 μ, subfusoid to broadly fusoid or fusoid-ventricose, thin-walled, hyaline to ochraceous in KOH, smooth. Caulocystidia in tufts, voluminous 40–120 × 15–40 μ, thin-walled, smooth, content homogeneous, clavate to clavate-mucronate to fusoid, some forked, wall yellowish in KOH.

Gill trama of a floccose central area of parallel to subparallel smooth thin-walled hyphae with the cells 4–12 μ diam., subhymenium of gelatinous narrow (2–3 μ) closely packed hyphae. Pileus cutis a thick gelatinous layer of hyaline to yellowish smooth hyphae 1.5–3 μ diam., over this veil hyphae occur in places; the latter nongelatinous 3–6 μ and with yellowish incrusted walls; hypodermium of dark rusty brown hyphae from coarse incrustations, walls thin to slightly thickened, hyphae 5–10 μ diam. Context hyphae inflated 9–20 μ ±, walls thin, smooth, yellowish in KOH. All hyphae inamyloid. Clamp connections present.

Habit, habitat, and distribution: Gregarious to caespitose on burned areas in the Pacific Northwest, fall, common after forest fires.

Observations: This species is very distinct as it occurs in the Pacific Northwest by its voluminous caulocystidia which are for the most part quite unlike any of the lamellar cystidia. It is also a larger fungus than *P. highlandensis* and with rather conspicuous zones of yellow veil remnants on the stipe. However, the flecks of veil fibrils forming the squamules on the pileus are pallid. Another interesting feature is the number of pleurocystidia which are forked. The thick-walled cells in the hypodermium of the pileus are most numerous in sections of older material.

Material examined: CALIFORNIA: Smith 3767, 9056, 9452. IDAHO: Smith 44678, 53782, 55283, 69248, 71307, 73889, 73890, 74092. OREGON: Smith 3411, 3462, 3525, (type), 3601, 3617, 3767, 55353.

154. Pholiota highlandensis (Pk.) comb. nov.
Agaricus carbonarius Fries, Obs. Myc. 2: 33. 1818.
Flammula carbonaria (Fr.) Kummer, Der Führer in die Pilzkunde, p. 82. 1871.
Flammula highlandensis (Pk.) Peck, New York State Mus. Ann. Rept. 50: 138. 1897.
Gymnopilus carbonarius (Fr.) Murrill, Mycologia 4: 256. 1912.
Pholiota carbonaria (Fr.) Singer, Agaricales, p. 517, 1951.
Dryophila carbonaria (Fr.) Quélet, Enchir. Fung., p. 70. 1886.
Illustrations: Text figs. 330, 332-335; pls. 67a, 70b, 72.

Pileus 2–4 (6) cm broad, viscid, convex, becoming somewhat depressed, at times with a low umbo, fulvous or reddish-cinnamon-brown to reddish brown, the margin usually paler, colors varying "russet," "tawny," "pecan brown," "verona brown," or in age almost "mummy brown," glabrous except for decidous veil-remnants along the margin, hygrophanous and fading to various shades around "ochraceous-buff," margin even. Context rather thin, yellow to subconcolorous; odor not distinctive, taste slightly disagreeable or none.

Lamellae adnate or rounded-adnate, pallid to pale-yellowish when young, becoming "snuff-brown" or "cinnamon-brown," broad, close, edges even or eroded.

Stipe (1) 2–4 cm long, (2) 3–6 mm thick, apex whitish to yellowish at first, becoming dingy brownish, lower portion pallid then dark brown (darker than apex), with zones or patches of the veil which is pallid yellow to "cinnamon-buff" (pale buff) and forms an evanescent, fibrillose annular zone, more or less glabrescent.

Spores "cinnamon-brown" in deposit (American material); 6–8 × 4–4.5 μ, smooth, apical pore distinct, mostly elliptic but varying to ovate in face view, in profile subelliptic to obscurely inequilateral, wall about 0.3 μ thick, dark rusty brown (near cinnamon brown) in KOH, paler and more ochraceous in Melzer's reagent.

Basidia 25–32 × 7–8 μ subcylindric to clavate, 4-spored, yellowish to hyaline in KOH, yellowish in Melzer's sol. (in American material often 18–24 × 5–6 μ). Pleurocystidia 38–65 (70) × 7–15 μ, fusoid-ventricose, apex obtuse, smooth, thin-walled, content often ochraceous in KOH. Cheilocystidia like pleurocystidia but smaller (30–50 × 7–12 μ) but varying to subfusoid to nearly clavate, content yellow to hyaline. Caulocystidia 45–88 × 7–12 (16) μ, cylindric, clavate or fusoid-ventricose.

Gill trama of a central area of subparallel floccose hyphae, cells short to long, walls thin smooth and yellowish to hyaline in KOH; subhymenium a well defined layer of hyaline branched narrow (± 2 μ) smooth hyphae. Pileus cutis a thick gelatinous pellicle of yellow narrow (2–3 μ) hyphae many appearing to have frequent refractive transverse septa; hypodermium of floccose distinctly encrusted tawny hyphae 4–12 μ in diam. Context hyphae compactly interwoven, having inflated cells and thin hyaline to yellow walls. All hyphae inamyloid. Clamp connections present.

HABIT, HABITAT, AND DISTRIBUTION: On burned-over soil, or on charred wood, New York, Maryland, Tennessee, Florida, Texas, Michigan, Colorado, Wyoming, Idaho, Washington, Oregon and California: reported from Jamaica and from Europe, spring-fall, winter (south).

OBSERVATIONS: This species grows on burned areas and varies somewhat in its characteristics. The pileus is brown, usually some shade of reddish brown, with the margin paler. One collection (Smith 65054, from Idaho) is obviously strongly faded, doubtless from exposure to sun and wind. The pileus flesh is pallid or yellowish. Peck (1897) described *Agaricus (Flammula) highlandensis* as differing from *Agaricus (Flammula) carbonarius* in its whitish flesh; but, in his description, he admits that the flesh is sometimes tinged with yellow under the cuticle. In *P. highlandensis* the lamellae are broad, in contrast to the narrow gills of another carbon-loving species, *P. carbonaria* Smith. The veil in *P. highlandensis* is pallid to yellowish or buff, becoming cinnamon brownish when sprinkled with spores; in *P. carbonaria* Smith the veil is cinnabar red to ferruginous, fading to ochraceous. In *P. highlandensis* the veil may be rudimentary or if better developed leaves on the stipe remnants which appear as scattered fibrillose remains or at times as thin yellowish patches (Smith 19894, from Oregon). The microscopic characters, although rather constant, show occasional variations. The spores usually are up to 7.5 μ long, but in Smith 51513, from Colorado, the upper limit is 8 μ, as it was in a collection of Bresadola's. In nearly all collections studied the pleurocystidia have a slender simple neck; but in Smith 17717, from Washington, some were forked and branched. The structure of the subhymenium at once distinguishes *P. harenosa* from this species.

A study of the "Highland" (near Highland Falls, N. Y.) collection which must be accepted as the type gave the following microscopic data.

Spores 6.5–8 × 4–4.5 μ, ellipsoid to ovoid in face view, inequilateral in profile, smooth, germ pore not evident. Basidia 23–27 × 5–6 μ, 4-spored. Pleurocystidia 47–72 × 7–12 μ, ventricose, at times slightly constricted, sometimes brown; cheilocystidia 33–44 × 6–10 μ, ventricose or subfusoid. Gill trama a mediostrate, hyphae slightly interwoven, hyphae 5–8 μ broad. Subhymenium a gelatinous zone. Pileus trama radial. Cuticle gelatinous, of loosely interwoven, pale brown hyphae, sometimes lightly incrusted. Clamp connections present. Pileus and gill trama yellowish brown or pale rusty in KOH; rusty brown in Melzer's reagent. Caulocystidia none.

Kauffman however had studied a specimen of *P. prolixa* under this name and Peck himself had sent Kauffman such a specimen. We designate those specimens having pleurocystidia 47–72 × 7–12 μ as the type since they unquestionably came from burnt ground.

MATERIAL EXAMINED: ALABAMA: Burke 680; Hesler 22978; CALIFORNIA: Cooke 18160; Copeland 455; Rea H-887 (MICH); COLORADO: Smith 51513; FLORIDA: Hesler 16152, 21600; IDAHO: Slipp UIFPH 1545, 3105 (both MICH); Smith 44665, 44803, 54354, 54446, 58605, 59449, 64933, 65019, 65054; LOUISIANA: Hesler 3958; MICHIGAN: Bartelli 2418; Harding 350, 390, Smith 32-10, 32-221, 32-221a, 32-513, 33-99, 1197, 4558, 6120, 33289, 33695, 71441; MARYLAND: Kauffman 6-16-19; NEW MEXICO: Barrows July 1955; NEW YORK: The type; Smith 3617, 7929, 19891, 19894, 55353; TENNESSEE: Hesler 4259, 4260, 10128, 18845, 21329, Smith 21647 (MICH); TEXAS: Thiers 1488; WASHINGTON: Smith 3063, 17717, (MICH) 14145; WYOMING: Smith 34357, 34434; ENGLAND: Austwick 403; GERMANY: Syd. Mycoth. Ger. 1411, 1812; SWEDEN: Fung. Suec. 20-X-1945; 5-V-1946.

Section **Spumosae** sect. nov.

Pileus viscidus; pleurocystidia fusoide ventricosa; sporae 7–11 × 4–6 μ. Typus. Pholiota spumosa.

Key to Stirpes*

1. Growing on *Sphagnum* or clumps of moss in bogs ....
   .... Stirps *Sphagnicola*

---

*If any pleurocystidia show some wall thickening up to about 0.5 μ try section *Flammuloides* also.

1. Habitat various but not as above 2
2. Odor pungent to fragrant; lamellae pale yellow young; many pleurocystidia with orange red content revived in KOH ....
  .... Stirps *Graveolens*
2. Not as above 3
3. Stipe 1–3.5 mm thick; pileus 1–3.5 cm wide .... Stirps *Scamba*
3. Pileus wider and stipe thicker 4
4. Spore deposit testaceous; taste bitterish .... Stirps *Subamara*
4. Not as above 5
5. Pileus appressed-squamulose at least around the disc (see *P. paludosella* also) .... Stirps *Stratosa*
5. Pileus glabrous or merely virgate .... Stirps *Spumosa*

Stirps Sphagnicola

Key

1. Spores 8–10 × 4.5–6 μ 2
1. Spores 7–9 × 4–4.5 μ 3
2. Gills whitish when young; pileus with reddish or reddish-brown spotted center; caulocystidia absent .... *P. sphagnicola*
2. Gills very soon yellowish; pileus disc tawny to dark yellow-brown; caulocystidia present .... *P. paludosella*
3. Pileus tinged flesh color when young and moist, pallid when faded .... *P. sphagnophila*
3. Pileus orange-fulvous over disc, greenish yellow over marginal area .... *P. chromocystis*

155. Pholiota sphagnicola (Pk.) comb. nov.
Flammula sphagnicola Peck, New York State Mus. Bull. 167: 43. 1913.
Gymnopilus sphagnicola (Pk.) Murrill, North Amer. Fl. 10: 196. 1917.
Illustrations: Text figs. 339-341.

Pileus 1–2.5 cm broad, convex or nearly plane, obtuse or umbonate, yellowish with reddish or reddish brown often spotted center, viscid, glabrous. Context thin, white.

Lamellae adnate or with a decurrent tooth, whitish becoming cinnamon color, thin, narrow, close.

Stipe 2.5–3.5 cm long, 1–3 mm thick, whitish, apex slightly white-fibrillose, base white-tomentose.

Spores 8–10 × 4.5–5.5 (6) μ smooth, apical pore distinct and a few spores seem to have a slight wall thickening around the pore; shape in face view elliptic to ovate, in profile somewhat inequilateral; color in KOH tawny to ochraceous-tawny (well colored), in Melzer's reagent slightly paler than in KOH; wall about 0.3 μ thick or slightly more.

Basidia 4-spored, 20–26 × 6.5–8 μ, clavate, yellowish in KOH and

Melzer's reagent. Pleurocystidia scattered to rare, 35–53 × 8–15 μ, fusoid-ventricose with obtuse apex to ovate-pedicellate or ventricose mucronate, content "empty," wall very thin; (in the type most cystidia remain collapsed), smooth. Cheilocystidia (28) 35–46 (53) × 4–12 μ, fusoid-ventricose to clavate or utriform (variable in shape), thin-walled, smooth, content homogeneous and hyaline. Caulocystidia none.

Gill trama a central area of parallel to interwoven thin-walled smooth hyphae 3–5 μ diam. but cells inflating in age, hyaline to yellowish in KOH, content not distinctive; subhymenium a thin layer of narrow gelatinous hyphae hyaline to yellowish in KOH. Pileus cuticle a tangled layer of hyphae 3–6 μ diam. with rather heavily incrusted walls and only subgelatinous in KOH, hyphae yellowish to tawny in KOH, those at or near surface collapsing in age; hypodermium a distinct region fulvous in KOH from incrusted floccose hyphae, hyphal cells 4–12 μ or more in diam. Context of interwoven inflated hyphal cells with smooth yellowish thin walls. All hyphae and hyphal end-cells inamyloid. Clamp connections present.

HABIT, HABITAT, AND DISTRIBUTION: Among sphagnum, in swamps, Massachusetts, September. Type studied.

OBSERVATIONS: In the type pleurocystidia are rare and we could find no caulocystidia. In *P. paludosella* we found the pleurocystidia more abundant, and caulocystidia are readily demonstrated. In both *P. sphagnicola* and *P. paludosella* the curious apical thickening around the germ pore of the spore shows on a few spores. A study in culture of both of these would be highly desirable. In recognizing both we are simply going on the evidence available but have reservations to the effect that both may simply be extremes of one species.

156. Pholiota paludosella (Atk.) comb. nov.
Naucoria paludosella Atkinson, Journ. Myc. 12: 193. 1906.
Illustrations: Text figs. 342-346; pls. 60b, 69a, 73.

Pileus (2) 3–5 (6) cm broad, obtuse to convex with an incurved margin, expanding to broadly convex to plane and at times with an obtuse umbo; ground color pale cream-color except for the tawny, scaly disc; surface more or less decorated with fibrillose squamules or patches from the remains of the buff-colored veil, eventually more or less glabrescent; margin fringed with veil remnants at first; viscid but soon dry. Content pliant, yellowish; odor mild or fragrant; taste not distinctive.

Lamellae sinuate, yellowish becoming cinnamon-brown and drying paler, close, narrow to moderately broad, pliant and gelatinous, edges even.

Stipe 3–6 (8) cm long, 3–4 (5) mm thick, apex pruinose and yellowish, becoming tawny to russet below, equal or nearly so, or bulbous, pliant, floccose-squamulose up to the annular fibrillose zone left by the broken veil, more or less glabrescent. Veil buff colored.

Spores 7–10 (12) × 4–5 (6) μ smooth, apical pore distinct and apex obscurely truncate, shape in face view mostly ovate varying toward elliptic, in profile somewhat inequilateral; dull ochraceous tawny to cinnamon in KOH, paler and more ochraceous in Melzer's reagent.

Basidia 20–26 × 5–7.5 μ, 4-spored (some 2-spored) clavate, yellowish in KOH, in Melzer's reagent duller yellowish. Pleurocystidia scattered, 36–52 × 9–12 μ, fusoid-ventricose, smooth, thin-walled, content often ochraceous and coagulated (as revived in KOH). Cheilocystidia 28–43 × 6–7 μ, versiform: fusoid-ventricose, subfusoid, to nearly clavate, thin-walled, smooth (or soon becoming so in KOH), content yellow to hyaline. Caulocystidia 38–66 × 4–8 μ and elongate, narrowly clavate ventricose, rostrate, subfusoid or 33–40 × 9–14 μ and utriform, mostly with yellowish walls in KOH, walls smooth and thin to slightly thickened.

Gill trama a somewhat interwoven strand of floccose hyphae 4–14 μ diam.; walls thin, yellowish in KOH and smooth; subhymenium a well developed layer of gelatinous narrow (1.5–3 μ wide) interwoven filaments giving rise at base of basidia to a palisade of septate hyphae each of which has a basidium as the terminal cell. Pileus cutis a thick layer of rusty brown hyphae 2.5–4 μ or more in diam. with incrusting bands and spirals of pigment, layer only subgelatinous in KOH, (space between hyphae slightly more refractive than normal for a non-gelatinous cutis); beneath this a hypodermial region of more enlarged (up to 12 μ) hyphae with thin yellow smooth walls. Context hyphae paler down to a ferruginous band (in KOH) of cells with somewhat thickened walls just above the subhymenium, the color intense in young caps. Clamp connections present. All hyphae inamyloid.

HABIT, HABITAT, AND DISTRIBUTION: On hummocks, in sphagnum, Michigan, Ohio and Tennessee, September—October. Type studied.

OBSERVATIONS: The habitat, medium large spores, projecting pleurocystidia, and scaly, tawny pileus disc are distinctive features of this species. The yellow context at maturity, and yellow young gills and stipe-apex, separate it from *P. sphagnicola*.

The anatomy of the apical pore of the spore is interesting in this species. There is a very slight inflation of the outer wall layer right around the pore which gives the apex a slightly different appearance than in other species of *Pholiota*. A second rather deceiving feature of the species is the almost pseudoparenchymatic band of cells with slightly thickened walls next to the subhymenium; in young material revived in KOH they are ferruginous red but in older caps almost colorless. This sort of pigment change has also been observed in *Psathyrella* species. In some older pilei areas of hymenium had apparently been destroyed by insects, and numerous pleurocystidia had replaced the basidia.

MATERIAL EXAMINED: MICHIGAN: Harding 391, 409, 432; Smith 33-1014, 33-1041, 988, 4921, 50585, 62203, 64746; OHIO: 20076 (CU) TENNESSEE: Hesler 10930.

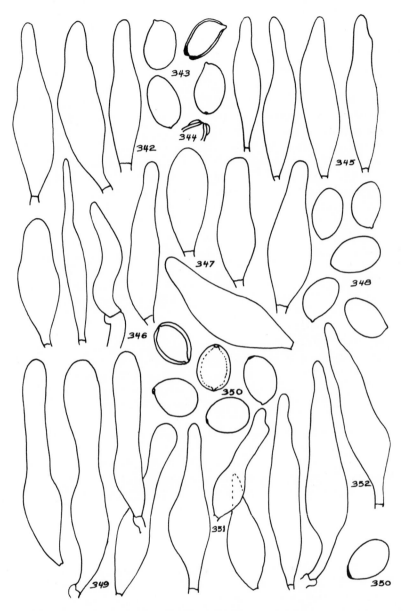

Text Fig. 24.

FIGS. 342-346, pleurocystidia, spores, spore apex enlarged, cheilo-cystidia and caulocystidia of *P. paludosella;* 347-349, cheilocystidia, spores and pleurocystidia of *P. sphagnophila;* 350-352, spores, cheilocystidia and pleurocystidia of *P. pulchella.*

157. **Pholiota sphagnophila** (Pk.) comb. nov.
Naucoria sphagnophila Peck, Bull. N.Y. State Mus. 139: 45. 1910.
Illustrations: Text figs. 347-349.

Pileus 1.2–2.5 cm convex becoming nearly plane, surface minutely appressed fibrillose to faintly squamulose, hygrophanous, tinged flesh color when young and moist, pallid when faded but near pinkish buff in dried material, grayish-ochraceous to rusty-brown when mature.

Lamellae thin, narrow, crowded, subsinuate, unequal, edges uneven, yellowish, becoming ferruginous.

Stipe 2.5–4.5 cm long, 2–3 mm thick, equal, flexuous, solid or at length hollow, yellowish, with a slight floccose tomentum at apex, white-tomentose at base, evenly pale pinkish buff or pinkish buff as dried, as dried thinly coated to near apex with grayish-pallid fibrils, dark fulvous in KOH.

Spores 7–9 × 4–5 μ, smooth, apical pore present but minute (no wall thickening at apex) ; shape in face view ovate to nearly elliptic, in profile somewhat inequilateral to nearly bean-shaped (ventral line straighter than dorsal line) ; wall about 0.3 μ thick; color in KOH bright ochraceous tawny singly but fulvous in masses, in Melzer's reagent merely slightly duller than in KOH.

Basidia 4-spored, 18–26 × 6–8 μ, subclavate, ochraceous in KOH and Melzer's reagent. Pleurocystidia 42–73 × 7–12 μ, neck 5–8 μ wide and apex obtuse, narrowly fusoid-ventricose, content ochraceous in KOH and homogeneous to refractive granular, in Melzer's reagent often granular and bright yellow but in some homogeneous; wall thin, exterior often coated with dried coagulated remains of mucilaginous material. Cheilocystidia subvesiculose to fusoid-ventricose, mostly with ochraceous content, wall with adhering mucilaginous material or smooth. Caulocystidia none found.

Gill trama a central area of apparently interwoven floccose smooth hyphae with thin weakly ochraceous walls in KOH, cells becoming variously inflated; subhymenium apparently gelatinous and of narrow interwoven hyphae. Pileus cutis a surface layer of narrow (3–5 μ), smooth scarcely gelatinous hyaline (in KOH) hyphae with thin walls; this intergrading with a tangled layer of wider heavily incrusted rusty brown hyphae at most subgelatinous next to the smooth-walled layer. Context of pale ochraceous thin-walled mostly smooth hyphae with inflating cells. Clamp connections present. All hyphae inamyloid.

HABIT, HABITAT, AND DISTRIBUTION: Riley's Bog, Stowe, Mass., 30 July 1909, S. Davis (type). Apparently known only from type locality.

OBSERVATIONS: This is a slender *Pholiota* like *P. pulchella*, but there is little resemblance between the two microscopically. *P. sphagnophila* features a very weak development of hyphal gelatinization in the cuticular area of the pileus, the spores lack the thickening around the apical pore which is present in the closely related *P. sphagnicola*, it has prominent pleurocystidia often coated over the exterior with a coagulated mucilaginous material, and though fusoid-ventricose the ventricose lower part is often not much wider than the neck. The color of the pileus and thickness of the stipe distinguish *P. chromocystis* immediately.

158. Pholiota chromocystis sp. nov.

Pileus 3–5 cm latus, obtusus deinde obtuse umbonatus, aurantio-brunneus, margine virido-flavus, viscidus, glabrosus vel subglabrosus. Caro olivacea deinde flavida; odore et gustu mitis. Lamellae adnatae, flavae deinde aurantio-brunneae, marginibus perflavae, angustae, confertae. Stipes 6–10 cm longus, 3–6 mm crassus, concolor, leviter fibrillosus. Sporae 6.5–8 × 4–4.5 μ, leves, ellipsoideae demum phasioliformes. Pleurocystidia 40–66 × 10–17 μ, aurea demum ferruginea vel hyalina; cheilocystidia similia, minora. Caulocystidia 26–50 × 10–18 μ, clavata demum subfusoidea. Cuticula gelatinosa. Specimen typicum in Herb. Univ. Mich. conservatum est; lectum in Sugar Island, Michigan, August 10, 1965. Smith 72040.

Pileus 3–5 cm broad, obtuse, expanding to obtusely umbonate, surface viscid, glabrous or nearly so, color bright greenish yellow over marginal half, becoming somewhat orange-fulvous over disc much as in *Naematoloma fasciculare*. Context thin, pliant, olivaceous moist, yellowish faded, with $FeSO_4$ green; odor and taste not distinctive.

Lamellae adnate, crowded, narrow, yellow when young, in age orange-fulvous, soon darker rusty brown where damaged, in some the edges bright yellow.

Stipe 6–10 cm long, 3–6 mm thick, equal, fibrous, becoming hollow, pith orange-fulvous and cortex pale greenish yellow, surface concolor with cap margin or base soon pale tawny and drying about this color (not darkening markedly), thinly fibrillose, no annulus or distinct veil line present.

Spore deposit bright rusty brown on surrounding debris; spores 6.5–8 × 4–4.5 μ, smooth, with a minute pore, in shape elliptic to slightly bean-shaped in profile, nearly oblong in face view, rusty brown in KOH, paler in Melzer's.

Basidia 22–24 × 5–6 μ, 4-spored, hyaline in KOH in fresh condition, lemon-yellow as revived in KOH. Pleurocystidia 40–66 × 10–17 μ, hyaline or with golden-ochraceous to rusty ochraceous content, thin-walled, smooth as revived in KOH but at first often with an incrusted zone above the ventricose portion, apex subacute to obtuse, thin-walled. Cheilocystidia clavate to subfusoid to shaped like the pleurocystidia only smaller, bright yellow in KOH to hyaline. Caulocystidia scattered to clustered, not abundant, 26–50 × 10–18 μ, clavate to subfusoid, yellowish to hyaline in KOH.

Gill trama with a central area of non-gelatinous parallel hyphae with inflated orange-fulvous to ochraceous cells (in KOH), some with incrusting debris; subhymenium of somewhat diverging narrow more or less gelatinous hyphae hyaline in KOH. Pileus cutis a thin gelatinous pellicle of incrusted to smooth hyphae 2–6 μ diam., yellow in KOH; hypodermium of inflated orange-fulvous hyphae (in KOH) many with incrustations on walls. Context hyphae yellow in KOH, floccose, thin-walled, hyphal cells inflated to 15 μ or more. Clamp connections present.

HABIT, HABITAT, AND DISTRIBUTION: Subcaespitose in sphagnum, Michigan, August; Smith 72040, type.

OBSERVATIONS: This species reminds one of subgenus *Flammula* but has prominent pleurocystidia. Actually, in mounts revived in KOH the pleurocystidia are seen to be of two types, those with a colored content of amorphous material not arranged in any particular pattern, and those that are hyaline and homogeneous. The dried specimens are bright yellow, but the spores are not dextrinoid.

Stirps Graveolens

159. **Pholiota graveolens** (Pk.) comb. nov.
Flammula graveolens Peck, New York State Mus. Bull. 150: 54. 1911.
Gymnopilus graveolens (Pk.) Murrill, North Amer. Fl. 10: 199. 1917.
Illustrations: Pl. 74.

Pileus often caespitose, 2.5–7 cm broad, obtuse to broadly convex or nearly plane with a low umbo, sometimes slightly depressed at the center, reddish brown or yellowish brown over disc, olive-yellow or paler on the margin, viscid, glabrous, at times very obscurely innately fibrillose, pellicle subseparable. Context pale yellow, in age olivaceous; odor strong at times like that of *Cortinarius percomis* (earthly), taste none.

Lamellae adnate or slightly decurrent, pale yellow, becoming subferruginous, close or moderately so, medium broad to broad, thin, obscurely white-fimbriate, at times spotted rusty where bruised.

Stipe (3) 5–8 (9) cm long, (4) 5–10 mm thick, pale yellow within and without, becoming dark brown at the base, silky-fibrillose, equal or tapering at the base, solid or with a very narrow cavity. Veil pale yellow, floccose or webby, visible in young basidiocarps, evanescent.

Spores (6) 7–9 × (3.5) 4–5 μ, smooth, apical pore minute, shape in face view oblong to elliptic, in profile somewhat bean-shaped to elliptic or oblong; color in KOH rusty cinnamon, pale and more yellowish in Melzer's reagent; wall about 0.25–0.3 μ thick.

Basidia 23–27 × 5.5–7 μ, 4-spored, clavate, yellowish in KOH and Melzer's reagent. Pleurocystidia 48–70 × 8–15 μ, fusoid-ventricose with obtuse apex, walls thin, typically smooth, content as revived in KOH orange-red to orange-brown in the neck and sometimes the ventricose part, in Melzer's the content paler even to ochraceous, in one collection (considered authentic by Murrill) it surrounded the neck as a congealed orange-brown mass in KOH. Cheilocystidia (30) 40–60 (67) × 8–14 μ, similar to pleurocystidia but smaller and more fusoid, the small ones usually colorless. Caulocystidia none.

Gill trama of a central area of parallel to interwoven floccose hyphae the cells long or short and with thin smooth ochraceous to nearly-hyaline wall; subhymenium a narrow gelatinous band of hyaline gelatinous hyphae curving out toward the hymenium, hyphae 2–3 μ diam. and with thin smooth walls. Pileus cutis a thick gelatinous pellicle of pale ochraceous hyphae 2–5 μ diam. with distinctly gelatinizing walls; hypodermium of floccose incrusted hyphae 4–10 (14) μ diam., orange-rusty to bright ferruginous in KOH (paler in young material). Context hyphae thin-walled, inflated; walls smooth and greenish-yellow in KOH; large orange-rusty oleiferous hyphae present. Clamp connections present, all hyphae inamyloid.

HABIT, HABITAT, AND DISTRIBUTION: On or near conifers (pine, hemlock), Massachusetts, New York, North Carolina, Tennessee, Michigan and Colorado. August-December.

OBSERVATIONS: As pointed out by Peck (1911), it is a species well marked by its yellow veil, and yellow flesh of both the stipe and pileus, and its strong odor. Kauffman (1926) considered it a segregate of *P. spumosa*. He also compared it with *P. condensa*. The latter shows slightly thickened cystidial walls and is not said to have an odor. The two should be carefully compared, however, on the basis of fresh material. One of the striking features in material revived in KOH is the orange-rusty colored content in the neck of the pleurocystidia in conjunction with the bright orange-rusty colored hypodermium. These features in addition to the larger spores distinguish it at once from the common American form of *P. spumosa*. However, it apparently is a rare species.

MATERIAL EXAMINED: COLORADO: Smith 68787; MASSACHUSETTS: Peck (type); MICHIGAN: Smith 33-762; NORTH CAROLINA: Hesler 19650; TENNESSEE: Hesler 9586.

Stirps Scamba

The slender stipe and relatively wide spores along with the short pleurocystidia of many species characterize the group. See *P. subtestacea* also.

Key

1. Spore wall 0.5 μ (or slightly more) thick .... *P. pulchella*
1. Spore wall 0.25 μ thick approximately 2
   2. Veil tawny as judged by flecks on pileus and zones on the stipe
   .... *P. calvini*
   2. Veil not as above 3
3. Pileus chrome yellow .... *P. tetonensis*
3. Pileus not colored as above 4

    4. Pileus dark cinnamon to vinaceous brown or at least reddish tawny
       on the disc 5
    4. Pileus essentially pale yellow to pale buff or pallid young 6
  5. Disc of pileus dark vinaceous brown to vinaceous drab ....
  .... *P. pseudopulchella*
  5. Disc of pileus reddish tawny (see *P. condensa* also) .... *P. totteni*
      6. Taste bitterish; spores 7–9 × 4.5–5.5 μ .... *P. gregariiformis*
      6. Taste mild; spores mostly slightly larger 7
    7. Pileus slimy viscid; veil rudimentary .... *P. scamboides*
    7. Pileus merely viscid; veil fairly well developed 8
      8. Spores 9–11 × 5–6 μ; subhymenium not gelatinous ... *P. subdefossa*
      8. Spores 7–9 (10) × 4.5–5.5 μ; subhymenium gelatinous ... *P. scamba*

    160. Pholiota pulchella sp. nov. var. **pulchella.**
Illustrations: Text figs. 350-352; pl. 65b.

    Pileus 2–3.5 cm latus, obtusus demum late campanulatus, obscure vinaceobrunneus, fibrillose squamulosus, glutinosus vel viscidus. Contextus subolivaceus. Lamellae adnatae, subdistantes, latae, subolivaceae. Stipes 3–6 cm longus, 3–4.5 mm crassus, aequalis, olivaceo-luteus, deorsum fibrillosus. Sporae (6) 6.5–8.5 (9) × 5–7 (7.5) μ, leves, crassotunicatae. Pleurocystidia (38) 50–81 × (8) 12–16 μ, fusoide ventricosa. Caulocystidia 37–56 × 8–15 μ, clavata vel subventricosa. Specimen typicum in Herb. Univ. Mich. conservatum est; legit prope Port Angeles, Wash. 21 Sept. 1941. Smith 17083.

    Pileus 2–3.5 cm broad, obtuse when young expanding to obtusely campanulate or finally nearly plano-umbonate in age, disc "Natal brown," sometimes becoming "wood-brown" to "avellaneous" (dark vinaceous brown to gray-brown); margin shading off to "pale olive-buff," usually decurved a long time; surface at first with scattered delicate yellow fibrillose scales from the broken veil; viscid to glutinous, fibrillose-streaked beneath the slime, usually with small patches of veil tissue along the margin. Context thick on the disc and tapered abruptly away from it, pliant, "olive-buff" or more or less greenish watery gray; odor none, taste mild or faintly bitterish.

    Lamellae bluntly adnate but soon slightly depressed and toothed, broad (more or less 6 mm), horizontal, subdistant (24–28 reach the stipe, 2–3 tiers of lamellulae), "pale olive-buff" or a little more green when young, near "buffy-brown" in age, or finally more rusty from the spores, edges fimbriate.

    Stipe 3–6 cm long, 3–4.5 mm thick, equal or narrowed below, hollow, "chartreuse-yellow" (greenish yellow) at least at the apex, surface "sea-foam-yellow" above, slightly brighter below, lower two-thirds covered by delicate zones or patches of more or less "clay-color" fibrils which are the darkened remains of the veil, apical region delicately fibrillose-farinose, base delicately fibrillose-strigose.

Spores (6) 6.5–8.5 (9) × 5–7 (7.5) μ, smooth, apical pore distinct but apex not truly truncate, wall up to 0.5 μ thick; shape in face view broadly ovate to almost angular-ovate at times varying to broadly elliptic, in profile mostly obscurely to merely somewhat inequilateral or obscurely angular-elliptic, apiculus very inconspicuous; color in KOH reddish tawny, paler in Melzer's reagent.

Basidia 4-spored, 22–30 × (5) 6–8 μ, clavate, hyaline in KOH, yellowish in Melzer's reagent. Pleurocystidia (38) 50–81 × (8) 12–16 μ, fusoid-ventricose with acute to subacute apex, varying to fusoid, walls thin and hyaline, content homogeneous or with scattered rods and granules. Cheilocystidia similar to pleurocystidia but smaller, content often evenly yellowish. Caulocystidia 37–56 × 8–15 μ, clavate to subventricose, in tufts, hyaline or with brown pigment, walls yellowish in KOH.

Gill trama of a central portion with parallel hyphae, 6–15 μ diam., the cells short or long, the walls thin smooth and yellowish in KOH; subhymenium a gelatinous layer of narrow hyphae hyaline in KOH and interwoven. Pileus cutis a thick gelatinous pellicle of loosely tangled narrow (2–4 μ) hyaline to yellow hyphae often with asperulate walls; hypodermial zone of floccose hyphae with pale to dark tawny incrustations on walls, hyphae 4–10 μ diam. Context hyphae inflated to 15 μ +, thin-walled, ochraceous to nearly hyaline and smooth, all hyphae inamyloid. Clamp connections present.

HABIT, HABITAT, AND DISTRIBUTION: Scattered or solitary, on conifer debris and humus, Washington, Oregon, and Idaho, September-October.

OBSERVATIONS: The broadly ovoid, dark brown, thick-walled spores are distinctive. The young gills are "olive-buff," or greenish watery gray. Field characters include the small size, and heavy veil development. It is related to *Pholiota pseudopulchella,* which has larger, paler, ellipsoid spores with thinner walls. It also is a connecting species to *P. subangularis* as the spore shape, color in KOH and the thickness of the wall are all very suggestive. The latter however, lacks pleurocystidia.

MATERIAL EXAMINED: IDAHO: Smith 55262, 55337; OREGON: Smith 24806, 25060, 28184; WASHINGTON: Cooke 18592, 18831, 21777 (MICH) ; Smith 17083 (type) , 17231.

160a. **Pholiota pulchella** var. **brevipes** var. nov.

Sporae 6.5–8 × 5–6.5 × 4–5 μ, stipes 1–2 cm longus, 2–3.5 cm crassus; lamellae ochracceae. Specimen typicum in Herb. Univ. Mich. conservatum est; legit prope Nordman, Idaho, Oct. 8, 1956. Smith 54284.

Pileus 2–3.5 cm broad, convex becoming plane, surface viscid but soon dry, disc pale "natal brown" (vinaceous brown) , margin pale olive buff drying near ochre yellow, at first decorated with fibrillose squamules from the veil, glabrescent; margin long remaining appendiculate; context yellow, when cut staining inky gray, pliant, no odor or taste.

Lamellae broad and ventricose, close, pale yellow becoming dull ochraceous tawny, adnate to adnexed.

Stipe 1–2 cm long, 2–3.5 mm thick, equal, solid, bright yellow within, surface at first with yellowish squamules up to the yellow fibrillose zone, silky and yellow above, becoming brownish to reddish at base.

Spores 6.5–8 × 5–6.5 × 4–5 μ, smooth, apex with a distinct pore and obscurely truncate in many spores, shape in face view more or less ovate, in profile more or less elliptic; color in KOH russet, paler in Melzer's reagent. Other characters as in the type form.

HABIT, HABITAT, AND DISTRIBUTION: Gregarious along a road in woods, Granite Creek, Nordman, Idaho, Oct. 8, 1956. Smith 54284, type.

OBSERVATIONS: The distinguishing features of this variety are the short relatively thick stipe for its length, the color change when the flesh is cut, and the generally more yellow coloration than in the type variety.

161. Pholiota calvini sp. nov.

Pileus 10–25 mm latus, viscidus, cinnamomeus, ad marginem fulvo squamulosus; lamellae pallidae demum fulvae, latae, confertae, adnatae; stipes 15–25 mm longus, 1–1.5 mm crassus, fibrillosus; sporae 6.5–8 × 4–4.5 μ; pleurocystidia 50–70 × 9–15 μ; subhymenium gelatinosum. Specimen typicum in Herb. Univ. Mich. conservatum est; legit prope Mt. Gretna, Penna. 15 Sept. 1924. C. H. Kauffman.

Pileus 10–25 mm broad, obtuse expanding to broadly convex or plane, at times with an obtuse umbo, viscid, "cinnamon" with appressed small darker ("russet") scales decorating the marginal area; context thin and pallid, odor and taste not distinctive.

Lamellae rather broad, broadly adnate, close to subdistant, pallid becoming dull tawny, edges entire.

Stipe 15–25 mm long, 1–1.5 mm thick, equal, straight or curved, at first peronate by a thin tawny fibrillosity terminating in an evanescent thin fibrillose ring.

Spores 6.5–8 × 4–4.5 μ smooth, apical pore hardly visible; shape in face view narrowly ovate to elliptic or oblong, in profile obscurely bean-shaped to obscurely inequilateral; color in KOH pale to medium dull cinnamon, in Melzer's reagent not much change (paler at first) ; wall about 0.25 μ thick.

Basidia 4-spored, 17–22 × 6–7.5 μ clavate, yellow to hyaline in KOH. Pleurocystidia abundant, 50–70 × 9–15 μ, fusoid-ventricose, obtuse at apex, smooth or some debris adhering, content hyaline to yellow or orange-ochraceous revived in KOH, (hyaline fresh), walls thin. Cheilocystidia similar to pleurocystidia but small and with more orange content and more adhering debris.

Gill trama with a central area of non-gelatinous smooth, thin-walled parallel (±) hyphae with inflated cells and a gelatinous subhymenium of narrow (2–4 μ) hyphae hyaline in KOH. Pileus cutis of appressed hyphae 3–5 μ diam., incrusted with rusty brown zones, rings and spirals, scarcely gelatinous revived in KOH; hypodermium of more compactly interwoven hyphae 4–8 μ diam., and highly colored (orange-rusty) from incrustations and wall pigment. Context hyphae closely arranged, thin-walled, somewhat translucent in KOH (as if subgelatinous) and pale yellowish. Clamp connections present.

HABIT, HABITAT, AND DISTRIBUTION: On mossy soil among chips and woody debris, Mt. Gretna, Penna. Sept. 15, 1924. C. H. Kauffman, type.

OBSERVATIONS: In stature this species is not too unlike *P. scamba* and the possible relationship is enhanced by the thin fibrillose veil. It differs from *P. scamba* in smaller spores, longer cystidia and a more cinnamon colored pileus with darker squamules of velar material decorating the cap surface near the margin. It is named in honor of its finder, Dr. C. H. Kauffman.

162. Pholiota pseudopulchella sp. nov.
Illustrations: Text figs. 353-355.

Pileus 1–2 cm latus, conicus demum conico-umbonatus, obscure vinaceo-brunneus, squamulosus demum glaber, viscidus. Contextus luteus. Lamellae subdecurrentes, luteae demum luteo-brunneae, confertae, latae. Stipes 3–4 cm longus, 2–4 mm crassus, pallide luteus, deorsum, sparse fibrillosus. Sporae 7–9.5 × 5–6.5 μ, leves. Pleurocystidia 43–80 × 9–15 μ, fusoide ventricose; tenuitunicata vel tunica 0.5 μ crassa.Caulocystidia nulla. Specimen typicum in Herb. Univ. Mich. conservatum est; legit prope Grants Pass, Ore., 14 Nov. 1956. Smith 55641.

Pileus 1–2 cm broad, more or less conic and umbonate, then expanding-convex, disc natal brown to near vinaceous-drab, elsewhere paler, veil squamules present at first, then glabrous, viscid, margin even. Context thin, yellow.

Lamellae adnate-decurrent, yellow at first, then "buckthorn brown," close, broad or medium broad, edges uneven to fimbriate.

Stipe 3–4 cm long, 2–4 mm thick, pale yellowish, with scattered fibrils or squamulose, equal, hollow. Veil copious, yellow.

Spores 7–9.5 × 5–6.5 μ, smooth, apical pore minute but distinct (NA 1.4 ob.) ; ovate to subelliptic in face view, in profile elliptic to obscurely inequilateral; color in KOH rusty brown, revived in Melzer's reagent more cinnamon; wall about 0.25 μ thick.

Basidia 25–35 (37) × 7–9 μ, 4-spored, narrowly clavate, yellowish to yellowish hyaline in KOH and more yellowish in Melzer's reagent. Pleurocystidia 43–80 × 9–15 μ, fusoid-ventricose, the neck tapered to a subacute apex, smooth or with some debris adhering (in KOH), walls thin to thickened up to 0.5 μ, content homogeneous. Cheilocystidia similar to pleurocystidia but usually shorter. Caulocystidia none.

Gill trama a floccose central strand of subparallel hyphae, the walls as revived in KOH thin smooth and yellowish to hyaline, cells very elongated; subhymenium of subparallel hyaline narrow (2–3 μ) gelatinous hyphae in a narrow to broad zone (very broad in young material). Pileus cutis a gelatinous layer up to 250 μ thick of somewhat radially arranged narrow (2 μ ±) smooth, thin-walled hyphae; hypodermial region of rusty brown encrusted hyphae 3–6 μ diam. in a narrow band. Context hyphae with thin smooth walls, yellowish in KOH. Clamp connections present. All hyphae inamyloid.

HABIT, HABITAT, AND DISTRIBUTION: On conifer debris, Grants Pass, Ore., Nov. 14, 1956; Smith 55641, type.

OBSERVATIONS: This species has duller colors than in *P. pulchella;* especially as dried the pileus has a dull brown tone, but the important difference is shown by the spores which have thinner walls and in no way remind one of the spores of *P. subangularis.* The absence of caulocystidia in *P. pseudopulchella* should be checked on additional fresh material as these cells are easily missed in mounts of revived material in species where the veil is heavy.

Stirps Scamba

163. **Pholiota scamba** (Fr.) Moser. in Helmut Gams Kleine Kryptogamenflora II. p. 228. 1955.

Agaricus scambus Fries, Epicr. Myc., p. 184. 1836-38.

Flammula scamba (Fr.) Saccardo, Syll. Fung. 5: 828. 1887.

Paxillus scambus (Fr.) Quélet, Enchir. Fung., p. 92. 1886.

Naucoria caespitosa Murrill, North Amer. Flora 10: 180. 1917.

Dryophila scamba (Fr.) Kühner & Romagnesi, Flore Anal Champ. Supér., p. 331. 1953.

Illustrations: Text figs. 356-358; pl. 75.

Pileus 1.5–2 (3) cm broad, gregarious to more or less caespitose, convex, with or without a low obtuse umbo, expanding to plane or broadly convex, pallid to "pinkish-cinnamon," silky fibrillose, viscid but soon dry, the surface fibrils glistening when dry, margin appendiculate with pinkish-cinnamon fibrils. Context very soft and watery cartilaginous, watery yellowish; odor faintly fragrant, taste mild.

Lamellae adnate with a slight tooth, pale yellow ("cartridge-buff") becoming pallid olive brownish, medium broad, close, edges even, some forked behind, three tiers of lamellulae, narrowed slightly outward, sometimes slightly ventricose.

Stipe 1.5–3 cm long, 1–3 mm thick, often curved, apex pale clear yellow ("sea-foam-yellow"), clay-brown and minutely woolly tomentose or fibrillose-squamulose below, base strigose, equal, solid.

Spores 7–9 (10) × 4.5–5.5 μ, smooth, apex with germ pore and in some apex obscurely truncate (under a 1.4 NA lens), shape in face view ovate to elliptic, in profile somewhat inequilateral to subelliptic; in KOH dull cinnamon, in Melzer's reagent paler and finally pale reddish cinnamon; wall about 0.25 μ thick.

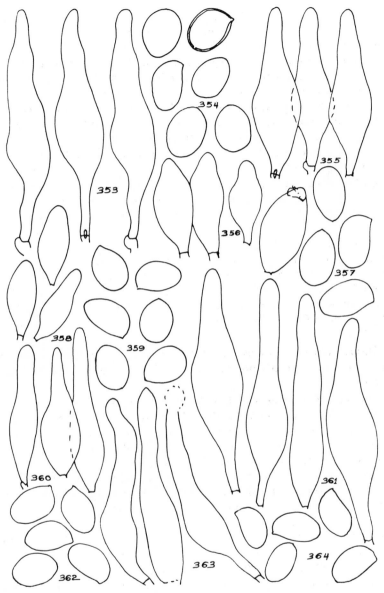

Text Fig. 25.

Figs. 353-355, pleurocystidia, spores, and cheilocystidia of *P. pseudo-pulchella;* 356-358, pleurocystidia, spores and cheilocystidia of *P. scamba;* 359-361, spores, cheilocystidia and pleurocystidia of *P. gregariiformis;* 362 & 363, spores and pleurocystidia of *P. tottenii;* 364, spores of *P. teto-nensis.*

Basidia 18–24 (26) × 7–9 μ, 4-spored, clavate, hyaline to yellowish in KOH or Melzer's reagent. Pleurocystidia 28–40 × 8–14 μ, subovate, broadly subfusoid utriform or fusoid-ventricose with a short neck and obtuse apex, thin-walled, in H_2O mounts with amorphous debris over apex, in KOH with some refractive particles in neck or an amorphous-refractive body filling the tip; smooth, content yellowish and homogeneous in Melzer's reagent. Cheilocystidia 24–33 × 7–10 μ, more frequently ovate to subfusoid than any other shape but generally like the pleurocystidia. Caulocystidia present (rarely) as scattered cells similar to cheilocystidia near stipe apex, walls thin, smooth and yellowish in KOH, content homogeneous.

Gill trama a central area of floccose subinterwoven hyphae 3–5 (10) μ broad (more inflated in age), hyphal walls thin, smooth, hyaline or nearly so in KOH and merely yellowish in Melzer's reagent; subhymenium a relatively broad well-developed layer of interwoven narrow hyaline gelatinous hyphae. Pileus cutis a well developed layer of subgelatinous hyphae 3–5 μ diam. with dull tawny bands and spirals of encrusting material; hypodermial zone of yellow to yellow-brown floccose nearly smooth hyphae more compactly arranged than in the epicuticular layer. Context hyphae interwoven, smooth, cells inflated, walls thin, yellowish to hyaline in KOH, yellowish in Melzer's reagent. Clamp connections present.

HABIT, HABITAT, AND DISTRIBUTION: On conifers, often mossy, logs and debris, June-October, Michigan, Idaho, and Washington; also in Canada (Ontario).

OBSERVATIONS: The small, pale, viscid, quickly drying pileus and the short, slender, woolly or fibrillose stipe are field characteristics of this species. It has shorter pleurocystidia and cheilocystidia than some of its relatives. European authors make no mention of an odor; in our collections a faint fragrance was noted. The pleurocystidia appear to be intermediate between chrysocystidia and leptocystidia. The very well developed gelatinous subhymenium and the brown spore deposit point clearly to *Pholiota* as the logical genus for this species.

MATERIAL EXAMINED: CALIFORNIA: Smith 3627, 3679, 3768, 3828, 8278, 8644, 8775, 8896, 8966, 9059, 9338, 9373, 9433, 55959, Dec. 1956; IDAHO: Smith 54637, 70661; MICHIGAN: Smith 141349, 43742, 44043, 64692; OREGON: Smith 19661, 19902, 24691, 28552, 28558; WASHINGTON: Murrill 691, (type of *Naucoria caespitosa*). Smith 13514, 14477, 14504, 14605, 29660, 30884, 40028, 40366, 48254, 48259; CANADA (ONTARIO): Smith 61521; ENGLAND: Smith 63151; SWITZERLAND: Favre 9-5-46.

164. **Pholiota gregariiformis** (Murr.) comb. nov.

Hebeloma gregariiforme Murrill, North Amer. Fl. 10: 217. 1917.
Illustrations: Text figs. 359-361; pl. 59b.

Pileus gregarious, 1–3.5 cm broad, convex to expanded, "light-buff" or pale yellowish brown with tints or stains of pale orange-brown, sometimes slightly darker on the disc, viscid, pellicle adnate, glabrous except for veil remnants on the even margin. Context whitish to watery brown; odor mild, taste slightly bitter.

Lamellae adnate or slightly sinuate, "olive-buff" or pale olivaceous at first, becoming yellowish brown, "buffy-brown" or "Isabella color," close, rather narrow, broad next to stipe, and subtriangular, several times inserted, edges fimbriate.

Stipe 4–6 cm long, 2–4 mm thick, at first whitish, then dingy, with scattered fibrils, tapering downward, tubular. Veil slight, arachnoid, evanescent.

Spores (6) 7–9 × 4.5–5.5 μ smooth, apical pore present but apex not truncate, shape in face view ovate to (rarely) subelliptic, in profile inequilateral, color in KOH near cinnamon-brown to tawny, paler in Melzer's reagent, wall about 0.25 μ thick.

Basidia 23–28 × 6–7 μ, 4-spored, narrowly clavate, yellow in KOH and in Melzer's reagent. Pleurocystidia 38–60 × 6–12 μ, narrowly fusoid-ventricose, apex obtuse, wall thin and smooth, content homogeneous, mostly yellow fading to hyaline in KOH, (often a plug of yellow colloidal material in neck). Cheilocystidia 30–50 × 6–9 (14) μ, similar to pleurocystidia but neck not as elongated. Caulocystidia 38–55 × 6–13 μ, more or less like the pleurocystidia, not readily demonstrated at times from dried material.

Gill trama of floccose subparallel hyphae with both short and elongated cells 4–12 μ diam., their walls thin smooth and hyaline to yellowish in KOH; subhymenium a gelatinous layer of somewhat interwoven hyphae 2–3.5 μ diam. and hyaline revived in KOH. Pileus cutis a thin pellicle of somewhat gelatinous hyphae mostly ochraceous in KOH and smooth to incrusted slightly, 2–3 μ diam.; hypodermial region of floccose rusty-fulvous hyphae (revived in KOH), walls of some of the cells incrusted and cells variable in diameter to 15 μ. Context hyphae closely interwoven, cells becoming inflated, walls thin, yellowish (in KOH) and smooth. Clamp connections present. All hyphae inamyloid.

HABIT, HABITAT, AND DISTRIBUTION: On soil, in pine woods Alabama, Georgia, and Tenessee, November—December.

OBSERVATIONS: This is related to *P. pulchella,* which has yellow fibrillose veil-remnants as scales, context "olive-buff" to greenish watery gray, horizontal gills, and smaller spores. The colors, together with the downward tapering of the stipe, help in field identification of *P. gregariiformis.* It is close to *P. tottenii,* which has a darker pileus, pale buff flesh, gills broad (not subtriangular) and at first melleous, and stipe shorter.

MATERIAL EXAMINED: ALABAMA: Hesler 22260; Murrill (type); GEORGIA: Hesler 22233; TENNESSEE: 22565.

165. **Pholiota totteni** (Murr.) comb. nov.
Hebeloma totteni Murrill, North Amer. Flora 10: 220. 1917.
Illustrations: Text figs. 362-363.

Pileus gregarious or caespitose, 2.5–4 cm broad, convex to plane, usually becoming depressed, often slightly umbonate, reddish tawny at the center, shading to whitish buff on the margin, or uniformly colored reddish brown, glabrous, shining. Context thin, pale buff; odor and taste not distinctive.

Lamellae sinuate or emarginate, melleous to ochraceous when young, then fulvous or brown, broad, not crowded.

Stipe 1.5–4 cm long, 2–3 mm thick, up to 7 mm when compressed, whitish buff above, apex yellowish mealy, reddish tawny below; sometimes decorated near the base with long, coarse, white hairs; dry. Veil arachnoid, leaving a few remnants on the stipe, evanescent.

Spores (6) 7–9 × 4–5 (10.5 × 6.5) μ, smooth, apical pore minute and apex not truncate; shape in face view elliptic to subovate, in profile subelliptic to obscurely inequilateral, dark tawny in KOH and merely paler and more cinnamon in Melzer's reagent, wall about 0.25 μ thick.

Basidia 18–23 × 5.5–7.5 μ, 4-spored, obscurely utriform to subclavate, yellow in KOH and Melzer's reagent. Pleurocystidia 45–65 (75) × 8–16 μ, fusoid-ventricose, apex obtuse to subcapitate neck outline usually wavy, wall thin and smooth; content amber brown to yellow, fading to nearly hyaline in KOH; neck often filled by a colloidal plug. Cheilocystidia 46–55 × 6–12 μ, subcylindric to narrowly fusoid-ventricose, otherwise similar to the pleurocystidia. Caulocystidia (not found on the dried material available for study).

Gill trama poorly revived but clearly a floccose central strand flanked on either side by a gelatinous subhymenium. Pileus cutis with a surface layer of somewhat gelatinous hyphae and a fulvous hypodermial region. Clamp connections present. All hyphae inamyloid.

HABIT, HABITAT, AND DISTRIBUTION: On soil, under pine, North Carolina, July and December.

OBSERVATIONS: We have studied the type as well as cotype from the Hebarium of the University of North Carolina. Both have the stature of a member of the naucorioid group around *P. scamba*, but are readily distinguished by the larger pleurocystidia. The arachnoid veil is typical of both. The relationships of this species actually are with the *P. spumosa* group. In fact the type collection consists of basidiocarps which in the dried state resemble those of *P. spumosa* except for being smaller and having a more poorly developed gelatinous pileus pellicle. It may be the same as *P. condensa*.

MATERIAL EXAMINED: NORTH CAROLINA: Totten 1509 (type), Hesler 10216.

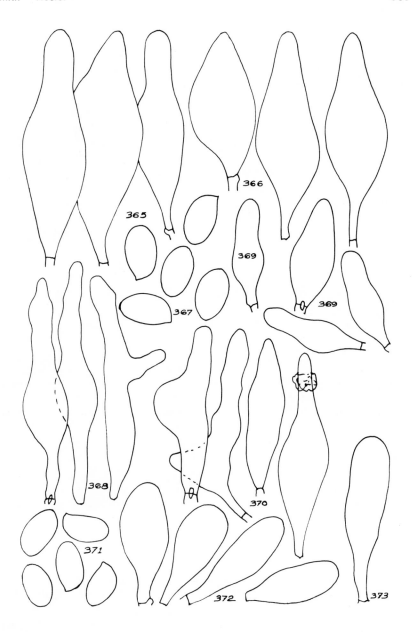

Text Fig. 26.

Figs. 365 & 366, pleurocystidia and caulocystidia of *P. tetonensis;* 367-370, spores, pleurocystidia, cheilocystidia and caulocystidia of *P. stratosa;* 371-373, spores and cheilocystidia of *P. baptistii.*

166. **Pholiota tetonensis** sp. nov.
Illustrations: Text figs. 364; 365-366.

Pileus 1–2.5 cm latus, convexus vel conicus, demum acute umbonatus, laete luteus ("deep chrome"), glaber. Lamellae adnatae, demum subdistantes, latae, luteae. Stipes 1.5–4 cm longus, 2–4 mm crassus, sursum pallide luteus, deorsum demum subfulvus, luteo fibrillosus. Sporae 7–9 × 4–5 μ. Pleurocystidia 40–70 × 10–22 μ, late ventricosa vel subfusoidea; tenuitunicata. Specimen typicum legit prope Jackson Lake, Wyoming, 29 June 1955, W. G. Solheim 3763, in Herb. Univ. Mich. conservatum est.

Pileus 1–2.5 cm broad, convex or conic, strongly and acutely umbonate, "deep chrome," center slightly darker, margin paler, glabrous. Context yellowish; odor and taste fungoid.

Lamellae adnate, yellowish at first, then yellowish brown, nearly subdistant, medium broad.

Stipe 1.5–4 cm long, 2–4 mm thick, pale yellow above, darker below, flesh yellowish, with scattered veil fibrils. Veil yellow, fibrillose.

Spores dull cinnamon ("Sayal-brown") in deposits; 7–9 × 4–5 μ, smooth, apical pore distinct but apex not truncate, wall dull cinnamon in KOH, in Melzer's reagent paler and more ochraceous, in face view oblong to elliptic, rarely ovate, in profile subelliptic to obscurely inequilateral, wall about 0.3 μ thick.

Basidia 25–28 × 6–8 μ, 4-spored, clavate, hyaline to yellow in either KOH or Melzer's reagent. Pleurocystidia 40–70 × 10–22 μ, abundant, broadly fusoid ventricose to broadly subfusoid varying to broadly ellipticpedicellate, walls thin and most cells remaining collapsed (in KOH), smooth, content amber-brown to dark ochraceous in neck, more homogeneous and paler in ventricose part, colored content tending to be reticulate folded or otherwise irregular in outline as seen on revived material under microscope, apex broadly rounded to obtuse and smooth. Cheilocystidia similar to pleurocystidia but on the average shorter and more obese. Caulocystidia none or a few clavate hyphal end-cells present.

Gill trama with a hyaline to yellowish central strand of parallel to subparallel hyphae with thin hyaline to yellowish smooth non-gelatinous walls and short to elongate cells 4–12 μ broad, some rusty ochraceous oleiferous hyphae present; subhymenium a narrow (2–3 μ), gelatinous zone of hyaline smooth interwoven hyphae. Pileus cutis a gelatinous pellicle of appressed-interwoven hyphae 3–5 μ diam. more or less ochraceous in KOH, and smooth to incrusted; hypodermium of more rusty-orange floccose hyphae 4–10 μ diam. with incrusted walls. Context hyphae with inflated cells, thin-walled, smooth to (rarely) incrusted, walls ochraceous in KOH; some large worm-like oleiferous hyphae present and rusty brown in KOH. Clamp connections present. All hyphae inamyloid.

HABIT, HABITAT, AND DISTRIBUTION: On rotting wood, Wyoming, Grand Teton National Park, June 29, 1955. Solheim 3763, type.

OBSERVATIONS: This species is very similar to *P. acutoconica* var. *acutoconica*, but is at once distinguished by its more obese pleuro- and cheilocystidia, and deep chrome colored pileus. The more distant gills are a possible additional difference but more collections are needed to substantiate this. It is very likely that there is a difference in the color of the spore deposit, but again more data are needed on the character. When found it is likely to be mistaken for one of the *P. alnicola* group.

167. Pholiota scamboides sp. nov.

Pileus 1–2.5(3) cm latus, obtusus, glutinosus, argillaceus. Lamellae pallidae demum pallide luteae, confertae, latae, adnatae. Stipes 1–2.5 cm longus, 2–2.5 mm crassus. Vellum sparsum, pallidum. Sporae 7–10.5 × 4–5.5 µ. Pleurocystidia 36–55 × 9–16 µ. Specimen typicum in Herb. Univ. Mich. conservatum est; legit prope Priest Lake, Idaho Oct. 5, 1964. Smith 71058.

Pileus 1–2.5 (3) cm broad, obtusely conic with a curved in margin, glabrous, slimy viscid, color whitish-buff to finally pinkish buff, when dried slightly darker on the disc than margin, the latter about pinkish buff; veil leaving only a few traces as fibrils on the pileus margin. Context pliant, pallid, odor and taste not distinctive, KOH, no reaction, FeSO₄ no reaction.

Lamellae yellowish white (pale ivory yellowish), becoming dingy clay-color close, broad, adnate, when dried dingy yellow-brown.

Stipe 1–2.5 cm long, 2–2.5 mm thick, equal coated to the gills with fine soft ivory yellowish fibrils (which are not part of the veil), color beneath the surface fibrils pinkish buff to cinnamon buff, finally clay color in basal part; veil pallid and very rudimentary (observable only on very small buttons).

Spores 7–10.5 × 4–5.5 µ, smooth, apical pore minute; shape in face view ovate to subelliptic, in profile elliptic to obscurely inequilateral; color in KOH tawny, in Melzer's reagent slightly more cinnamon but paler; wall about 0.3 µ thick.

Basidia 22–30 × 7–8.5 µ, 4-spored (rarely 2-spored), clavate, hyaline to ochraceous in KOH. Pleurocystidia abundant, 36–48 (55) × 9–16 µ, fusoid-ventricose with obtuse apex, smooth or with incrustations variously distributed, walls thin, content yellowish in KOH but not coagulated into a distinct body as revived in KOH, neck often rather short. Cheilocystidia similar to pleurocystidia. Caulocystidia more or less similar to pleurocystidia but usually the neck not as well differentiated varying more to clavate, often with yellow (in KOH) incrusting material on the upper part.

Gill trama with a central area of regularly arranged hyphae of narrow (4–7 µ) greatly elongated cells, inflating in age; walls thin, smooth and hyaline; subhymenium a gelatinous layer of narrow (3–4 µ) diverging hyaline hyphae. Pileus cutis a thick gelatinous pellicle of hyphae

2.5–4.5 μ diam., many with ochraceous incrustations on the wall; hypodermium a rusty brown (in KOH) layer of non-gelatinous hyphae with smooth or incrusted walls. Context hyphae compactly arranged, hyaline, thin-walled, cells inflating by maturity, oleiferous hyphae present. Clamp connections present.

HABIT, HABITAT, AND DISTRIBUTION: Gregarious on wet sand (apparently from buried wood) Mosquito Bay, Priest Lake, Idaho. Oct. 5, 1964. Smith 71058, type.

OBSERVATION: This species is obviously a segregate of *P. scamba* but excellent specimens of all stages were present and it differs in the truly slimy pileus and very reduced veil. The pleurocystidia especially when young remind one of chrysocystidia in being clavate-mucronate but by maturity a distinct neck develops and they are fusoid ventricose. They lack the content characteristic of chrysocystidia when revived in KOH.

168. Pholiota subdefossa sp. nov.

Pileus 8–17 mm latus, late convexus, siccus, fibrillosus, albo-luteus; lamellae pallidae demum fulvae, latae, subdistantes, adnato-decurrentes; stipes 1–1.5 cm longus, 1–2 mm crassus, pallide luteus; sporae 9–11 × 5–6 μ, laete fulvae (in KOH). Pleurocystidia 20–35 × 8–15 μ, subovata vel clavato-mucronata. Specimen typicum in Herb. Univ. of Mich. conservatum est; legit prope Sinclair, Maine, 17 Juli 1956, Bigelow 3331.

Pileus 8–17 mm broad, broadly convex with an incurved margin expanding to plane or nearly so, at times with a low broad umbo, surface dry and unpolished, matted fibrillose under a lens, margin opaque and even, color cream-buff varying to pale yellow on margin, colors slightly more intense on disc, hygrophanous and fading to whitish; context thin, whitish, no odor or taste.

Lamellae adnate with a short decurrent tooth, broad, close to subdistant, not forked or intervenose, arched, 2–3 mm broad, edges undulating and finely eroded.

Stipe 1–1.5 cm long, 1–2 mm thick, equal, curved, terete, central, hollow, fibrous, with a tuft of tomentum at base, surface fibrillose, apex with fine filaments from veil, when young, concolorous with pileus.

Spores 9–11 × 5–6 μ, smooth but tending to be obscurely angular, apical pore present but minute (apex not truncate); color in KOH rusty-fulvous, in Melzer's paler; shape in face view ovate to subelliptic; in profile obscurely inequilateral to suboblong; wall about 0.25–0.3 μ thick (thickest in KOH).

Basidia 4-spored, 20–26 × 8–9, clavate, mostly yellow in KOH. Pleurocystidia rare, 20–35 × 8–15 μ, ovate, clavate-submucronate to subelliptic, content homogeneous, yellow in KOH, wall thin and smooth, cheilocystidia similar to pleurocystidia but some seen with adhering debris. Caulocystidia versiform but mostly like the cheilocystidia.

Gill trama of ochraceous-walled hyphae with inflated cells; subhymenium of narrow branched non-gelatinous hyphae. Pileus cutis a loosely interwoven layer of non-gelatinous, hyaline to ochraceous hyphae 4–7 μ diam; hypodermial region continuous with the pileus context, the hyphae inflated and with ochraceous walls fading to hyaline. Clamp connections present.

HABIT, HABITAT, AND DISTRIBUTION: Gregarious on wet humus beneath a conifer log, July 17, 1956, near Sinclair, Maine, Bigelow 3331.

OBSERVATIONS: The spores in KOH are the color of a *Conocybe* but are not truncate and the pileus lacks an hymeniform or cellular epicutis. The species might be placed in *Galerina* where it would go in section *Porospora*. The stature, however, is more like *P. scamba* than of any other species, and its essential characters place it in *Pholiota* or in *Galerina*.

Stirps Subamara

169. Pholiota subamara sp. nov.
Illustrations: Text figs. 514-516.

Pileus 3–9 cm latus, convexus, demum planus vel late depressus, rare subumbonatus, viscidus, luteus, ad marginem striatulus. Contextus subluteus. Sapor tarde amarus. Stipes 4–10 cm longus, 3–6 mm crassus, flexuosus, luteus, siccus, fibrillosus, cavus. Sporae in cumulo hepaticolor, 7–9 × 4–5 μ, leves. Pleurocystidia 48–70 × 9–15 μ, fusoide ventricosa. Specimen typicum in Herb. Univ. Mich. conservatum est; legit prope Cades Cove, G.S.M.N.P., 9 Nov. 1940. L. R. Hesler 12950.

Pileus 3–9 cm broad, convex, then expanded, finally plane and slightly depressed, at times slightly umbonate, very viscid, at first "ochraceous-buff" to "antimony-yellow," then "yellow-ochre," disc usually darker, radiately brown-fibrillose, at times with scale-like patches of veil remnants margin striatulate when wet, even when dry. Context thin, pliant, yellowish with an olive-ochre tint; odor like wood, taste mild then slightly bitter.

Lamellae adnate, with a decurrent tooth, seceding (as the pileus expands), "amber-yellow," at first, then "tawny-olive" to "buckthorn brown," close, broad, rounded behind, many short, edges fimbriate.

Stipe 4–10 cm long, 3–6 mm thick, flexuous, concolorous with the pileus, dry, fibrillose, hollow. Veil usually evanescent.

Spores 7–9 × 4–5 μ, smooth, apical pore distinct; liver color in deposit; shape ovate to elliptic in face view, in profile obscurely inequilateral to slightly bean-shaped; in KOH dull tawny, in Melzer's reagent ochraceous buff; wall about 0.3 μ thick.

Basidia 25–28 × 5–7 μ, 4-spored, clavate, yellow in KOH and merely duller in Melzer's reagent. Pleurocystidia 48–70 × 9–15 μ, fusoid-ventricose, apex obtuse, rarely forked, walls thin and smooth, content homogeneous and ochraceous to hyaline. Cheilocystidia 25–38 × 7–10 μ, fusoid to fusoid-ventricose; narrowly clavate or irregular in outline, thin-walled, smooth, content ochraceous to hyaline. Caulocystidia voluminous: 1) clavate and 18–28 × 9–14 μ, smooth, thin-walled, wall ochraceous in KOH, content homogeneous; 2) utriform, 46–70 × 9–16 μ, smooth, thin-walled. Content yellow to hyaline; 3) versiform-inflated and up to 60 × 30 μ.

Gill trama a central area of floccose hyphae with greatly elongated, wide cells yellow in KOH, thin-walled and smooth; subhymenium a thin gelatinous layer of hyaline narrow (2–3 μ) hyphae. Pileus cutis a gelatinous pellicle up to 200 μ thick with narrow ochraceous hyphae dispersed in it, hyphae smooth but collapsing and then wrinkled; hypodermial zone of tawny distinctly incrusted hyphae 4–10 μ diam. Clamp connections present. All hyphae inamyloid.

HABIT, HABITAT, AND DISTRIBUTION: On stumps and logs of oak and pine, Tennessee, November; Hesler 12950, type.

OBSERVATIONS: Although apparently related to *P. spumosa* this species is distinct in the complex by its dark liver-colored spore deposit. Under the microscope, however, the color is normal for the group. Its spores are too large for *P. flavida* (6–7 × 4–4.5 μ as compared to 7–9 × 4–5 μ) in the sense of Moser.

Stirps Stratosa

Pholiota bakerensis will key out here if no thick-walled cystidia are observed.

170. Pholiota stratosa sp. nov.
Illustrations: Text figs. 367-370; pl. 76.

Pileus 2–4 cm latus, demum campanulatus vel late convexus, viscidus, subvirgatus, vinaceo-cinnamomeus. Contextus pallide subluteus, crassus, firmus; sapor mitis; odor fragrans. Lamellae confertae, latae, brunneolae demum ligno-brunneae. Stipes 3–6 cm longus, 4–10 mm crassus, solidus, fibrillosus. Vellum luteum. Sporae 7–10 × 4.5–5.5 μ. Pleurocystidia 50–78 × 7–12(15) μ, tenuitunicatae. Specimen typicum in Herb. Univ. Mich. conservatum est; legit prope Whitmore Lake, Mich. 14 Oct. 1961, Smith 64684.

Pileus 2–4 cm broad, obtuse with an incurved sterile margin, becoming campanulate to broadly convex, viscid but soon dry, covered by a vinaceous-tawny (almost "Mikado brown") epicutis which breaks up into obscure patches and streaks, margin paler in some (pinkish-buff to pale pinkish-buff) and typically fringed with fibrils from an almost cortinate veil. Context pale buff, thick, firm; odor faintly fragrant, taste mild; FeSO$_4$ olive, KOH orange brown.

Lamellae adnexed, pallid brownish becoming near wood-brown, close, moderately broad, edges even.

Stipe 3–6 cm long, 4–10 mm thick, solid, pallid within, covered over all to near apex with fibrils paler than those of cap and leaving an apical zone when veil breaks. Veil yellow.

Spores 7–10 × 4.5–5.5 μ, smooth, ochraceous twany in KOH, apical pore small but distinct, in face view elliptic varying more rarely to ovate and a very few somewhat angular, in profile elliptic to obscurely inequilateral; color pale reddish tawny in Melzer's reagent or a very few spores dark bay; wall as revived in KOH about 0.5 μ thick.

Basidia 4-spored, 25–32 (37) × 6–8 (10) μ, both 2-, and 4-spored, clavate, hyaline in KOH, yellowish hyaline in Melzer's reagent. Pleurocystidia 50–78 × 7–12 (15) μ, basically fusoid-ventricose with flexuous walls in neck in many, also tending to branch either in ventricose part or above, pedicel narrow and thin-walled, neck often incrusted with amorphous material, with homogeneous content in either KOH or Melzer's reagent, thin-walled. Cheilocystidia similar to pleurocystidia but often smaller. Caulocystidia none.

Gill trama of hyaline subparallel hyphae 3–6 μ broad, the walls thin, hyaline in KOH, smooth, non-gelatinous, cells short to elongated and inflating only in age; subhymenium a broad zone of narrow gelatinous interwoven hyaline hyphae, smooth, and thin-walled, the gelatinization extending to base of basidia near gill edge. Pileus cutis a poorly formed narrow zone of subgelatinous hyphae incrusted with ochraceous-brown pigment, hyphae 3–5 μ broad; beneath this a thick hypodermium of nongelatinous hyphae 5–15 μ broad with rusty brown bands and spirals of pigment. Context hyphae yellow to hyaline in KOH, walls thin and smooth, cells inflated to 60 μ at times, mostly 10–15 μ diam., some bright ochraceous oleiferous hyphae present. Clamp connections present. All hyphae inamyloid.

HABIT, HABITAT, AND DISTRIBUTION: On decayed hardwood (*Acer rubrum*), Mud Lake Bog, Washtenaw County, Michigan. Oct. 14, 1961, Smith 64684, type.

OBSERVATIONS: This species resembles *P. graveolens* but has slightly larger spores, only a faint pleasant odor, and a very poorly developed gelatinous pellicle. The pleurocystidia, in addition, are much more versiform in *P. stratosa*, and the structure of the pileus context also appears to be different.

Stirps Spumosa

Key

1. Pileus pellicle gelatinous but thin and easily obliterated. Veil very thin; spores with apical pore distinct (some spores obscurely truncate) .... *P. baptistii*
1. Not as above 2

2. Pileus dingy yellow to olive-yellow (finally) on margin and tawny
   to dingy yellow-brown on disc .... *P. spumosa*
2. Pileus bright yellow on margin and disc bay to orange or red 3
3. Stipe 2–4 mm thick; veil fibrillose and copious, yellowish becoming
   pallid .... *P. velata*
3. Stipe 4–15 mm; veil thin 4
4. Caulocystidia absent .... *P. vialis*
4. Caulocystidia present at stipe apex ....
   .... (see *P. subflavida* also) *P. piceina*

171. Pholiota baptistii sp. nov.
Illustrations: Text figs. 371-373; 375-376.

*Pileus 3–6 cm latus, convexus demum late convexus, subviscidus,
glaber, sordide luteus, ad centrum subfulvus. Contextus luteus. Lamellae
confertae, latae, adnatae, pallide luteae. Stipes 3–7 cm longus, 4–8 mm
crassus, aequalis, sparse fibrillosus, sursum pruinosus, pallide luteus,
deorsum subfulvus. Sporae 7–9 × 4–4.5(5) μ. Pleurocystidia 45–82 × 7–18
μ, tenuitunicata, ad apicem obtusa vel late obtusa. Specimen typicum in
Herb. Univ. Mich. conservatum est; legit prope Carney Lakes, Ada
County, Idaho, Mr. C. F. D. Baptist, 15 Oct. 1956, (Trueblood 542).*

Pileus 3–6 cm broad, convex to nearly plane or with a low umbo,
surface glabrous, slightly viscid, colors dull yellowish (ochraceous) or
over center dull pale tawny, drying to pale yellow except for brownish
disc. Context thin, yellowish, odor and taste not recorded.

Lamellae close, moderately broad, adnate to adnexed, pale yellowish and retaining this tone on drying, edges minutely fimbriate.

Stipe 3–7 cm long, 4–8 mm thick, equal or nearly so, thinly fibrillose; pruinose at apex and yellowish, drying greenish yellow; subfulvous
below but color fading somewhat in drying; veil scarcely leaving an
annular zone.

Spores 7–9 × 4–4.5 (5) μ smooth, wall slightly thickened (± 0.25 μ),
rusty fulvous in KOH and more ochraceous in Melzer's reagent, (much
paler than in KOH), apical pore distinct, some spores obscurely truncate; in face view oblong to elliptic, in profile slightly bean-shaped to
elliptic, more rarely obscurely inequilateral.

Basidia 23–30 × 5–7 μ, 4-spored, clavate, ochraceous in KOH or
paler, merely yellowish in Melzer's. Pleurocystidia 45–82 × 7–18 μ,
narrowly to broadly fusoid-ventricose; walls thin or thickened, in some
to 0.5 μ in ventricose part, smooth, apex obtuse to rounded, content
homogeneous or some with some rod-like crystals, yellow to hyaline in
KOH. Cheilocystidia 35–50 × 9–15 μ, and ellipsoid-pedicellate to clavate
or subfusoid, thin-walled, hyaline or with yellowish content in KOH and
in some the content amorphous and coagulated; some fusoid-ventricose
cells like the pleurocystidia also present. Caulocystidia 40–65 × 10–20 μ
ellipsoid pedicellate to clavate, rarely subfusoid, content often of rusty-

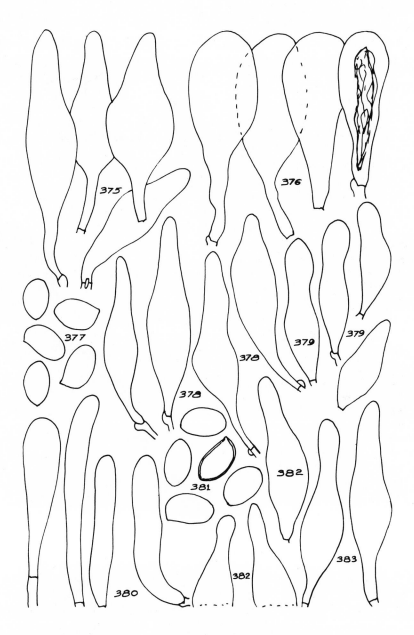

Text Fig. 27.

FIGS. 375 & 376, pleurocystidia and caulocystidia of *P. baptistii;* 377-380, spores, pleurocystidia, cheilocystidia and caulocystidia of *P. spumosa;* 381-383, spores, cheilocystidia and pleurocystidia of *P. velata.*

ochraceous coagulated material; walls thin and hyaline to yellowish (in KOH).

Gill trama of parallel to interwoven hyphae with elongate cells 6–18 μ diam. (inflated at maturity); the walls thin, smooth, and yellowish to hyaline in KOH; subhymenium of gelatinous interwoven narrow hyaline hyphae. Pileus cutis a thin layer of narrow (2–4 μ) ochraceous hyphae with gelatinizing walls (layer becoming obliterated); hypodermium of floccose hyphae 5–12 μ diam. with coarse dark tawny, incrusting patches of pigment (layer dark orange-brown). Content hyphae inflated (8–18 μ ±) cells with thin smooth walls yellow to hyaline in KOH; hyaline to yellow oleiferous hyphae also present. All hyphae inamyloid. Clamp connections present.

HABIT, HABITAT, AND DISTRIBUTION: On conifer debris, Carney Lakes, Ada County, Idaho. C.F.D. Baptist, Oct. 15, 1956. (Trueblood 542, type).

OBSERVATIONS: This species is very close to P. *tetonensis* but is broadly convex, has voluminous caulocystidia and duller colors—more like P. *spumosa*. From the latter it differs in having a thin gelatinous pellicle which may become obliterated in age, the more rounded pleurocystidia, and the more erratic distribution of clamp connections—they were difficult to locate in some mounts and readily demonstrated in others. This last features is probably of no taxonomic value but in the light of how the presence and absence of clamps is now being used generally as a character of value in basidiomycete taxonomy such observations as recorded here are worth mentioning. The spores are the same size as for P. *spumosa* in Europe. The germ pore is broad enough so that with a 1.4 NA oil ob. the apex appears obscurely truncate in some spores. In some pilei the pleurocystidia were seen to fork as in P. *tetonensis*.

172. **Pholiota spumosa** (Fr.) Singer Lilloa 22: 517. 1951.

Agaricus spumosus Fries, Syst. Myc. 1: 252. 1821.

Flammula spumosa (Fr.) Kummer, Der Führer in die Pilzkunde, p. 81. 1871.

Dryophila spumosa (Fr.) Quélet, Enchir. Fung. p. 70. 1886.

Illustrations: Text figs. 377-380; pl. 77-78.

Pileus caespitose to gregarious, (2) 3–6 cm broad, at first broadly and obtusely conic to convex, becoming expanded-plane, with or without an umbo, or at times with a prominent conic umbo, when young "Isabella-color" over all, or the margin "olive-ocher," "ecru-olive," darker and more brownish toward the "tawny" to "ochraceous-tawny" or "buck-thorn-brown" disc, at maturity the marginal portion yellowish, often with a greenish tint, glutinous or viscid, glabrous but appearing fibrillose-streaked, sometimes the center roughened by the drying gluten. Context yellow, sometimes a watery "bright green-yellow," soft; odor and taste mild.

Lamellae adnate to adnexed, or with a decurrent tooth, at first "sulphur-yellow" to "citron-yellow," "massicot-yellow," or "pale greenish-yellow," becoming tawny or cinnamon-brown, often retaining a greenish hue, close, medium broad.

Stipe 3–5 (10) cm long, 4–5 (8) mm thick, "amber-yellow" within, surface "napthalene-yellow," "barium-yellow" to "pale greenish-yellow" above, becoming sordid brown from the base upward, surface covered by a thin coating of yellow fibrils from the veil remnants, apex pruinose and greenish yellow, becoming hollow, equal.

Spores 7–9 × 4–4.5 μ, smooth, germ pore distinct but apex not truncate; shape in face view oblong to elliptic, in profile slightly bean-shaped to somewhat inequilateral; in KOH dull tawny, in Melzer's reagent paler and more cinnamon; wall about 0.3 μ thick.

Basidia 26–32 × 6–7 μ, 4-spored, narrowly clavate hyaline to yellowish in KOH and yellowish in Melzer's reagent. Pleurocystidia 40–60 (68) × 7–14 (16) μ, fusoid-ventricose with subacute to obtuse apex, smooth or rarely with an ochraceous (in KOH) mucilaginous coating, thin-walled; content hyaline to yellowish, colloidal in the neck. Cheilocystidia (28) 35–55 × 9–13 μ, subclavate, broadly subfusoid, to fusoid-ventricose, thin-walled, smooth or with incrusting ochraceous material, hyaline to yellowish in KOH. Caulocystidia (24) 40–80 (120) × (5) 10–20 μ, mostly clavate, wall thin, ochraceous in KOH, smooth or with bands of incrusting material.

Gill trama of a central area of floccose hyphae the cells inflated to 15 μ or more, yellowish in KOH or in Melzer's and smooth; subhymenium a well developed gelatinous layer of narrow hyaline interwoven hyphae. Pileus cutis a thick gelatinous pellicle of hyaline to yellowish, narrow (2–3 μ) gelatinous hyphae; hypodermial region of incrusted brown hyphae (in KOH). Context of interwoven inflated smooth yellowish-walled hyphae (as revived in KOH). Clamp connections present. All hyphae in amyloid.

HABIT, HABITAT, AND DISTRIBUTION: On soil, in coniferous woods and on logs, stumps, buried wood, sawdust, duff, and humus; more rarely reported on hardwood (birch, oak, aspen); New York, North Carolina, Tennessee, Michigan, Colorado, Idaho, Montana, Wyoming, Washington, Oregon, California, and Canada (Nova Scotia), June—December; also in Europe.

OBSERVATIONS: This is the most common and variable species in the "spumosa complex" which among others is composed of *P. vialis, P. piceina, P. subflavida, P. graveolens, P. fulviconica, P. squalida, P. subamara* and *P. velata.*

In our description we have taken our microscopic data from a collection made in Sweden by Nannfeldt. In it the spore size is 7–9 × 4–5.5 μ. In most collections under the name *Flammula spumosa* in American herbaria (we have not studied all of them) the spores measure 5.5–8 × 4–4.5 μ. This will be noted by anyone examining our material cited.

The lack of macroscopic data on most of the herbarium material we have studied prevents accurate identification of it. The problem here, however, is that of the group as a whole. In order to focus on the features of importance in the recognition of species one first must study the group to ascertain what characters are present, and if possible obtain data on their variability. The only way this can be done scientifically is to set up a classification as we have done here and use it as a testing mechanism with reference to further field studies and studies in culture. The time to pass judgement on the species concepts is after the data have been accumulated and studied, not before, as has been done all too frequently in the past.

We have evidence that the same problem of variants within this complex is present in Europe as well as in North America. A collection by Romell (no. 9782) is an example. The following are our data on it:

Spores 6–7.5 (8) × 4–4.5 μ, smooth, apical pore minute and inconspicuous (under oil) ; shape in face view elliptic to oblong, in profile very obscurely inequilateral; color in KOH pale ochraceous tawny, in Melzer's scarcely changing; wall about 0.25 μ thick.

Basidia 4-spored, 18–22 × 6–7 μ, clavate hyaline in KOH, yellowish in Melzer's reagent. Pleurocystidia scattered, 36–58 (63) × 8–12 (15) μ, fusoid-ventricose with the "neck" narrowly elliptic in optical section varying to typically fusoid ventricose with a straight neck and obtuse apex; wall thin, smooth, hyaline to yellowish in KOH. Content "empty" or with a plug of yellowish colloidal material in the apex. Cheilocystidia clavate to fusoid-ventricose or ventricose with the "neck" enlarged and apex rounded, smooth, thin-walled, content hyaline to yellowish. Caulocystidia in clusters 40–80 × 7–12 μ, cylindric to clavate, thin-walled, walls smooth, yellowish in KOH; content "empty."

Gill trama with a central area of parallel hyaline thin-walled smooth hyphae 4–8 μ in diam. which are non-gelatinous in KOH; subhymenium of loosely arranged non-gelatinous to subgelatinous (near gill edge) hyphae 2.5–3.5 μ in diam. Pileus cutis a gelatinous pellicle of narrow hyaline to yellowish hyphae with numerous transverse creases as revived (appearing crinkled) ; hypodermial region rusty-fulvous in KOH, hyphae floccose and fairly heavily incrusted. Context hyphae interwoven, thin-walled, walls smooth (except near hypodermium) and cells inflated. All hyphae inamyloid. Clamp connections present.

Romell's painting with the collection (no. 9782) , shows a *Pholiota* with olive in the coloration and a somewhat dingy stipe much as we know the species in North America but the microscopic features are different and as dried the basidiocarps are a very bright yellow. The subhymenium is not truly gelatinous as revived in KOH. Sections compared give quite a different picture. The pleurocystidia are smaller and have a strong tendency for a secondary enlargement beyond the main ventricose portion in the area normally described as the neck. Also, the spores are "small," as in some American collections.

Kühner and Romagnesi (1953) write: "dans la chair, au moins a la ligne cornée (où l'on voit au microscope de grosses masses jaune-verte intercellulaires, qui manquent chez la précédente" . . . (meaning *Dryophila lubrica*). We have not seen such pigment masses in the course of our study, indicating that very likely the French authors have still another variant. Pilat (1932) gives the spores as 7–8.5 × 4.5–5.5 μ. These are wider in relation to length than in any of the American variants grouped here.

The following is a description of fresh material which appears to belong in this species.

Pileus 3–8 cm broad, convex with an incurved margin, expanding to plane with the margin usually remaining decurved, surface slimy-viscid, at first obscurely spotted with agglutinated veil particles but these soon obliterated, color pale dull tawny, with the margin pale yellow, or at times "tawny" on disc and "warm-buff" on margin, water-soaked margin olivaceous in age, margin fringed at first from fibrils of yellow veil. Context pale yellow with a watery green line above the gills, taste mild, odor faint but reminding one of freshly husked green corn, with FeSO$_4$ olivaceous.

Lamellae pale yellow when young, pale dull cinnamon when mature, more or less subdistant at maturity, broad, adnexed-seceding, becoming ventricose near the stipe.

Stipe 5–11 cm long, 9–17 mm at apex, slightly enlarged downward, yellow over all when young, soon olive-brown to very dingy rusty brown from the base up, thinly fibrillose from the yellow veil but the fibrils discoloring over lower part of stipe, apex silky to fibrillose, no distinct veil-line left at maturity.

Spores in deposit dull rusty brown, 7–9 × 4–5 μ, smooth, with a small but distinct apical germ pore; shape elliptic to ovate in face view, in profile slightly bean-shaped to obscurely inequilateral; color in KOH dull cinnamon, not much different in Melzer's reagent, wall about 0.3 μ thick.

Basidia 15–26 × 5–6 (7) μ, 4-spored, clavate, hyaline in KOH. Pleurocystidia 55–75 (80) × 9–18 μ, fusoid-ventricose, content dull yellow in KOH as revived from a colloidal material in the neck, walls thin and smooth. Cheilocystidia similar to pleurocystidia but with less of a neck, often tapered from ventricose part to the obtuse apex, walls smooth, thin; content ochraceous in KOH. Caulocystidia 50–120 × 10–18 μ, fusoid-ventricose to clavate, often with a secondary cross wall near the base, thin-walled and hyaline in KOH, scattered.

Gill trama with a central area of parallel hyphae the cells of which finally inflate to about 15 μ, walls brownish to hyaline, smooth or nearly so; subhymenium a poorly defined gelatinous to subgelatinous layer. Pileus cutis of narrow gelatinous hyphae 2–3 μ diam., hyaline to ochraceous in KOH, loosely tangled, hypodermium a compactly interwoven layer of hyphae with more or less platelike rusty brown incrustation, the hyphae of various diameters but thin-walled. Context hyphae thin-walled, hyaline in KOH or nearly so, cells greatly inflated in some hyphae. Clamp connections present.

HABIT, HABITAT, AND DISTRIBUTION: Caespitose on chip dirt in a mill yard, Cusick, Wash. Oct. 12, 1966. Smith 74157. The mill had been cutting conifer wood entirely.

OBSERVATIONS: This is a common variant, which as far as a comparison of dried material goes is the closest to *P. vialis* of any *Pholiota* collected. It was a brighter yellow than material referred to *P. spumosa*, but does have occasional caulocystidia and a slight odor. The subhymenium is not as gelatinous as it is in specimens assigned to *P. spumosa*.

Because of the confusion involving the variants of *P. spumosa* we are not including a list of material studied. Herbaria are full of specimens in this group but the data to accurately classify them are lacking for the most part. As mentioned many times previously for other groups, carefully correlated field and culture studies seem to be the approach most likely to furnish a better understanding of the complex.

173. Pholiota velata (Pk.) comb. nov.

Flammula velata Peck, Bull. Torrey Bot. Club 30: 96. 1903.
Gymnopilus velatus (Pk.) Murrill, North Amer. Fl. 10: 196. 1917.
Illustrations: Text figs. 381-383.

Pileus 2–4 cm broad, convex, sulphur-yellow, center reddish or orange, margin persistently incurved. Context thin, especially toward the margin, yellow or greenish yellow; taste mild.

Lamellae adnate or slightly decurrent, arcuate, pale yellow, becoming rusty brown or snuff-brown in age, medium narrow.

Stipe 2.5–4.5 cm long, 2–4 mm thick, sulfur-yellow above, brownish below, fibrillose, somewhat tomentose at the base, flexuous, solid. Veil arachnoid, yellowish white, strongly developed.

Spores 7–9 × 4–4.5 (5) μ, smooth, apical pore minute and apex not truncate; shape in face view oblong to elliptic, in profile obscurely inequilateral; tawny to ochraceous in KOH, not much different in Melzer's reagent; wall about 0.3 μ thick.

Basidia 18–24 × 5–6.5 μ, obese, 4-spored, yellowish revived in KOH or Melzer's reagent. Pleurocystidia 45–62 × 7–14 μ, fusoid-ventricose, broadly obtuse or subacute at apex, neck in outline often wavy; wall thin to slightly thickened (–0.5 μ), smooth or coated or capped with hardened amber mucilaginous material; content of coagulated amber-colored material gradually dissolving in KOH and content then yellowish to hyaline. Cheilocystidia 30–45 × 7–12 μ, subfusoid to fusoid-ventricose, similar to pleurocystidia in remaining features. Caulocystidia not studied.

Gill trama of floccose subparallel hyphae hyaline to yellowish in

Text Fig. 28.

Figs. 384-386, pleurocystidia, cheilocystidia and spores of *P. vialis;* 387-389, cheilocystidia, spores and pleurocystidia of *P. piceina;* 390-392, caulocystidia, spores and pleurocystidia of *P. astragalina;* 393 & 394, pleurocystidia and spores of *P. coloradensis.*

KOH (not reviving well) ; subhymenium a gelatinous layer of narrow (± 2.5 μ) hyaline hyphae. Pileus cutis a gelatinous pellicle of interwoven narrow (1.5–2.5 μ) hyaline to yellowish hyphae; hypodermial region highly colored. Clamp connections present. All hyphae non-amyloid.

HABIT, HABITAT, AND DISTRIBUTION: In woods along streams, Idaho, July; type studied.

OBSERVATIONS: The small size, strongly developed yellowish white veil, and the yellow to greenish yellow flesh are distinctive. It is close to *P. tottenii*, in which brown tints are in the pileus, the flesh pale-buff, and the gills emarginate and broad. We have found no record of its occurrence other than the type.

The microscopic data are from the type. The species is typical of subgenus *Flammuloides* and appears close to *P. graveolens*.

174. Pholiota vialis (Murr.) comb. nov.

Flammula vialis Murrill, Mycologia 4: 262. 1912.
Gymnopilus vialis Murrill, Mycologia 4: 255. 1912.
Illustrations: Text figs. 384-386.

Pileus 5 cm broad, convex to expanded, at length depressed, dark flavo-luteous with bay center or the entire surface bay, splitting radially at the margin, viscid, glabrous, smooth, at length rimose.

Lamellae adnate, citrinous to ferruginous-fulvous, ventricose, broad, rather crowded.

Stipe 5 cm long, 10–15 mm thick, citrinous, equal or inflated, solid or hollow, fibrillose, especially at the top where a slight trace of the fugacious veil remains.

Spores (6) 7–9 × 4–4.5 (5) μ, smooth, apical pore minute; shape in face view oblong to elliptic, more rarely ovate, in profile mostly somewhat inequilateral; color revived in KOH, dull cinnamon-brown, in Melzer's reagent paler; wall about 0.3 μ thick.

Basidia 23–30 × 5–7 μ, 2- and 4-spored, clavate, yellowish in KOH and in Melzer's reagent. Pleurocystidia 36–75 × 7–15 μ, fusoid-ventricose varying (rarely) toward utriform or subclavate, wall thin smooth and hyaline, content amber-brown to yellow and on standing in KOH gradually becoming hyaline, homogeneous. Cheilocystidia 33–52 × 7–12 μ, subfusoid, utriform, or fusoid-ventricose, smooth, thin-walled, walls yellowish in some, content soon homogeneous (in KOH). Caulocystidia none found.

Gill trama with a central floccose area of somewhat interwoven hyphae, cells elongate and up to 15 μ broad, walls thin and smooth, yellowish to hyaline in KOH; subhymenium a distinct gelatinous layer of somewhat interwoven hyphae 2–3 μ broad. Pileus cutis a well developed pellicle of interwoven narrow (1.5–3 μ) hyaline to ochraceous hyphae with smooth walls but toward hypodermium some with tawny incrustations; hypodermial region of rusty fulvous floccose encrusted hyphae 5–15 μ diam. Context hyphae interwoven, cells inflated, walls thin smooth and yellowish to hyaline. Clamp connections present. All hyphae inamyloid.

HABIT, HABITAT, AND DISTRIBUTION: On wood, Oregon, November. Type studied.

OBSERVATIONS: We recognize this species with great reluctance, but if caulocystidia really are absent this would distinguish it from European specimens of *P. spumosa* we have studied. Also, the utriform cheilocystidia mixed in with the normal type for the *P. spumosa* group may be an additional character. In fact the presence of utriform cheilocystidia indicates a connection to *P. graveolens* but for *P. vialis* we have no data on the odor. The bay colored pileus disc would seem to exclude *P. spumosa*, but the dried basidiocarps are not too convincing. They resemble those of *P. spumosa*. *P. piceina* differs in its clear bright yellow pileus as dried. No thick-walled pleurocystidia were found.

175. Pholiota piceina (Murr.) comb. nov.

Gymnopilus piceinus Murrill, North Amer. Flora 10: 202. 1917.
Illustrations: Text figs. 387-389; pl. 79a.

Pileus scattered or caespitose, 3–5 cm broad, convex to expanded, obtuse, bright yellow, darker and reddish on the disc, very viscid, glabrous, margin not striate. Context greenish yellow; taste mild.

Lamellae sinuate-decurrent, yellow to pale fuscous, subcrowded, heterophyllus, rather broad, plane.

Stipe 3–5 cm long, 4–6 mm thick, concolorous but darker at the base, cylindric, somewhat fibrillose, stuffed, becoming hollow.

Spores 7–9 × 4–5 μ smooth, apical pore present but minute; shape in face view oblong to elliptic or slightly ovate, in profile obscurely inequilateral; color in KOH tawny to ochraceous tawny, more ochraceous in Melzer's reagent; wall about 0.25 μ thick.

Basidia 18–24 × 4–6 μ, 4-spored, obese, yellow in KOH and Melzer's reagent. Pleurocystidia 38–66 × 9–12 μ, fusoid-ventricose with obtuse apex, smooth, thin-walled, content ochraceous to pale tawny, fading on standing. Cheilocystidia 27–34 × 7–12 μ fusoid ventricose, apex obtuse, content mostly pale rusty brown to ochraceous; walls smooth or thinly coated with ochraceous material. Caulocystidia at very apex of stipe, similar to cheilocystidia.

Gill trama of a central area of floccose, parallel to interwoven hyphae with elongate cells; walls thin and pale ochraceous in KOH, smooth; subhymenium a thick layer of gelatinous narrow (1.5–3 μ) interwoven branched hyphae hyaline in KOH. Pileus cutis a gelatinous pellicle of hyphae 2–3 μ, ochraceous in KOH and soon collapsing, smooth (as far as observed); hypodermial region of floccose hyphae about like those of context only slightly more ochraceous in KOH, smooth-walled as far as observed. Context hyphae inflated; walls smooth, thin and pale ochraceous. Clamp connections present. All hyphae inamyloid.

HABIT, HABITAT, AND DISTRIBUTION: On spruce, Maine, August. Type studied.

OBSERVATIONS: The microscopic data are all from the type. The species should be compared carefully with *P. graveolens.* As dried the gills of the type are about "buckthorn brown" (yellow-brown). The dried pileus is a pale bright yellow. Also, *P. vialis* and *P. piceina* should be compared on the basis of additional collections and culture studies if possible. We are not completely satisfied that all three are distinct from each other.

We have notes and a photograph (pl. 71) of an Idaho collection which may belong here:

Pileus 3–6 cm broad, broadly convex becoming nearly plane, with a few faint fibrils from the veil but soon glabrous, color pale bright yellow ("Naphthaline yellow") margin finally decoloring to yellowish white, disc pale orange-brown at maturity, ochraceous at first. Context thickish, yellow, when cut staining a brighter yellow then (finally) dingy brownish; taste mild, odor of corn husks ($\pm$), with FeSO$_4$—olive, with tincture of Guaiac quickly green.

Lamellae pale yellow becoming dull cinnamon brown, broad, adnate, close to subdistant.

Stipe 3–8 cm long, 6–10 mm thick, equal, soon hollow, bright yellow in cortex, surface pale yellow above, soon rusty fulvous below, drying pale bright yellow like the pileus with the basal discoloration not pronounced, thinly fibrillose from the pale yellow veil.

Spore deposit dark cinnamon. Spores 6.5–8 × 3.8–4.2 μ smooth, with a minute apical pore; shape elliptic varying to subovate in face view, nearly elliptic in profile; color in KOH dull cinnamon, paler in Melzer's reagent; wall about 0.25 μ thick.

Basidia 4-spored, 18–24 × 6–8 μ clavate, mostly yellow in KOH (as spores begin to form), dingy ochraceous in Melzer's. Pleurocystidia 50–85 × 9–17 μ, fusoid ventricose, apex obtuse, thin-walled, with a long narrow pedicel (originating at edge of central non-gelatinous strand in gill trama), smooth. Cheilocystidia similar to pleurocystidia but shorter, caulocystidia in fascicles, clavate to fusoid-ventricosa 30–80 × 10–18 μ, mostly thin-walled and smooth.

Gill trama with a central strand of parallel hyphae of relatively short cells and in area toward the pileus trama the cells inflating markedly, thin-walled, hyaline to yellowish in KOH, some oleiferous hyphae present; subhymenium a gelatinous zone of hyaline branched narrow hyphae. Pileus cutis a pellicle of mixed narrow (2–3 μ) and wider (4–7 μ) hyphae with disintegrating walls yellowish to hyaline in KOH; hypodermium of interwoven non-gelatinous somewhat roughened to smooth hyphae ochraceous to ochraceous brown in KOH. Context hyphae yellowish to greenish hyaline in KOH, smooth, thin-walled, very compactly arranged. Clamp connections present.

Gregarious on or around old conifer logs, Binarch Creek, Priest Lake, Idaho, Sept. 17, 1966. Smith 73446.

We identify this collection as *P. piceina* not only because of the dark gills when fresh (we cannot be sure what Murrill meant by "pale fuscous") but especially by the bright yellow color which is preserved in drying. The spores are a shade smaller than in the type but not enough so to appear significant. If Smith 73446 is indeed *P. piceina* the species is further distinguished by the green Guaiac reaction, the slight peculiar odor, and the cut context becoming brighter yellow and then brownish. The wide hyphae in the gelatinous pellicle may or may not be distinctive. We did not note them in the type, but their apparent absence would not necessarily be critical since several problems arise concerning them—are they stray filaments from the context which gelatinize less than the narrow hyphae, is their presence merely evidence of shreds of the veil too sparse to show macroscopically (they were mostly near the surface) or is the cutis truly "dimitic"—if the latter is the case the character should be regarded as significant.

Section **Lubricae** (Fr.) Singer, emended

Lilloa 22: 516. 1951.

Pleurocystidia prominent but not of the type generally known as chrysocystidia; spores 5–8 (9) × 3–4.5 (5) μ; pileus glutinous to viscid. Type: *P. lubrica.*

Key to Stirpes

1. Taste bitter .... Stirps *Astragalina*
1. Taste mild to farinaceous 2
   2. Pileus color in bright ferruginous-red, orange-red or brilliant orange-yellow range .... Stirps *Fibrillosipes*
   2. Pileus color darker or duller at least over disc 3
3. Pileus cinnamon to dark cinnamon brown, subtestaceous or bay-brown; marginal area not yellow (may be pallid to tan, *etc.*) ....
.... Stirps *Lubrica*
3. Pileus variously colored but at least the pileus margin some shade of yellow varying to pallid (old or faded specimens of stirps *Fibrillosipes* will key here also) 4
   4. Pileus muticolored-mixed green, violaceous, purple-drab and yellow at different stages .... Stirps *Polychroa*
   4. Not as above 5
5. Typically *on* decaying wood; spores 3.5–4.5 μ (see stirps *Lenta* also)
.... Stirps *Crassipedes*

5. Typically near decaying wood or on very decayed wood 6
6. Spores 2.8–3.5 (4) μ broad .... Stirps *Innocua*
6. Spores 4–4.5 (5) μ broad .... Stirps *Lenta*

Stirps Astragalina

The bitter taste is the central feature. We recognize one species in the group at present. *Flammula amara* Fr. sensu Kauffman probably belongs here but we finally decided to exclude it pending further study.

176. Pholiota astragalina (Fr.) Singer Agar. in Mod. Tax., p. 516. 1951.

Agaricus astragalinus Fries, Syst. Myc. 1: 251. 1821.
Agaricus neesii Barla, Champ. Prov. Nice, p. 46. 1859.
Flammula astragalina (Fr.) Kummer, Der Führer in die Pilzkunde, p. 82. 1871.
Dryophila astragalina Quélet, Enchir. Fung., p. 71. 1886.
Gymnopilus laeticolor Murrill, Mycologia 4: 251. 1912.
Flammula laeticolor Murrill, Mycologia 4: 262. 1912.
Illustrations: Text figs. 390-392; pls. 80, 81.

Pileus 2–4 cm broad, obtusely conic or obtusely umbonate when young, expanding to obtusely campanulate and finally with a spreading or uplifted margin which may become wavy, usually retaining a slight obtuse umbo, smooth, viscid to glutinous when wet, soon dry, glabrous except for pallid, fibrillose remains of the veil along the margin, color brilliant pinkish orange ("flame-scarlet" to "bittersweet-orange"), fading somewhat in age and soon developing blackish discolorations. Context moderately thick, tapered evenly to the margin (about 4 mm in the disc), pliant and watery, "Mikado-orange" but soon paler yellowish orange; odor none, taste bitter.

Lamellae sharply and deeply adnexed, at times appearing to be almost free, close, 2–3 tiers of lamellulae, moderately broad (3–4 mm), "capucine-yellow" (orange-yellow) but discoloring somewhat where bruised, edges even.

Stipe 5–9 cm long, 4–7 mm thick, equal, terete, hollow, flexuous, apex "cream-color" within, in the base sordid orange buff, surface more or less fibrillose and pallid yellowish from the yellow veil, base tinged faintly like the pileus and soon sordid orange, brown where handled, glabrescent.

Spores 5–7 × 3.8–4.5 μ, smooth, germ pore minute and apex not truncate; shape in face view ovate to elliptic, in profile somewhat inequilateral to obscurely so; revived in KOH rusty brown, in Melzer's reagent paler and more cinnamon; wall about 0.3 μ thick.

Basidia 18–26 × 5–7 μ, 4-spored, narrowly clavate, yellowish in KOH and in Melzer's reagent. Pleurocystidia 35–60 × 8–14 μ, fusoid-ventricose to clavate-mucronate, base often 6–8 μ or more broad, wall thin and smooth, apex obtuse to subacute; content amorphous-refractive and in some organized into a solid refractive mass, in others more or less resembling coagulated material and somewhat granular in appearance, both types intergrading, the coagulated content bright yellow in KOH and orange to orange-red in Melzer's reagent. Cheilocystidia 40–75 × 4–8 × 3–4.4 μ, ventricose at base and neck a long cylindric tube ending in an obtuse apex, walls at times with adhering debris and often yellowish in KOH. Caulocystidia none found except for a few clavate hyphal end-cells.

Gill trama with a central area of greatly inflated hyphal cells (to 20 μ or more); subhymenial area of narrower (3–6 μ), non-gelatinous hyphae, yellow pigment in solution pervading the section. Pileus cutis a gelatinous pellicle of hyaline to yellow interwoven hyphae 2–5 μ diam.; hypodermial region more ochraceous, cells compactly arranged and 8–12 (20) μ broad. Context hyphae interwoven, of very broad cells, smooth, yellow pigment spreading throughout the mount. Clamp connections present. All hyphae inamyloid.

HABIT, HABITAT, AND DISTRIBUTION: On logs, stumps, and rotting wood of conifers, California, Michigan, Tennessee, Idaho, Oregon and Washington. August to October.

OBSERVATIONS: The bright colors of the pileus, bitter taste, and the development of black discolorations are distinctive features of this species. It appears related to *P. piceina,* which is bright yellow with a darker, reddish disc, with greenish yellow context, smaller cheilocystidia, narrow tramal hyphae of the lamellae, and in having a distinct hypodermium.

The pileus trama and gill trama are brown or yellowish brown in KOH but slowly fade out to nearly hyaline. When sections dipped in 95% alcohol and then in water are mounted in 2% KOH, a greenish yellow pigment diffuses into the mounting fluid. The curious cheilocystidia are a unique character in the genus.

MATERIAL EXAMINED: CALIFORNIA: Smith 8812: IDAHO: Smith 70251; MICHIGAN: Smith 33-750, 25881, 37409, 38522, 38655; MONTANA: Kauffman 7-8-28; NORTH CAROLINA: Hesler 19298; OREGON: Gruber 687; KAUFFMAN: 10-14-22, 10-15-22; Smith 18747, 20187, 20231, 20243, 28419, 28249; WASHINGTON: Kauffman 10-17-15a, 10-17-15b, 10-14-25, 10-25-25; Smith 3094, 16246, 16446, 16704, 16749, 16856, 17102, 17844, 30108, 31493, 31780. CANADA: ONTARIO: Smith 4533. FRANCE: Josserand 30-8-37. SWEDEN: Kauffman 10-1808. SWITZERLAND: Favre.

Stirps Fibrillosipes

This group contains the non-bitter bright red, orange-red to orange or brilliant yellow species.

Key

1. Stipe 6–12 (15) mm thick (see *P. spinulifera* also) 2
1. Stipe 3–6 (8) mm thick 4
　2. Veil with an outer gelatinous layer .... *P. coloradensis*
　2. Veil dry and fibrillose 3
3. Veil remnants on pileus pallid tan to yellowish; spores ochraceous tawny in KOH .... *P. sublubrica*
3. Veil remnants whitish; spores in KOH merely pale yellowish ....
　... *P. armeniaca*
　4. Growing on soil; lamellae narrow .... *P. subcarbonaria*
　4. Not with above combination of features 5
5. Some fibrils on the stipe brilliant orange .... *P. fibrillosipes*
5. Not as above 6
　6. Spores in KOH pale rusty cinnamon .... *P. luteola*
　6. Spores merely yellowish in KOH .... *P. spinulifera*

　177. **Pholiota coloradensis** sp. nov.
Illustrations: Text figs. 393-394; 395.

　Pileus 5–6 cm latus, campanulatus, glaber, viscidus, aurantiacus ("ochraceous-orange"), ad marginem albofibrillosus. Contextus albus. Lamellae subdecurrentes, angustae pallide griseo-olivaceae demum sub-fulvae. Stipes 5–6 cm longus, 9–10 mm crassus, solidus, albidus, deorsum demum subfulvus. Sporae 6–7.5 × 4–4.5 μ. Pleurocystidia 45–65 × 9–15 μ, utriformia, tenuitunicatus. Specimen typicum in Herb. Univ. Mich. conservatum est; legit prope Tolland, Colo. 12 Sept. 1920. C. H. Kauff-man.

　Pileus 5–6 cm broad, campanulate-convex, obtuse when young, broadly umbonate in age, glabrous, viscid, pale orange ("ochraceous-orange") when fresh (all ochraceous as dried), in age at times spotted from the gluten. Margin whitish from veil remnants disposed along it. Context white to whitish, thick, scissile.

　Lamellae adnexed becoming subdecurrent, rather narrow, close to crowded, almost "dark olive-buff" then "Isabella-color" to "tawny-olive," edges entire, concolor.

　Stipe 5–6 cm long, 9–10 mm thick, solid, persistently fibrous-stuffed, white at first, very thinly peronate to the annular zone, concentrically arranged shreds or patches of veil material lower down, becoming rusty brown in base. Veil gelatinous outside—fibrillose to interior.

　Spores 6–7.5 × 4–4.5 μ, pale tawny in KOH and about the same in Melzer's reagent, smooth, apical pore very minute, in face view elliptic to ovate; in profile mostly obscurely inequilateral to subovate, apiculus indistinct.

　Basidia 18–23 × 5–6.5 μ, 4-spored, clavate, yellowish in KOH and Melzer's reagent. Pleurocystidia 45–65 × 9–15 μ, subcylindric to utri-

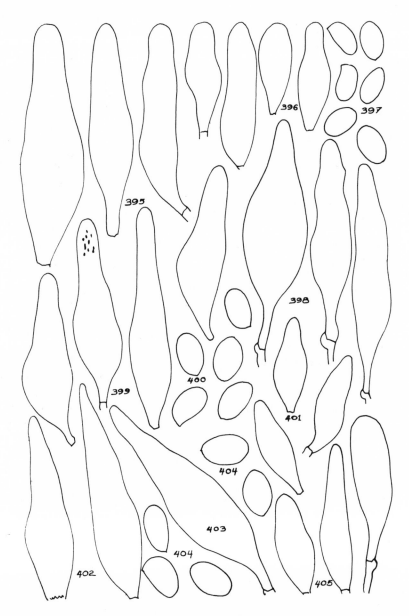

Text Fig. 29.

Figs. 395, pleurocystidia of *P. coloradensis;* 396-398, cheilocystidia, spores, and pleurocystidia of *P. sublubrica;* 399-401, pleurocystidia, spores, and cheilocystidia of *P. subcarbonaria;* 402-405, pleurocystidia (403 also), spores and cheilocystidia of *P. luteola.*

form, apex broadly rounded, wall thin smooth and hyaline; content homogeneous ochraceous in KOH and slowly bleaching. Cheilocystidia similar to pleurocystidia or more obese. Gill trama typical of *P. lubrica* group. Pileus cutis a thick pellicle of interwoven narrow (2–3 μ) hyaline to yellowish hyphae with minutely asperulate walls; hypodermial zone of orange-rusty incrusted broader hyphae and context hyphae 6–15 μ ± broad, smooth, thin-walled and nearly hyaline. Clamp connections present. All hyphae inamyloid.

HABIT, HABITAT, AND DISTRIBUTION: On humus under spruce, Tolland, Colorado. 9500 ft. Sept. 12, 1910. C. H. Kauffman, type.

OBSERVATIONS: This species was identified by Kauffman as *Flammula lubrica* but the broadly rounded pleurocystidia do not check with European material. It is close to *P. tetonensis* in cystidial features. The colors approach those shown for *Agaricus (Flammula) lubricus* in Fries' Icones.

178. Pholiota sublubrica sp. nov.
Illustrations: Text figs. 396-398; pl. 85.

Pileus 4–10(15) cm latus, convexo-umbonatus aurantio-fulvus demum pallide fulvus, ad marginem appendiculatus, viscidus. Contextus albus. Lamellae adnatae latae, confertae demum fulvomaculatae. Stipe 4–10 cm longus, 10–15 mm crassus, aequalis, solidus, subalbidus; deorsum squamulosus, demum fulvus. Sporae 5.5–7 × 3.2–4 μ. Pleurocystidia 45–83 × 9–16 μ, pallide lutea, tenui-tunicata. Cheilocystidia 32–50 × 8–12(8) μ, fusoide ventricosa vel subclavata. Specimen typicum in Herb. Univ. Mich. conservatum est; legit prope Stanley, Idaho, 19 Aug. 1954. Smith 46383.

Pileus 4–10 (15) cm broad, obtuse when young, expanding to obtusely umbonate, disc ochraceous tawny to ochraceous orange, margin pale pinkish buff to more yellowish, with brownish veil remnants in zones or patches along the margin, surface in old caps somewhat watery spotted, viscid, margin even. Context white, no color change on bruising; odor or taste not distinctive.

Lamellae bluntly adnate, often with a decurrent tooth, dull rusty brown at maturity, occasionally rusty-spotted in age, moderately broad, close, pallid when young.

Stipe 4–10 cm long, 10–15 mm thick, equal, solid, fibrous-tough, whitish but base soon rusty brown and color change progressing upward, in age brown over all, apex silky, with a superior fibrillose zone or annulus, below this ragged-fibrillose to squamulose from the pallid veil remnants.

Spores 5.5–7 × 3.2–4 μ, smooth ochraceous tawny in KOH, merely yellowish in Melzer's reagent, apical pore minute; shape in face view oblong to slightly ovate, in profile obscurely to distinctly bean-shaped; wall thin (± 0.35 μ).

Basidia 17–20 (24) × 4–5 (6) μ, 4-spored, clavate (hymenium bright yellow in KOH, duller yellow in Melzer's reagent). Pleurocystidia abundant, 45–83 × 9–16 μ, prominently projecting, broadly to narrowly fusoid-ventricose with greatly elongated neck of uneven diameter and apex obtuse to subacute, in KOH and Melzer's the content evenly ochraceous (rarely with solid matter), walls thin to slightly thickened (up to 0.5 μ) in ventricose part in some, smooth. Cheilocystidia 32–50 × 8–12 (18) μ, fusoid-ventricose and similar to pleurocystidia or shorter and more obese or utriform to subclavate, hyaline to evenly pale ochraceous in KOH. Caulocystidia none.

Gill trama of floccose parallel hyphae with hyaline smooth thin walls as revived in KOH, merely yellowish in Melzer's reagent, cells short to elongate, becoming inflated in age (8–15 μ); subhymenium a hyaline gelatinous narrow zone of interwoven hyphae. Pileus cutis a thick (to 250 μ) gelatinous layer of hyphae 2–3 μ diam., with smooth or nearly smooth walls and interwoven; hypodermial zone of narrow (3–8 μ) orange-rusty hyphae with incrusted walls. Context hyphae 5–15 μ diam., thin walled, smooth, interwoven and hyaline to yellowish in KOH. Clamp connections none. All hyphae inamyloid.

HABIT, HABITAT, AND DISTRIBUTION: On or near rotting conifer logs, Idaho Washington and California, summer and fall.

OBSERVATIONS: This species has some characters in common with *P. lubrica,* but differs chiefly in the brown color of the veil remnants on the pileus. This color is limited to the outer layer of the veil and shows best on remnants left on the pileus. Those on the stipe are usually whitish from the pulling apart of the veil layer as the stipes elongate. The stipe elongation is somewhat like that in subgenus *Bulbopodium* of *Cortinarius* where the outer veil if present connects to the rim of the basal bulb and the veil remnants on the stipe represent mostly partial veil material. See *P. lubrica* and *P. avellaneifolia* for further comment.

MATERIAL EXAMINED: CALIFORNIA: Smith 56086. IDAHO: Smith 46383 (type), 65714, 69588, 69784. WASHINGTON: 17278.

179. Pholiota armeniaca sp. nov.

Pileus 3–9 cm latus, hemisphericus, viscidus, glaber, persicinus vel laete luteus; lamellae confertae latae, brunneolae demum olivaceo-brunneae; stipes 5–7 cm longus, 6–12 mm latus, sursum pallidus; velum pallidum; sporae 6–7.5(8) × 3.5–4.5 μ in "KOH" lutealae; pleurocystidia 43–68 × 9–14 μ. Specimen typicum in Herb. Univ. of Mich. conservatum est; legit prope Tolland, Colorado, 17 Sept. 1920. C. H. Kauffman.

Pileus 3–9 cm hemispheric becoming nearly plane, margin undulating, glabrous, viscid, shining when dry, color "apricot-orange" on disc and "antimony-yellow" toward the margin, "zinc-orange" to tawny in age; margin with whitish particles of veil. Context white, taste slightly disagreeable, odor none.

Lamellae broadly adnate becoming subdecurrent, crowded, rather broad (5–8 mm), "pinkish-buff" young becoming "cinnamon-buff" and finally "buffy-brown" (olive-brownish).

Stipe 5–7 cm long, 6–12 mm, equal, base slightly bulbous, surface covered by the veil forming a sheath of floccose fibrils, sheath terminating in an annular zone, whitish above the sheath and silky-pruinose, apex striate from gill-lines in some.

Spores in deposit (on annulus, nearly fuscous—Kauffman), (5.5) 6–7.5 (8) × 3.5–4 (4.5) μ, smooth, apical pore minute, in face view oblong to narrowly ovate and often with a truncate base, in profile obscurely bean-shaped to nearly oblong, in KOH *pale* ochraceous, in Melzer's reagent nearly hyaline, wall thin (less than 0.25 μ).

Basidia 4-spored, 20–24 × 5–6.5 μ, content ochraceous in KOH, paler in Melzer's. Pleurocystidia 43–68 × 9–14 μ fusoid-ventricose, neck 7–10 μ thick and apex obtuse to rounded, wall thin, smooth and hyaline, content homogeneous or in some "colloidal" in the neck, hyaline to yellowish. Cheilocystidia similar to pleurocystidia but content in neck with rod-like hyaline particles.

Gill trama of floccose parallel hyphae hyaline to pale tan in KOH; subhymenium gelatinous. Pileus cuticle of narrow gelatinous hyphae 3–4 μ diam., walls yellow to hyaline and smooth to incrusted, hypodermial zone bright ochraceous in KOH, the hyphae floccose. Context hyphae hyaline to yellow in KOH, interwoven, walls thin and smooth. Clamp connections present. All hyphae inamyloid.

HABIT, HABITAT, AND DISTRIBUTION: On duff under spruce-fir, near Tolland, Colorado, Sept. 17, 1920, C. H. Kauffmann. 9500 ft. elevation; type.

OBSERVATIONS: The outstanding feature of this species is the pale ochraceous spores as revived in KOH. They are also more thin-walled than in most species of *Pholiota*. In stature it closely resembles *P. sublubrica*.

180. Pholiota subcarbonaria (Murr.) comb. nov.

Gymnopilus subcarbonarius Murrill, Mycologia 4: 256. 1912.
Flammula subcarbonaria Murrill, Mycologia 4: 262. 1912.
Illustrations: Text figs. 399–401.

Pileus gregarious, 3–4 cm broad, convex to expanded, rarely umbonate, red to bay, yellow on the margin, sometimes darker at the center, rather thin, surface smooth, glabrous, very viscid.

Lamellae adnate or sinuate, pale yellow to ochraceous or fulvous, not crowded, rather narrow, inserted.

Stipe 3–4 cm long, 4–8 mm thick, white, somewhat enlarged below, scaly, hollow. Veil fibrillose, evanescent, not leaving an annulus.

Spores 6–7.5 × 4–4.5 μ smooth; apical pore present but apex not truncate; shape in face view elliptic to ovate, in profile elliptic to very obscurely inequilateral; color in KOH pale cinnamon, in Melzer's reagent paler, cinnamon to ochraceous; wall about 0.25 μ thick.

Basidia 16–22 × 5–6 μ, 4-spored, yellowish to hyaline in KOH and yellowish in Melzer's reagent. Pleurocystidia 36–58 (65) × 7–15 μ, fusoid-ventricose with obtuse apex, smooth, thin-walled, content in the neck in most amber-brown to raw-sienna and appearing wrinkled to striate or near apex with needle-like crystals, some hyaline and homogeneous. Cheilocystidia 17–26 × 4–9 μ, clavate to fusoid-ventricose, hyaline, thin walled, content homogeneous and hyaline. Caulocystidia (none found but very little material available for examination).

Gill trama with a floccose hyaline central strand of hyphae with elongated cells 5–8 μ in diam. (inflating finally to larger) with smooth hyaline walls; subhymenium a gelatinous layer of narrow hyaline hyphae subparallel to interwoven. Pileus cutis a thick gelatinous pellicle of interwoven narrow (1.5–4 μ) ochraceous to hyaline smooth hyphae; hypodermial region rusty-fulvous from incrusted floccose hyphae of various diameters (to 15 μ ± at times). Context hyphae yellowish to hyaline, thin-walled, smooth, interwoven and cells more or less inflated. Clamp connections present. All hyphae inamyloid.

HABIT, HABITAT, AND DISTRIBUTION: On soil, California, January. Type studied.

OBSERVATIONS: The description of microscopic features in the above description are taken from the type collection. This species has a brightly colored pileus even in the dried condition but is somewhat similar to *P. highlandensis* in stature aside from the thicker stipe and the features placing it in Subgenus *Flammuloides*. It differs further from *P. highlandensis* in not growing on burned ground, in brighter colored lamellae when young and scaly stipe (as described by Murrill).

181. Pholiota fibrillosipes (Murr.) comb. nov.
Gymnopilus fibrillosipes Murrill, North Amer. Flora 10: 199. 1917.
Illustrations: Text figs. 406-407; pl. 82.

Pileus 2–6 cm broad, viscid, convex to conic or campanulate, then umbonate, at first "Kaiser-brown," then "tawny," or "cinnamon-rufous," "mars-orange" to "Sanford's-brown," disc "burnt-sienna" (bright ferruginous to orange-ferruginous) viscid, margin even, incurved and appendiculate, glabrous except for evanescent veil-remnants. Context "light ochraceous-salmon" to pale yellow, moderately thick in the disc, but thin on margin; odor and taste mild.

Lamellae adnate to adnexed or emarginate, "straw-yellow" to "Naples-yellow," finally "snuff-brown," broad, ventricose, close, or crowded, edges at first fimbriate, finally even.

Stipe 4–8 cm long, 2–8 mm thick, apex pallid or yellow, dark or dingy olive below, fibrillose, moist, stuffed, then hollow, often compressed, narrowed below. Veil copious, webby, pale yellow with some fibrils "Mars-orange," appendiculate, leaving a fugaceous apical ring.

Spores 6.5–8.5 × 4–4.5 μ, smooth, apical pore not distinct; shape in face view elliptic, in profile elliptic to very obscurely inequilateral; color in KOH ochraceous tawny, in Melzer's reagent paler and slightly yellower; wall thin (–0.25 μ).

Basidia 4-spored 20–25 (27) × 5.5–7 μ, clavate, yellowish in KOH and in Melzer's reagent. Pleurocystidia 45–88 × 9–15 μ, fusoid-ventricose, apex obtuse, neck often plugged with ochraceous material (as revived in KOH); wall thin, smooth, hyaline to yellowish. Cheilocystidia 31–60 × 5–13 μ, subfusoid to fusoid-ventricose, smaller than pleurocystidia for the most part. Caulocystidia 36–54 × 8–12 μ scattered, clavate to fusoid ventricose, walls hyaline to yellowish in KOH but not appreciably thickened.

Gill trama a central area of subparallel floccose hyphae 5–9 μ or more broad, yellowish to orange-brown as revived in KOH; subhymenium a thin layer of narrow gelatinous hyphae. Pileus cuticle a thick gelatinous pellicle of narrow (–3 μ) appressed-interwoven hyphae hyaline to yellowish in KOH; hypodermial region of orange-brown incrusted hyphae, the hyphal cells variable in size. Context hyphae yellowish to hyaline in KOH, interwoven. Clamp connections present. All hyphae inamyloid.

HABIT, HABITAT, AND DISTRIBUTION: Caespitose on soil, humus or sawdust, Tennessee, Alabama and Montana—summer and fall.

OBSERVATIONS: This species structurally is related to *P. subcarbonaria* but differs as shown in our key. Its individual features are the ferruginous colors (typical of the stirps) combined with spores ochraceous tawny under the microscope in KOH, bright yellow gills and copious colored veil.

In the Montana collection Cotner 570060 (MICH) the pileus was light vinaceous buff with the disc "cinnamon-rufous" and so is assigned here provisionally. There is not enough material of *P. fibrillosipes* known to indicate its pattern of color variation.

MATERIAL EXAMINED: ALABAMA: Murrill, (type); MONTANA: Cotner 570060 (MICH); TENNESSEE: Hesler 14106, 20755 (TENN).

182. Pholiota luteola sp. nov.
Illustrations: Text figs. 402-405.

Pileus 2.5–3.5 cm latus, obtusus demum campanulatus glaber, virgatus, viscidus, aurantiacus vel ad marginem laete luteus. Contextus luteus. Lamellae pallide luteae demum cinnamomeae, confertae, adnatae demum emarginatae, latae. Stipes 3–4 cm longus, 3–5 mm crassus, aequalis, solidus; intus sursum laete luteus, deorsum olivaceus; fibrillosus. Sporae 6.5–8 × 4–4.5 μ. Pleurocystidia 45–65 × 9–15 μ acuta, fusoidea, tenuitunicata. Specimen typicum in Herb. Univ. Mich. conservatum est; legit prope McCall, Idaho. 17 Sept. 1956. Smith 53487.

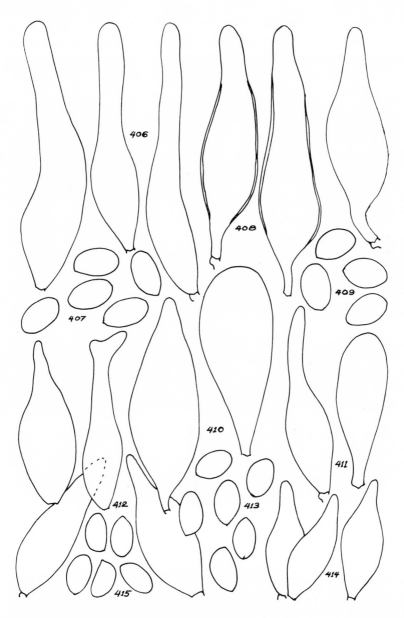

Text Fig. 30.

Figs. 406 & 407, pleurocystidia and spores of *P. fibrillosipes;* 408-411, pleurocystidia, spores, caulocystidia and cheilocystidia of *P. spinulifera;* 412-414, pleurocystidia, spores and cheilocystidia of *P. subtestacea;* 415, spores of *P. avellaneifolia.*

Pileus 2.5–3.5 cm broad, obtuse when young, expanding to obtusely conic-campanulate, glabrous but virgate from streaks beneath pellicle, "Xanthine-orange" (bright orange) and disc and streaks, "pale orange-yellow" near margin (bright yellow), margin fringed at first with yellow veil remnants. Context yellow, odor and taste mild.

Lamellae yellowish pallid when young (paler than context of pileus), near cinnamon-brown mature, close, moderately broad, adnexed.

Stipe 3–4 cm long, 3–5 mm thick at apex, equal, solid becoming hollow, picric yellow within above and in base olivaceous, surface brownish at base, yellowish pallid above, thinly fibrillose from yellow veil.

Spores 6.5–8 × 4–4.5 μ, smooth, apical pore minute, wall thickened (± 0.25 0.3 μ), shape ovate to subelliptic (often tapered slightly at apex) in face view, in profile somewhat bean-shaped to obscurely inequilateral, in KOH rusty pale cinnamon, in Melzer's reagent paler.

Basidia 4-spored 20–25 × 6–7 μ, yellowish in KOH and also in Melzer's reagent; pleurocystidia numerous, 45–65 × 9–15 μ, fusoid to fusoid-ventricose, apex subacute, walls thin and smooth, content homogeneous (or yellow coagulated material present when first revived in KOH). Cheilocystidia similar to pleurocystidia but smaller or some clavate to fusoid and 30–40 × 9–14 μ, content yellow or hyaline, walls thin and smooth, apex obtuse. Caulocystidia 60–100 × 10–18 μ fusoid-ventricose, walls yellowish in KOH and with some adhering material tending to flake off at times, content homogeneous, walls thin.

Gill trama of parallel floccose short-celled hyphae with thin yellowish to hyaline walls in KOH, cells inflated in age; subhymenium a gelatinous narrow zone of hyaline narrow (2–3 μ) hyphae. Pileus cutis a thick gelatinous pellicle with collapsed hyphae scattered through it and these ochraceous in KOH; hypodermial region rusty orange in KOH slowly becoming duller, hyphae 5–12 μ diam. and conspicuously incrusted. Context hyphae of greatly inflated, smooth, yellowish to hyaline thin walls. Clamp connections present. All hyphae inamyloid.

HABIT, HABITAT, AND DISTRIBUTION: Gregarious on wet conifer wood, near McCall, Idaho. Sept. 17, 1956. Smith 53487, type.

OBSERVATIONS: This is one of the brightly colored species of the subgenus *Flammuloides*. It is amply distinct from *P. spumosa* in its bright colors, paler gills when young and more acute pleurocystidia. The species epithet refers to the pale yellow gills.

183. Pholiota spinulifera (Murr.) comb. nov.

Gymnopilus spinulifer Murrill, Mycologia 4: 254. 1912.
Flammula spinulifer Murrill, Mycologia 4: 262. 1912.
Illustrations: Text figs. 408-411.

Pileus 3.5–8 cm broad, convex, umbonate, at length expanding and losing the umbo, light yellow with bay center, surface smooth, glabrous, viscid, margin entire. Context cremeous; taste and odor not distinctive.

Lamellae adnate or very slightly sinuate, yellowish to ferruginous, plane, medium broad, subdistant.

Stipe 5–9 cm long, 7–11 mm thick, equal, hollow, subglabrous, with conspicuous mycelium at the base, yellowish-white or tinged with bay. Veil arachnoid, whitish, leaving a small ring of fibrils near the apex of the stipe.

Spores 6–7.5 (8) × 4–4.5 μ, smooth, no apical pore visible, shape in face view elliptic, in profile elliptic or nearly so; color in KOH ochraceous singly, in Melzer's reagent ochraceous; wall about 0.25 μ diam.

Basidia 20–25 × 5–6 μ, 4-spored, clavate, hymenium in sections yellowish in KOH and Melzer's reagent. Pleurocystidia 45–75 × 9–16 μ fusoid-ventricose, apex obtuse, wall thin to slightly thickened (rarely), smooth, yellowish to hyaline in KOH, content yellowish to hyaline (a plug of yellow material in the neck) and rods and particles of refractive debris often also present. Cheilocystidia 41–50 × 7–15 μ, fusoid-ventricose, fusoid, or clavate to subelliptic-pedicellate, some with brown content (mostly like pleurocystidia but smaller). Caulocystidia versiform 36–60 × 9–20 μ clavate, vesiculose, fusoid-ventricose and variously intermediate, thin-walled, smooth to incrusted somewhat, thin-walled, content mostly homogeneous but some with refractive debris.

Gill trama with a central floccose strand merely ochraceous in KOH; subhymenium gelatinous, well differentiated. Pileus with a thick gelatinous pellicle of narrow hyaline to ochraceous hyphae; hypodermial zone rusty brown in KOH. Clamp connections present. All hyphae inamyloid.

HABIT, HABITAT, AND DISTRIBUTION: Scattered to clustered on soil under redwoods, California, January. Type (McMurphy 10) studied.

OBSERVATIONS: The distinguishing features of this species are the ochraceous spores revived in KOH or Melzer's reagent, their lack of a germ pore, and the bright colors. *P. subcarbonaria* is very close but its spores have a distinct germ pore, and no caulocystidia were found. *P. fibrillosipes* is equally close in spore features but its veil is yellow with some fibrils "Mars-orange." Its pileus is more evenly ferruginous than in *P. spinulifera*. The tendency of the cystidial walls to swell slightly in KOH may cause one to look in section *Flammuloides* first.

We regard the species epithet as an adjective.

Stirps Lubrica

We group here the species without distinct yellow tones over the margin of the pileus. This is in accord with the Friesian descriptions but not with the illustration of Fries in the Icones.

Key

1. Stipe 1–2.5 mm thick 2
1. Stipe (3) 4–12 mm or more thick 3
    2. Pileus testaceous .... *P. subtestacea*
    2. Pileus dull cinnamon color .... *P. harenosa*
3. Cespitose under larch; spores 7–9 × 3.5–4 μ .... *P. gruberi*
3. Not as above 4
    4. Young lamellae avellaneous; veil yellow, copious ....
    .... *P. avellaneifolia*
    4. Not as above 5
5. Pileus virgate with dark brown streaks; stipe rooting and with much
    sand adhering (as in *Laccaria trullisata*) .... *P. trullisata*
5. Not as above 6
    6. Lamellae almost blackish brown when mature; pileus reddish
       cinnamon; on the ground under oak .... *P. foedata*
    6. Not as above 7
7. Lamellae yellow when young 8
7. Lamellae not yellow at first 9
    8. Veil gelatinous; stipe viscid when young .... *P. groenlandica*
    8. Veil dry .... *P. lubrica* var. *luteifolia*
9. Lamellae pallid when young (see *P. fulvozonata* and *P. bakerensis*
    also) .... *P. lubrica*
9. Lamellae dull brown when young .... *P. milleri*

183a. Pholiota groenlandica M. Lange, Meddelser on Grønland Bd.
148, Nr. 2 p. 7. 1957.

Pileus 6–7 cm broad, subglobose with strongly incurved margin, then
convex and finally almost flat or even slightly depressed, at first covered
by whitish coating, which soon disappears without breaking up in patches,
leaving the cap naked, viscid-shining, pale Russet (h l); cuticle detach-
able, elastic, hyaline; flesh thick almost to the edge, firm, pallid watery
brownish; cap margin with a dense white slimy veil; gills rather broad,
narrow towards margin, moderately crowded, 40 L, many very short l,
decurrent, pale yellowish brown (k 4, Cream-Buff), slightly darker and
less bright when spores ripen, margin concolorous, entire; stipe 8 × 1.2–
1.5 cm, cylindrical, slightly widened above, base thickened, pallid yellowish brown above, darker, Cinnamon Rufous (e 4) in lower two thirds,
especially where touched, hollow, flesh concolorous, base felty, apex
finely white-pruinose, fibrillose downwards, somewhat slimy when young,
especially above.

Smell and taste faible. Sporeprint Tawny-Olive Clay Color.

Cuticle a thick layer of strongly gelatinizing hyphae, often with
thickened slightly and bright golden brown; gill trama similar, sub-
banded structure; trama of loosely woven, subhyaline hyphae, in places

regular, hyphae 6–8 μ broad, some yellowish lactifers seen; pleurocystidia numerous, springing from deep subhymenial layer, lower half inflated, tapering towards apex, some of them subcapitate or forked, upper part filled with yellowish brown refractive content, 50–65 × 11–14 μ; cheilocystidia similar; basidia very small, about 16 × 4–6 μ, 4-spored, sterigmata long; spores small 5.3–6.7 × 3.2–4 μ, elliptic subphasaeoliform, pale Clay Color, with very small apiculus and an obscure small germ-pore.

Quite closely related to *Pholiota lenta* (Pers. ex Fr.) Singer from which it differs but slightly in microscopic characters, but the covering of the cap never breaks up in scales, the colours are darker, and the whole plant of coarser stature.

DISTRIBUTION: Only known from the type locality, where it was found in three places in the same large *Salix glauca* copse, in deep moss with *Deschampsia flexuosa*. We have not examined material since the species is very readily characterized.

The above account is from Lange's original description and in the main his format is retained. The species belongs in stirps *Lubrica* of our classification by virtue of the cystidia and small spores, but we have seen nothing like it. In veil features it reminds one of our *P. velaglutinosa*. It is a most interesting *Pholiota* because of its occurrence in relation to *Salix,* the viscid stipe, large pleurocystidia, and veil remnants over the pileus. Anyone collecting in northern Canada should be on the lookout for it.

184. Pholiota subtestacea (Murr.) comb. nov.

Hebeloma subtestaceum Murrill, North Amer. Flora 10: 226. 1917.
Illustrations: Text figs. 412-414.

Pileus 8 mm broad, 5 mm high, broadly conic, not fully expanding, umbonate, pale testaceous on the umbo, paler elsewhere, viscid, margin fibrillose from the evanescent veil, incurved.

Lamellae adnate, white to subfulvous, broad, rather distant, edges entire and concolorous.

Stipe 3 cm long, 2 mm thick above, 4 mm below, stramineous, with loose tufts of testaceous fibrils from the remains of the fibrillose, evanescent, testacteous veil.

Spores 5.5–7.5 × 4–4.5 μ, smooth, no germ pore evident; shape in face view oval, in profile obscurely inequilateral; color in KOH ochraceous tawny, in Melzer's reagent dingy ochraceous; wall about 0.25 μ thick.

Basidia 4-spored, 18–22 × 5–6 μ, hyaline in KOH and Melzer's reagent, somewhat clavate. Pleurocystidia very abundant, 40–56 × 8–16 μ, broadly fusoid-ventricose, apex obtuse to subacute, tapered to apex from broadest point; wall thin and smooth, hyaline; content "empty" or with a few rods and particles of refractive material in the upper part, rarely bifurcate at tip. Cheilocystidia similar to pleurocystidia, 30–38 × 7–8 μ. Caulocystidia none.

Gill trama of a floccose central strand of subparallel hyphae somewhat ochraceous in KOH, thin-walled, cells becoming inflated; subhymenium a gelatinous layer of narrow interwoven hyphae. Hypodermium a conspicuous zone of dark brown (in KOH) hyphae some with incrusted walls. Clamp connections present. All hyphae inamyloid.

HABIT, HABITAT, AND DISTRIBUTION: On soil, Jamaica, December-January; type studied.

OBSERVATIONS: The testaceous colors of pileus and veil are distinctive. In other features it somewhat resembles *P. subflavida* and *P. carbonaria*. The rather distant lamellae, occurrence on soil and southern distribution distinguish it from the latter. The pleurocystidia distinguish it from both. They are very abundant and lack the long neck of the typical *"Flammuloides"* species.

185. Pholiota avellaneifolia sp. nov.
Illustrations: Text figs. 415; 416-417; pl. 83.

Pileus 4–7 cm latus, convexus, viscidus, badius, luteo-squamulosus. Lamellae avellaneae adnatae vel decurrentes, confertissimae, angustae. Stipe 4–8 cm longus, 10–20 mm crassus, aequalis, solidus, deorsum demum fulvus et badio-squamulosus, sursum luteus. Velum luteum. Sporae 6–7 × 3–3.5 μ. Pleurocystidia 48–75 × 9–20 μ obese fusoide ventricosa. Cheilocystidia 26–48 × 7–15 μ, obese ventricosa, intus cinnamomae et reticulata. Specimen typicum in Herb. Univ. Mich. conservatum est; legit prope. McCall, Idaho, 5 Aug. 1958. Smith 59589.

Pileus 4–7 cm broad (immature), convex with an incurved margin, becoming broadly convex to nearly plane, viscid, bay-brown with yellowish patches of veil fibrils. Context thick, firm, whitish; slowly becoming pinkish buff when cut, odor and taste mild.

Lamellae avellaneous young, more rusty in age, adnate to short-decurrent, close or crowded, narrow, edges even.

Stipe 4–8 cm long (immature), 10–20 mm thick, equal, solid, cortex yellowish in apex, pallid elsewhere, slowly pinkish-buff where cut, and eventually dark brown at least below, surface with pale bay squamules over basal portion, yellowish silky up to the zone left by the copious veil, pallid silky above zone. Veil very thick, fibrillose, yellowish.

Spores 6–7 × 3–3.5 μ, oblong to elliptic in face view, rarely ovate or obscurely angular, in profile mostly somewhat bean-shaped, wall rather thin for the genus, pore at apex extremely minute, in KOH pale tawny, in Melzer's reagent about the same.

Basidia 18–24 × 4–5 μ, 4-spored, narrowly clavate, yellowish to hyaline in KOH and Melzer's sol. Pleurocystidia 48–75 × 9–20 μ, broadly fusoid-ventricose to pedicellate-subclavate, pedicel rather narrow (3–5 μ), thin-walled, often with debris adhering over apex, walls thin. Cheilo-

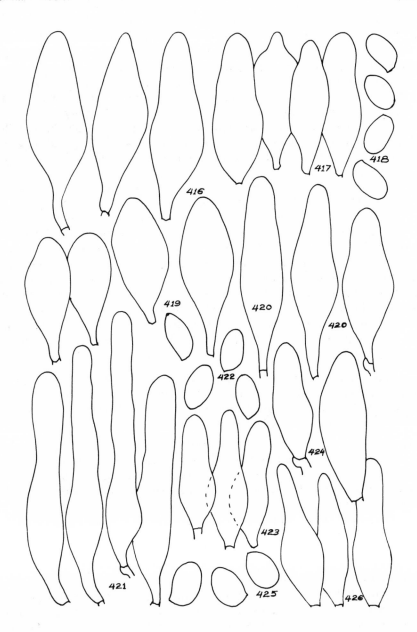

Text Fig. 31.

Figs. 416 & 417, pleurocystidia and cheilocystidia of *P. avellaneifolia;* 418-424, spores, cheilocystidia and pleurocystidia, spores and cheilocystidia of *P. gruberi;* 425 & 426, spores and cheilocystidia of *P. foedata.*

cystidia 26–48 × 7–15 μ, broadly ventricose, content cinnamon brown and reticulate as revived in KOH. Caulocystidia none.

Gill trama of parallel hyphae ochraceous to rusty in thick sections (in KOH) narrow (but all relatively immature), smooth; subhymenium gelatinous. Pileus cutis a very thick gelatinous pellicle of narrow (2–3 μ) hyphae with walls slightly thickened and also some ornamented inconspicuously; hypodermium of bright rusty brown floccose hyphae 3–8 μ diam. and with tawny incrustations. Context hyphae with inflated cells, walls thin, smooth and yellowish in KOH or Melzer's sol. (hyaline when single hyphae are isolated). Clamp connections present. All hyphae inamyloid.

HABIT, HABITAT, AND DISTRIBUTION: On soil under spruce. McCall, Idaho. 5 Aug. 1958. Smith 59589, type.

OBSERVATIONS: This species is distinguished by the heavy yellow veil and an outer layer which leaves brown squamules over the lower part of the stipe. The ·avellaneous gills were conspicuous in the young basidiocarps but became olivaceous in drying. The species is closely related to *P. sublubrica*. However the pleurocystidia of that species do not have the brown content revived in KOH as noted for *P. avellaneifolia*, and for the latter they more closely resemble those of *P. polychroa* in shape than those of *P. sublubrica*. The spores of the latter are paler in Melzer's reagent than in KOH, whereas they are about the same in *P. avellaneifolia*.

186. Pholiota lubrica (Fr.) Singer. Agar. In Mod. Tax. p. 516. 1951.
Agaricus lubricus Fries, Syst. Myc. 1: 252. 1821.
Dryophila lubrica (Fr.) Quélet, Enchir. Fung. p. 70. 1886.
Illustrations: Text figs. 418-420; pl. 84.

var. lubrica

Pileus 4–8 cm broad (estimated), glabrous, very viscid, when young almost ivory-colored (pale yellowish) and with an almost blackish-red central spot, when older pale brown ochre with the spot more extended and dark reddish brown.

Lamellae almost white at first, finally colored as in *P. lenta* close, medium broad.

Stipe 5–8 cm long, 4–6 mm thick (estimated). Pallid in young specimens and faintly white floccose, as dried evenly melleous overall (about like the dried gills in color).

Spores 6–7.5 × 3.5–4.2 μ, smooth, apical pore barely visible under a 1.4 NA oil im. lens; shape in face view elliptic to oblong, in profile more or less oblong; color in KOH ochraceous to pale tawny, in Melzer's reagent about the same; wall about 0.25 μ thick.

Basidia 4-spored, 20–24 × 5–6.5 μ, narrowly clavate, hyaline in KOH and merely yellowish in Melzer's reagent. Pleurocystidia abundant 35–64 × 13–18 (20) μ fusoid-ventricose with obtuse apex to utriform, neck tapered from ventricose part to apex and 6–8 μ diam. near apex, smooth, thin-walled, wall hyaline to slightly yellowish; content homogeneous or with a plug of yellowish colloidal material (in KOH) in apical part, refractive particles present in this material in some, or present in cells not showing the colloidal material. Cheilocystidia 30–45 × 12–20 μ broadly subutriform to clavate, thin-walled, smooth, walls yellowish to hyaline, content yellowish to hyaline and homogeneous. Caulocystidia none found.

Gill trama a central strand of floccose thin-walled, yellowish parallel to somewhat interwoven hyphae 4–10 μ diam. or cells finally more inflated; subhymenium a thick layer of narrow gelatinous hyaline hyphae. Pileus with a thick gelatinous pellicle of narrow (2–5 μ) hyaline to yellowish smooth to incrusted hyphae grading into a hypodermial region of heavily incrusted brown hyphae 4–12 μ diam. Context of yellowish smooth hyphae, thin-walled (0.25–0.3 μ estimated), interwoven, and with cells inflated to 15 μ. All hyphae inamyloid and hyphae at apex of stipe yellowish to hyaline in KOH. Clamp connections present.

HABIT, HABITAT, AND DISTRIBUTION: Among mosses and *Calamagrostis arundinacea* on bouldery slope under beech and birch. Sweden (Lundell 5683).

OBSERVATIONS: That the problem of the identity of *P. lubrica* is an acute one is an understatement. Konrad (1936) gave the spore size as 8–9.5 × 4.5–5.5 μ. For this reason our data are all taken from a Lundell (no. 5683) specimen collected in Sweden. A Moser specimen studied by Hesler had thick walled cystidia and Moser (1953) gives the spores as 5–6 × 3–4 μ, a broader spore in relation to its length than we have found in any of this group. Fries' illustration Icones pl. 116 of *Agaricus* (Flammula) *lubricus* shows an ochraceous marginal area to the pileus and a brown disc. The stipe is white, staining brown at the base. In Systema, however, Fries described the pileus as "cinnamomeus." This is in line with (copied from) Persoon's description and hence is accepted as authentic for the color.

The following is a description of collections Smith 73892, 73678, 74181, and 74071 all from Upper Priest Lake in Idaho:

Pileus 4–8.5 cm broad, broadly convex with an incurved margin, expanding to plane or shallowly depressed, surface with patches of the pallid fibrillose veil over marginal area *on* the slime covering the surface, slime often dripping from edge of pileus; color reddish tawny over disc and pallid over margin mature, when very young the margin ivory yellow; veil pallid, leaving a fringe on margin at first. Context whitish with watery brownish line next to gills; taste mild, odor none, with FeSO₄ green.

Lamellae whitish becoming dull cinnamon, broad, bluntly adnate, crowded, edges even.

Stipe 6–8 cm long, 9–11 mm thick, equal, pallid, soon rusty red to bay below, whitish above, fibrillose scurfy from remains of the veil, apex silky and yellowish pallid.

Spore deposit cinnamon brown. Spores 6–7 × 3.5 μ; pleurocystidia 50–65 × 9–16 μ, thin-walled mostly (especially when fresh or revived in Melzer's reagent), in KOH wall swelling to ± 0.5 μ in a fair number. The critical features of these basidiocarps are: 1) relatively large size, 2) reddish tawny colors (which are within the "cinnamomeus" range, copious slime over the pileus on which at first are perched whitish (pallid) squamules of veil remnants, 3) whitish context, 4) whitish lamellae; and white veil and stipe with the latter staining brown to rusty brown from the base upward. The spores (6–7 × 3.5 μ) are the same as for the Lundell specimen and as given by Kühner & Romagnesi. This comes about as close to the type concept as one can expect in this group.

The problem in North America is greatly complicated by rather similar populations to the above, but differing to such an extent that one dealing mainly with morphological characters must give recognition to them if his classification is to be "honest." We have the following which are very close to *P. lubrica*: *Pholiota coloradensis* with subcylindric to utriform pleurocystidia, *P. sublubrica* with brownish patches of veil on pileus margin, and the stipe elongating as in *Cortinarius* subg. *Bulbopodium*, *P. armeniaca* with exceptionally pale colored spores in KOH and in Melzer's sol., but with colors about like Fries' illustration in the Icones, and *P. avellaneifolia* with a heavy pale but distinctly yellow veil and grayish brown gills when young. All of these are on conifer debris. *P. verna* has cystidia with thickened walls and occurs on debris of cottonwood.

186a. Pholiota lubrica var. luteifolia var. nov.

Pileus 3–9 cm latus, late convexus, glutinosus, ad centrum aurantio-cinnamomeus, ad marginem subsulphureus; lamellae pallide sulphureae vel luteae. Vellum copiosum, subsulphureum, sporae 6–7 × 3.5–4 μ. Pleurocystidia obtusa vel late obtusa. Specimen typicum in Herb. Univ. of Mich. conservatum est; legit prope Goose Lake, Brundage Mt., McCall, Idaho, 18 Aug. 1962, Smith 66012.

Pileus 3–9 cm broad, broadly convex with an inrolled margin, becoming more broadly convex to plane, surface slimy viscid, often decorated with small patches of yellowish veil near the margin; color over disc tawny to orange-cinnamon, paler and with a sulphur tone showing in some degree. Context pallid, odor and taste not distinctive, yellow with KOH and olive with $FeSO_4$ (blue gray in Smith 73475).

Lamellae pale yellow to bright yellow when young, close, moderately broad, dull cinnamon when mature, broadly adnate to slightly decurrent.

Stipe 4–7 cm long, 10–15 mm thick, equal, cortex lemon yellow in apex, soon rusty brown in the base, surface coated with the remains of the copious dry fibrillose yellow veil leaving an evanescent annular zone when it breaks, silky fibrillose above and yellowish.

Spores 6–7 × 3.5–4 μ smooth, apical pore very minute, shape in face view oblong to elliptic or slightly ovate, in profile obscurely inequilateral to slightly bean-shaped, dull cinnamon in KOH and slightly paler in Melzer's reagent, wall –0.25 μ thick.

Basidia 4-spored, 17–20 × 5–6 μ, narrowly clavate, ochraceous in KOH, dull orange in Melzer's (as seen on sections of hymenium). Pleurocystidia abundant, 46–70 × 10–16 μ, ovate-pedicellate, utriform or fusoid ventricose with an obtuse apex, wall thickened to 1 μ in some, mostly with amorphous rods and particles in the neck which also often contains a plug of colloidal material yellow in KOH, in Melzer's reagent content merely orange-ochraceous or merely dull ochraceous. Cheilocystidia smaller than pleurocystidia but the same shape and with much more dried mucilaginous material adhering to them, mostly ochraceous in KOH. Caulocystidia 40–60 × 9–18 μ, clavate to utriform or fusoid-ventricose, mostly hyaline, thin-walled and empty (revived in KOH).

Gill trama typical for group, a gelatinous subhymenium of narrow branched hyphae hyaline in KOH, and a central area of hyaline to yellowish thin-walled smooth hyphae with elongated cells in parallel arrangement; some ochraceous oleiferous hyphae also present. Pileus pellicle a thick layer of narrow (2–3 μ) hyaline to yellowish gelatinous hyphae with smooth (rarely roughened) walls; hypodermium of rusty brown to ochraceous nongelatinous hyphae with smooth to roughened walls. Context hyphae mostly with some "colloidal" content becoming ochraceous to orange red in Melzer's reagent. Clamp connections present.

HABIT, HABITAT, AND DISTRIBUTION: Mostly solitary to scattered along very rotten conifer logs near meadows at high elevations in late summer and fall, Colorado, Idaho and Washington.

OBSERVATIONS: The cystidia of this variety are more like those of *P. avellaneifolia*, but the same provoking situation prevails in regard to the thickness of the cystidial wall that one finds in var. *lubrica,* only more of the cystidia in var. *luteifolia* show some wall thickening. The yellow veil and yellow gills distinguish it from typical *lubrica* in the field. It is another of the puzzling series of variants among the species with typically white to pallid gills, and is included here as part of the documentation for this particular type of variant.

MATERIAL EXAMINED: COLORADO, Mains 5257; IDAHO, Smith 66012 (type), 69560; WASHINGTON, Smith 47622, 48025.

187. Pholiota gruberi sp. nov.
Illustrations: Text figs. 421-424.

Pileus 2–5 cm latus, late convexus, glaber, viscidulus, rufo-brunneus. Lamellae confertae, latae adnatae. Stipes 3–5 cm longus, 3–6 mm crassus, aequalis, sursum subpruinosus, deorsum sparse fibrillosus, sordide pallide luteus. Sporae 7–9 × 3.5–4 μ. Pleurocystidia 50–70 × 9–14 μ fusoide ventricosa, ad apicem obtusa vel late rotundata. Cheilocystidia 35–48 ×

9–15 µ, utriformia. Specimen typicum in Herb. Univ. of Mich. conservatum est; legit prope Lewiston, Idaho, 2 Juni 1943, Wm. B. Gruber 41.

Pileus 2–5 cm broad, broadly convex with a decurved margin, thinly viscid and soon dry (but pellicle distinct) glabrous, color as dried dull pinkish buff over disc with redder tones near and on margin (reddish brown fresh—Gruber). Context pallid, odor and taste mild to slightly mealy.

Lamellae close, broad, adnate becoming slightly decurrent, seceding in age, color when young not known, dingy cinnamon when mature, edge even to slightly flocculose.

Stipe 3–5 cm long, 3–6 mm thick, equal, yellowish to buff and merely dingy buff as dried, not darkened appreciably at base when dried, apex faintly pruinose, appressed fibrillose-downward, veil very thin (color not known).

Spore print about cinnamon-brown. Spores 7–9 × 3.5–4 µ, smooth, apical pore present and distinct; shape in face view narrowly elliptic to narrowly ovate, in profile obscurely inequilateral to subelliptic; wall about 0.3 µ thick; color in KOH dark cinnamon, in Melzer's paler and more ochraceous; with a distinct apiculus.

Basidia 18–23 × 6–7.5 µ clavate, 4-spored, yellowish to hyaline in KOH, yellowish in Melzer's reagent. Pleurocystidia abundant, 50–70 × 9–14 µ, fusoid ventricose with obtuse to rounded apex, walls smooth thin and hyaline in KOH, and in Melzer's varying to slightly yellowish; content homogeneous, yellowish to hyaline in KOH. Cheilocystidia abundant, 35–48 × 9–15 µ, utriform, thin-walled, smooth, mostly hyaline in KOH. Caulocystidia scattered to rare and more or less like the cheilocystidia.

Gill trama of a central area of subparallel floccose hyphae the cells greatly inflated, hyaline to yellowish in KOH with walls thin and smooth; subhymenium of gelatinous branched narrow (2 µ ±) hyaline hyphae forming a rather wide band. Pileus cutis a thin layer of loosely tangled ochraceous gelatinous narrow (1.5–2 µ) hyphae (revived in KOH); hypodermium very well defined, of floccose hyphae the cells 8–20 µ wide, bright fulvous in KOH and with distinct incrusting patches of pigment adhering. Context hyphae of greatly inflated cells, walls yellowish to hyaline in KOH, thin and smooth. All hyphae inamyloid. Clamp connections present.

HABIT, HABITAT, AND DISTRIBUTION: Cespitose in masses under the needle cover under *Larix occidentalis,* near Lewiston, Idaho. June 2, 1943, Wm. B. Gruber 41, type.

OBSERVATIONS: The vernal appearance and the stature of this species remind one of the complex of variants around *Hebeloma maesophaeum* but the microscopic features clearly place the fungus in *Pholiota* subg. *Flammuloides.* The relatively long narrow spores, abundant utriform cheilocystidia smaller than the pleurocystidia, manner of fruiting and occurrence under larch in relatively dry situations distinguish it. The longer narrow spores distinguish it from *P. subcarbonaria.*

188. **Pholiota trullisata** sp. nov.
Illustrations: Text figs. 517-519.

Pileus 4–10 cm latus, convexus, viscidus, aurantio-brunneus, virgatus. Lamellae albidae demum subolivaceo-griseae dein luteo-brunneae, confertae. Stipes 5–12(14) cm longus, 8–18 mm crassus, radicatus, sursum albidus, deorsum luteus. Sporae 5.5–6.5 × 4–4.5 μ. Pleurocystidia 36–52 × 9–15 μ. Specimen tipicum in Herb. Univ. Mich. conservatum est; legit prope Santa Maria, Calif. 9 Jan. 1954, John L. Moore.

Pileus 4–10 cm broad, broadly convex with an inrolled margin, becoming nearly plane, with a whitish band of fibrils along the margin from the veil, glabrous and slimy-viscid otherwise, virgate with dark brown streaks against and orange brown disc and a light tan margin; hygrophanous and fading on disc first to dingy yellowish tan. Context pallid and without a distinctive odor and taste.

Lamellae white when veil breaks, becoming olive-drab and finally dingy brown, close, adnexed, moderately broad, edges wavy.

Stipe 5–12 (14) cm long, single or compound, often sunken deeply in the sand and clavate to trowel-shaped over the underground portion (like *Laccaria trullisata*), 8–15 mm thick above ground line, with a superior veil-line and white fibrillose above it, bright yellow below it but this color soon fading, in addition with brown patches of fibrils (of outer veil material ?) which soon disappear, darkening in base around worm holes, stuffed becoming hollow.

Spores rusty brown in deposit, 5.5–6.5 × 4–4.5 μ, smooth; apical pore extremely minute; shape in face view broadly ellipsoid, in profile merely ellipsoid, very slightly compressed; color in KOH dull cinnamon, about the same color in Melzer's reagent; wall about 0.3 μ thick.

Basidia 4-spored, 17–23 × 6–7 μ, hyaline in KOH. Pleurocystidia 36–52 × 9–15 μ, fusoid-ventricose, distinctly projecting, thin-walled, smooth, apex obtuse, content in KOH orange-ochraceous in neck and homogeneous. Cheilocystidia similar to pleurocystidia but smaller. Caulocystidia none or at very apex a few and these resembling cheilocystidia.

Gill trama a central area of parallel hyaline thin-walled hyphae with inflated cells in age (up to 15 μ), ochraceous contorted oleiferous hyphae also present (as seen in mounts revived in KOH); subhymenium of narrow (2–4 μ) hyaline hyphae in a gelatinous matrix. Pileus cutis a thick gelatinous pellicle of narrow (2–4 μ) hyaline to ochraceous hyphae (revived in KOH), the hyphal walls becoming transversely crinkled and collapsing; hypodermium of rusty brown compactly interwoven hyphae with smooth to incrusted walls, the hyphae not of greater diameter than those of the context. Context hyphae 5–10 μ diam., not much inflated, hyaline in KOH, yellowish in Melzer's reagent. Clamp connections present.

HABIT, HABITAT, AND DISTRIBUTION: Caespitose near a stump (pine ?), Santa Maria, Calif. Jan. 9, 1954, Coll. John L. Moore, type.

OBSERVATIONS: This is a very odd *Pholiota* because of the long rooting base often giving rise to a number of secondary stipes (merismoid) and with adhering sand much as in *Laccaria trullisata,* the rather broadly ellipsoid spores, and the relatively short pleurocystidia for the group. It's relationships appear to be in the *P. lubrica* complex but the spores at once distinguish it from all of these.

189. Pholiota foedata (Pk.) comb. nov.
Hebeloma foedatum Pk., Bull. Torrey Bot. Club 22: 202. 1895.
Gymnopilus foedatus (Pk.) Murrill, North Amer. Fl. 10: 206. 1917.
Cortinarius foedatus (Pk.) Kauffman, Amer. Journ. Bot. 13: 28. 1926.
Illustrations: Text figs. 425-426.

Pileus 3.5–7.5 cm broad, convex, becoming plane or centrally depressed, reddish cinnamon, very viscid or glutinous, glabrous.

Lamellae emarginate and with a decurrent tooth, cinnamon colored, becoming mummy brown, medium broad, subcentricose, crowded.

Stipe 3.5–6.5 cm long, 4–8 mm thick, paler than the pileus, fibrillose, equal or slightly thickened at the base, solid.

Spores 6–7.5 × 4–4.5 μ, smooth, apical pore minute, wall up to 0.25–0.5 μ thick, shape elliptic to oval in face view, elliptic to very obscurely inequilateral in profile, in KOH rusty cinnamon and about the same color in Melzer's reagent.

Basidia 18–24 × 5–6 μ, 4-spored, clavate, yellowish-hyaline in KOH, yellowish in Melzer's reagent. Pleurocystidia abundant, 36–70 × 9–15 μ fusoid-ventricose, apex obtuse, wall thin and smooth in KOH but content at times reticulate-wrinkled and ochraceous in KOH as coagulated (often clearing on standing). Cheilocystidia similar to pleurocystidia or shorter and more fusoid, apex obtuse. Caulocystidia none found on type or on Sipe 248.

Gill trama a central strand of floccose hyphae not distinctively colored as revived in KOH, the walls thin and smooth; subhymenium a layer of hyaline branched gelatinous hyphae 2–3 μ diam. Pileus cutis a gelatinous pellicle of yellowish collapsed hyphae as revived in KOH; hypodermium of rusty brown hyphae 3–7 μ diam. with rusty colored incrustations. Context hyphae smooth and thin-walled, yellowish in KOH, hyphal cells greatly inflated. All hyphae inamyloid. Clamp connections present.

HABIT, HABITAT, AND DISTRIBUTION: Along streets, or among oak leaves. California (Pasadena). Type studied.

OBSERVATIONS: The type was from under oak in southern California and had adnexed gills. McClatchie's specimens which we have studied had dark reddish-rust colored spores much as in *P. subangularis* but in Sipe's 248 from conifer duff in the mountains they were paler. The gill color of McClatchie's material seen by us is now rusty cinnamon not a blackish brown (mummy brown). For these reasons the microscopic

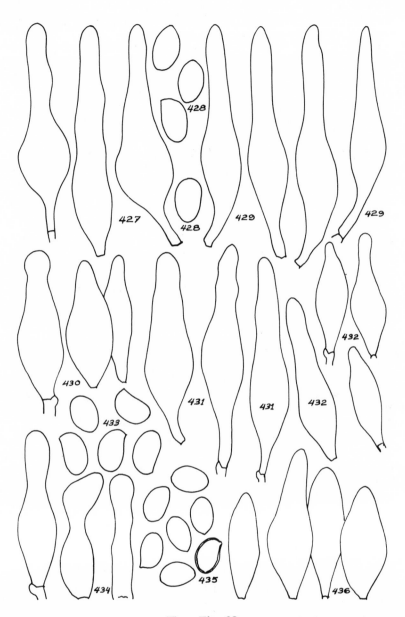

Text Fig. 32.

Figs. 427, pleurocystidia of *P. foedata;* 428-430, spores, pleurocystidia and cheilocystidia of *P. harenosa;* 431-433, pleurocystidia, cheilocystidia and spores of *P. polychroa;* 434 & 435, cheilocystidia and spores of *P. macrocystis;* 436, cheilocystidia of *P. subflavida.*

data and drawings are all taken from McClatchie's material. We suspect that when properly redescribed this species will be found to have other features than given in McClatchie's notes to distinguish it. There is no reason for referring the species to *Cortinarius* as Kauffman did, since the spores in the material studied by us were smooth. Kauffman in his notes, however, (unpublished) indicated that the spores were "under high power—roughish." This may have been an artifact, since his "high power" was a 3 mm dry objective, not an oil immersion lens. However, it cannot be denied that the possibility of a description based on two different species exists. If this can be proven the species should be abandoned as a source of confusion. At present, however, on th basis of the spore features it is possible to recognize it. The material we have studied is clearly a *Pholiota*.

190. Pholiota harenosa sp. nov.
Illustrations: Text figs. 428-430.

Pileus 2–3 cm latus, convexus, viscidus, glaber, subcinnamomeus. Lamellae confertae angustae vel sublatae, cinnamomeae. Stipes 2–2.5 cm longus, 1.5–2.5 mm crassus, sursum citrinus, deorsum subcinnamomeus, sparse fibrillosus. Sporae 6–8.5 × 4–4.5 μ. Pleurocystidia 45–70 × 9–14 μ. Specimen typicum in Herb. Univ. of Mich. conservatum est; legit prope Milford, Mich. 16 Nov. 1958, Smith 60810.

Pileus 2–3 cm broad, broadly convex, "Sayal-brown" to "cinnamon-brown," viscid, glabrous. Context pliant, concolorous; odor and taste mild or slightly farinaceous.

Lamellae adnexed, close, narrow to moderately broad, "Sayal-brown" to "cinnamon-brown," edges even to minutely eroded.

Stipe 2–2.5 cm long, 1.5–2.5 mm thick at apex, equal or narrowed downward, pale citrine near apex, pale dull cinnamon at base, lower part covered with very faint remains of a veil.

Spores 6–8.5 × 4–4.5 μ, smooth, apical pore minute; shape in face view elliptic to slightly ovate, in profile obscurely inequilateral to sub-elliptic; color in KOH rich cinnamon and groups of spores dark cinnamon, paler cinnamon or more ochraceous in Melzer's reagent; wall about 0.25–0.4 μ thick.

Basidia 20–25 (27) × 5.5–7 μ, 4-spored, narrowly clavate (base 3–4.5 μ broad), yellowish to hyaline in KOH and yellowish in Melzer's reagent. Pleurocystidia 45–70 × 9–14 μ, fusoid-ventricose, apex obtuse, some coated with mucilage (?) as first revived in KOH but soon smooth, wall thin (less than 0.3 μ), content yellowish to hyaline. Cheilocystidia (28) 32–56 × 6–12 (14) μ, broadly fusoid with obtuse apex to fusoid-ventricose, rarely subcapitate, thin-walled, smooth, hyaline to yellowish in KOH. Caulocystidia in fascicles, subfusoid, fusoid-ventricose to nearly clavate and 33–50 × 9–13 μ, some 48–70 × 4–6 μ and cylindric-acuminate, walls thin, yellowish in KOH; often with subgelatinous hyphae 2–3 μ diam. mixed in or around the cluster (resembling hyphae of pileus cutis).

Gill trama a central area of floccose hyphae 4–8 μ diam. (or more after cells have inflated), walls smooth and hyaline to ochraceous or pale rusty in KOH; subhymenium a thin cellular zone not distinctly gelatinizing but outlines of cells including the base of the basidia (but not cystidia) soon indistinct. Pileus cutis a gelatinous pellicle of narrow (2–3 μ) ochraceous hyphae collapsing in age, often filled with ochraceous pigment; hypodermium a region of inflated rusty brown hyphal cells, walls incrusted on some, cells 8–18 μ broad; context hyphae paler than the hypodermial hyphae, nearly hyaline near subhymenium; wall thin and smooth. Clamp connections present. All hyphae inamyloid.

HABIT, HABITAT, AND DISTRIBUTION: On sandy humus. Proud Lake Recreation Area. Oakland County, Michigan, Nov. 16, 1958. Smith 60810, type.

OBSERVATIONS: This species is at once distinguished from *P. highlandensis* (*Flammula carbonaria* Fries) in lacking the characteristic gelatinous type of subhymenium found in most species of subgenus *Flammuloides*. It also differs in habitat (on sandy soil under beech-maple instead of a burned area).

191. Pholiota milleri sp. nov.
Illustrations: Text figs. 511-513.

Pileus 2–3.5 cm latus, obtuse conicus, subviscidus, virgatulus, sordide cinnamomeus. Contextus albus. Lamellae brunneolae, anguste confertae; stipes 3–5 cm latus, 4–8 mm crassus, sursum citrino-pallidus, deorsum pallidus vel subsordidus. Sporae 6–8 × 4–4.5 μ. Pleurocystidia 50–70 × 10–15 μ, tenuitunicata. Specimen typicum in Herb. Univ. of Mich. conservatum est; legit prope Priest River Experimental Forest, 6 Juli 1964. O. K. Miller 2382.

Pileus 2–3.5 cm broad, obtuse, expanding to obtusely conic or campanulate, umbonate, surface slightly viscid but soon dry and appearing obscurely fibrillose or streaked, near "Verona-brown" unless darkened from spores. Context white, odor none, taste mild; $FeSO_4$ olive, KOH on cutis no reaction.

Lamellae adnate, dull brown when young, darker than "Verona-brown" when mature, crowded, narrow, edges even.

Stipe 3–5 cm long, 4–8 mm thick, equal or base with a slight rounded bulb, surface above citrine-pallid and with very inconspicuous fibrils or squamules from a rudimentary veil, base not darkening.

Spores 6–8 × 4–4.5 μ smooth, apical pore small but evident; shape in face view oblong to elliptic, in profile elliptic to obscurely inequilateral; in KOH dark rusty, cinnamon, paler but reddish cinnamon in Melzer's reagent; wall about 0.3 μ thick.

Basidia 24–27 × 5–7 μ, 4-spored, short-clavate, ochraceous in KOH and in Melzer's reagent. Pleurocystidia 50–70 × 10–15 μ, fusoid-ventricose, apex obtuse, wall thin, smooth; content homogeneous or with refractive rods and particles near apex, yellow to hyaline, often yellow only in the neck. Cheilocystidia 30–54 × 8–12 μ obtusely fusoid to fusoid-ventricose, obclavate to nearly ellipsoid, smooth, often with refractive particles near or at apex. Caulocystidia 45–70 × 5–14 μ, clavate, subcylindric, fusoid-ventricose or irregular, walls thin but yellow in KOH, content homogeneous.

Gill trama of subparallel floccose hyphae with enlarged cells, the walls thin, smooth, yellowish to hyaline in KOH; subhymenium a narrow gelatinous layer, structure very soon indistinct. Pileus cutis a thick layer of narrow mostly hyaline hyphae collapsing and becoming reticulate, incrusted near hypodermium, 2–3.5 μ diam.; hypodermium of floccose heavily incrusted rusty-brown hyphae in KOH. Context hyphae inflated, smooth thin-walled and yellowish in KOH. Clamp connections present. All hyphae inamyloid.

HABIT, HABITAT, AND DISTRIBUTION: On soil, Idaho, July, type. Miller 2382.

OBSERVATIONS: The distinctive characters of this species include its narrow gills which are dull brown at first, and its brown, umbonate pileus. It has some relationship to P. subtestacea, which has a brick-red to pinkish pileus as dried, broad gills which are at first white, and a testaceous veil. The non-darkening stipe base and consistently thin-walled pleurocystidia distinguish it from P. decorata.

Stirps Polychroa

192. Pholiota polychroa (Berk.) Smith & Brodie Bot. Gaz. 96: 533-546. 1935.
Agaricus polychrous Berkeley, Lond. Journ. Bot. 6: 313. 1847.
Agaricus ornellus Peck, N.Y. State Mus. Ann. Rept. 34: 42. 1883.
Flammula polychroa (Berk.) Saccardo, Syll. Fung. 5: 824. 1887.
Pholiota appendiculata Peck, N.Y. State Mus. Bull. 94: 33. 1905.
Pholiota ornella (Pk.) Peck, N.Y. State Mus. Bull. 122: 151. 1908.
Gymnopilus polychrous (Berk.) Murrill, North Amer. Fl. 10: 204. 1917.
Illustrations: Text figs. 431-433; pls. 86a, 87.

Pileus 1.5–10 cm broad, obtuse to convex when young, with the margin incurved, expanding to broadly convex or obtusely umbonate, surface glutinous to viscid, cuticle separable, glabrous, but at first decorated with the remnants of the veil as creamy to avellaneous superficial squamules, margin often appendiculate with veil remnants, of many colors: pale grass-green, blue-green ("turquoise green"), dark olive, or dark purplish-drab to purple-gray, gradually developing yellow hues, often mottled, often becoming dull orange to yellow on the disc, the margin olivaceous (color extremely variable). Context soft, moist, thick on the disc, white above, greenish below, thin on the margin; odor and taste not distinctive.

Lamellae varying in attachment from adnexed to decurrent, often seceding, close to crowded, moderately broad, at first lilaceous, or pale cream color to pallid young, soon gray-fuscous or avellaneous to wood brown, finally a dark purplish brown with an olive tone, edges white-fimbriate.

Stipe 2–6 (8) cm long, 3–5 (8) mm thick, often narrowed downward, fibrous and solid, finally hollow at times, with fairly copious veil remnants distributed over the lower part as squamules or patches and these terminating in a fibrillose to submembranous, greenish to dingy, evanescent annulus, glabrescent below in age, light blue-green or pallid to yellowish over the apical portion, becoming reddish brown below, often attached to the substratum by a mat of tawny hairs.

Spore deposit brown with a slight purplish tinge in moist state, after escape of moisture near cinnamon brown. Spores 6–7.5 × 3.5–4.5 μ, smooth, apical pore minute; shape oblong to elliptic in face view, rarely ovate, in profile mostly bean-shaped; color dark dull cinnamon in KOH, in Melzer's reagent paler; wall about 0.25 μ thick.

Basidia 18–25 × 4.5–6 μ, 2- and 4-spored, subclavate, hyaline to yellowish in Melzer's reagent or in KOH. Pleurocystidia 40–60 (70) × 9–15 μ, fusoid-ventricose, apex obtuse, wall thin and smooth; content homogeneous or containing some rodlike particles (in Melzer's), yellowish to amber-brown in KOH fading to hyaline and then granular-colloidal in consistency; often with a slender pedicel. Cheilocystidia 28–42 × 7–10 (23) μ, broadly fusoid with obtuse apex to fusoid ventricose and similar to pleurocystidia. Caulocystidia 22–75 (150) × 5–9 (30) μ, large ones hyaline thin-walled and clavate to fusoid; smaller ones versiform: utriform, fusoid-ventricose, clavate etc., wall in some slightly thickened and ochraceous.

Gill trama of somewhat interwoven floccose hyphae, the hyphal cells 6–20 μ broad; walls thin hyaline and smooth; subhymenium a broad layer (relatively) of narrow hyaline interwoven gelatinous hyphae. Pileus cutis a thick gelatinous pellicle with narrow (2–3 μ) hyaline hyphae rather widely dispersed through it, the hyphal walls breaking down; hypodermial zone of smooth floccose hyphae 5–15 μ diam., the walls thin to slightly thickened and hyaline to ochraceous or brownish. Context hyphae hyaline smooth, the wall thin but seen as two walls cemented together, cells greatly enlarged. Clamp connections present. All hyphae inamyloid.

HABIT, HABITAT, AND DISTRIBUTION: On hardwood logs, stumps, and fallen limbs, more rarely on conifers, occasionally sawdust, New York, Pennsylvania, Maryland, North Carolina, Florida, Louisiana, Tennessee, Texas, Michigan, and Oregon, July—November; reported from New England to Alabama, and west to Wisconsin (Murrill 1917), and from Canada (Güssow & Odell 1927).

OBSERVATIONS: This species is well marked for field identification by its varied colors, especially the olive and green hues in the earlier stages. These green tints often show to some degree in mature caps. The spore-color is essentially brown, but in a good print there is a slight purplish tinge. Despite this spore-color, agaricologists consider it close to *Pholiota* (or *Flammula*, in older publications) than to any of the purple-spored genera, but this only goes to help point out the intergradations in spore color between *Psilocybe, Stropharia* and *Pholiota*.

MATERIAL EXAMINED: INDIANA: Kanouse 10-11-47; FLORIDA: Hesler 21436; MICHIGAN: Harding 487; Kauffman & Pennington 8-27-06, Kauffman 9-107a, 9-12-07b, 9-12-07c, 9-23-12, 9-25-29; Smith 10-10-31, 32-598, 11008, 11083, 14952, 15255, 21155, 21909, 32054, 43545, 43711, 51216, 68743, 68782; MARYLAND: Kelly 435, 1447; Kauffman 9-1-19; NEW YORK: Kauffman 7-17-03; Peck (types of *Agaricus (Flammula) ornellus* and *Pholiota appendiculata*); NORTH CAROLINA (GSMNP): Hesler 17654; OREGON: Smith 68741; PENNSYLVANIA: Kauffman 9-24-09; TENNESSEE: Hesler 3682, 4261, 5396, 5397, 8076, 8019, 9545, 13797, 19522, 19840, 22180; TEXAS: Thiers 1905; VIRGINIA: Kelly 348, 349, 1696; CANADA (Ontario) : Smith 4589.

Stirps Crassipedes

The distinctly lignicolous species not included in any previous stirps are placed here.

Key

1. Pileus clay-color to pinkish-buff 2
1. Pileus distinctly yellow at least on the margin 3
  2. Pileus context slowly staining cinnamon-buff when cut; pleuro-cystidia 60–104 μ long; subhymenium thin and cellular (not gelatinous) .... *P. macrocystis*
  2. Pileus context white and unchanging; pleurocystidia 40–80 μ long .... see *P. harenosa*
3. Pileus spotting green when handled .... *P. subflavida*
3. Not as above 4
  4. Pileus dark yellow brown but drying bay-red; lamellae sulphur yellow when young .... *P. bigelowii*
  4. Not as above 5
5. Pleurocystidia 40–56 × 12–17; spores 5–6 × 3–3.5 μ ....
.... see *P. flavopallida*
5. Pleurocystidia 38–73 × 7–21 μ; spores 5.5–7 × 3.5–4.5 μ ....
.... *P. crassipedes*

193. **Pholiota macrocystis** sp. nov.
Illustrations: Text figs. 434-435, 437-439.

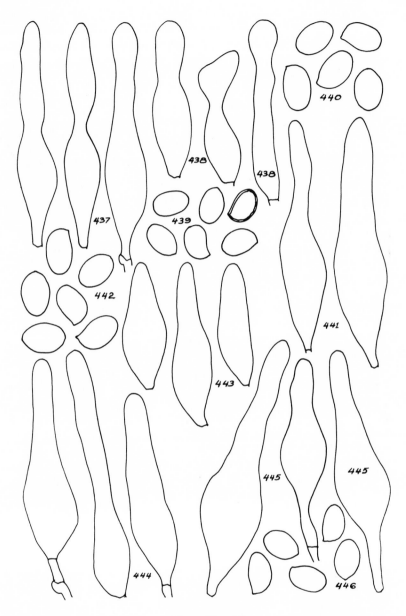

Text Fig. 33.

Figs. 437-439, pleurocystidia, cheilocystidia and spores of *P. macrocystis;* 440 & 441, spores and pleurocystidia of *P. subflavida;* 442-444, spores, cheilocystidia and pleurocystidia of *P. crassipedes;* 445 & 446, pleurocystidia and spores of *P. virescentifolia.*

*Pileus 4–8 cm latus, late convexus, glaber, viscidus pallide argillaceus.
Contextus crassus, pallidus tactu argillaceus. Lamellae latae, confertae, sub-
cinnamoneae. Stipes 3–7 cm longus, 7–10 mm crassus, intus subargillaceus,
extus albidus. Sporae 5.5–6.5(7) × 4–4.5 μ. Pleurocystidia 60–104 × 7–12
(16) μ, fusoide ventricosa. Specimen typicum in Herb. Univ. Mich. conservatum est; legit prope Lake Fork Creek, Payette National Forest,
Idaho. 29 Juni 1962, Smith 65070.*

Pileus 4–8 cm broad, broadly convex to plane, viscid, glabrous,
"pinkish-buff," youngest pale pinkish buff. Context thick pallid; odor
and taste mild. With FeSO$_4$ greenish, with KOH dark brownish; slowly
staining cinnamon-buff when cut.

Lamellae adnexed, broad, close, pale cinnamon-brown mature.

Stipe 3–7 cm long, 7–10 mm thick, pinkish-buff, cortex watery cinnamon buff, surface white and unpolished, with a faint zone of fibrils from
the thin veil, pith silky and pallid.

Spores 5.5–6.5 (7) × 4–4.5 μ, smooth, apical pore (for all practical
purposes) none; in shape elliptic to ovate in face view, in profile obscurely bean-shaped to obscurely inequilateral; color dull cinnamon in
KOH, pale and more ochraceous in Melzer's reagent, wall thin (less
than 0.2 μ by estimate) .

Basidia 20–25 × 6–7 μ, 4-spored, clavate, hyaline to yellowish in
KOH, more yellowish in Melzer's reagent. Pleurocystidia 60–104 × 7–
12 (16) μ fusoid ventricose with apex obtuse, often constricted at base
of neck, neck 30–50 μ long, occasionally capitate, thin-walled, content
homogeneous or with some rod-shaped debris in neck near apex, hyaline
to yellowish in KOH. Cheilocystidia 40–77 × 8–12 μ similar in shape to
pleurocystidia. Caulocystidia 53–110 × 9–15 μ versiform-cylindric, subclavate, ventricose rostrate to fusoid-ventricose, or variously shaped, wall
thin, and smooth, content homogeneous.

Gill trama of parallel hyphae with elongate cells 6–12 μ or more
broad, walls thin, smooth more or less ochraceous in KOH; subhymenium
cellular, the layer thin and inconspicuous, rather translucent in old gills.
Pileus cutis a hyaline gelatinous pellicle, the hyphae 2–4 μ diam., walls
thin smooth and in age only the refractive cross wall showing; hypodermium of smooth orange-brown hyphae 4–12 μ diam., non-gelatinous.
Context hyphae of inflated cells with thin smooth walls pale tan in KOH
becoming paler on standing. Clamp connections present. All hyphae
inamyloid.

HABIT, HABITAT, AND DISTRIBUTION: On a conifer log, McCall, Idaho,
June 29, 1962. Smith 65070, type.

OBSERVATIONS: The pinkish buff (not truly yellow) pileus, the green
FeSO$_4$ reaction, very large distinctly thin-walled pleurocystidia, essentially cellular subhymenium, context staining when cut, and relatively
broad spores for their length are distinctive. It is an odd combination
to have such pleurocystidia with the thin cellular subhymenium.

194. **Pholiota bigelowii** sp. nov.

Pileus 3–4.5 cm latus, late convexus, sordide brunneus, in siccati laterarius; vellum sulphureum; lamellae sulphureae; stipes sursum sulphureus, deorsum sordide brunneus; spore 6–7.5 × 3.8–4.5 μ; pleurocystidia fusoide ventricosa vel subclavata, tenuitunicata; specimen typicum in Herb. Univ. Mich. conservatum est; legit prope Mackinaw City, Mich. Aug. 27, 1953 (Smith 42423).

Pileus 3–4.5 cm broad, broadly convex with an incurved margin, expanding to plane or nearly so, color dull dark yellowish brown on disc ("Saccardo's umber") slightly paler to the sulphur yellow margin, in drying becoming evenly brick red, with flecks of veil tissue over marginal area at first, glabrous in age, slimy-viscid; veil yellow. Context thin and pliant yellowish, odor and taste not recorded.

Lamellae crowded, short-decurrent, narrow (caps all young) sulphur yellow, edges even.

Stipe 2–4 cm long, 3–6 mm thick, equal, hollow, collapsing in drying, surface sulphur yellow above, dingy yellow-brown below, veil leaving only an evanescent sulphur colored fibrillose zone.

Spores 6–7.5 × 3.8–4.5 μ, smooth with a minute apical pore, shape in face view ovate to subelliptic, in profile bean-shaped to obscurely inequilateral; color in KOH pale ochraceous to brownish ochraceous, in Melzer's about the same; wall about 0.25 μ or less thick.

Basidia 4-spored, 20–25 × 5–6.5 μ, pale sulphur in KOH from content. Pleurocystidia abundant, 46–68 × 11–16 μ fusoid-ventricose varying to clavate or elliptic-pedicellate, but projecting prominently, smooth, thin-walled, neck with yellow colloidal content in KOH, about the same color in Melzer's. Cheilocystidia similar to pleurocystidia but more subclavate to broadly ventricose with short neck and obtuse apex. Caulocystidia elongate-clavate, (36) 40–90 × 6–11 μ or near stipe-apex fusoid-ventricose and up to 90 × 14 μ, yellowish hyaline in KOH or with ochraceous coagulated content.

Gill trama a central strand of greenish ochraceous (in KOH) smooth, thin-walled hyphae in parallel arrangement; subhymenium of diverging narrow hyphae in a slime matrix. Pileus pellicle *thick,* of interwoven narrow gelatinous hyphae with disentegrating walls, yellow to hyaline in KOH, walls roughened as one approaches the hypodermium, reddish fulvous, of compactly arranged narrow (3–10 μ) non-gelatinous hyphae. Context hyphae, greenish yellow in KOH, thin-walled, smooth, cells inflated to 15 μ +. Clamp connections present.

HABIT, HABITAT, AND DISTRIBUTION: Gregarious on an old hardwood log, Mackinaw City, Hardwoods, Emmet County, Mich., Aug. 27, 1953. H. E. Bigelow, Smith 42423, type.

OBSERVATIONS: The species was thought to be an unusually bright colored collection of *Pholiota spumosa* when it was collected but the color change in drying and the variation in shape of the pleurocystidia make it amply distinct.

195. Pholiota subflavida (Murr.) comb. nov.
Gymnopilus subflavidus Murrill, 4: 252. 1912.
Flammula subflavida Murrill, Mycologia 4: 262. 1912.
Illustrations: Text figs. 436; 440-441; pl. 88.

Pileus 3–5 cm broad, thin, conic or convex to expanded, umbonate when young, melleous with fulvous center, becoming green-spotted when handled, slimy, glabrous, smooth, margin entire, strongly incurved.

Lamellae sinuate or adnate, citrinous to fulvous, medium broad, subdistant.

Stipe 4–7 cm long, 5–8 mm thick, equal, cremeous above, pale fulvous below, smooth, fibrillose. Veil slight, citrinous, membranous in young stages, soon breaking into fibrils and leaving no annulus.

Spores 5.5–7.5 (8.5) × 3.5–4.5 (5) μ, smooth, apical pore small but distinct; shape in face view elliptic to ovate, in profile obscurely inequilateral; color tawny in KOH under microscope, in Melzer's reagent about the same color; wall about 0.25 μ thick.

Basidia 17–22 × 4–5 μ, 4-spored, clavate, yellowish and KOH and Melzer's reagent. Pleurocystidia abundant, 48–72 × 9–15 μ, fusoid-ventricose, apex subacute to obtuse, walls thin and smooth, content ochraceous tawny to yellowish fading to hyaline and homogeneous. Cheilocystidia 28–45 (60) × 8–13 μ, subfusoid with obtuse apex varying to fusoid-ventricose, walls thin, some with debris adhering, content homogeneous. Caulocystidia not studied.

Gill trama a central area of floccose hyphae, the cells yellowish in KOH (poorly revived); subhymenium of narrow gelatinous hyphae in a distinct layer. Pileus cutis a thick gelatinous layer of hyaline to yellowish hyphae 2–4 μ diam.; hypodermial region of bright fulvous hyphae with incrusted walls, cells 4–12 μ diam. Context hyphae interwoven, smooth, yellowish in KOH. Clamp connections present. All hyphae inamyloid. (Above microscopic data all from type).

HABIT, HABITAT, AND DISTRIBUTION: On conifer debris or near it, fall, Idaho and Washington. Type studied.

OBSERVATIONS: This is another member of the *P. spumosa* complex which has been named as a distinct species from North America. We suspect that the spotting green when handled is some sort of artifact due to wet weather and the general tendency of olive tints to develop in the context in age. The type specimen reminds one of *P. spumosa*. We recognized the species here as an aid to future studies, but Smith in all of his collecting in the Northwest has not been able to recognize it on any other feature than the smaller spores. It may well be merely a small spored variety of *P. spumosa*. *P. subfulva* has thick-walled pleurocystidia.

We have a number of collections from Idaho (Smith 73387, 73388,

73389, 73415, 73457, 73663) which appear to belong here. Some stained yellow slightly and some did not and all show more fulvous in their coloration than is evident in *P. piceina.* The following is a description of Smith 73387:

Pileus 3–6 cm broad, broadly convex, expanding to nearly plane, surface viscid (not glutinous), disc ochraceous tawny to dark tawny, glabrous but developing aggregations of fibrils beneath the cuticle, margin pale yellow (about "cartridge-buff"); margin stained sulphur (greenish yellow) where bruised. Context bright yellow, odor pungent, taste mild, FeSO$_4$ olive, Guaiac quickly blue on gills.

Lamellae close to subdistant, adnexed, moderately broad, pale sulphur yellow young, soon duller and near "Verona brown" mature (sordid cinnamon), edges even.

Stipe 5–8 cm long, 4–7 mm thick, equal, interior bright yellow soon fulvous below, surface pale yellow above, paler than "Naphthaline yellow" near apex, fulvous below, glabrescent. Veil thin, yellowish.

Spores 6.5–8 × 4–4.5 μ, smooth, with a minute apical pore; shape in face view oblong to elliptic varying to ovate; in profile somewhat bean-shaped to obscurely inequilateral, color in KOH rusty cinnamon, in Melzer's sol. paler; wall over 0.25 μ thick.

Basidia 4-spored, 20–25 × 6–8 μ, clavate, hyaline to yellow in KOH. Pleurocystidia 40–70 (80) × 10–18 μ, fusoid ventricose, apex obtuse to subacute, wall thin, surface smooth, content colloidal as revived ("empty" in fresh material), yellowish to hyaline revived in KOH, nearly hyaline in Melzer's reagent. Cheilocystidia smaller than the pleurocystidia, mostly with yellowish content in KOH. Caulocystidia scattered, clavate to fusoid-ventricose thin-walled, yellow to hyaline.

Gill trama of a central area of more or less parallel hyphae the cells of which finally inflate markedly (+ 15 μ), walls thin to scarcely thickened, hyaline to yellowish, smooth, some ochraceous oleiferous hyphae present; subhymenium a gelatinous zone of hyaline branched hyphae 2–4 μ diam. Pileus cutis a gelatinous layer of ochraceous to hyaline more or less encrusted hyphae 3–6 μ diam.; hypodermium of rusty to ochraceous-fulvous non-gelatinous hyphae with encrusted walls and cells 4–12 (15) μ diam., compactly arranged, walls thin, smooth, pale yellowish olive in KOH. Clamp connections present.

On conifer debris, abundant in the Priest Lake area.

In this material colors are duller and are more rusty brownish generally than in *P. piceina* in either the fresh or dried condition. The sulphur stains which develop slowly on the injured pileus margin are not "green" as described for *P. subflavida,* but close enough to raise doubts, since no truly green-staining fungus has been found. As for the type, the dried specimens cited above resemble those referred to *P. spumosa.* Because of the slight odor the above collections might be referred to *P. graveolens.* Because the characters on which *P. spumosa, P. graveolens* and *P. subflavida* are distinguished appear to be rather minor, it is urgent that a study in culture be made of the variants which closely resemble *P. spumosa*.

196. Pholiota crassipedes nom. nov. (not **P. lata** Kummer p. 85, 1871)
Gymnopilus latus Murrill, Mycologia 4: 257. 1912.
Flammula lata Murrill, Mycologia 4: 262. 1912.
Illustrations: Text figs. 442-444.

Pileus gregarious, reaching 9 cm broad, convex to plane, not umbonate, ferruginous-fulvous at the center, ochroleucous on the margin, glabrous, shining, viscid, radiate-lineate. Context rather thin; taste mild.
Lamellae sinuate or adnate, pallid to fulvous, plane, not crowded, rather narrow.
Stipe 5–7 cm long, 1–1.3 cm thick, equal or slightly larger below, dry smooth, subglabrous, fleshy, white or somewhat yellowish, with yellow or orange mycelium at the base. Veil pale yellow, membranous in young hymenophores, soon breaking into fibrils and disappearing.
Spores 5.5–7 × 3.5–4.5 μ, smooth, germ pore present but very minute; shape in face view elliptic to ovate, in profile subelliptic to obscurely inequilateral; as revived in KOH more or less ochraceous tawny, paler cinnamon in Melzer's reagent; wall about 0.25 μ thick.
Basidia 20–27 × 5–7 μ, 4-spored, pale ochraceous in KOH and in Melzer's reagent. Pleurocystidia: 1) abundant, 38–73 × 7–21 μ, fusoid-ventricose, apex obtuse, wall thin smooth and hyaline, content usually ochraceous to amber-brown from colloidal content which in some is shrunken and coagulated: 2) 12–20 × 4–9 μ, subfilamentous to clavate, with thin smooth hyaline walls, content consisting of an irregular mass of hyaline-refractive material (not as well organized as in "chryso-cystidia") or the refractive material in rods, bars or particles and variously distributed in the cell (the same material seen in some basidia and in some of the large fusoid-ventricose cells). Cheilocystidia 43–57 × 7–14 μ, similar to pleurocystidia or subfusoid (neck not elongated). Caulo-cystidia none found.
Gill trama a central area of floccose subparallel hyphae (3) 4–10 μ diam. cells finally inflated, walls thin smooth and yellowish to hyaline in KOH; subhymenium of gelatinous narrow (2 μ) hyaline hyphae. Pileus cutis a gelatinous pellicle of loosely interwoven ochraceous narrow (2–4 μ) smooth to encrusted hyphae; hypodermial region of floccose rusty brown incrusted hyphae 3–9 μ diam. Context hyphae interwoven, of inflated cells with smooth thin yellowish to hyaline walls in KOH. Clamp connections present. All hyphae inamyloid.
HABIT, HABITAT, AND DISTRIBUTION: On a log of a deciduous tree in woods, Washington, fall. Known only from the type.
OBSERVATIONS: Our microscopic data are from the type. This is near *P. jalapensis*, which becomes slightly greenish where bruised, has stramineous gills and pale spores. Kauffman (1926) examined specimens from

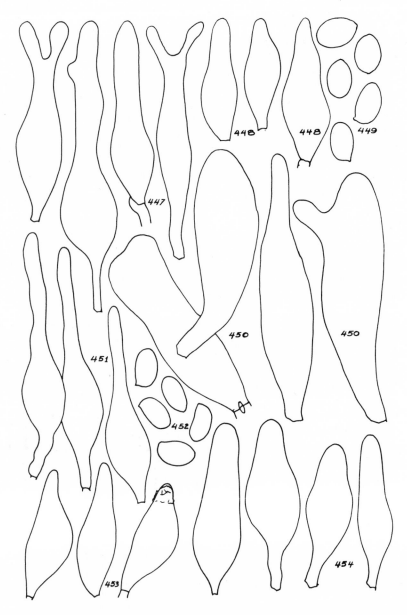

Text Fig. 34.

FIGS. 447-450, pleurocystidia, cheilocystidia, spores and caulocystidia of *P. brunnescens;* 451-453, pleurocystidia, spores and cheilocystidia of *P. jalopensis;* 454, pleurocystidia of *P. innocua.*

dead willow trunks and found the stipe apparently viscid (Murrill described it as dry). Kauffman stated that the large pilei and solid stipe would separate it from the "spumosa" group. He apparently had some other species. *P. crassipedes* is close to *P. lubrica* but the latter has white mycelium around the base and grows under conifers. However, both should be critically compared from fresh material.

Because of the bright color, even of dried specimens, one is reminded of the *P. alnicola* group but the large hymenial cystidia and the failure of the spores to become dark reddish cinnamon in Melzer's reagent rule it out. *P. crassipedes* has the stature of *P. lubrica* and the cystidia are consistently thin-walled. We are not inclined to emphasize the "chrysocystidioid cells" in the hymenium as a taxonomic character in the present stage of our knowledge of this species, but they are not without interest from the standpoint of the evolution of chrysocystidia from basidioles. It differs from *P. sublubrica* in growing on hardwood logs and in having yellow to orange mycelium at the stipe base. Also *P. sublubrica* typically has veil remnants on the pileus. The color of the spores in KOH, however, is the same in both.

Stirps Innocua

Terrestrial or appearing terrestrial and the spore width 2.8–3.5 (4) μ are the two features in combination which delimit this group. See *P. perniciosa* also; it has long pleurocystidia but actually they are chrysocystidia.

Key

1. Lamellae pallid but soon becoming pale greenish yellow .... *P. virescentifolia*
1. Not as above 2
   2. Some spores with a dark violet-brown coagulated content as revived in Melzer's; pleurocystidia 38–52 × 8–15 μ .... *P. brunneodisca*
   2. Not as above 3
3. Stipe 3–5 mm thick; pileus broadly conic .... (see *P. flavopallida* and *P. agglutinata*)
3. Stipe (4) 5–10 mm thick 4
   4. Pileus margin slightly greenish when bruised; pileus context white .... *P. jalapensis*
   4. Not as above 5
5. Pleurocystidia 30–46 × 10–15 μ, utriform caulocystidia not distinctive .... *P. innocua*
5. Pleurocystidia 50–70 × 11–15 μ; fusoid-ventricose; caulocystidia conspicuous and versiform (fig. 459) .... *P. lurida*

197. **Pholiota virescentifolia** sp. nov.
Illustrations: Text figs. 445-446.

Pileus 4–5 cm latus, conicus, demum conico-umbonatus, sordide luteo-brunneus, viscidus. Contextus albus, lamellae adnato-decurrentes, albidae demum olivaceo-lutea, confertae, latae, fimbriate. Stipes 3.5–4 cm longus, 8–12 mm crassus, subradicatus, sursum albidus, deorsum sordidus, siccus. Velum luteum, copiosum. Sporae 5.5–6.5(7) × 3.5–4 μ. Pleurocystidia (40)50–75(85) × 10–17 μ, fusoide ventricosa. Caulocystidia 36–80 × 7–15 μ, clavata. Specimen typicum in Herb. Univ. Tenn. conservatum est; legit prope Mt. LeConte G.S.M.N.P. 5 Sept. 1952. Hesler 20591.

Pileus 4–5 cm broad, conic, then more or less expanding, "tawny-olive," pellicle separable, viscid, rivulose under lens, margin even. Context white, thick on disc, thin on margin; odor and taste slight.

Lamellae adnate, short-decurrent, white at first, then pale greenish yellow, finally brownish yellow, close, broad, edges fimbriate.

Stipe 3.5–4 cm long, 8–12 mm thick, subradicate, apex white, dingy below, dry fibrillose, spongy-hollow. Veil copious, yellow, submembranous-webby.

Spores 5.5–6.5 (7) × 3.5–4 μ, smooth, apex with a very minute pore; shape in face view elliptic to ovate, in profile obscurely inequilateral to elliptic; color pale tawny in KOH, about the same color in Melzer's reagent; wall about 0.25 μ thick.

Basidia 4-spored, 20–25 × 5–6 μ, narrowly clavate, hyaline to yellowish in KOH. Pleurocystidia abundant, (40) 50–75 (83) × 10–17 μ, fusoid-ventricose with usually a long narrow pedicel (14–27 μ) and an obtuse apex, thin-walled, hyaline and smooth as revived in KOH, but often ochraceous when first revived; content of homogeneous colloidal material in the neck, only a few with some amorphous to crystaline material in the apical region, this material more or less dextrinoid. Cheilocystidia similar to pleurocystidia but smaller and more of them tending to remain ochraceous in KOH, many with somewhat stringy ochraceous content as seen in KOH. Caulocystidia 36–80 × 7–15 μ, clavate, in tufts.

Gill trama of short- to long-celled parallel hyphae with thin non-gelatinous walls hyaline to yellowish in KOH and Melzer's sol.; subhymenium a gelatinous to subgelatinous zone of narrow (2–3.5 μ), interwoven hyaline filaments. Pileus cutis a thick gelatinous layer of appressed-interwoven hyphae 2–5 μ diam., with band-like to spiral incrustations, yellowish to hyaline in KOH, hyphae hyaline to yellowish individually; hypodermium of bright tawny floccose hyphae 4–12 μ diam. with more or less incrusted walls. Context hyphae hyaline to yellowish in KOH, cells variously inflated, thin-walled, hyphae interwoven. All hyphae inamyloid.

HABIT, HABITAT, AND DISTRIBUTION: On soil and humus, under hemlock, Tennessee, September; Hesler 20591, type.

OBSERVATIONS: The tawny olive pileus, white context, white young lamellae which become greenish yellow, subradicate stipe which is white above, and the large, clavate caulocystidia in tufts all characterize this species. When collected, it appeared to be a form of *P. spumosa,* but its microscopic characters separate it.

198. Pholiota brunneodisca (Pk.) comb. nov.

Flammula brunneodisca Peck, New York State Mus. Bull. 167: 42. 1913.
Gymnopilus brunneodiscus (Pk.) Murrill, North Amer. Flora 10: 199. 1917.

Pileus caespitose, 2.5–6 cm broad, broadly convex or nearly plane, umbonate, ochraceous-yellow, center brown, viscid, cuticle separable, slightly innately fibrillose. Context thin, white.

Lamellae adnate with a decurrent tooth, pale yellow, becoming rusty brown, thin, close, rather narrow.

Stipe 2–3 cm long, 4–6 mm thick, pale yellow within and without, paler at the apex, glabrous, equal, solid.

Spores 5–7 × 3–3.5 (4) μ, smooth, apical pore present but very minute, apex not truncate; shape in face view ovate to subelliptic, in profile subovate to obscurely inequilateral; in KOH ochraceous tawny, in Melzer's reagent mostly about the same color but one or two in a microscopic field seen to have dark violet brown coagulated contents; wall about 0.25 μ thick.

Basidia 4-spored, 20–25 (27) × 5–6.5 μ, yellowish in KOH or in Melzer's reagent, mostly obscurely utriform when immature. Pleurocystidia 38–52 × 8–15 μ, fusoid-ventricose, neck with somewhat undulating walls and apex obtuse to rounded, wall thin, smooth or some with adhering coagulated amorphous material, content often amber-brown to ochraceous but fading out to pale yellowish or hyaline. Cheilocystidia 30–48 × 6–12 μ, subfusoid with obtuse apex, utriform or clavate, walls thin, content in KOH usually ochraceous. Caulocystidia not studied.

Gill trama a central area of floccose subinterwoven hyphae yellowish to hyaline in KOH, hyphae 4–9 μ broad, walls thin and smooth; subhymenium gelatinous, of tangled, narrow ($\pm$ 2 μ) hyaline hyphae. Pileus cutis a thick gelatinous pellicle of narrow (1.5–3 μ) hyaline to yellowish interwoven hyphae; hypodermial region of rusty ochraceous floccose hyphae some with encrusted walls. Context hyphae paler (poorly revived). Clamp connections present. All hyphae inamyloid.

HABIT, HABITAT, AND DISTRIBUTION: Caespitose, on soil, probably growing from a buried root, Massachusetts, October. Type studied.

OBSERVATIONS: This species appears to be close to *P. inocua* but is the only *Pholiota* known to us with the curious almost amyloid (violet-brown) inclusion filling or nearly filling some spores.

199. **Pholiota jalapensis** (Murr.) comb. nov.
Gymnopilus jalapensis Murrill, Mycologia 5: 25. 1913.
Flammula jalapensis Murrill, Mycologia 5: 36. 1913.
Illustrations: Text figs. 451-453.

Pileus reaching 8 cm in diameter, expanded, at length depressed at the center, ochraceous toward the disc and ferruginous-isabelline to fulvous at the center, slightly greenish when bruised, cremeous at the margin, surface smooth, moist to viscid, glabrous, margin curved downward and irregular or undulate. Context white, 5 mm thick near stipe; taste mild.

Lamellae adnate, stramineous, crowded, about 5 mm broad, ventricose near stipe, arcuate near the margin.

Stipe reaching 8 cm long and 10 mm thick, stramineous, equal below, slightly enlarged at the apex, glabrous. Veil showing a trace of a slight cortina at the middle.

Spores 5.5–6.5 (7) × 3–3.5 μ, smooth, apical pore very minute, often not visible; shape in face view oblong to elliptic, in profile slightly bean-shaped to subelliptic, color as revived in KOH ochraceous, not much different in Melzer's reagent; wall thin (–0.25 μ thick).

Basidia 18–23 (25) × 5–6 μ mostly 4-spored, clavate, yellowish to hyaline in KOH, yellowish in Melzer's reagent. Pleurocystidia abundant, 50–77 × 10–16 μ, fusoid-ventricose, apex subacute to obtuse, neck narrow (4–6 μ), walls thin and smooth, content with some particles of amorphous material, ochraceous to yellowish or finally pallid, content often "colloidal." Cheilocystidia 38–60 × 5–18 μ, similar to pleurocystidia or merely subfusoid. Culocystidia none found on specimen studied.

Gill trama with a gelatinous subhymenium, details of central area not too clear in revived material but hyphal cells about 5–8 μ broad. Pileus cutis a gelatinous pellicle (with some of the hyphae incrusted) over a rusty brown hypodermial zone of floccose, incrusted hyphae. Context hyphae poorly revived. Clamp connections present. All hyphae inamyloid.

HABIT, HABITAT, AND DISTRIBUTION: On soil, in woods, Mexico, December. Type studied.

OBSERVATIONS: This species has spores and lamellae paler than in most other terrestrial species. It is near *P. hypholomoides,* which has broader and darker spores.

200. **Pholiota innocua** sp. nov.
Illustrations. Text figs. 454; 455-457; pl. 89.

Pileus 3–7 cm latus, convexus, demum late convexus, viscidus, subfulvus vel fulvus, ad marginem laete luteus. Contextus luteus. Lamellae laete luteae confertae, latae, demum subdecurrentes. Stipes 4–6 cm longus, 9–12 mm crassus, solidus, pallide luteus, sursum pruinosus, deorsum de-

mum fulvus. Velum subfulvum, fibrillosum. Sporae 4.4–6.5 × 2.8–3.5 μ.
Pleurocystidia utriformia 30–46(60) × 10–15 μ. Specimen typicum in
Herb. Univ. Mich. conservatum est; legit prope Warrensburg, New York,
12 Sept. 1934. Smith 798.

Pileus 3–7 cm broad, convex with a bent in margin which remains decurved a long time, nearly plane or more rarely slightly depressed in age but some slightly umbonate, margin at first appressed fibrillose from patches of tawny fibrils, surface covered by a thin gelatinous layer; color "tawny" (tawny) on disc and pale lemon-yellow ("pinnard-yellow" to "baryta-yellow") over marginal area. Context watery firm, yellowish, odor and taste not distinctive, $FeSO_4$ slowly green on dried pileus cutis, finally inky black.

Lamellae pale yellow ("Baryta-yellow"), close, moderately broad, equal, adnate to decurrent (not at all sinuate or adnexed), edges even.

Stipe 4–6 cm long, 9–12 mm equal or nearly so, solid pale yellow above ("pale chalchedony-yellow") and pruinose to fibrillose-pruinose, below dull yellow but soon rusty stained, base with matted yellowish mycelium as dried.

Spores 4.5–6 (6.5) × 2.8–3.5 μ, smooth, apical pore not distinct; shape in face view oblong, slightly bean-shaped in profile; yellow in KOH, in Melzer's sol. merely pale cinnamon brown; wall slightly thickened (–0.25 μ).

Basidia 4-spored, 18–22 × 5–6 μ, hyaline in KOH, yellowish in Melzer's. Pleurocystidia abundant and projecting, 30–46 (60) × 10–15 μ, utriform (broadly fusoid-ventricose with rounded apex), when first revived in KOH with reddish to rusty ochraceous content but clearing on standing, finally hyaline, in Melzer's yellowish to hyaline or retaining some brown debris, walls thin to rarely slightly thickened (± 0.5 μ) and either smooth or with some debris adhering, as revived often with rod-like bodies and particles in neck. Cheilocystidia smaller than pleurocystidia (26–35 × 10–16 μ) and many varying in shape to clavate to nearly vesiculose-pedicellate, becoming hyaline in KOH and with no distinct reaction in Melzer's reagent the walls frequently thickened and yellow in KOH. Caulocystidia not characteristic, a few clavate hyphal ends present above the veil line.

Gill trama in KOH of ochraceous to pale tawny parallel hyphae with non-gelatinous walls which in Melzer's reagent are dull pale rusty brown; subhymenium of narrow interwoven much-branched hyphae only obscurely gelatinous in KOH. Pileus cutis a pellicle of appressed narrow (2–3 μ) hyphae yellow to tawny as revived in KOH, the hyphal walls smooth to minutely incrusted by bands or spirals and the walls not obviously gelatinous though the hyphae are imbedded in a gelatinous matrix; beneath this the context hyphae 4–11 μ diam., loosely interwoven and non-gelatinous. No hypodermium evident. Clamp connections readily observed at nearly all septa.

HABIT, HABITAT, AND DISTRIBUTION: Caespitose gregarious around

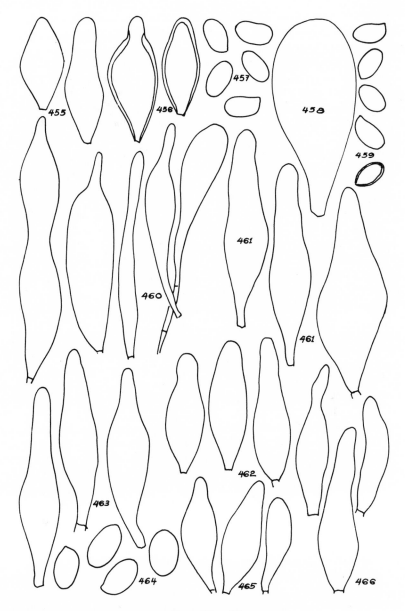

Text Fig. 35.

FIGS. 455-457, cheilocystidia (two types) and spores of *P. innocua;* 458-462, caulocystidia, spores, pleurocystidia, and cheilocystidia of *P. lurida;* 463-465, pleurocystidia, spores and cheilocystidia of *P. acuto-conica;* 466, cheilocystidia of *P. lenta.*

beech logs and debris but not on the wood, Warrensburg, New York, Sept. 12, 1934. Smith 798, type.

OBSERVATIONS: This species by virtue of small spores and broadly rounded pleurocystidia appears to be closely related to *P. polychroa* but is readily distinct by the rusty to yellow pilei. Its distinctive features in addition to those relating it to *P. polychroa* are the typically convex to depressed pileus, cespitose-gregarious fruiting pattern and moderately thin veil. We did not find any thick-walled pleurocystidia in any of the mounts we made, but the presence of so many thick-walled cheilocystidia causes one to speculate as to whether the same feature will not be found eventually in the pleurocystidia of some collections of this species.

201. Pholiota lurida sp. nov.
Illustrations: Text figs. 458-462.

Pileus 3–7 cm latus, se expandens, margine "cartridge-buff," vel "cream-color," disco "tawny." Caro flavido-alba; odore et gustu mitis vel tenuis. Lamellae adnatae demum adnexae, pallido-flavae, subdistantes, medio-latae. Stipes 4–9 cm longus, 4–9 mm crassus, supra albus, infra brunnaceus, fibrillosus. Velum arachnoideum, album. Sporae 5.5–7 × 3–3.7 μ, ellipsoideae demum ovoideae, leves. Pleurocystidia 49–68 × 9–15 μ, ventricosa; cheilocystidia 28–47 × 9–4 μ, ventricosa, subellipsoides, obclavata. Cuticula gelatinosa. Caulocystidia fasciculata, clavata, fusoidea, ventricosa. Specimen typicum in Herb. Univ. Mich. conservatum est; lectum prope Pellston, Michigan, 30 Sept. 1962. Smith 66386.

Pileus 3–7 cm broad, convex with an incurved margin, expanding to broadly convex or nearly plane, "cartridge-buff" to "cream-color" on margin, more or less ochraceous tawny on disc, marginal area streaked with agglutinated fibrils or nearly glabrous, margin for a time decorated with a fringe of pallid veil fibrils. Context yellowish white; odor none, taste slight; in $FeSO_4$ instantly olive, flesh and cutis with KOH instantly yellow to finally tawny brown.

Lamellae adnate to adnexed, yellowish pallid, nearly subdistant, moderately broad, edges becoming uneven.

Stipe 4–9 cm long, 4–9 mm thick, whitish above, soon dull rusty below from handling, equal, to slightly enlarged downward, cartilaginous, hollow, lower half fibrillose from veil, but not leaving a distinct annulus, scurfy above. Veil arachnoid, whitish.

Spores 5.5–7 × 3–3.7 μ, smooth, apical pore very minute (under 1.4 N.A.) to absent, shape in face view suboblong to ovate, in profile obscurely inequilateral; color pale tawny in KOH, nearly hyaline in Melzer's reagent; wall less than 0.25 μ thick (estimated).

Basidia 4-spored, 18–25 × 4.5–6 μ, clavate, hyaline in KOH. Pleurocystidia 42–58 (68) × 9–15 μ, fusoid-ventricose with obtuse apex to utriform, thin-walled, content ochraceous to rusty brown but slowly hyaline in KOH (or hyaline from the beginning), wall thin and smooth. Cheilocystidia 28–47 × 9–14 μ, subfusoid to utriform or clavate, smooth, thin-walled. Caulocystidia numerous over apex of stipe, in rosettes, versiform, fusoid, clavate, vesiculose, or ventricose above and below a median constriction, pedicel often greatly elongated, apex in any of above types may be drawn into a filamentous crooked prolongation 3–6 μ diam., walls thin smooth and hyaline or some of the vesicular elements golden yellow.

Gill trama with a distinct gelatinous subhymenium and a floccose central strand of subparallel hyphae 4–8 μ broad, and walls hyaline to pale tawny in color. Pileus cutis a gelatinous pellicle of narrow (2–5 μ) ochraceous smooth to encrusted hyphae, hypodermium of rusty brown floccose hyphae. Clamp connections present. All hyphae inamyloid.

HABIT, HABITAT, AND DISTRIBUTION: Scattered on debris, among fallen aspen, Michigan, September; Smith 66386, type.

OBSERVATIONS: The pale, although rather bright, buff to cream-color margin and the tawny disc make it a striking agaric. The flesh, gills, and stipe are likewise pale, and the veil white. In addition, the stipe base is also pallid, but becomes dull rusty from handling. The caulocystidia are in rosettes and are rather striking in form.

Stirps Lenta

Terrestrial species or basidiocarps appearing to be terrestrial (not located directly on wood such as logs, stumps, or branch material above ground) : spores 4–5 μ wide; colors various but not as in stirpes *Lubrica, Fibrillosipes,* or *Polychroa.*

Key

1. Pileus conic, in age with a conic umbo 2
1. Pileus convex to plane, rarely with a low umbo 3
   2. Lamellae ferruginous at maturity .... *P. fulviconica*
   2. Lamellae clay-color at maturity .... *P. acutoconica*
3. Pileus pallid to grayish and developing yellow tones in age .... *P. lenta*
3. Pileus yellow (at least on margin when young) 4
   4. Lamellae pallid when young (see *P. lubrica* also) ....
   .... *P. squalida*
   4. Lamellae yellow at first .... see *P. spinulifera*

202. Pholiota fulviconica (Murr.) comb. nov.
Gymnopilus fulviconicus Murrill, Florida Acad. Sci. Proc. 7: 120. 1945.
Flammula fulviconica (Murr.) Murrill, Florida Acad. Sci. Proc. 7: 127. 1945.

Pileus 3 cm broad, conic, not fully expanding, fulvous on the disc, paler toward the margin, solitary, viscid, surface smooth, glabrous, margin even, entire, incurved when dry. Context thin, pallid; odorless, taste mild.

Lamellae adnate with decurrent tooth, ferruginous at maturity, inserted, broad, medium distant, entire.

Stipe about 5 cm long, 7 mm thick, subequal, smooth, glabrous, pale yellowish above, fulvous below.

Spores 6–7.5 × 3.8–4.5 μ, more rarely 8–9 × 5 μ, elliptic or more rarely subovate in face view, inequilateral in profile; smooth; germ pore minute. Basidia 22–25 × 5–6 μ, 4-spored. Pleurocystidia 48–65 × 8–10 μ, ventricose, usually colorless, sometimes brown, apices sometimes with an exudate; cheilocystidia 30–58 × 8–10 μ, similar.

Gill trama with a central stratum of hyphae subparallel and 3–5 μ broad. Pileus trama radial. Cuticle a gelatinous zone of loose, narrow (1–2.5 μ broad), colorless hyphae, resting on a hypodermium of incrusted, brown hyphae. Clamp connections present. Caulocystidia none. Pileus and gill trama pale yellowish in KOH; dark dingy brown in Melzer's reagent (data by Hesler).

HABIT, HABITAT, AND DISTRIBUTION: On soil, humus, and rotten logs, Florida, California, and Idaho, August and December. Type studied.

OBSERVATIONS: This may be too close to *P. spumosa* to recognize it as a separate taxon, but the ferruginous gills may be distinguishing features, the gill color no doubt reflects a similar color in the spore deposit though this remains to be established.

MATERIAL EXAMINED: CALIFORNIA: Smith 3789. FLORIDA: type; IDAHO: Smith 65898.

203. Pholiota acutoconica sp. nov.
Illustrations: Text figs. 463-465.

Pileus 3–6 cm latus, conicus demum conico-campanulatus, viscidus, virgatus, ad marginem appendiculatus, laete vel sordide ochraceus. Lamellae late adnatae vel subdecurrentes, confertae, latae (5–6 mm), pallide citrino-luteae demum sordide argillaceae. Stipes 5–7 cm longus, 5–8 mm crassus, aequalis, citrino-luteus, deorsum subfulvus, luteo-fibrillosus. Sporae 6–8 × 4–4.5 μ, leves. Pleurocystidia 46–70 × 8–16 μ, fusoide ventricosa, tenuitunicata. Specimen typicum legit prope Rhododendron, Oregon, 2 Oct. 1944. Smith 19315, in Univ. of Mich. conservatum est.

Pileus 3–6 cm broad, conic with an incurved margin, expanding to conic-campanulate, or conic umbonate, the umbo acute, surface viscid, fibrillose-streaked (virgate) beneath the viscid pellicle, margin with thin patches of the fibrillose remains of the veil, "tawny-olive" on disc "honey-yellow," on margin or at extreme edge "Reed's yellow." Context pliant, thin except on the disc, near "honey-yellow" (more dingy than gills); odor none, taste mild.

Lamellae broadly adnate becoming subdecurrent, moderately close, 3 tiers of lamellulae, moderately broad (5–6 mm near stipe) tapered to cap margin, "Reed's yellow" young, finally dingy clay-color, edges even.

Stipe 5–7 cm long, 5–8 mm thick, equal, hollow, when young "Reed's yellow" over all and fibrillose from "Reed's yellow" veil remnants, apex silky and "citron-yellow," gradually becoming "sepia" inside and out from the base upward, cortex yellow, pith usually worm-eaten and tawny in color. Veil yellow, arachnoid.

Spores 6.5–8 × 4–4.5 (9 × 5) μ, smooth, ochraceous tawny revived in KOH, in Melzer's reagent pale cinnamon with a minute apical pore, in face view elliptic varying to ovate, in profile subelliptic to obscurely inequilateral; wall less than 0.3 μ thick and becoming appreciably thicker in KOH.

Basidia 18–25 × 6–7 (8) μ, 4-spored, clavate, yellowish in KOH and Melzer's reagent. Pleurocystidia abundant, 46–70 × 8–16 μ, broadly to narrowly fusoid-ventricose varying to subfusoid, neck usually greatly elongated and apex obtuse, walls thin and many cells remaining collapsed, smooth, content homogeneous and yellowish to hyaline in either KOH or Melzer's reagent. Cheilocystidia similar to pleurocystidia but usually shorter and more frequently varying to subfusoid to nearly clavate and 30–45 × 8–12 μ, content homogeneous in KOH and Melzer's sol., walls thin and smooth. Caulocystidia present as clavate end-cells 9–14 μ broad.

Gill trama of parallel to somewhat interwoven hyaline (in KOH) to yellowish thin-walled, smooth non-gelatinous hyphae 3–8 μ diam. with short (near pileus) to elongate hyphal cells; cells becoming somewhat inflated in age; subhymenium of gelatinous or subgelatinous narrow (3–5 μ) hyaline smooth-walled hyphae in a zone intergrading with the central strand. Pileus cutis a gelatinous layer of hyphae 2–5 μ diam., the walls collapsing and disintegrating, in the process becoming crinkled and often appearing ornamented with incrustations; hypodermium a layer of interwoven hyphae dark orange-brown in KOH and of hyphae 5–12 μ diam. with heavily incrusted walls. Context hyphae interwoven, walls yellow in KOH and smooth, cells inflated to 15+ μ, inamyloid (yellow in Melzer's reagent). Clamp connections present.

HABIT, HABITAT, AND DISTRIBUTION: Caespitose to gregarious around conifer wood, Rhododendron, Oregon. Oct. 1, 1944. Smith 19315, type.

This species bears a strong resemblance to species of subg. *Flammula* but is at once distinguished by its large pleurocystidia. It is a brighter yellow than *P. spumosa* and the color is more persistent, in fact it is an outstanding field character along with the sharply conic pileus. There is a difference in spore color on spores revived in KOH also. In *P. acutoconica* they are near ochraceous tawny.

204. Pholiota lenta (Fr.) Singer.

Agaricus lentus Fries, Syst. Myc. 1: 253. 1821.
Flammula lenta (Fr.) Kummer, Der Führer in die Pilzkunde, p. 82. 1871.
Flammula betulina Peck, Bull. Torrey Bot. Club 34: 100. 1907.

Gymnopilus lentus (Fr.) Murrill, North Amer. Fl. 10: 204. 1917.
Dryophila lenta (Fr.) Quélet, Enchir, Fung. p. 70. 1886.
Illustrations: Text figs. 466; 467-470; pls. 11b, 25a, 90.

Pileus 3–7 (10) cm broad, convex-hemispheric to convex, finally expanded, whitish to pallid, at times "pinkish-buff," or smoky gray, the disc becoming slightly darker ("avellaneous or even yellowish"), viscid to glutinous, with scattered, white fibrillose-squamulose scales from the broken veil, and often for a long time appendiculate from veil remnants, glabrescent. Context white, firm; odor and taste mild.

Lamellae adnate, or with a decurrent tooth, white, then gray-tawny or grayish brown or "clay-color," close, rather narrow to meidum broad, abruptly narrowed in front, edges even to fimbriate.

Stipe 3–8 (12) cm long, 4–12 mm thick, white above, brownish at the base, fibrillose, apex white-mealy, equal or sub-bulbous, solid or spongy. Veil white, copious, cortinate, leaving an evanescent annulus.

Spores 5.5–7 × 3.5–4.5 μ, smooth, apical pore minute, in face view elliptic to oblong, in profile slightly bean-shaped to subelliptic, in KOH more or less ochraceous tawny, in Melzer's reagent ochraceous, wall relatively thin ($\pm$ 0.2 μ).

Basidia 18–23 × 5–6 μ, yellowish in Melzer's reagent, in KOH hyaline or nearly so, almost narrowly elliptic or some slightly ventricose before sporulating, varying to obscurely clavate. Pleurocystidia 42–60 (65) × 8–14 μ, fusoid-ventricose, apex obtuse, wall thin and hyaline, content homogeneous, hyaline in KOH (in well dried material). Cheilocystidia 26–30 × 7–10 μ, broadly subfusoid, and 28–42 × 9–13 μ, thin-walled, hyaline in KOH, smooth. Caulocystidia scattered or in tufts on a gelatinous "subhymenium," 25–100 × (4) 5–18 μ, fusoid-ventricose with subacute apex, utriform or clavate or clavate-mucronate, thin-walled or wall slightly thickened (less than 0.5 μ), content homogeneous and hyaline ("empty").

Gill trama a central area of floccose thin-walled smooth hyaline hyphae parallel to subparallel and with the cells greatly inflated in age; subhymenium of narrow gelatinous branched hyphae hyaline in KOH. Pileus cutis a thick gelatinous layer of narrow hyaline to yellowish hyphae 1–3 μ diam., appearing to have numerous refractive cross walls at times, smooth, loosely dispersed in gelatinous matrix; hypodermial region of ochraceous to brownish ochraceous floccose hyphae 6–12 μ diam. and with smooth to slightly encrusted walls. Context hyphae inflated, thin-walled, smooth, walls yellowish to hyaline in KOH. All hyphae inamyloid. Clamp connections present.

HABIT, HABITAT, AND DISTRIBUTION: On humus, debris, or humus charged soil, Massachusetts, North Carolina, Tennessee, Michigan, and California, July—December; reported from New York to South Carolina in the eastern United States by Murrill (1917).

OBSERVATIONS: The pallid color, small spores, medium sized pleuro-

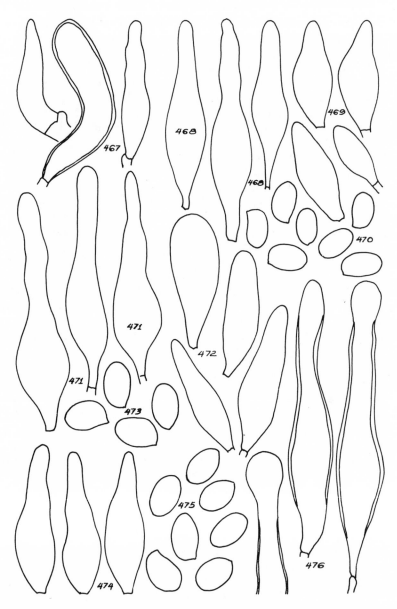

Text Fig. 36.

Figs. 467-470, caulocystidia, pleurocystidia, cheilocystidia and spores of *P. lenta;* 471-473, pleurocystidia, cheilocystidia and spores of *P. squallida;* 474-476, cheilocystidia, spores and pleurocystidia of *P. sequoiae.*

cystidia, small cheilocystidia and typically white gills when young feature this species. Sterile or semisterile basidiocarps may develop yellow gills, and have caused confusion between this species and *P. gummosa*. Interesting "abnormal" basidiocarps are rarely found, one of which is described as follows:

  Pholiota lenta—abnormal variant?

Pileus 5 cm broad, plane with a decurved inrolled margin, glutinous when wet, soon merely viscid, disc near "hair brown," toward margin "wood-brown" to "avellaneous" (dark gray to pale grayish brown), staining rusty slightly when bruised. Context pallid, slowly olive in $FeSO_4$; odor none, taste mild.

Hymenophore poroid near stipe and lamellate near pileus margin, adnate to pileus and short decurrent on stipe, creamy buff when young and staining tan when injured.

Stipe 3 cm long, 14 mm thick, eccentric, equal, solid, surface pallid (concolorous with incurved margin of pileus), with a thin distribution of grayish veil fibrils but lacking a distinct apical zone, staining rusty brown at base when handled.

Spores 6–8.5 × 3.5–4 μ, elliptic to subovate in face view, bean-shaped in profile view, smooth, germ pore present but obscure. Basidia 4-spored. Pleurocystidia 48–64 × 9–11 μ, fusoid ventricose, thin-walled, neck broad and apex obtuse to rounded, hyaline to yellowish in KOH. Cheilocystidia similar to pleurocystidia but necks often shorter.

Hymenophoral trama of yellowish hyphae (in KOH), the walls smooth; subhymenium gelatinous. Pileus cutis a tangled layer of gelatinous hyaline narrow (2–4 μ) hyphae or possibly the layer trichodermial in origin, in Melzer's yellowish and hyphae showing frequently a peculiar transverse banding; hypodermium of hyphae 8–15 μ diam., walls yellowish in KOH, smooth and non-gelatinous. Context hyphae interwoven, non-gelatinous and merely yellowish in Melzer's. Clamp connections present.

HABIT, HABITAT, AND DISTRIBUTION: On soil in mixed woods, Huron Mts., Big Bay, Mich. June 15, 1963. Smith 66381.

OBSERVATIONS: The gills are parasitized by one of the *Fungi Imperfecti* with narrow hyaline hyphae. This may account for the configuration of the hymenophore. In the fresh condition there was no macroscopic evidence of parasitism. This variant—or whatever one chooses to call it— reminds one of the type of hymenophore described for *Psiloboletinus* by Singer but of course there is no phylogenetic connection between the two. It does raise the question again, however, as to whether there is any real taxonomic significance in the type of hymenophoral configuration that is part lamellate and part poroid. We know for instance that *Amanita muscaria* occasionally produces basidiocarps with a poroid to daedalioid hymenium, and now we have this brown spored variant clearly in *Pholiota* as far as its microscopic features are concerned.

Only the basidiocarp illustrated was found in the collection cited

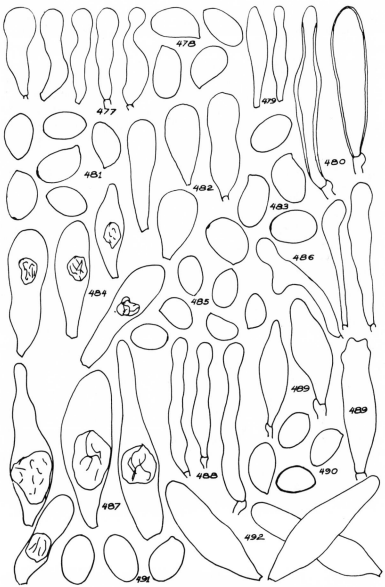

Text Fig. 37.

Figs. 477-479, cheilocystidia, spores, and pleurocystidia of *P. murrilii;* 480-482, caulocystidia, spores, cheilocystidia of *Flammula limulata* sensu Romell; 483 & 486, spores and cheilocystidia of *P. anomala;* 484 & 485, pleurocystidia and spores of *P. johnsonsiana;* 487, 488 & 491, pleurocystidia, cheilocystidia, and spores of *P. perniciosa;* 489, 490 & 492, cheilocystidia, spores and pleurocystidia of *P. subpapillata.*

but we have encountered this variation on more than one occasion and old specimens were clearly attacked by a parasite.

MATERIAL EXAMINED: (typical specimens) CALIFORNIA: Smith 3787; MASSACHUSETTS: Peck (type of *Flammula betulina,* on dead birch, from Stow, leg. S. Davis, Oct. 4, 1906) ; MICHIGAN: Harding 440; Hoseney 10-20-65; Kuaffman 9-16-29; Smith 5041, 14965, 20894, 33955, 34097, 35997, 38147, 38250, 43426, 44049, 58203, 67338, 67699; NEW YORK: Smith 300; NORTH CAROLINA: (GSMNP): Hesler 10903, 17231. CANADA, ONTARIO: Smith 4433. FRANCE: Josserand 1937. SWEDEN: Fungi Sueici 2692; Hagland 424, 726. SWITZERLAND: Favre 1948.

205. Pholiota squalida (Pk.) comb. nov.

Flammula squalida Peck, New York State Mus. Ann. Rept. 44: 131. 1891.
Gymnopilus squalidus (Pk.) Murrill, North Amer. Fl. 10: 197. 1917.
Illustrations: Text figs. 471-473.

Pileus 2.5–3.5 cm broad, convex or plane, dingy-yellowish or rufescent, viscid, glabrous. Context firm, whitish but under the separable cuticle concolorous to pileus surface.

Lamellae adnate, pallid, becoming dark-ferruginous, rather broad, close.

Stipe 3.5–7.5 cm long, 2–4 mm thick, pallid or brownish, subcartilaginous, at first the apex pale yellow, flexuous, fibrillose, hollow.

Spores 6–8 × 4.2–5 μ, smooth, apical pore obscure under NA 1.4 obj.; shape in face view elliptic, in profile elliptic to very obscurely inequilateral, color in KOH pale ochraceous-tawny, in Melzer's reagent about the same; wall 0.25 μ thick.

Basidia 18–22 × 5–6.5 μ, somewhat clavate, 4-spored, yellowish in KOH and Melzer's reagent. Pleurocystidia abundant, 46–68 (76) × 9–17 μ, fusoid-ventricose, apex blunt to subacute, smooth, thin-walled, neck filled with a plug of ± colloidal-coagulated material but appearing homogeneous under microscope. Caulocystidia none found.

Gill trama with a central area of subparallel floccose hyphae, yellowish to nearly hyaline in KOH; but subhymenium gelatinous of narrow interwoven hyphae. Pileus cutis a thick pellicle; hyphae narrow (2–3 μ diam.), gelatinous, transversely creased (as revived in KOH); hypodermial region of rusty orange to orange-brown incrusted hyphae (revived in KOH), the hyphal cell 5–8 (15) μ diam. Context hyphae interwoven, inflated (and often not reviving well) thin-walled smooth hyaline to yellowish in KOH, clamp connections present. All hyphae inamyloid.

HABIT, HABITAT, AND DISTRIBUTION: Often very caespitose on soil, in bushy places and alder swamps, New York, September. Type studied.

OBSERVATIONS: This is very close to *P. spumosa* in the sense of European material but differs in the uniform color of the pileus, its whitish flesh, slender habit and dingy appearance. Peck in describing the flesh

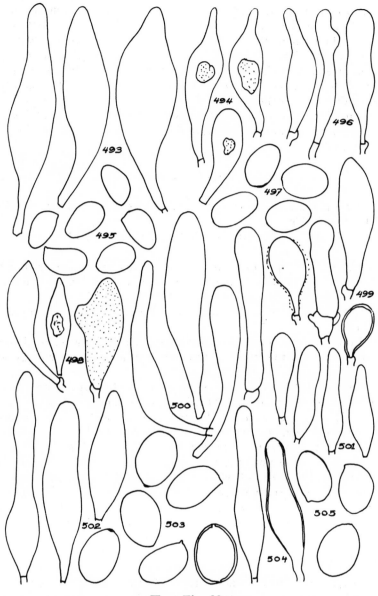

Text Fig. 38.

Figs. 493-496, pleurocystidia, pleuro-chrysocystidia, cheilocystidia and spores, of *P. schraderi;* 497-499, spores and cheilocystidia of *P. hiemalis;* 498, 500, 501, pleurocystidia, caulocystidia and cheilocystidia of *P. fila-mentosa;* 502 & 503, cheilocystidia and spores of *P. iterata;* 504 & 505, cheilocystidia and spores of *P. subminor.*

as whitish, also says that the flesh, under the cuticle, is concolorous with the pileus. The lamellae are at first pallid, and Peck says nothing of a yellow coloration of the young gills. He does say that he observed the species several times in different localities always finding it constant in its character and readily distinguishable. This has influenced us in recognizing it as a species. *P. spinulifera* may be the same as *P. squalida,* but both should be re-collected and studied fresh before making such a disposition of it. The aspect of the basidiocarps in the type of *Flammula squalida* is rather similar to those of *P. prolixa* but the cystidia distinguish them readily.

Doubtful Species

Phaeomarasmius alnicola (Murrill) Singer, Schweiz. Zeitschrift fur Plizk. 34: 61. 1956.
Crinipellis alnicola Murrill, North Amer. Fl. 9: 288. 1915.

Pileus 5–8 mm broad, subglobose to convex, rather firm. Surface densely villose, chestnut colored, not becoming glabrous, margin concolorous, involute, strongly inflexed on drying.

Lamellae adnate, rather broad and distant, pallid, the edges finely notched.

Stipe 5–10 mm long, 1–1.5 mm thick, clothed and colored like the pileus, pallid and tomentose at the apex, cylindric, equal, spongy stuffed with a cortex.

Spores 7.7–9.7 × 5.5–7.7 μ, some with a callus, pale honey-brownish. Cheilocystidia polymorphous, 28–52 × 5–10 μ. Hairs of pileus composed "of single members" separated by normal septa with clamp connections, incrusted by a membranous-pigment (from Singer).

On dead alder trunks, near Seattle Wash. W. A. Murrill 561 (N.Y.).

Note: We have not restudied the type for this paper because of the very limited material and when a critical study of *Tubaria* is made it will be essential to study it again. Obviously the species is similar in many ways to *P. erinacea* but we exclude it from *Pholiota* for the present because of the spore color as indicated by Singer. The above account is Murrill's original description with Singer's type study added.

Phaeomarasmius floridanus Singer, Schweiz. Zeitschrift fur Pilzk. 34: 59. 1956. This is a new name for Murrill's interpretation of *Agaricus curcuma.*

Pileus 15 mm broad, uniformly dark fulvous, or "convexo- vel acute conico-verrucoso . . ."; lamellae subdistant to distant, horizontal, broad, nearly free, pale isabelline, edge white and fimbriate; stipe 20 × 2–2.5 mm, squamulose with erect squamules the color of the pileus forming a sheath, apex white pruinose, base thickened; veil pallid, somewhat con-

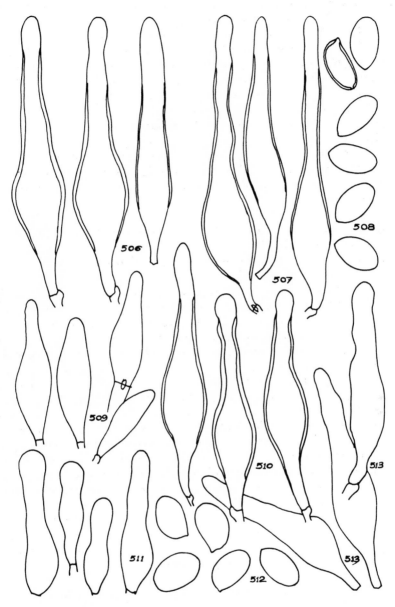

Text Fig. 39.

Figs. 506, pleurocystidia of *P. iterata;* 507, pleurocystidia of *P. sub-minor;* 508, 509, 510, spores cheilocystidia and pleurocystidia of *P. pseudo-graveolens;* 511, 512, 513, cheilocystidia, spores and pleurocystidia of *P. milleri.*

tinuous with the stipe covering. Spores melleous or ferrugineous, smooth, ovoid to ellipsoid or subinequilateral-elliptic ("vel subamygdalifor-mi-ellipsoideis"), wall hardly distinctly double, 6–8 × 4.2–4.5 μ; basidia 24–26 × 5.8 μ; cystidia none; cheilocystidia 61–72 × 5.8–10.1 μ. Clavate, very rarely subcylindric, epicutis of pileus of cells 21–28 × 15–20 μ, with encrusting pigment. On dead wood. Florida Singer F10003 (FLAS). It is under the name *Naucoria curcuma* in the Florida herbarium.

This is another instance where a study of the type should be postponed until a critical revision of *Phaeomarasmius* sensu Singer can be made. In the meantime it is obvious that if the species is a *Pholiota* in our sense it is in stirps *Curcuma* near *P. fagicola* but the latter has arcuate gills. In these agarics with small basidiocarps seldom collected in quantity, type material is too valuable to be expended in any but final critical studies.

Phaeomarasmius parvuliformis (Murr.) Singer, Schweitz. Zeitschrift für Pilzk. 34: 59. 1956.
Galerula parvuliformis Murrill, Proceed. Florida Acad. Sci. 7: 119. 1944.

Pileus 1.3 cm broad, conic to plane, with a prominent conic umbo, surface dry, floccose-scaly, finely striate to umbo, pale rosy isabelline, dark isabelline at center, margin entire, appressed when young; context very thin, pallid; lamellae adnexed, rounded behind, ventricose, inserted, medium distant, entire, soon pale-isabelline; stipe 20 × 1 mm, white, finely floccose, equal.

Spores 8–11 × 5–7.2 μ, smooth, lacking a germ pore, elliptic, occasionally ear-shaped from a slight side projection, smooth, lacking a germ pore, wall thin and not distinctly double (spore not *Tubaria*-like), brownish to pale honey colored. Basidia 25.5 × 9 μ. Cheilocystidia 30–43 × 10.7–14.5 μ, ventricose, often constricted, or flash-shaped with a broad neck (utriform), hyaline to light brown. Epicutis cellular (granulose ?) with pigment incrusted interwoven hyphae forming hypoderm. All hyphae in the type were brown, incrusted, and had clamp connections.

Again, the above description is that of Murrill with Singer's type study for the microscopic features. If the cells of the epicutis disarticulate this species would be close to our *P. pseudosiparia*. At present it does not seem advisable to transfer *G. parvuliformis* to *Pholiota*.

Phaeomarasmius muricatus (Fr.) Singer, in Singer & Digilio, Lilloa 25: 387. 1951.

We have avoided using the name *Pholiota muricata* for a North American species because of more than one concept extant in Europe for this species at the present time. Singer (1963, p. 597) indicates that *Naucoria mexicana* is a synonym of it. It is clear to us that much of

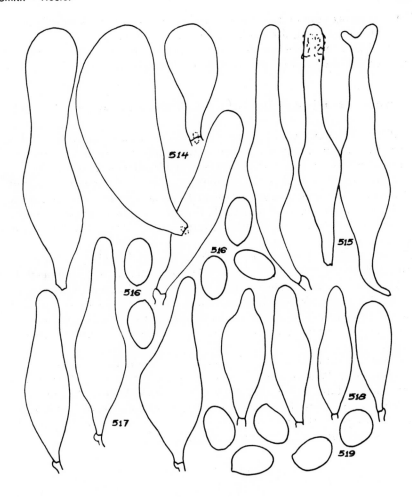

Text Fig. 40.

FIGS. 514-516, caulocystidia, pleurocystidia and spores of *P. sub-amara;* 517-519, pleurocystidia, cheilocystidia and spores of *P. trullisata.* Illustrations: Text figs. 514-516.

what has passed under the name *Pholiota muricata* in North America is the species we recognize under the name *Pholiota granulosa* (Peck in White). We prefer not to recognize *Naucoria mexicana* as a *Pholiota* until a critical revision of *"Phaeomarasmius"* is made.

Pholiota retiphylla Atkinson, Proc. Amer. Phil. Soc. 57: 356. 1918.

Pileus 1–2.5 cm broad, convex or expanded, lateritious or hazel to vinaceous cinnamon, when very young with indistinct scales, finally with appressed fibrils, margin incurved. Context tinged vinaceous.

Lamellae adnate to slightly emarginate, reddish vinaceous, narrow and narrowed in front, close or crowded, surfaces venose and reticulate.

Stipe 2–3 cm long, 4–8 mm thick, flesh tinged vinaceous, occasionally bulbous, at length equal, fibrillose-striate, hollow, Annulus thin, membranous, delicate, vinaceous.

Spores 5.5–7 × 4–4.5 μ, subovoid, smooth, lacking a germpore. Basidia 20–24 × 5–6 μ, 4-spored. Pleurocystidia none; cheilocystidia 18–22 × 5–6 μ, rare, slightly ventricose-capitate. Gill trama subparallel, hyphae 2–4 μ broad; subhymenium not distinctive. Pileus trama more or less radial; surface bearing a trichodermium of brownish, septate, more or less constricted at the septa, incrusted hyphae. Clamp connections present.

HABIT, HABITAT, AND DISTRIBUTION: On very rotten, moss-covered log, in woods, leg. Whetzel and Jackson (type, no. 18540), Malloryville moor, Cayuga Lake Basin near Ithaca, New York August 18, 1904.

We do not know if the pileus was hygrophanous beneath the fibrils. The species is in the *Phaeomarasmius—Hygrotrama* complex, and reminds us very much of *Pholiota confragosa*.

EXCLUDED SPECIES

Pholiota acericola (Peck) Saccardo, Syll. Fung. 5: 759. 1887.
Agaricus acericola Peck, Buffalo Soc. Nat. Sci. 1: 50. 1873.
This is now *Agrocybe acericola* (Pk.) Singer.

Pholiota aegerita (Brig.) Quélet, Champ. Jura & Vosges p. 229. 1872.
This is now *Agrocybe aegerita* (Brig.) Singer.

Pholiota aeruginosa Peck, Ann. Rep. N. Y. State Mus. 43: 8 (75). 1890.
see *Gymnopilus aeruginosus* (Pk.) Singer.

Pholiota aggericola (Pk.) Saccardo, Syll. Fung. 5: 740. 1887.
Singer (1963) placed this in subg. *Aporus* of *Agrocybe*.

Pholiota autumnalis Peck, Bull. N. Y. State Mus. 122: 156. 1908.
see *Galerina autumnalis* (Peck) Smith & Singer.

Pholiota avellanea Murrill, Mycologia 5: 32. 1913.
A study of the type shows this to be either an *Agrocybe* or a *Conocybe* sect. *Pholiotina*.

Pholiota blattaria (Fr.) Gillet, Champ. France p. 433. 1876.
see *Conocybe (Pholiotina) blattaria* (Fr.) Fayod.

Pholiota broadwayii Murrill, Mycologia 5: 32. 1913.
see *Agrocybe broadwayii* (Murr.) Dennis.

Pholiota brittonia Murrill, Mycologia 5: 35. 1913.
see *Gymnopilus pampeanus,* in Singer p. 635 (1963).

Pholiota bryophila Murrill, Mycologia 5: 33. 1913.
see *Galerina bryophila* (Murr.) Smith & Singer.

Pholiota candicans (Schaeff.) Schroet., Krypt. Fl. Schles. 3: 608. 1889.
see *Agrocybe praecox* (Fr.) Fayod.

Pholiota caperata (Fr.) Gillet, Champ Fr. p. 435. 1876.
see *Rozites caperata* (Fr.) Karsten.

Pholiota cerasina (Pk.) Saccardo, Syll. Fung. 5: 744. 1887.
This is a *Gymnopilus,* probably *G. spectabilis.*

Pholiota dactyliota (Berk. & Mont.) Saccardo, Syll. Fung. 5: 750. 1887.
said to be the same as *P. squarrosa;* we have seen no material. (see Overholts 1927: 174).

Pholiota dura (Fr.) Kummer, Der Führer in die Pilzkunde p. 84, 1871.
see *Agrocybe dura* (Fr.) Singer.

Pholiota erebia (Fr.) Gillet, Champ. Fr. p. 432. 1876.
see *Agrocybe erebia* (Fr.) Kühner.

Pholiota fallax Vel. České Houby p. 501. 1922.

Pholiota filaris (Fr.) Peck, Bull. N. Y. State Mus. 122: 144. 1908.
see *Pholiotina filaris* (Fr.) Singer.

Pholiota furcata Overholts, North Amer. Flora 10: 272. 1924.
This is a *Galerina*. The combination with that genus has not been made since we prefer to see fresh material first. The specimens and description appear to indicate an abnormality somewhat like that described for *P. lenta* in this work (pl. 84b).

Pholiota fusa (Fr.) Singer, Agar. Mod. Tax. p. 516. 1951.

Reported from Ohio by Hard. We have examined his collection and it is unsuitable for critical study.

Pholiota hormorpha (Mont.) Saccardo, Syll. Fung. 5: 754. 1887.

It is said to resemble *P. tuberculosa*. We have seen no authentic material.

Pholiota howeana (Pk.) Peck, N. Y. State Mus. Bull. 122: 147. 1908; see also Rept. N. Y. State Mus. 26: 59. 1874. Also, *Stropharia howeana* Peck, Buffalo Soc. Nat. Sci. 4: 53. 1873.

see *Agrocybe howeana* (Pk.) Singer.

Pholiota intermedia Smith, Ann. Myc. 32: 479. 1934.

see *Pholiotina septentrionalis* (Smith) Singer.

Pholiota langei Singer, Nor. Acta Inst. Bot. Komarov Acad. Sci. USSR. ser. 2 pe Crypt. fasc. 6. p. 417. 1950 (replaces *P. intermedia* Lange).

Pholiota lapponica (Fr.) Singer. Lilloa 22: 517. 1951.

Pholiota lutea Peck, Ann. Rep. N. Y. State Mus. 51: 288. 1898.

probably *Gymnopilus spectabilis.*

Pholiota luteifolia (Pk.) Saccardo, Syll. Fung. 5: 756. 1887.

see *Gymnopilus luteofolius* (Pk.) Singer.

Pholiota maackiae Singer, Pap. Mich. Acad. Sci. Arts & Letters 32: 142. 1948.

Pholiota magnivelata Morse, Mycologia 33; 367. 1941.

either a *Thaxterogaster* or a *Cortinarius.*

Pholiota marginata (Fr.) Quélet, Champ Jura & Vosges p. 94. 1872 (see p. 127 in the reprint).

see *Galerina marginata* (Fr.) Smith & Singer.

Pholiota mcmurphyi Murrill, Mycologia 4: 260. 1912.

an examination of the type shows it to be a *Cortinarius.*

Pholiota martinicensis Patouillard, in Duss, Enum. Champ. Guad. p. 54. 1903.

Probably in section *Flavidula* of *Pholiota* but should be studied critically in a restudy of *Phaeomarasmius* and *Tubaria.*

Pholiota megalosperma Singer, Sydowia 7: 216. 1953.

Pholiota minima Peck, Ann. Rep. N. Y. State Mus. 41: 65. 1888.

see *Galerina minima* (Pk.) Smith and Singer.

Pholiota mollicula Bann. apud Peck, New York State Mus. Rept. 44: 182. 1892.

We were unable to locate the type.

Pholiota musae (Earle) Murrill, Mycologia 5: 34. 1913.

see *Pholiotinia musae* Earle, Inf. An Estac. Agron. Cuba 1: 241. 1906. In the type material examined, the spores were found to be 13–18 × 7–12 μ ellipsoid, smooth, pale, germ pore not evident. Pleurocystidia and cheilocystidia were not found. Probably not a *Pholiota.*

Pholiota mycenoides (Fr.) Gillet, Champ. France p. 432. 1876.

see *Galerina jaapii* in Smith & Singer (1964) and also *Conocybe.*

Pholiota ombrophila (Fr.) Saccardo, Syll. Fung. 5: 737. 1887.

see section *Aporus* of *Agrocybe* in Singer (1963).

Pholiota platyphylla Kauffman, Pap. Mich. Acad. Sci. Arts and Letters 1: 145. 1923.

see *Galerina platyphylla* (Kauff.) Smith & Singer.

Pholiota praecox (Fr.) Kummer, Der Führer in die Pilzkunde p. 85. 1871.

see *Agrocybe praecox* (Fr.) Fayod.

Pholiota pumila see discussion in Smith & Singer (1964).

Pholiota radicosa (Fr.) Kummer, Der Führer in die Pilzkunde p. 84. 1871.

see Overholts 1927; we have not seen this collection.

Pholiota retiphylla Atkinson, Proc. Amer. Phil. Soc. 57: 356. 1918.

see the doubtful species (under Phaeomarasmius).

Pholiota rubecula Bann. apud Peck, New York State Mus. Ann. Rept. 44: 182. 1892.

Overholts (1927) states that the spores are rough so we assume it is probably a *Gymnopilus*. The type could not be found at Albany.

Pholiota rugosa Peck, Ann. Rept. N. Y. State Mus. 50: 102. 1897.

see *Pholiotina rugosa* (Pk.) Singer.

Pholiota separata Kummer, p. 84. 1871.

see *Panaeolus semiovatus* ? Kummer did not indicate an authority for the name, but we assume he had *Agaricus semiovatus* in mind.

Pholiota sabulosa Peck, Bull. Torrey Bot. Club 23: 414. 1896.

The type has rough spores. Overholts (1927) thought it was in the *P. marginata* complex which in our classification would make it a *Galerina!* We would like additional data on fresh specimens as the habitat is very peculiar. It was inadvertently overlooked in the *Galerina* work of Smith and Singer.

Pholiota scobifera (Berk. & Curt.) Saccardo, Syll. Fung. 5: 753. 1887.

This is probably in the *Phaeomarasmius* complex and should be studied in connection with a revision of that group.

Pholiota speciosa Clements, Bot. Surv. Nebr. 2: 41. 1893.

As Overholts pointed out, the description is inadequate. We have not been able to study the type.

Pholiota spectabilis (Fr.) Gillet, Champ. Fr. p. 443. 1876 (in many citations). (Fr.) Kummer, Der Führer in die Pilzkunde p. 84. 1871.

see *Gymnopilus spectabilis* (Fr.) Singer.

Pholiota sphaleromorpha (Fr.) Quélet, Champ. Jura et Vosges p. 91. 1872.

see *Agrocybe sphaleromorpha* (Fr.).

Pholiota subnigra Murrill, Mycologia 4: 258. 1912.

see *Agrocybe erebia*, it is said to be a synonym of that species.

Pholiota subsquarrosa (Fr.) Saccardo, Syll. Fung. 5: 750. 1887.

see *P. subvelutipes* of the present work.

Pholiota temnophylla (Pk.) Saccardo, Syll. Fung. 5: 740. 1887.

see *Agrocybe temnophylla* which probably is a variant of *A. praecox*.

Pholiota terrigena (Fr.) Saccardo, Syll. Fung. 5: 737. 1887.

This has been reported and illustrated from Wisconsin by Harper

(1913). We have studied his collection (2827) and find it to be *P. terrestris.*

Pholiota togularis (Fr.) Kummer, Der Führer in die Pilzkunde p. 85. 1871.

see *Pholiotina togularis* (Fr.) Fayod ex Singer.

Pholiota trachyspora C. & C. apud Overholts, Missouri Bot. Gard. Annals. 14: 125. 1927. This is a *Rozites* or a *Cortinarius.*

Pholiota tuberculosa (Fr.) Kummer, Der Führer in die Pilzkunde p. 83. 1871.

Reported from Michigan by Harper (1913: 489). We have studied Harper's collection from Michigan and conclude that it is *P. flammans* (the variant with a distinct gelatinous pellicle). It is clearly not the same as material of *P. tuberculosa* from Great Britain identified by P. D. Orton.

Pholiota unicolor (Fr.) Gillet, Champ. Fr. Hymen. p. 436. 1878.

see *Galerina unicolor* (Fr.) Singer.

Pholiota ventricosa Earle, Bull. N. Y. State Bot. Garden 2: 341. 1902.

A probable synonym of *Gymnopilus spectabilis* see Singer (1963).

Pholiota vermiflua (Pk.) Saccardo, Syll. Fung. 5: 739. 1887.

see *Agrocybe dura.*

Pholiota villosa (Fr.) Saccardo, Syll. Fung. 5: 752. 1887.

Reported from the Pacific Coast. Overholts (1927) thought it was *Pholiota (Gymnopilus) spectabilis.*

Pholiota viscida (Pk.) Kauffman, Amer. Journ. Bot. 13: 29. 1926.

see *Galerina viscida* (Pk.) Smith & Singer, Monogr. on the Genus Galerina Earle, p. 244. 1964.

Pholiota washingtonensis Murrill, Mycologia 4: 259. 1912.

see *Agrocybe ombrophila.*

APPENDIX

In the course of studying *Gymnopilus* Hesler has studied the types of *Flammula olivacea* Pat., *F. aureoviridis* Pat. and *F. vinicolor* Pat. His type studies are given below; New combinations are withheld pending study of fresh material.

Flammula aureoviridis Pat.

Coll. by Duss, No. 816, on decayed wood, Camp Jacob, Guadeloupe, Farlow Herb.

Spores 6–8.5 × (3.5) 4–4.5 μ, ellipsoid to subovoid, inequilateral in profile, smooth, truncate (germ pore large), brownish in KOH, yellowish brown in Melzer's reagent. Basidia unsuitable for study. Pleurocystidia and cheilocystidia none found. Gill trama subparallel, hyphae 3–5 μ broad; subhymenium not distinctive. Pileus trama radial. Cuticle of brown, repent hyphae; no pileocystidia. Caulocystidia none. Clamp connections present.

This is a *Pholiota (Kuehneromyces).*

Flammula olivacea Pat.

Coll. by Duss, on dead wood, near Basse-Terre, Martinique, No. 53, Patouillard, Farlow Herb.

Spores 5.5–7.5 × 3.5–4.5 μ, ellipsoid to subovoid, truncate from a broad germ pore, smooth, brown in 2% KOH, and in Melzer's reagent. Basidia (not in condition for study). Pleurocystidia and cheilocystidia none found. Cuticle repent, bearing clusters of brownish more or less erect hyphae. Clamp connections present. Caulocystidia none.

This is a *Pholiota* (*Kuehneromyces*-type).

Flammula vinicolor Pat.

Coll. Duss, Saint Pierre, Martinque, on dead wood, July 1889 (type), Farlow Herb.

Spores (5.5) 6.5–8 × (3.5) 4–4.5 μ, ellipsoid to subovoid, truncate from a broad germ pore, smooth, brown in KOH, yellowish brown in Melzer's reagent. Basidia unsuitable for study. Pleurocystidia and cheilocystidia not found. Gill trama undulating subparallel, hyphae 3–5 μ broad; subhymenium not distinctive. Pileus trama radial. Cuticles repent, with scattered, low mounds of colorless, clavate to cylindric pileocystidia, 23–32 × 3–6 μ. Clamp connections none found. Caulocystidia none.

This is a *Pholiota* (*Kuehneromyces*).

Selected Bibliography

Selected Bibliography

Atkinson, G. F. 1900. Studies of American Fungi, mushrooms, edible, poisonous, etc. Henry Holt & Co. New York.

————. 1918. Preliminary notes on some new species of agarics Proc. Amer. Phil. Soc. 57: 354-356.

Bach, Erna. 1956. The agaric *Pholiota aurea,* Physiology and Ecology. Dansk. Bot. Arkiv. 16 (2) : 1-216.

Bresadola, J. 1930-31. Iconographia Mycologica vols. 14, 15, 16. Milan.

Dennis, R. W. G. 1953. Les Agaricales de L'ile de Trinité: Rhodosporae-ochrosporae. Bull. Soc. Myc. Fr. 69: 145-198.

Dennis, R. W. G., P. D. Orton, and F. B. Hora. 1960. New check list of British agarics and boleti. British Myc. Soc. Trans. Suppl. June pp. 1-225.

Donk, M. A. 1949. Nomenclatural notes on generic names of agarics. Bot. Gard. Buitenzorg, Ser. III. 18: 271-402.

————. 1962. Nomenclatural notes on generic names of agarics. Beihefte zur Nova Hedwigia 5: 1-320.

Earle, F. S. 1902. Mycological studies, I. New York Bot. Garden Bull. 2: 331-350.

————. 1909. The genera of the North American gill fungi. Bull. N. Y. Bot. Garden 5 (18) : 373-451.

Farlow, W. G. 1929. Icones Farlowianae (text by E. A. Burt) Harvard University, Cambridge, Mass. pp. 119: pl. 102.

Favre, Jules. 1960. Catalogue descriptif des champignons supérieurs de la zone subalpine du Parc National Suisse pp. 325-610. National Park Museum, Chur.

Fries, E. M. 1821. Systema Mycologicum I: 1-508. Lund.

————. 1836-38. Epicrisis System. Mycologici, pp. 1-610. Upsala.

————. 1872. Icones Selectae Hymenomycetum II. Upsala.

————. 1874. Hymen. Europaei. pp. 1-757. Upsala.

Groves, J. Walton. 1962. Edible and Poisonous Mushrooms of Canada: *Pholiota.* pp. 184-190; *Flammula,* pp. 190-191. Ottawa.

Gussow, H. T. and W. S. Odell. 1927. Mushrooms and Toadstools. pp. 274. Ottawa.

Harding, Paul R. 1952. A Monograph of the North American Species of *Gymnopilus.* Thesis. pp. 1-247. University of Michigan (microfilm) .

Harper, Edward T. 1913. Species of *Pholiota* of the Region of the Great

Lakes. Wisconsin Acad. Sciences, Arts and Letters 17: 470-502. pls. 25-55.

―――. 1914a. Species of Pholiota and Stropharia in the Region of the Great Lakes. Wisconsin Acad. Sciences, Arts and Letters 17: 1011-1026. pls. 59-67.

―――. 1914b. Note on Pholiota erebia Fr. Wisconsin Acad. Sciences, Arts and Letters 17: 1163. pl. 84.

Hongo, Tsuguo. 1959. The Agaricales of Japan I (1). Mem. Faculty Lib. Arts. Educ. Shiga Univ. 9: 47-94.

Hora, F. B. and P. D. Orton. 1955. Three new British agaric records. Brit. Myc. Soc. Trans. 38: 400-404.

Imai, Sanshi. 1938. Studies on the Agaricaceae of Hokkaido II. pp. 179-378. Sapporo, Japan.

Imazeki, Rokuya and Tsuguo Hongo. 1962. Colored illustrations of Fungi of Japan, vol. I.

Imazeki, Rokuya and Tsuguo Hongo. 1965. Colored illustrations of Fungi of Japan, vol. II.

Josserand, Marcel. 1937. A propos de l'existence en Europe de *Pholiota albocrenulata* Peck. Rev. Mycol. Paris N. S. 2: 18.

―――. 1965. Notes critiques sur quelques champignons de la Région Lyonnaise. Bull. Soc. Mycol. de Fr. 81: 517-565.

―――. and Alexander H. Smith 1941. Notes on the Synonymy of French and American Agarics II. Mycologia 33: 483-505.

Kauffman, C. H. 1918. The Agaricaceae of Michigan: *Pholiota* and *Flammula*, pp. 289-314 and 483-492.

―――. 1926. The Genera *Flammula* and *Paxillus* and the status of the American Species. Amer. Journ. Bot. 13: 11-32. 1926.

―――. 1930. The fungous flora of the Siskiyou Mountains of Southern Oregon. Mich. Acad. Science, Arts and Letters 11: 151-210.

―――. and Alexander H. Smith 1933. Agarics collected in the vicinity of Rock River, Michigan in 1929. Mich. Acad. Science, Arts and Letters 17: 153-200.

Konrad, P. 1936. Notes critiques sur quelques Champignons du Jura. Bull. Soc. Myc. Fr. 52: 35-53.

Kühner, R. 1946. Étude morphologique et caryologique du hycélium et des formations mycéliennes du *Flammula gummosa* Lasch. Rev. Mycol. Paris N. S. 11: 3-30.

Kühner, R. et Henri Romagnesi. 1953. Flore Anal. des Champ. Superieurs. Dryophila Quélet (1886) emend. pp. 326-333. Paris.

―――. 1956-57. VII. Especes nouvelles, critiques ou rares des Naucoriacees, Coprinacees et Lepiotacees. Bull. de la Soc. des Nat. d'Oyonnax nos. 10-11. suppl. pp. 1-94.

Kummer, Paul. 1871. Der Führer in die Pilzkunde pp. 1-146.

Lange, Jakob. 1921. The genus Pholiota. Dansk Bot. Arkiv. 2 (11) : 1-11.

―――. 1928. The genus Flammula. Dansk Bot. Arkiv. 5 (5) : 7-15.

―――. 1935-40. Flora Agaricina Danica. Vols. I-V. Copenhagen.

Larsen, Poul. 1932. Fungi of Iceland. The Botany of Iceland II. pp. 449-607 Copenhagen.

Matsuda, Ichiro and Tsuguo Hongo. 1955. Larger fungi from the sand dunes in Niigata-prefecture (2). Journ Jap. Bot. 30: 259-263.

Metrod, Georges. 1938. Descriptions de quelques agarics peu commun. Rev. Mycol. 3: 148-156.

Møller, F. H. 1945. Fungi of the Faeroes pp. 1-294. Einar Munkagaard. Copenhagen.

Morse, Elizabeth E. 1941. A new western Pholiota. Mycologia 33: 367-370.

Moser, M. 1950. Neue Pilzfunde aus Tirol. Ein Beitrag zu Kenntnis der Pilzflora Tirols. Sydowia 4: 84-122.

———. 1955. Pholiota, Flammula and Kuehneromyces. Die Rohrlinge, Blatter-und Bauchpilze, pp. 224-228. (in Helmut Gams, Kleine Kryptogomenflora).

Murrill, W. A. 1912. The Agaricaceae of the Pacific Coast II. Mycologia 4: 231-262.

———. 1917. *Gymnopilus*. North Amer. Fl. 10: 193-215.

Orton, P. D. 1960. New check list of British agarics and boleti. Part III. Notes on genera and species in the list. British Myc. Soc. Trans. 43: 159-439.

Overholts, L. O. 1924. *Pholiota* (Fr.) Quél. North Amer. Fl. 10: 261-277.

———. 1927. A Monograph of the genus *Pholiota* in the United States. Ann. Missouri Bot. Gard. 14: 87-210.

———. 1932. *Hypodendrum*. North Amer. Fl. 10: 277-281.

Paulet, Jean J. 1793. Traite des Champignons. Paris.

Pearson, A. A. 1949. New Records and Observations IV. British Myc. Soc. trans. 32: 258-272.

Peck, Charles H. 1872. Report of the Botanist. N. Y. State Mus. Ann. Rept. 24: 41-108.

———. 1879. Report of the Botanist. N. Y. State Mus. Ann. Rept. 31: 19-60.

———. 1888. Report of the Botanist. N. Y. State Mus. Ann. Rept. 41: 51-122.

———. 1895. New species of fungi. Bull. Torrey Club 22: 198-211.

———. 1898. New York species of *Flammula*. N. Y. State Mus. Ann. Rept. 50: 133-142.

———. 1899. New species of fungi. Bull. Torrey Club 26: 63-71.

———. 1901. Report of the State Botanist, 1900. N. Y. State Mus. Ann. Rept. 54: 130-195.

———. 1903a. New species of fungi. Bull. Torrey Club 30: 95-101.

———. 1903b. Report of the State Botanist for 1902. N. Y. State Mus. Bull. 67: 3-194.

———. 1906. New species of fungi. Bull. Torrey Club 33: 213-221.

———. 1907. Report of the State Botanist, 1906. N. Y. State Mus. Bull. 116: 5-117.

———. 1908. New York species of Pholiota. N. Y. State Mus. Bull. 122: 141-158.

———. 1909. New species of fungi. Bull. Torrey Club 36: 329-339.

———. 1911. New species and varieties of extralimital fungi. N. Y. State Mus. Bull. 150: 50-65.

———. 1912. Report of the State Botanist, 1911. N. Y. State Mus. Bull. 157: 5-139.

———. 1913. New species of extralimital fungi. N. Y. State Mus. Bull. 167: 38-50.

Pilát, A. 1932. Additamenta ad florem Asiae Minoris Hymenomycetum. Pars secunda Agaricineae. Bull. Soc. Myc. Fr. 48: 283-323.

———. 1933. Additamenta ad floram Sibiriae Asiaeque orientalis mycologicam. Bull. Soc. Myc. Fr. 49: 256-339.

———. 1951. Hymenomycetes novi vel minus cogniti Cechoslovakiae. Studia Bot. Cechoslovacia 12: 1-72.

———. 1959. Nase Houby. Prague.

Quélet, L. 1886. Enchiridion Fungorum. Paris.

Rea, Carleton. 1922. British Basidiomycetae, pp. 1-799. Cambridge Univ. Press.

Ricken, A. 1915. Die Blätterpilze Deutschlands. Leipzig.

Romagnesi, Henri. 1956.

Robak, Hakon. 1933. *Pholiota mutabilis* (Schaeff.) Quel. Som Råtesopp På Tremasse. Friesia 1: 93-94.

Sawyer, W. H. Jr. 1917. Development of Some Species of *Pholiota*. Bot. Gaz. 64: 206-208. 1917.

Shaffer, Robert. 1965. Poisoning by *Pholiota squarrosa*. Mycologia 57: 318-319.

———. 1966. On the terms Viscid, Gelatinous and Ixo. Mycologia 58: 486-490.

Singer, R. 1943. Type studies on Basidiomycetes II. Mycologia 35: 142-163.

———. 1948. New and interesting species of Basidiomycetes II. Papers Mich. Acad. Science Arts and Letters 32: 103-150.

———. 1950. New and interesting Basidiomycetes III. Sydowia 4: 130-157.

———. 1951. The Agaricales in Modern Taxonomy. Lilloa 22: 1-832.

———. 1955. Type Studies on Basidiocymetes VIII. Sydowia 9: 367-431.

———. 1957. New Genera of Fungi X.-Pachylepyrium. Sydowia 11: 320-321.

———. 1962. Diagnoses Fungorum novarum agaricalium II. Sydowia 15: 45-83.

———. 1963. The Agaricales in Modern Taxonomy 2nd Ed.: *Pholiota* pp. 550-558. (Title page indicates publication as 1962 but this is incorrect). Weinheim.

Singer, Rolf and Alexander H. Smith. 1946a. Proposals concerning the nomenclature of the gill fungi including a list of proposed lectotypes and genera conservanda. Mycologia 38: 240-299.

————. 1946b. The taxonomic position of *Pholiota mutabilis* and related species. Mycologia 38: 500-523.

————. 1959. Studies in Secotiaceous Fungi—V. Nivatogastrium Gen. Nov. Brittonia 11: 224-228.

Smith, Alexander H. 1934. New and unusual agarics from Michigan. Ann. Myc. 32: 471-484.

————. 1944a. Unusual North American Agarics. The Amer. Midland Nat. 32: 669-698.

————. 1944b. New North American Agarics. Mycologia 36: 242-262.

————. 1949. Mushrooms in their Natural Habitats. Sawyers Inc. Portland, Oregon.

————. 1951. The North American species of *Naematoloma*. Mycologia 43: 467-521.

————. 1956. Additional new or unusual North American Agarics. Sydowia, Suppl. 1: 46-61.

————. and Harold J. Brodie. 1935. Cultural characters and pairing reactions of monosporus mycelia and development of the fruit body of *Pholiota* (*Flammula*) *polychroa* Bot. Gaz. 96: 533-546.

————. and Rolf Singer. 1964. A Monograph on the Genus *Galerina* Earle pp. 1-384, pls. 1-20 Hafner Pub. Co. New York.

Smith, Alexander H. and S. M. Zeller. 1966. A Preliminary account of the North American species of Rhizopogon. Mem. N. Y. Bot. Garden 14 (2) : 1-178.

Soehner Ert. 1922. *Pholiota subsquarrosa*. Zeitschr. für Pilzk. 1: 33-38.

Stuntz, D. E. and B. F. Isaacs. 1962. Pacific Northwestern fungii. Mycologia 54: 272-298.

Thomas, G. P. and D. G. Podmore. 1953. Studies in forest pathology. Canadian Journ. Bot. 31: 675-692.

Vandrendries, Rene. 1933. Nouvelles Investigations dans le domaine sexual des Hymenomycetes. Bull. Soc. Myc. Fr. 49: 130-164.

————. 1934. Les polarites sexuelles dans le genre *Pholiota*. Bull. Soc. Myc. Fr. 50: 270-277.

Wells, Virginia and Phyllis Kempton. 1965. *Togaria aurea* in Alaska Mycologia 57: 316-318.

Zeller, S. M. 1933. New or noteworthy agarics from Oregon. Mycologia 25: 376-391.

List of Plates by Species

List of Plates by Species

1. *P. abietis* pls. 53-54.
2. *P. albivelata* pl. 24.
3. *P. albocrenulata* pls. 25c, 26-27.
4. *P. astragalina* pls. 80, 81.
5. *P. aurantioflava* pl. 11a.
6. *P. aurea* pls. 5-6.
7. *P. aurivella* pls. 49-50.
8. *P. avellaneifolia* pl. 83.
9. *P. bakerensis* pl. 60a.
10. *P. brunnea* pl. 10.
11. *P. brunnescens* pls. 40a, 71.
12. *P. carbonaria* pl. 68.
13. *P. castanea* pl. 59a.
14. *P. confragosa* pl. 9a.
15. *P. conica* pl. 18b.
16. *P. curvipes* pl. 4a.
17. *P. decorata* pls. 63, 64, 79b.
18. *P. destruens* pls. 21-23.
19. *P. elongata* pl. 29a.
20. *P. erenacea* pl. 8b.
21. *P. erinaceella* pls. 4a, 7b.
22. *P. fibrillosipes* pl. 82.
23. *P. filamentosa* pls. 56-57.
24. *P. flammans* pl. 47.
25. *P. flavida v. flavida* pl. 34.
26. *P. flavida v. graveolens* pl. 35.
27. *P. granulosa* pl. 29b.
28. *P. graveolens* pl. 74.
29. *P. gregariiformis* pl. 59b.
30. *P. hiemalis* pl. 51.
31. *P. highlandensis* pls. 67a, 70b, 72.
32. *P. innocua* pl. 89.
33. *P. lenta* pls. 11b, 25a, 90.
34. *P. lubrica* pl. 84.
35. *P. lutescens* pl. 30.
36. *P. malicola v. malicola* pls. 36, 37.
37. *P. malicola v. macropoda* pls. 38, 39.

38. *P. molesta* pl. 70c.

39. *P. multifolia* pls. 2-3.

40. *P. mutabilis* pls. 12-14.

41. *P. mutans* pls. 7d, 8c.

42. *P. myosotis* pl. 28.

43. *P. occidentalis* pl. 67b.

44. *P. pallida* pl. 18a.

45. *P. paludosella* pls. 60b, 69a, 73.

46. *P. parvula* pl. 7c.

47. *P. piceina* pl. 79a.

48. *P. polychroa* pls. 86a, 87.

49. *P. prolixa* pls. 33, 70a.

50. *P. prominans* pl. 8a.

51. *P. pseudograveolens* pl. 58.

52. *P. pulchella* pl. 65b.

53. *P. rubronigra* pl. 65a.

54. *P. scamba* pl. 75.

55. *P. sola* pl. 40b.

56. *P. spumosa* pls. 77-78.

57. *P. squarrosa* pls. 41-43.

58. *P. squarroso-adiposa* pl. 55.

59. *P. squarrosoides* pls. 45-46.

60. *P. stratosa* pl. 76.

61. *P. striatula* pl. 9b.

62. *P. subangularis* pl. 1.

63. *P. subcaerulea* pl. 25b.

64. *P. subcastanea* pl. 48.

65. *P. subflavida* pl. 88.

66. *P. sublubrica* pl. 85.

67. *P. subochracea* pls. 31-32, 86b.

68. *P. subsaponacea* pl. 69b.

69. *P. subvelutipes* pl. 52.

70. *P. tennessensis* pl. 15.

71. *P. terrestris* pl. 44.

72. *P. velaglutinosa* pl. 62.

73. *P. veris* pls. 16-17.

74. *P. verna* pl. 66.

75. *P. vernalis* pls. 19, 20.

76. *P. vinaceobrunnea* pl. 61.

Index

Index

Abies, 174, 218, 219
  concolor, 107
Acer, 267
  negundo, 214
  rubrum, 313
  saccharum, 36
Agaricus, 3
  Tribe Flammula, 37
  Tribe Pholiota, 37
  Species
    acericola, 383
    adiposus, 224
    albocrenulatus, 127
    alnicola, 3, 171
    angustipes, 227
    aridus, 75
    astragalinus, 3, 326
    aureus, 54
    aurivellus, 211
    caperatus, 3
    confraosus, 42
    carbonarius, 3, 287, 288
    curcuma, 37
    curvipes, 50
    destruens, 124, 125
    detersibilis, 56
    discolor, 84
    elatior, 141, 142
    elongatipes, 143
    erinaceellus, 56
    erinaceus, 75
    flammans, 206
    flavidus, 177
    gummosus, 82
    highlandensis, 288
    johnsonianus, 137
    lentus, 3, 371
    lingnicola, 117, 119
    limonellus, 220
    lubricus, 3, 239, 330, 342, 343
    lucifera, 226
    muricatus, 61
    mutabilis, 92
    myosotis, 141
    neesii, 326
    ornellus, 352, 354
    polychrous, 352
    scambus, 4, 302

    semiovatus, 385
    spumosus, 3, 316
    squarrosoides, 201
    udus var. elongata, 143
    vahlei, 54
    vernalis, 118, 119
Agrocybe, 7, 82, 128, 131, 135, 137, 383
  Subgen. Aporus, 383
  Sect. Aporus, 384
  Species
    acericola, 383
    dura, 383, 386
    erebia, 128, 383, 385
    ombrophila, 386
    praecox, 383, 385
    sphaleromorpha, 385
    temnophylla, 385
Alnicola, 176
Alnus, 210, 267
Amanita muscaria, 374

Betula, 210
  lutea, 218
Boletaceae, 21
Boletus truncatus, 89

Calamogrostis arundinacea, 343
Carpophilus, 77
Clitocybe illudens, 214
Conocybe, 311, 383
  Sect. Pholiotina, 383
    blattaria, 383
Coprinus, 15
Cortinariaceae,
Cortinarius, 23, 32, 33, 331, 344, 350, 384, 386
  Subgen. Bulbopodium, 331, 334
    foedatus, 348
    percomis, 296
Corylus, 76
Crepidotus, 23
Crinipellis alnicola, 378
Cystoderma, 27

Deschampsis flexuosa, 339
Dryophila, 3, 4, 31, 35, 37
  alnicola, 171
  astragalina, 326

carbonaria, 287
curvipes, 50
destruens, 124
erinacea, 75
flavida, 177
gummosa, 82
lenta, 372
lubrica, 319, 342
lucifera, 226
mutabilis, 92
ochropallida, 204
scamba, 302
sordida, 4
spumosa, 316
Conocybe, 7, 45

Fagus, 52
Flammula, 3, 4, 8, 18, 37, 46, 91, 296,
    354
  var. marginalis, 180, 181
  alnicola, 178
  amara, 326
  anomala, 40
  astragalina, 326
  aureoviridis, 386
  betulina, 371, 376
  brunneodisca, 364
  californica, 168
  connisans, 181
  carbonaria, 35, 158, 280, 287, 351
  condensa, 248
  decorata, 254
  duroides, 136
  expansa,
  flavida, 4, 29, 177
  fulviconica, 369
  granulosa, 60
  graveolens, 296
  fummosa, 82, 83
  highlandensis, 158, 159, 287
  hypholomoides, 262
  jalapensis, 365
  laeticolor, 326
  lata, 360
  lenta, 371
  limulata, 74
  lubrica, 239, 330
  multifolia, 47, 50
  olivacea, 386, 387
  ornatula, 160
  polychroa, 352

pusilla, 156
scamba, 302
spinulifer, 336
sphagnicola, 290
spumosa, 316
squalida, 376, 378
subcarbonaria, 332
subflavida, 358
subfulva, 277
sulphurea, 180, 181
velata, 320
vialis, 322
vinicolor, 386, 387
Flammopsis, 37
Flocculina, 77
Fungi Imperfecti, 374

Galerina, 20, 31, 32, 35, 68, 70, 74, 88,
    383, 385
  Sect. Inoderma, 46
  Stirps Sideroides, 88
  Species
    autumnalis, 35, 84, 85, 86, 383
    bryophila, 383
    cortinarioides, 32
    jaapii, 384
    marginata, 384
    minima, 384
    odorata, 32
    platyphylla, 384
    sideroides, 46, 88, 110
    triscopa, 102
    unicolor, 386
    viscida, 386
Galerula parvuliformis, 380
Geophila, 16, 30, 31, 32, 33, 148
Gymnopilus, 4, 40, 67, 385, 386
  aeruginosus, 383
  alabamensis, 247
  alnicola, 171
  aromaticus, 67
  californicus, 168
  carbonarius, 287
  condensus, 248
  decoratus, 254
  fibrillosipes, 333
  foedatus, 348
  fulvellus, 54
  fulviconicus, 369
  graveolens, 296
  hypholomoides, 262

jalapensis, 365
laeticolor, 326
latus, 360
lentus, 372
luteofolius, 384
multifolius, 47
ornatula, 160
pampeanus, 383
piceinus, 323
polychrous, 352
squalidus, 376
squamulosus, 52
spectabilis, 176, 383, 384, 385, 386
sphagnicola, 290
spinulifera, 336
subcarbonarius, 332
subflavidus, 358
subfulvus, 277
velatus, 320
vialis, 322

Hebeloma, 36, 205
albocrenulatum, 127
appendiculatum, 204, 205
foedatum, 348
kalmicola, 90
maesophaeum, 346
subtestaceum, 339
totteni, 306
Hyalophila myosotis, 141
Hymenogastraceae, 34
Hypholoma, 82
anomalum, 140
elongatipes, 143
elongatum, 143
olympianum, 145
subochraceum, 153
sublateritium, 263
Hypodendron, 37
adiposum, 225
albocrenulatum, 127
angustipes, 227
aurvelloides, 210
aurivellum, 211
flammans, 206
fulvosquamosum, 184
limonellum, 220
oregonense, 176
squarrosoides, 201

Inocybe, 24, 33, 185, 187

Juglans, 220

Kuehneromyces, 4, 16, 24, 28, 29, 33,
    37, 44, 87, 91, 386, 387
carbonicola, 44
depauperatus, 121
latifolia, 91
mutabilis, 92
rostratus, 98
vernalis, 118

Laccaria trullisata, 347, 348
Larix, 51
Leccinum, 21, 24
Lepiota prynenacea, 54
Lepista, 56

Macowanites, 21, 24
Mycena, 20
corticola, 69

Naematoloma, 29, 30, 96, 144, 257, 273
capnoides, 87
elongatum, 143
fasiculare, 83, 99, 101
humidicola, 142
myosotis, 141
olympianum, 145
radicosum, 146
subochraceum, 153
Naucoria caespitosa, 302, 304
corticola, 74
curcuma, 380
cyathicola, 75
horizontalis, 69
humidicola, 142
elatior, 141
erinaceus, 75
limulata, 62, 74
lignicola, 118
mexicana, 60
muricata, 61
myosotis, 141
obtusissima, 143, 144
paludosella, 291
praecox, 118
sphagnophila, 294
vernalis, 118
Nivatogastrium, 34

Pachylepyrium, 4, 29, 33, 37, 44, 69

Panaeolus semiovatus, 385
Panus, 23
Paxillus, 40
  scambus, 302
Phaeolepiota, aurea, 54
Phaeomarasmius, 24, 25, 27, 28, 46,
    75, 77, 384, 385
  Sect. Confragosi 39
  Species
    alnicola, 378
    aridus, 75
    confragosus, 42
    curcuma, 63
  erinacellus, 56
    erinaceellus, 56
    floridanus, 378
    muricatus, 380
    parvuliformis, 380
    suberinaceellus, 64
Pholiota, 3, 4, 7, 8, 9, 10, 11, 12, 14,
    15, 16, 17, 18, 19, 20, 21, 22, 23,
    24, 25, 27, 28, 29, 30, 31, 32, 33,
    34, 35, 36, 37, 38, 40, 44, 46, 60,
    69, 70, 74, 82, 88, 91, 97, 105,
    119, 131, 138, 144, 160, 181, 184,
    187, 188, 190, 205, 207, 208, 214,
    260, 263, 274, 286, 292, 294, 318,
    320, 332, 339, 346, 348, 354, 364,
    374, 378, 380, 384, 386, 387
  Subgenus
    Adiposae, 4
    Flammula, 4, 6, 17, 24, 35, 88, 170,
      296, 371
    Flammuloides, 6, 13, 17, 18, 19,
      23, 28, 29, 30, 31, 34, 38, 83, 230,
      238, 260, 273, 322, 333, 336, 351,
      346
    Flavidula, 22, 27, 28, 29, 30, 31,
      38, 45, 46, 55, 75
    Hemipholiota, 4, 5, 18, 29, 30, 31,
      32, 38, 39, 77, 78
    Hygrotrama, 5, 29, 38
    Phaenaematoloma, 6, 30, 32, 131

    Pholiota, 4, 6, 11, 27, 30, 38, 44,
      184, 208, 273
    Subflammantes, 4
  Section
    Adiposae, 6, 38, 278
    Albivelatae, 6, 132
    Albocrenulatae, 4

Carbonicola, 7, 232, 278
Confragosae, 5, 29, 39
Flammula, 4, 6
Flammuloides, 6, 231, 232, 337
Flavidula, 5, 384
Glutinigerae, 4
Hemipholiota, 5, 121
Hygrotrama, 5, 39, 44
Kuehneromyces, 97
Lubricae, 4, 7, 83, 231, 325
Mutabiles, 5, 77, 91
Myxannulatae, 4
Pholiota, 6, 31, 184
Phaeonamaetoloma, 38, 46, 132,
  138
Privignae, 4
Sericellae, 4
Sordidae, 4, 77, 78
Spumosae, 7, 231, 289
Subflammentes, 278
Variabilisporae, 5, 130
Stirps
  Adiposa, 6, 184, 192, 194, 205
  Adirondackensis, 6, 231, 238
  Albivelata, 6
  Albocrenulata, 5, 122, 126
  Astragalina, 7, 325, 326
  Aurea, 5, 36, 67
  Cinchonensis, 5, 47, 62
  Condensa, 6, 231, 242, 267
  Confragosus, 41
  Corticola, 5, 47, 73
  Crassipedes, 7, 325, 354
  Cubensis, 6, 135
  Curcuma, 5, 47, 63, 380
  Curvipes, 5, 46, 77
  Decorata, 7, 231, 250
  Depauperata, 5, 91, 121
  Destruens, 5, 124
  Discolor, 5, 78
  Elongata, 6, 138, 141, 143
  Erinacea, 5, 47, 75
  Ferruginea, 7, 231, 259
  Fibrillosipes, 325, 327, 369
  Graveolens, 7, 290, 296
  Innocua, 7, 326, 362
  Lenta, 7, 325, 326
  Lubrica, 7, 325, 337, 369
  Marginella, 5, 91, 114
  Mutabilis, 5, 91, 92
  Myosotis, 6, 138, 141

Obscura, 5, 92, 107
Occidentalis, 7, 232, 259, 266
Olivaceophylla, 6, 231, 234
Polychroa, 7, 325, 352, 369
Scamba, 7, 290, 297, 302
Schraderi, 6, 184, 185
Serotina, 5, 78, 88, 290
Silvatica, 6, 138
Sphagnicola, 7, 289, 290
Spumosa, 7, 290
Squarrosa, 6, 184, 189
Squarrosoides, 6, 184, 192, 194
Stratosa, 7, 312
Subamara, 7, 290, 311
Subochracea, 6, 138, 146
Vernalis, 5, 30, 92, 113, 114
Virgata, 6, 232
Species
  aberrans, 6, 69, 139, **140**
  abieticola, 6, 171, **172**
  abietis, 6, 206, 216, **218**, 220, 224
  abruptibulba, 7, 259, **267**
  acericola, 383
  acutoconica, 7, 309, 369, **370**
  adiposa, 3, 4, 6, 13, 14, 22, 34, 205, 214, 216, **224**, 225
  adirondackensis, 6, **238**
  aegerita, 383
  aggericola, 383
  aeruginosa, 383
  agglutinata, 6, 24, 238, **240**, 247, 362
  alabamensis, 7, 242, **247**
  albivelata, 6, 14, 30, 132, **133**
  albocrenulata, 4, 17, 36, **127**
  albo-olivascens, 5, 92, 99, **103**, 104, 107
  albovirescens, 5, 99, **100**
  alnicola, 6, 13, **171**, 309, 362
  angustifolia, 6, 13, 21, 146, 193, 203, **204**
  angustipes, 6, 193, 206, **227**, 230
  anomala, 5, 21, 28, **39**, 140
  appendiculata, 204, 352, 354
  armeniaca, 7, 328, **331**, 344
  aromatica, 67, 181
  astragalina, 7, 13, 154, **326**
  atripes, 5, 21, 107, 111, 113, **114**
  aurantiobrunnea, 13
  aurantioflava, 5, 78, **87**, 88
  aurea, 5, 7, 19, 27, 30, 35, 53, **54**,

56
  aurivella, 3, 6, 34, 205, 210, **211**, 212, 214, 220, 224, 225
    var. cerifera, 212
  aurivelloides, 6, 28, 205, 207, **208**
  autumnalis, 383
  avellanea, 383
  avellaneifolia, 7, 12, 261, 271, 331, 338, **340**, 342, 344, 345
  bakerensis, 6, 242, **243**, 312, 338
  baptistii, 7, 231, 313, **314**
  barrowsii, 6, 34, 193, **199**, 200, 201
  biglowii, 7, 354, **357**
  blattaria, 383
  bridgii, 5, 20, 99, **106**, 116
  broadwayii, 383
  brittonia, 383
  brunnea, 5, 21, 78, **84**
  brunneodisca, 7, 24, 266, 362, **364**
  brunnescens, 7, 279, 284, **286**
  bryophila, 383
  burkei, 6, 146, **148**
  caespitosa, 5, 77, 92, **96**, 138, 166, 206
  californica, 6, 147, **168**
  calvinii, 7, 297, **300**
  candicans, 383
  canescens, 5, 22, 26, 28, 39, **41**
  caperata, 383
  carbonaria, 7, 12, 35, 278, **279**, 280, 282, 287
  carbonicola, 4, 44, 279, 280
  castanea, 6, **235**, 238
  cerasina, 383
  cerifera, 214
  chromocystis, 7, 290, **295**
  cinchonensis, 5, 23, 25, **62**
  coloradensis, 7, **328**, 344
  comosa, 5, 125
  condensa, 6, 242, **248**, 297, 306
  conica, 5, 113, **116**
  confragosa, 5, 25, 39, 41, **42**, 382
  connata, 6, 205, **213**, 214, 218
  contorta, 6, 77, 147, **167**
  corticola, 5, 26, 28, 69, 73, **74**, 75
  crassipides, 7, 354, **360**, 362
  cubensis, 6, 132, **135**
  curcuma, 5, 25, **63**
    var. lanatipes, 26, **65**
  curvipes, 5, 25, 27, 45, 47, 48, **50**, 51, 52, 67, 72, 73

cyathicola, 5, 26, 28, **73,** 75
dactyliata, 383
davidsonii, 5, 78, **86**
deceptiva, 5, 99, **101**
decorata, 7, 35, 250, 253, **254,** 258,
  260, 272, 352
depauperata, 5, **121**
destruens, 4, 5, 11, 30, 36, **124,** 126
  var. edmundii, **125**
discolor, 5, 29, 32, 77, 78, **84**
dura, 137, 383
duroides, 6, 21, 132, 135, **136**
elongatipes, 6, 141, **143**
erebia, 383
erinacea, 5, 25, 27, 28, 56, **73, 75**
erinaceella, 5, 25, 51, 53, 55, **56,**
  58, 61, 66, 67, 160
fagicola, 5, 20, 52, 63, **72,** 380
fallax, 224, 383
ferruginea, 7, 259, **263,** 266
ferrugineo-lutescens, 7, 254, 259,
  261, 264
fibrillosipes, 7, 328, **333,** 334, 337
filamentosa, 6, 206, **223**
filaris, 383
flammans, 3, 6, 14, 17, 205, **206,**
  208, 222, 386
flavescens, 6, 147, **162**
flavida, 6, 13, 170, **177,** 312
  var. graveolens, 171, **179**
flavopallida, 6, 24, 238, **241,** 354,
  362
foedata, 7, 338, **348**
fulvella, 5, 53, **54**
fulviconica, 7, 317, **369**
fulvodisca, 7, 267, **274,** 278
fulvosquamosa, 6, 13, 23, **184**
fulvozonata, 7, 278, **280,** 284, 338
furcata, 383
fusa, **383**
fusca, 127
galerinoides, 5, 107, **112**
glutinigera, 4
granulosa, 5, 25, 31, 53, 55, 58, **60,**
  61, 62, 63, 64, 67, 71
graveolens, 7, 12, 234, **296,** 313,
  317, 322, 323, 324, 359
gregariiformis, **304**
groenlandica, 7, **338**
gruberi, 7, 338, **345**
gummosa, 5, 78, **82,** 83, 273

haerenosa, 7, 13, 231, 289, 338,
  350, 354
heteroclita, 5, 125
hiemalis, 6, 20, 206, **215,** 216
highlandensis, 7, 12, 159, 279, 280,
  284, 286, **287,** 333, 351
harmorpha, 384
howeana, 384
humidicola, 5, 141, **142**
humii, 7, 12, 250, **251,** 253, 259
hypholomoides, 7, 13, 259, **262,** 365
innocua, 7, 20, 21, 231, 362, 364,
  365
intermedia, 220, 222, 384
iterata, 6, 242, **245**
jalapensis, 7, 360, 362, **365**
johnsoniana, 6, 13, 132, **137**
kalmicola, 5, 89, **90,** 91
kauffmaniana, 206, 208
kodiakensis, 6, 189, **191**
lactea, 5, 25, 63, **69,** 70
langei, 384
lapponica, 384
lenta, 7, 83, 273, 339, 369, **371,** 374,
  383
limonella, 6, 21, 24, 206, **220,** 222
limulata, 61
lubrica, 4, 7, 35, 233, 271, 325, 330,
  331, 338, **342,** 343, 344, 348, 362
  var. luteifolia, 259, 338, **344,** 345
lucifera, 6, 25, 205, **226**
lurida, 7, 24, 362, **368**
lutea, 384
luteifolia, 384
luteola, 7, 328, **334**
luteobadia, 7, 278, **284**
lutescens, 6, 11, 147, **150,** 166
  var. robusta, **152**
macrocystis, 7, 9, 18, 21, 24, **354**
magnivelata, 384
malicola, 6, 85, **180,** 181
  var. macropoda, 13, 171, **181**
marginella, 5, 99, 103, **105, 106**
martinicensis, 384
megalosperma, 384
mcmurphyi, 384
melliodora, 6, 12, 146, **161**
milleri, 7, 24, 338, **351**
minima, 38
minor, 22
minutula, 5, 26, 28, 63, **68**

molesta, 7, 24, 279, **284**
mollicula, 384
multifolia, 5, 13, **47,** 50, 51, 52
muricata, 53, 56, 57, 61, 380, 382
murrillii, 5, 26, 28, 63, **67**
musae, 384
mutabilis, 3, 34, 35, 91, **92,** 121, 180
mutans, 5, 29, 32, 78, 80, **81,** 82, 86
mycenoides, 384
myosotis, 6, 91, 138, **141**
nameko, 4
nigripes, 5, 14, 107, **110**
obscura, 5, 107, **108,** 109
ochrochlora, 100, 148
occidentalis, 7, 263, **271,** 273, 274
var. luteifolia, **272,** 274
oedopus, 78, 82
olivaceodisca, 5, 15, **128**
olivaceophylla, 6, 235, **236,** 239
olympiana, 6, 99, 141, **145,** 146
ombrophila, 384
oregonensis, 6, 13, 171, **176**
ornatula, 6, 146, **160,** 161, 162
ornella, 352
pallida, 5, 21, **113**
paludosella, 7, 89, 290, **291**
parvula, 6, 146, **155**
penningtoniana, 6, 193, **194**
perniciosa, **159**
piceina, 7, 314, 317, **323,** 324, 325, 327, 359
platyphylla, 384
polychroa, 4, 7, 11, 16, 35, 83, **352,** 368
populicola, 5, 113, **120**
praecox, 385
privigna, 4
prolixa, 6, 19, 146, 147, 159, **166,** 289
proximans, 5, 25, 27, 63, **70**
var. subauripes, 25, **71**
pseudograveolens, 6, 232, **233**
pseudolimulata, 5, 26, 28, **73,** 74
pseudopulchella, 7, 231, 298, 299, **301,** 302
pseudosiparia, 5, 25, 53, 56, **58,** 60, 380
pulchella, **7,** 16, 29, 33, 160, 245, 294, 297, **298,** 302, 305
var. brevipes, 245, **299**

pumila, 385
punicea, 5, 26, 39, **40**
pusilla, 6, 80, 146, 155, **156**
radicosa, 385
retiphylla, 382, 385
rigidipes, 6, **193,** 206
rivulosa, 7, 267, **273**
romagnesiana, 6, 193, **203**
rostrata, 98
rubecula, 385
rubronigra, 7, 12, 250, **257,** 258
rufodisca, 7, 259, **264,** 266
rugosa, 385
sabulosa, 385
scabella, 6, 13, 21, 185, 186, **188**
scamba, 12, 298, 301, **302,** 306, 310
scamboides, 7, 298, **309**
schraderi, 6, 13, 185, 186, **187,** 188
scabifera, 385
separata, 385
sequoiae, 7, 242, **246**
serotina, 5, **89,** 91
sienna, 7, **259**
silvatica, 6, **139**
simulans, 6, 19, 193, 206, **228**
sipei, 6, **132,** 134
sola, 6, 20, 185, **186**
speciosa, 385
spectabilis, 385, 386
sphagnicola, 7, 12, **290,** 291, 292, 294
spagnophila, 7, 290, **294**
sphaleromorpha, 385
spinulifera, 7, 231, 328, **336,** 337, 369, 378
spumosa, 4, 35, 87, 236, 250, 263, 273, 276, 297, 306, 312, 314, **316,** 320, 323, 336, 357, 358, 359, 364, 371, 376
squalida, 7, 317, 369, **376,** 378
squarrosa, 3, 4, 6, 11, 12, 14, 21, 29, 34, 35, 38, 184, **189,** 192, 195, 199, 200, 202, 204
var. faginea, 202
squamulosa, 5, 26, 47, **52**
squarrosa-adiposa, 6, 14, 21, 199, 200, 201, 206, 212, 218, 220, **222,** 223
squarrosoides, 6, 11, 34, 36, 191, 192, 193, 195, 196, 200, **201,** 204
stratosa, 7, 12, 21, 24, 231, **312,** 313

striatula, 5, 29, 32, **78,** 82
subamara, 7, **311,** 317
subangularis, 5, 38, **44,** 299, 302, 348
subcaerulea, 6, 146, **147,** 148
subcarbonaria, 7, 328, **332,** 334, 337, 346
subcastanea, 6, 193, **198**
subdefossa, 7, 298, **310**
subechinata, 5, 25, 53, 63, **66,** 67
subflammans, 4, 278
subflavida, 7, 317, 354, **358,** 359
subfelina, 7
subfulva, 7, 230, 267, 272, 276, **277,** 358
subgelatinosa, 6, 146, **154**
sublubrica, 7, 231, 238, 271, 328, **330,** 332, 342, 344, 362
subminor, 6, 242, **244**
subrugosa, 385
subochracea, 6, 107, 146, **153,** 242
subpapillata, 5, 113, **117**
subsaponacea, 7, 278, **282**
subsquarrosa, 218, 222, 385
subsulphurea, 5, 47, **51**
subtestacea, 7, 297, **338,** 352
subvelutina, 171, **174**
subvelutipes, 6, 206, **217,** 218, 385
tahquamenonensis, 5, 102, 107, **109**
temnophylla, 385
tennessensis, 5, 77, 92, **94,** 96, 138
terrestris, 6, 11, 35, 193, **195,** 273, 282, 386
terrigena, 194, 385
tetonensis, 7, 297, **308,** 316, 330
togularis, 386
totteni, 7, 298, 305, **306,** 322
trachyspora, 386
trullisata, 7, 338, **347**
tuberculosa, 25, 50, 57, 73, 384, 386
umbilicata, 5, 99, **102**
unicolor, 386
variabilispora, 5, 78, **130**
velata, 7, 314, 317, **320**
velaglutinosa, 7, 13, 14, 250, **253,** 259, 262
ventricosa, 386
veris, 5, 82, 97, **98,** 104, 110
vermiflua, 386
verna, 7, 267, **268,** 344
vernalis, 5, 12, 32, 106, 113, 115,

117, **118,** 159
vialis, 7, 314, 317, 320, **322,** 323, 324
villosa, 386
vinaceobrunnea, 7, 250, **252,** 253, 259
virescentifolia, 7, 362, **363**
virgata, 6, **232**
viscida, 386
washingtonensis, 386
Pholiotina filaris, 383
musae, 384
rugosa, 385
septentrionalis, 384
togularis, 386
Pinus ponderosa, 128
Pluteus, 26, 27
cercinus, 26
Populus, 125, 126, 128
trichocarpa, 121, 271
Psathyrella, 15, 20, 292
Pseudotsuga, 224
Psilocybe, 16, 29, 30, 32, 99, 113, 118, 122, 126, 137, 354
Psiloboletinus, 374
Rhizopogon, 44, 56
Rozites, 386
caperata, 383
Russula, 15
Salix, 339, 210
Sequoia, 242
Sphagnum, 144
Stropharia, 16, 29, 30, 128, 131, 133, 137, 138, 354
aeruginosa 148
albocrenulata, 127
caesiipora, 188
hardii, 188
howeana, 384
johnsoniana, 137
kauffmanii, 184, 188
silvatica, 139
schaderi, 187
Thaxterogaster, 384
Thuja plicata, 103, 140
Tilia glabra, 36
Togaria aurea, 35, 54, 56
Tsuga hereophylla, 140
Tubaria, 28, 46, 56, 77, 82, 378, 384
Visculus, 3, 37
Xeromphalina 159

PLATES
(Illustrations)

PLATE 1

Pholiota subangularis × 1   Smith 34354

Pholiota subangularis × 1   Smith 34435

PLATE 2

Pholiota multifolia × 1 Smith 33868

PLATE 3

Pholiota multifolia   × 1   Harding 11

PLATE 4

Pholiota curvipes × 1 Smith 15050

Pholiota erinaceella × 2 Smith 67028

PLATE 5

Pholiota aurea   × 1   Smith 31103

PLATE 6

Pholiota aurea × 1   Smith 3050

PLATE 7

a) *Pholiota molesta* × 1   Smith 65008
b) *Pholiota erinaceella* × 1   Smith 67028
c) *Pholiota parvula* × 1   Smith 43158
d) *Pholiota mutans* × 1   Smith 1471

PLATE 8

Pholiota proximans × 1 Smith 63516

Pholiota erinacea × 1 Smith 4282

Pholiota mutans × 1 Smith 6205

PLATE 9

a) *Pholiota confragosa* × 1 Photo A. H. Smith

b) *Pholiota striatula* × 1 Smith 43158

PLATE 10

Pholiota brunnea × 1 Smith 66294

PLATE 11

Pholiota aurantioflava × 1   54274

Pholiota lenta × 1   Smith 34097

PLATE 12

Pholiota mutabilis   × 1   Photo A. H. Smith   Smith 14534

PLATE 13

Pholiota mutabilis   Photo AHS Mt. Hood Oregon   Smith 30906

PLATE 14

Pholiota mutabilis × ½ Smith 30906

PLATE 15

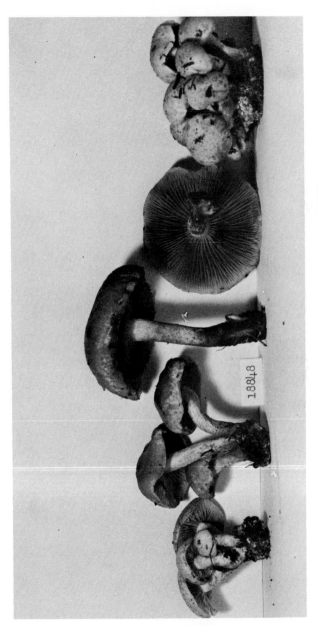

Pholiota tennesseensis × 1 Hesler 18848

PLATE 16

Pholiota veris   × 1   Smith 9510

PLATE 17

Pholiota veris × 1 Smith 15002

PLATE 18

a) *Pholiota pallida*   × 1   Smith 68837

b) *Pholiota conica*   × 1   Smith 68254

PLATE 19

Pholiota vernalis × 1½   Smith 1278

PLATE 20

Pholiota vernalis   × 1   Smith 13399

PLATE 21

Pholiota destruens   × 1   Smith 64741

PLATE 22

Pholiota destruens × 1 Smith 64741

PLATE 23

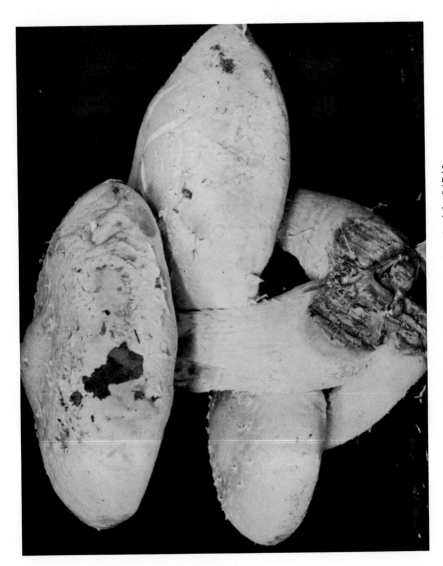

Pholiota destruens × 1 Smith 64741

PLATE 24

Pholiota albivelata × 1 Smith 3914

PLATE 25

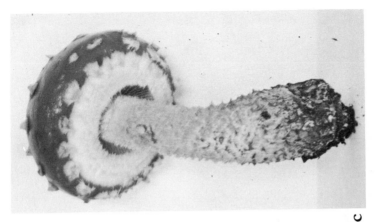

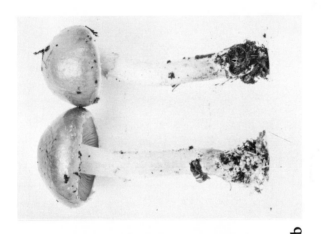

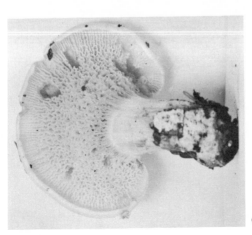

a

b

c

a) *Pholiota lenta* × 1 poroid form, Smith 66381
b) *Pholiota subcaerulea* × 1 Smith 73971
c) *Pholiota albocrenulata* × 1 Harding 10

PLATE 26

Pholiota albocrenulata × 1 Harding #12

PLATE 27

Pholiota albocrenulata × 1 Smith 74999

PLATE 28

Pholiota myosotis   × 1   Smith 207

PLATE 29

Pholiota elongata × 1   Smith 14942

Pholiota granulosa × 1   Photo A. H. Smith

PLATE 30

Pholiota lutescens × 2 Smith 63406

PLATE 31

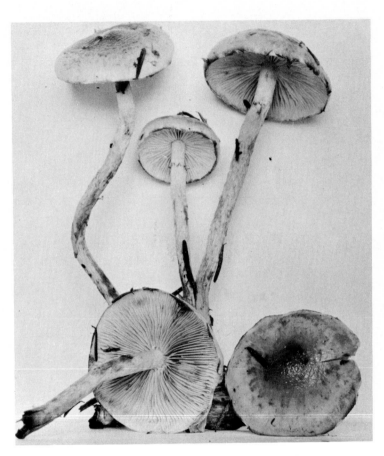

Pholiota subochracea   × 1   Smith 54319

PLATE 32

Pholiota subochracea　× 1　Smith 70627

PLATE 33

Pholiota prolixa × 1   Smith 33-1034

PLATE 34

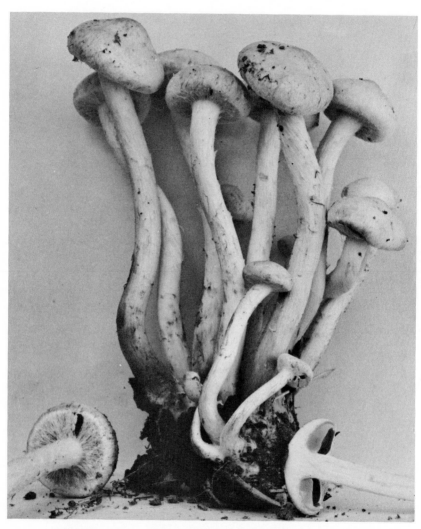

Pholiota flavida var. flavida   × 1   Bigelow 14186

PLATE 35

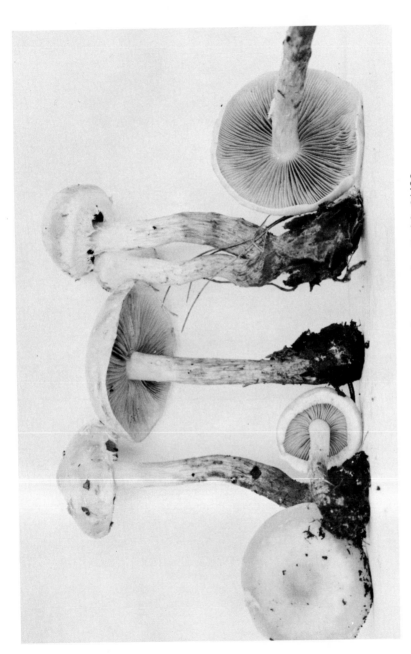

Pholiota flavida var. graveolens   × 1   Smith 64496

PLATE 36

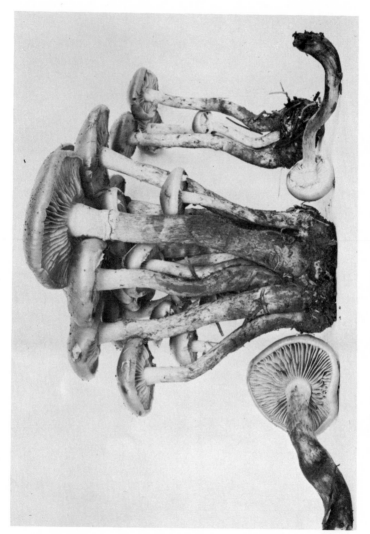

Pholiota malicola var. malicola × 1 Smith 2817

PLATE 37

Pholiota malicola var. *malicola*   × 1   Smith 32-506

PLATE 38

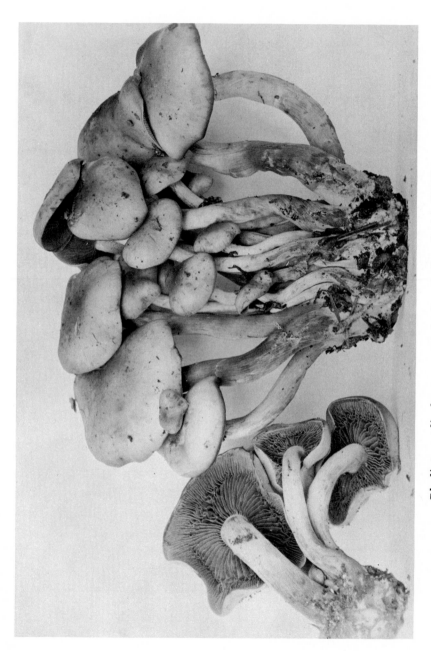

Pholiota malicola var. macropoda   × 1   Smith 59660

PLATE 39

Pholiota malicola var. *macropoda* × 1   Smith 70887

PLATE 40

a) *Pholiota brunnescens* × 1   Smith 53782

b) *Pholiota sola* × 1   Smith 37424

PLATE 41

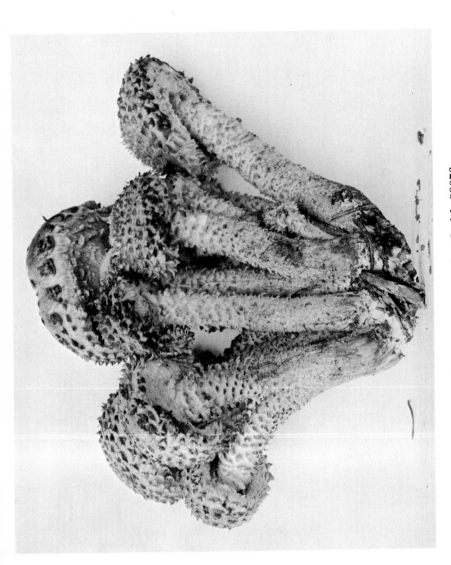

Pholiota squarrosa   × 1   Smith 59873

PLATE 42

Pholiota squarrosa × 1   Smith 51602

PLATE 43

Pholiota squarrosa × ½ Smith 26545

PLATE 44

Pholiota terrestris × 1 Smith 8194

PLATE 45

Pholiota squarrosoides × 1 Smith 31427

PLATE 46

Pholiota squarrosoides × 1 Smith 67151

PLATE 47

Pholiota flammans   × 1   Smith 73628

PLATE 48

Pholiota subcastanea × 1 Smith 75074

PLATE 49

Pholiota aurivella × 1 Smith 54702

PLATE 50

Pholiota aurivella × 1 Smith 3779

PLATE 51

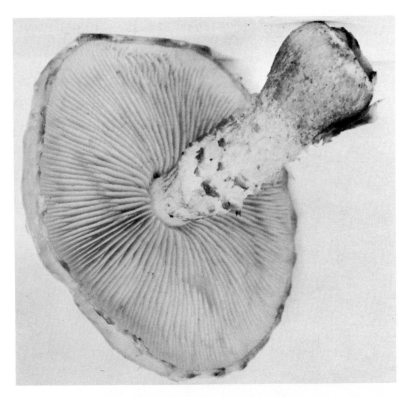

Pholiota hiemalis   × 1   Smith 74173

Pholiota hiemalis   × 1   Smith 74173

PLATE 52

Pholiota subvelutipes × 1 Photo A. H. Smith

PLATE 53

Pholiota abietis $\times$ 1   Smith 34227

PLATE 54

Pholiota abietis × 1   Smith 70684

PLATE 55

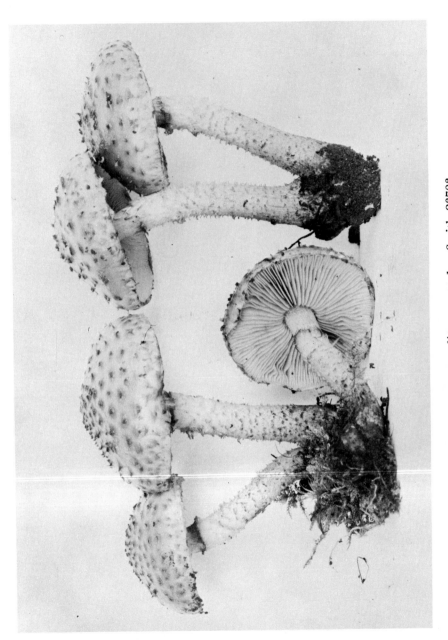

Pholiota squarroso-adiposa × 1 Smith 23783

PLATE 56

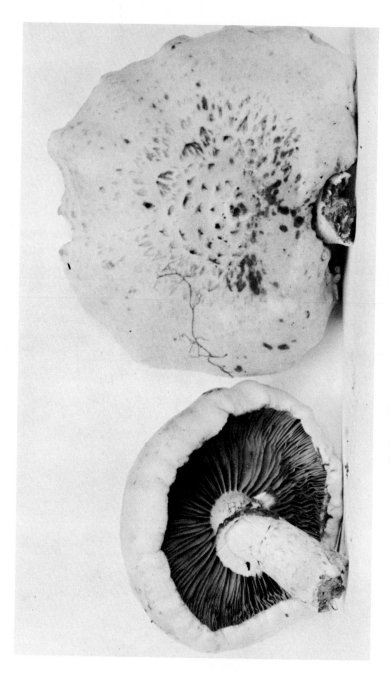

Pholiota filamentosa × 1 Smith 73615

PLATE 57

Pholiota filamentosa × 1 Smith 73615

PLATE 58

Pholiota pseudograveolens × 1 Smith 73302

PLATE 59

a) *Pholiota castanea* × 1   Hesler 24974

b) *Pholiota gregariiformis* × 1   Hesler 22565

PLATE 60

a) *Pholiota bakerensis* × 1   16727

b) *Pholiota paludosella* × 1   Smith 33-1092

PLATE 61

Pholiota vinaceobrunnea × 1 Smith 71217

PLATE 62

Pholiota velaglutinosa × 1   Smith 3560

PLATE 63

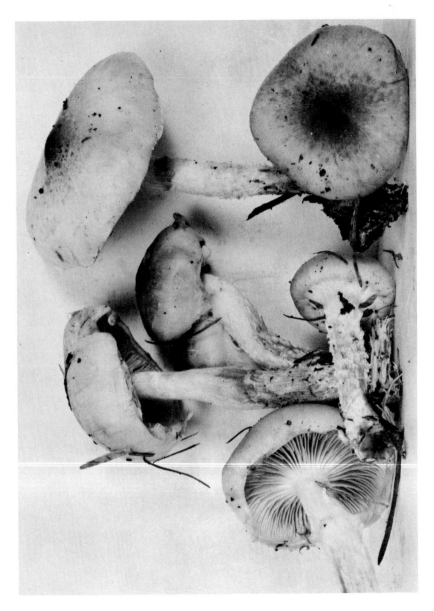

Pholiota decorata × 1 Smith 71104

PLATE 64

Pholiota decorata × 1 Smith 70844

PLATE 65

a) *Pholiota rubronigra* × 1 Smith 56192

b) *Pholiota pulchella* × 1 Smith 55630

PLATE 66

Pholiota verna × 1 Smith 14692

PLATE 67

Pholiota highlandensis × 1   Photo A. H. Smith 33695

Pholiota occidentalis × 1   Smith 27374

PLATE 68

a) *Pholiota carbonaria* × 1 Smith 9342

b) *Pholiota carbonaria* × 1 Smith 54261

PLATE 69

a) *Pholiota paludosella* × 1 Smith 4921

b) *Pholiota subsaponacea* × 1 Smith 73315

PLATE 70

Pholiota prolixa × 1 73281

Pholiota highlandensis × 1 33-289

Pholiota molesta × 1 44665

PLATE 71

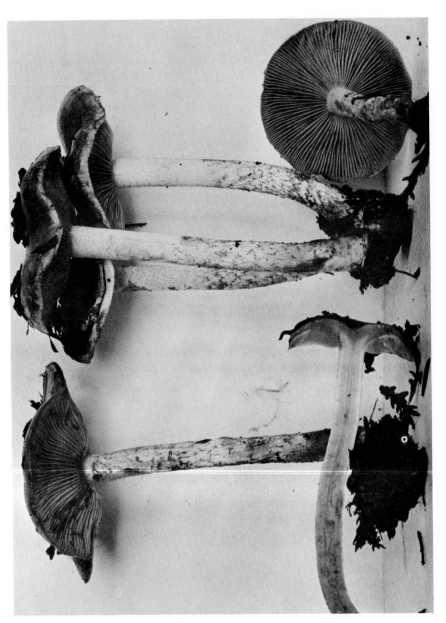

Pholiota brunnescens × 1 Smith 3767

PLATE 72

Pholiota highlandensis × 1   Smith 32-10

PLATE 73

Pholiota paludosella   × 1   Smith 33-104

PLATE 74

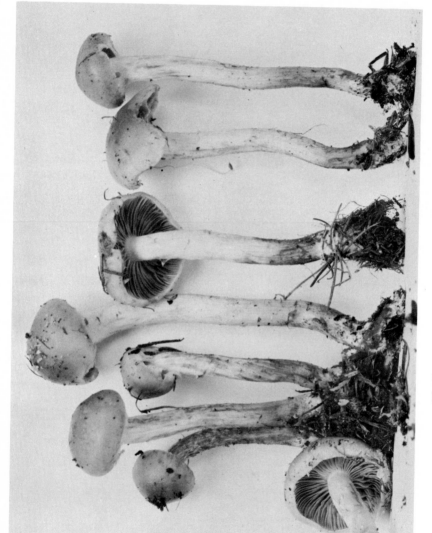

Pholiota graveolens × 1 Smith 73626

PLATE 75

Pholiota scamba × 1   Smith 3627

Pholiota scamba × 1   Smith 6205

PLATE 76

Pholiota stratosa   × 1   Smith 64684

PLATE 77

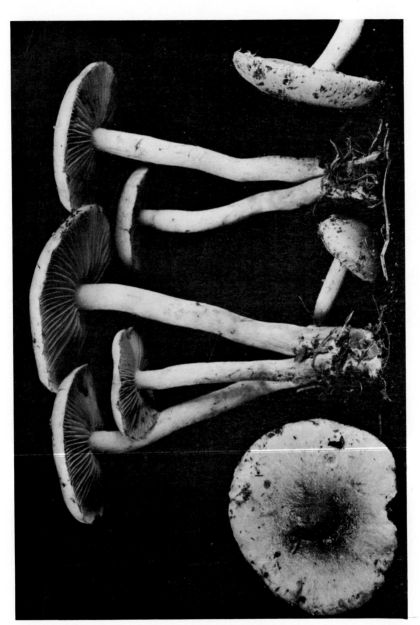

Pholiota spumosa × 1 H. E. Bigelow 8696

PLATE 78

Pholiota spumosa × 1 Smith 64712

PLATE 79

a) *Pholiota piceina* × 1   Smith 73446

b) *Pholiota decorata* × 1 (wet) .   Smith 54770

PLATE 80

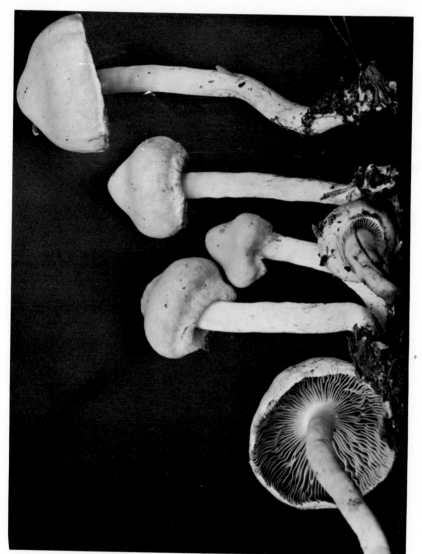

Pholiota astragalina × 1 Smith 73471

PLATE 81

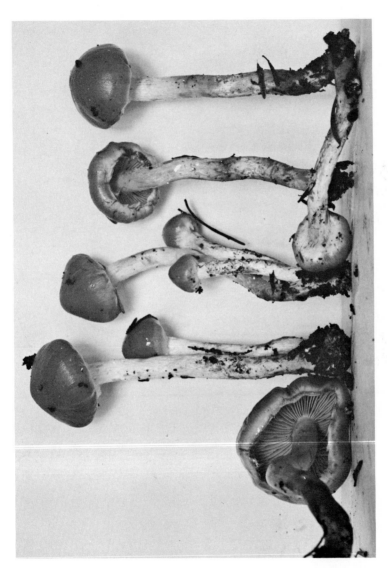

Pholiota astragalina   × 1   Smith 17102

PLATE 82

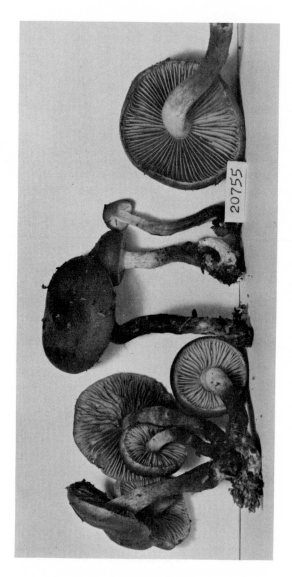

Pholiota fibrillosipes × 1   Hesler 20755

PLATE 83

Pholiota avellaneifolia × 1 Smith 59589

PLATE 84

Pholiota lubrica × 1 Smith 74071

PLATE 85

Pholiota sublubrica × 1 Smith 69588

PLATE 86

Pholiota polychroa × 1 Smith 75231

Pholiota subochracea × 1 Smith 73969

PLATE 87

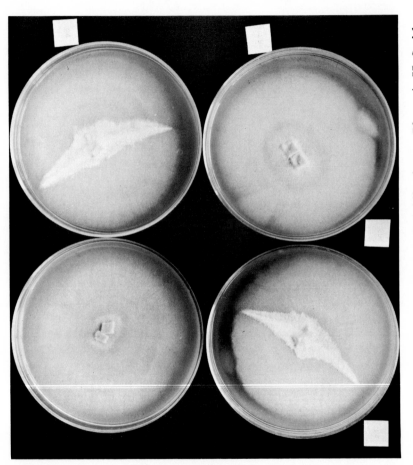

Pholiota polychroa cultures showing diploidization   Photo A. H. Smith

PLATE 88

Pholiota subflavida   × 1   Smith 73388

PLATE 89

Pholiota innocua   × 1   Smith 798

PLATE 90

Pholiota lenta × 1 Smith 59730